STRUCTURAL
IN CONCRE

TO BS8110

STRUCTURAL DESIGN IN CONCRETE
TO BS8110

L.H. Martin, P.C.L. Croxton and J.A. Purkiss

Edward Arnold

A division of Hodder & Stoughton

LONDON   MELBOURNE   AUCKLAND

© 1989 L. H. Martin, P. C. L. Croxton and J. A. Purkiss

First published in Great Britain 1989

British Library Cataloguing in Publication Data
Martin, L.H. (Laurence Harold, *1928–*
   Structural design in concrete to BS8110.
   1. Prestressed & reinforced concrete structural
  components. Design
  I. Title   II. Croxton, P.C.L. (Peter Charles Lester),
  1924–   III. Purkiss, J.A.
  624.1'8341

  ISBN 0–7131–3659–6

Typeset in 10/12 pt Times by Wearside Tradespools, Fulwell,
Sunderland. Printed and bound in Great Britain for Edward Arnold,
the educational, academic and medical publishing division of Hodder
and Stoughton Limited, 41 Bedford Square, London WC1B 3DQ by
JW Arrowsmith Ltd, Bristol

Contents

Preface	ix
Acknowledgements	xi
Guide to Readers	xiii
Glossary	xv
List of Symbols	xxi

1. Introduction — 1

1.1	The design process	1
1.2	Limit state design	2
1.3	Statistical basis for design	3
1.4	BS8110 (1985)	6
1.5	Drawings for reinforced concrete designs	7
1.6	Tutorial problems	11
	References	

2. Properties of Materials — 12

2.1	Characteristic strength	12
2.2	Design strength	14
2.3	Modulus of elasticity of concrete	14
2.4	Creep, shrinkage and thermal strains	15
2.5	Stress–strain curves for design	18
2.6	Tutorial problems	21
	References	

3. Loads — 23

3.1	Characteristic loads	23
3.2	Adverse and beneficial loads	24
3.3	Design load, partial safety factor for load	26
3.4	Design envelopes	27
3.5	Tutorial problems	29
	References	

4.   Analysis of the Structure   34

4.1   Introduction   34
4.2   Design philosophies   34
4.3   Stability   35
4.4   Braced and unbraced frames   39
4.5   Frame analysis   39
4.6   Column loads   64
4.7   Redistribution of moments   67
4.8   Plastic analysis for continuous beams   73
4.9   Approximate analysis of continuous beams and one-way spanning slabs   75
4.10 Tutorial problems   76
      References   79

5.   Durability, Serviceability and Fire   80

5.1   Introduction   80
5.2   Corrosion of the reinforcement   80
5.3   Alkali–aggregate reaction   83
5.4   Sulphate attack   84
5.5   Serviceability limit states   84
5.6   Deflections   86
5.7   Crack widths   94
5.8   Early thermal cracking   98
5.9   Fire design of structures   101
5.10 Tutorial problems   112
      References   114

6.   Reinforced Concrete Beams   116

6.1   Introduction   116
6.2   General principles – singly reinforced beams   117
6.3   Design formulae for rectangular sections   121
6.4   Flanged beams   131
6.5   Design procedure for beams   137
6.6   Tutorial problems   142

7.   Shear and Torsion in Reinforced Concrete   148

7.1   Shear resistance of reinforced concrete   148
7.2   Torsional resistance of reinforced and prestressed concrete members   169
7.3   Tutorial problems   176
      References   181

8.   Anchorage, Bar Connections, Curtailment and Member Connections   182

8.1   Anchorage   182
8.2   Bar connections   187

8.3   Curtailment of reinforcing bars   189
8.4   Member connections   196
8.5   Tutorial problems   215
      References   218

9.   Reinforced Concrete Columns   219

9.1   General principles   219
9.2   Axially loaded short columns   227
9.3   Combined bending and axial load   228
9.4   Biaxial bending   231
9.5   Slender columns   232
9.6   Shear strength of columns   242
9.7   Serviceability limit states   242
9.8   Tutorial problems   242

10.   Reinforced Concrete Slabs   247

10.1   Introduction   247
10.2   Methods of construction   247
10.3   Design philosophy   248
10.4   Plastic methods of analysis   250
10.5   Johansen yield – line method   250
10.6   Hillerborg strip method   262
10.7   One-way spanning slabs   265
10.8   Two-way-spanning slabs   265
10.9   Slab design and detailing   267
10.10 Support beams   281
10.11 Shear in one- and two-way spanning slabs   283
10.12 Flat slabs   284
10.13 Waffle slabs   284
10.14 Staircases   285
10.15 Retaining walls   288
10.16 Tutorial problems   300
       References   303

11.   Foundations   304

11.1   Introduction   304
11.2   Bearing pressures from pad foundations   306
11.3   Design of pad foundations   309
11.4   Pile caps   315
11.5   Tutorial problems   317
       References   321

12.   Prestressed Concrete   322

12.1   Bending resistance of prestressed concrete members at ultimate load   322

12.2   Bending resistance of prestressed concrete at service load   329
12.3   Loss of prestress   342
12.4   Shear resistance of prestressed concrete members   349
12.5   End blocks   356
12.6   Tutorial problems   363
      References   368

13.   Design Studies   369

13.1   Reinforced concrete lintel beam   369
13.2   Continuous beam   371
13.3   Pad foundation for a column   385
13.4   Flat slab   390
13.5   Prestressed concrete floor beam   403
13.6   Counterfort retaining wall   411
13.7   Bending, shear and torsion reinforcement   427
13.8   Design in lightweight concrete   429

Appendices   438

A1   Bar area tables   438
A2   Maximum and minimum percentages of reinforcements   439
A3   Properties of prestress tendons   446

B1   Design graphs   447
B2   Derivation of design graphs   462

C1   Densities and specific weights of some building materials   469
C2   Imposed floor loads for some buildings   470
C3   Imposed roof loads   471
C4   Wind pressures   472

Index   473

Preface

This book conforms with the latest recommendations for the design of reinforced and prestressed concrete as set out in British Standard 8110: 1985 – *Structural Use of Concrete*. It may be used as a stand-alone text or in conjunction with BS 8110. Comprehensive references to the relevant clauses of the Standard are given, and wherever possible the symbols used are the same as in the Standard. Verbatim quotations from British Standards are printed in different type. (Cross references within such quotations use the numbers in the BS publication.)

All the material necessary for the design of concrete elements in normal structures is provided, including a complete set of design graphs to facilitate the design of reinforced and prestressed concrete and also of pad foundations. The design graphs and other information regularly needed by a designer are placed in Appendices for easy reference.

No previous knowledge of structural design is assumed, but it is expected that readers will have received elementary instruction in structural analysis or mechanics of structures. The book contains detailed explanation of the principles underlying concrete design and is intended for the use of students reading for engineering degrees in universities and polytechnics. It should be especially useful to third-year students involved in design projects. It should also be sufficiently practical for practising engineers and architects who require an introduction to BS 8110.

The authors are convinced of the value of examples in learning and accordingly almost every topic is illustrated with a fully worked example. Tutorial problems, with answers, are also provided for practice. Links between individual topics are provided by a series of design studies at the end of the main text.

This book replaces *Elementary Structural Design in Concrete to CP 110* by A. W. Astill and L. H. Martin, which proved to be very popular with both students and engineers. Replacement became necessary when CP 110 was superseded by BS 8110 and sadly a change in authorship was forced by the death of Mr A. W. Astill. The book has been completely rewritten and extended. In particular greater coverage has been given to detailing and connections, deflections and crack control, and methods of designing for durability and fire resistance.

Acknowledgements

Dr Purkiss would like to thank Mrs G. Jones and Miss S. Fulford for typing his section of the manuscript. The extracts from BS 8110 and other British Standards are reproduced with the permission of the British Standards Institution, 2 Park Street, London W1A 2BS. Complete copies can be obtained from Linford Wood, Milton Keynes, MK14 6LE. Figure 5.11 is reproduced from the I Struct E/Concrete Society publication *Design and Detailing of Concrete Structures for Fine Resistance* by permission of the Institution of Structural Engineers.

Guide to Readers

References to BS 8110 are given in the form of the clause (or other) number followed by the relevant part number, for example (cl 3.4.1.5, Pt 1), (Table 7.1, Pt 2).

Arithmetical expressions are in general written as a single line in a form that can be entered directly into an electronic calculator. Exponential notation is used throughout. For example:

$$1\,234 \text{, i.e. } 1.234 \times 10^6 \text{, is written as } 1.234E6$$
$$0.001\,234 \text{, i.e. } 1.234 \times 10^{-3} \text{, is written as } 1.234E{-}3.$$

Glossary

alkali–aggregate reaction   deleterious chemical reaction between aggregates and cement

aspect ratio   long dimension/short dimension for a rectangle

balanced section   steel and concrete reach their design strengths simultaneously

bay   the space between two columns of a building framework

bearing   a support for a structure

bearing stress   a local compressive stress at a support, concentrated load, or inside the bend of a steel reinforcing bar

bedded bearing   a bearing with contact surfaces having an intermediate padding of cementitious material

bent-up bar   a tensile reinforcing bar that is bent up, usually at 45°, to resist shear forces

bond stress   shear stress developed between concrete and steel reinforcement

bracing   a system of members designed to stiffen a structure, or prevent it from behaving as a mechanism, or becoming unstable

bundled bars   reinforcing bars in close contact

butt weld   a fusion of two components, one or both of which is attached by its cross section

carbonation   chemical reaction between atmospheric carbon dioxide, moisture and hydrated cement minerals

characteristic load   the load above which not more than 5% of the loads applied to the member (or structure) are greater

characteristic strength   the strength of a material such that not more than 5% of the sample strengths are less

clearance   a small distance left intentionally between components of a structure to facilitate construction

coefficient of friction   the ratio of the frictional force to the normal force on sliding surfaces

collapse mechanism   the unique mechanism produced by the formation of plastic hinges in a structure at ultimate load, i.e. at collapse

column   vertical strut

column head   local enlargement of the top of a column providing support to the slab over a larger area than the column section alone

compaction   method of vibration to produce dense concrete by excluding entrainedair

compatibility   the relationship between displacements or strains that ensure a geometric fit

connection an assemblage of components which connect one member to another and which is generally capable of resisting forces

conservative design more safe than strictly necessary

construction depth vertical distance allowed, or available, for the structural component.

continuous construction a beam or column continued beyond a support without a break, or through a suitably designed splice

contraflexure point of zero bending moment where curvature changes from convex to concave, or vice versa

corrosion of steel a chemical reaction causing degradation and pitting on the surface

creep increase in strain at constant stress

cube crushing strength the crushing strength of a standard cube (usually 150 mm) of hardened concrete after a specified curing period

cylinder crushing strength compressive strength of a cylinder (usually 150 mm diameter and 300 mm high) of hardened concrete

dead load the permanent load of constant magnitude and position, e.g. self-weight

deemed to satisfy judged to comply with the code of practice without further analysis

deformation change in dimension of a member relative to its original dimensions

design load characteristic load multiplied by a partial safety factor (greater than 1 for ultimate loads)

design stress characteristic strength divided by a partial safety factor (1.5 for concrete and 1.15 for steel)

distortion a gross deformation where the cross section of a member changes shape

doubly reinforced beam concrete beam with tension and compression reinforcement

drop thickening of a slab in the region of the column

dry bearing a bearing with no intermediate padding material

durability ability of a material to resist the deleterious effects of the environment over a period of years

effective depth the depth from the most highly compressed face of a member to the centroid of a layer of tension reinforcement

effective length the effective length of a strut is that length which, if the strut were pin-ended, would produce the same buckling load as the actual strut

effective width a width, less than the real width, over which, for simplicity, a uniform stress is assumed to act

elastic limit maximum load, or stress, to which a material (or structure) can be loaded without causing permanent deformation

elastic material (or structure) a material (or structure) which if initially loaded regains its original dimensions and geometry when unloaded

elongation increase in length of a member due to a tensile force

encastré built into a support

end block end section of a post-tensioned prestressed concrete beam where the prestressing cables are anchored

factor of safety see **safety factor**

failure degeneration of a material, or structure, so that it is unable to support loads

fatigue premature loss of strength in a material, or structure, due to the action of varying loads

fillet weld a fusion of the surfaces of two components which are generally at right angles to each other

finishes   non-structural coating to floors and walls, e.g. plaster

fixing steel   placing, arranging and tying reinforcement

formwork   timbers, props and shuttering required to support *in situ* cast concrete work

gross cross-section   cross-section of a member with no deduction for bars, holes, etc.

high-yield steel   steel which has the relatively high characteristic strength of 460 N/mm^2

hyperstatic structure   a statically indeterminate structure

imposed load   load that is not permanent, e.g. furniture, snow, people, vehicles, etc.

initial tangent modulus   modulus of elasticity based on the tangent to the stress–strain curve at the origin

in-plane behaviour   the behaviour of a member or structure which deforms only in a selected plane of loading

in-situ **concrete**   concrete cast in its final position

instability   a condition of unstable equilibrium, usually manifested by sudden buckling or overturning

isostatic structure   a statically determinate structure

isotropic   having the same material properties in all directions

joint   see connection

lateral   in a plane perpendicular to the web of the section

lateral support   member or restraint member which prevents lateral buckling

lateral support for a wall   an element (which may be a prop, buttress, floor, cross-wall or other horizontal or vertical element) able to transmit lateral forces from a braced wall to the principal structural bracing or to the foundations

lateral torsional buckling   a form of instability in beams involving lateral buckling combined with twisting

linear elastic behaviour   behaviour of an elastic material, or structure, in which the relationship between stress and strain is linear

link   reinforcement in the form of a closed loop used as shear reinforcement or as a binder in a column – sometimes called a stirrup

live load   a load produced by acceleration or deceleration of masses, e.g. by vehicles or machinery. May sometimes mean an imposed load

lower-bound fit   an equation which fits the lower values of a scatter of experimental results

mechanism   a configuration of hinged members not capable of maintaining stable equilibrium under load

micro-strain $1E-6$ or 1×10^{-6}

mild steel   steel with the relatively low characteristic strength of 250 N/mm^2

minimum guaranteed yield stress   the yield stress, determined from tensile tests of samples taken during manufacture of steel, so that only 5% of the samples have yield strengths which are less

mix of concrete   the relationship between the quantities by weight of cement, fine aggregate (sand), and coarse aggregate (usually gravel)

moment of inertia   second moment of mass

moment redistribution   further distribution of elastic bending moments to allow for the formation of plastic hinges

net cross section   the reduced cross-section of a member after allowing for bars or holes

neutral axis   the axis in the plane of the section, separating tension and compression zones

node   a point in a structure where several members intersect

nominal reinforcement   steel not required for strength purposes but used to form a reinforcement cage

orthogonal reinforcement   reinforcement at right angles

out-of-plane behaviour   the behaviour of a member or structure in a plane perpendicular to the selected plane of loading

over-reinforced section   section in which the tension reinforcement does not reach the design strength at failure

partition   an internal non-permanent wall used for subdividing a storey, but carrying no load other than its own weight; i.e. not part of the dead load

pinned joint   a connection which allows relative motion between members with little or no transfer of moment

plastic   condition of highly stressed material when large permanent deformations occur

plastic design   a method of design which computes the collapse load based on the occurrence of sufficient hinges for a collapse mechanism to occur

polar second moment of area   second moment of area about the centroidal axis perpendicular to the plane of the section (polar axis)

precast member   concrete member which is cast at floor level or in a casting yard before erection to its place in a structure

prestressed concrete   concrete reinforced with steel which is pre-tensioned or post-tensioned

principal axes   sectional axes about which the product moment of area is zero, and the second moments of area are a maximum and a minimum

proof stress   stress at which a specified amount of permanent plastic strain occurs in a tensile test (0.2% for high-yield steel)

prop   strut member used to support formwork, or to improve the stability of a structure

punching shear   strictly the type of shear failure of a concrete section where the failure plane is parallel with the shear force, but is also applied to failure on an inclined plane in BS 8110

radius of curvature   radius to which a member is bent when subject to pure bending

radius of gyration   the radius (r) at which the whole area (A) of a section can theoretically be concentrated, for the calculation of the second moment of area, i.e. $I = Ar^2$

rafter   a beam spanning from ridge to eaves

redundant member or reaction   a member, or reaction, that is in excess of those required for a statically determinate (isostatic) structure, or part of a structure

reinforced concrete   concrete reinforced with steel that is not prestressed

relaxation   reduction in steel stress at constant strain, associated with loss of prestress force in the steel in prestressed concrete

restraint   anything that effectively prevents movement at a point in a structure

rigid joint   a connection which allows a transfer of moment between members with little or no rotation

safety factor   a factor relating design strength and characteristic strength or loads

secant modulus   modulus of elasticity based on a line connecting the origin with a selected point on the stress–strain curve

second moment of area   the sum of elements of area multiplied by the square of their distance from a given axis

semi-rigid joint   a connection which has characteristics which are between those of pinned and rigid connections

service load   load on a structure at the serviceability limit state

serviceability limit state   the limiting condition acceptable in a structure when subject to the service load or from adverse environmental conditions, e.g. exposure, fire, etc.

shear wall   a structural wall preventing sidesway in a building

short column   where l_{ex}/h or l_{ey}/b are less than 15 (braced) and 10 (unbraced)

shrinkage of concrete   reduction in size of members due to the evaporation of water in excess of that required for the hydration of the cement

shuttering   a mould, usually made of timber or steel, used to cast concrete members

simple bearing   a support which offers no significant resistance to rotation

single curvature   having no contraflexure

singly reinforced concrete beam   beam with tension reinforcement only, e.g. a lintel

slender   having a high slenderness ratio such that the effect of lateral buckling cannot be neglected

slenderness ratio   ratio of effective length to radius of gyration (l/r), classical definition, or to the overall width or depth of a section (BS 8110)

soffit   underside of a beam or slab

split cylinder strength   tensile strength of concrete obtained by splitting a cylinder (100 mm diameter and 200 mm high) by a compressive force applied across a diameter

stiffness of a member   resistance of a member to bending, expressed as EI/L. The corresponding value for torsion is GJ/L

storey   the space between floors, or floor and roof, of a building

strain energy   the potential energy, or work, stored in a linear elastic material when subjected to strain

strain hardening   the permanent increase in strength (and hardness) of a material, which occurs when it is stressed beyond the elastic limit

stress concentration   a localized high stress produced in a material due to defects, holes, discontinuities, etc.

strut   a member which supports a predominantly axial compressive load

sub frame   part of a structure that is isolated and idealized structurally to determine the forces and moments

tangent modulus   modulus of elasticity which is tangent at some specified point to a non-linear stress–strain curve

tendon   high-strength longitudinal steel in a prestressed member

tie   a member which supports a predominantly tensile axial force

tolerance   a limit placed on unintentional inaccuracies that occur in dimensions when marking out for cutting, bending reinforcement, or casting concrete, etc.

toughness   the ability of material to absorb energy, measured approximately by the Charpy V-notch impact test

transmission length   distance from the end of a beam required for a pretensioned wire to develop full prestress

transverse   in the plane of, or parallel to, the web of a section, and perpendicular to the longitudinal axis of the member

ultimate limit state   the condition of a structure when collapse occurs, or when it becomes unstable

under-reinforced section   a section in which the tensile reinforcement reaches its design strength before the concrete reaches its limiting strain

wall   a vertical load-bearing member whose length exceeds four times its thickness

warping   distortion of a section in torsion so that plane sections are no longer plane

water–cement ratio   ratio of the weight of water to the weight of cement in a concrete mix

work hardening   see strain hardening

working load   see service load

yield line   line across a slab where the stress in the tensile steel is at the design strength and a plastic hinge can be assumed to have developed

yield stress   stress in a material at which large plastic strains start to occur, with little or no increase in stress

List of Symbols

A	area of a cross-section
A_c	area of concrete
A_{ps}	area of prestressing tendons
A_s'	area of compression reinforcement
A_s	area of tension reinforcement
A_{sb}	area of steel in bent-up bars
A_{sc}	area of longitudinal reinforcement for columns
A_{sl}	area of longitudinal reinforcement for torsion
$A_{s,prov}$	area of tension reinforcement provided
$A_{s,req}$	area of tension reinforcement required
A_{sv}	total cross-sectional area of links at the neutral axis
a	deflection
a'	distance from compression face to crack point
a_b	centre-to-centre distance between bars
a_c	long-term creep deflection
a_{cr}	distance from the cracking point to the nearest bar
a_e	short-term elastic deflection
a_t	chord offset
a_u	lateral deflection of a slender column
a_{uav}	average computed lateral deflection at a level in an unbraced frame
a_v	shear span

B	total breadth
b	width of a section, or effective width of flange of 'T' beam section
	dimension at right angles to the plane of bending
b'	shorter section dimension
	shorter effective depth of a biaxially bent column
b_e	flange width
b_s	width of beam at soffit
b_t	width of section at level of tension reinforcement
b_v	breadth of member for shear resistance
b_w	average web width of a flanged beam

C	torsion constant
	compression force
c	column width
	cover to reinforcement
c_1, c_2	shear stress distribution factors between columns and slabs
d	effective depth of tension reinforcement
d'	depth to centroid of compression reinforcement
d_n	depth to the centroid of the compression zone
d_s	slab depth
d_t	effective depth for shear resistance in a prestressed beam
E_c	static secant modulus of elasticity of concrete
$E_{c,t.}$	modulus of elasticity of concrete at time t
$E'_{c,t}$	effective creep modulus $= Ec/(1 + \phi)$
E_n	nominal earth load
E_s	modulus of elasticity of steel
E_v	deformation modulus
$e.$	eccentricity of prestressing force from centroidal axis
	eccentricity of axial load on a column or base
	base of Napierian logarithm
e_{min}	minimum or nominal eccentricity
e_p	practical eccentricity of prestressing force from centroidal axis
e_1	eccentricity of prestressing force at lowest cable position
e_2	eccentricity of prestressing force at highest cable position
F	total ultimate design load
F_{bst}	tensile bursting force in a post-tensioned end block
F_{bt}	tensile force in bars at ultimate load
F_c	compressive force from concrete stress block
F_k	characteristic load
F_s	force in tension reinforcement
F'_s	force in compression reinforcement
F_T	tying force
F_1, F_2	factors
f_b	bond stress
f_{bg}	concrete bearing stress
f_{bu}	design ultimate bond stress
f_c	stress in concrete adjacent to steel
f'_c	cylinder crushing strength
f_{ci}	concrete strength at transfer of the prestressing force
f_{co}	stress in concrete at level of tendon due to initial prestress and dead load
f_{cp}	compressive stress at centroidal axis due to prestress
f_{ct}	concrete cube strength at transfer
f_{cu}	characteristic concrete cube strength at 28 days
$f_{cu,t}$	characteristic concrete cube strength at time t in days
f_k	characteristic strength
f_{pb}	design tensile stress in tendons at ultimate load in bending

f_{pe}	effective prestress in a tendon
f_{pi}	initial stress in the prestressing steel
f_{pt}	stress due to prestress
f_{pu}	characteristic strength of prestressing tendons
f_s	service stress in reinforcement
	stress, less than the design strength, in tension reinforcement at the ultimate limit state
f'_s	loss of stress in prestressing steel
	stress, less than the design strength, in compression reinforcement at the ultimate limit state
f_{sc}	design service compressive stress in concrete at service load
f_{st}	design tensile stress in concrete at service load
f_{sv}	design tensile stress in a link
f_{s1}	stress in the tension fibres at service load
f_{s2}	stress in the compression fibres at service load
f_t	design tensile strength of concrete
f_{tc}	design compressive stress in concrete at transfer
f_{tt}	design tensile stress in concrete at transfer
f_{t1}	stress in the tension fibres at transfer
f_{t2}	stress in the compression fibres at transfer
f_y	characteristic strength of reinforcement
f_{yb}	characteristic strength of inclined bars
f_{yv}	characteristic strength of link reinforcement ($<460\ \text{N/mm}^2$)
f_1, f_2	stress in reinforcement at level 1, 2
G	shear modulus
G_k	characteristic dead load
g_k	characteristic dead load per unit area or per unit length
H	horizontal force
h	overall depth of a section in the plane of bending
h'	longer section dimension
	longer effective depth of a biaxially bent column section
h_{agg}	maximum size of aggregate
h_c	effective diameter of column or column head
h_{cr}	crack height
h_f	flange thickness
h_{max}	larger dimension of a section
h_{min}	smaller dimension of a section
I	second moment of area
i	radius of gyration
	ratio of hogging to sagging moment of resistance
j	number of joints
K	bending stiffness of a member (EI/L)
	bending moment coefficient for the Hillerborg strip method

	friction coefficient in a prestressed duct
	reduction factor for additional moment in a slender column
	shrinkage constant
	$M/(bd^2 f_{cu})$
K'	maximum $M/(bd^2 f_{cu})$ for a singly reinforced concrete section
K_a	active soil pressure coefficient
K_b	stiffness of a beam
K_1	stiffness of lower column length
K_p	passive soil pressure coefficient
K_t	coefficient associated with transmission length for a pre-tensioned prestressed concrete beam
K_u	stiffness of upper column length
K_0	constant related to the modulus of elasticity of a concrete aggregate
k	a constant with appropriate subscripts
	joint stiffness
	stiffness
k_1	shear strength enhancement factor
k_2	concrete shear strength factor
L	effective span of a beam, cantilever or slab
	total length
l	general length term
	bond length
l_c	half the spacing between column centres, or the distance to the edge of a pad foundation whichever is the greater
l_e	effective height of a column or wall
l_{ex}	effective height for bending about the major axis
l_{ey}	effective height for bending about the minor axis
l_g	length of gap between welds
l_n	length of a nib in a half joint
l_o	clear height of column between end restraints
l_r	spacing of ties
l_t	transmission length for a pretressed concrete member
l_r	maximum span of beam set framing into a column
l_s	clear height (floor to soffit)
l_w	length of weld
l_x	length of the shorter side of a rectangular slab
l_y	length of the longer side of a rectangular slab
l_z	distance between points of zero bending moment in a flanged beam
M	bending moment
M_A, M_B	initial end moments in an unbraced slender column
M_{add}	maximum additional moment
M_{bx}, M_{by}	bending moments on critical sections due to design ultimate loads
M_i	maximum initial moment in a column due to ultimate design loads, but not less than $0.05Nh$
	bending moment from imposed load
M_{max}	maximum bending moment

M_{min}	minimum bending moment, generally due to self-weight of beam
M_r	moment of resistance
M_s	bending moment due to design service load, i.e. dead load + imposed load
M_s	bending moment at a distance s from the origin
M_{sx}, M_{sy}	design bending moments at midspan on strips of unit width for spans l_x and l_y respectively
M_t	design moment transferred between slab and column
M_u	moment of resistance at ultimate load
M_{ux}	maximum moment capacity of a short column at ultimate axial load and bending moment about the major axis only
M_{uy}	maximum moment capacity of a short column at ultimate axial load and bending moment about the minor axis only
M_x, M_y	applied moments about the major and minor axes of a short column, or a pad foundation
M'_x, M'_y	equivalent design moments in a biaxially bent column
M_0	moment necessary to produce zero stress in the extreme fibres of a prestressed beam
M_1, M_2	smaller and larger end moments in a braced slender column due to ultimate design loads
m	moment per unit width
	non-dimensional moment
N	ultimate axial design load at section considered
N_{bal}	ultimate axial design load on a column corresponding to the balanced condition
N_d	number of discontinuous edges
N_{uz}	ultimate axial load capacity of a column ignoring all bending
n	total ultimate design load per unit area, i.e. $1.4g_k + 1.6q_k$
	number of wires or bars
	number of unbraced columns
	number of samples in statistics
n_0	number of storeys
P_k	characteristic force in a tendon
P_o	jacking force
P_{op}	practical jacking force
P_s	prestressing force after long-term losses
P_t	prestressing force at transfer after immediate losses
P_{t1}	prestressing force at transfer corresponding to the lowest cable position
P_{t2}	prestressing force at transfer corresponding to the highest cable position
P_w	force in one prestressing wire or cable
P_x	prestressing force at a distance x from the jack
p	tensile reinforcement ratio $(A_{st}/(bd))$
p'	compression reinforcement ratio $(A_{sc}/(bd))$
Q_k	characteristic imposed load
q	distributed imposed load
q_k	characteristic imposed load per unit area

R	fan radius in yield-line method
	reaction force
	restraint parameter
	low-strength bar
r	internal radius of a bend in reinforcement
	ratio $\sigma_{max}/\sigma_{min}$
r_b	radius of curvature of a deflected beam
r_{ps}	radius of curvature of a prestressing tendon
$1/r_{cs}$	curvature due to shrinkage
$1/r_{ip}$	instantaneous curvature due to permanent loading
$1/r_{it}$	instantaneous curvature due to total load
$1/r_{lp}$	long-term curvature due to permanent loading
$1/r_x$	total curvature
S	crack spacing
	local snow load
	settlement
S_o	characteristic snow load with a return period of 50 years
	limiting distance at which cracking will not affect stress state
S_s	first moment of area about the neutral axis of the reinforcement
s	clear space between bars
	distance along a member from the origin
s_b	spacing of bent-up bars
s_v	spacing of links
T	torsional moment due to ultimate design loads
	tension force
	temperature
	high-strength bar
t	time
	temperature rise
t_e	effective section thickness
u	shear perimeter
u_0	shear perimeter which touches a loaded area
V	shear force at ultimate design load
V_b	design ultimate shear resistance of bent-up bars
V_c	design ultimate shear resistance of a concrete section
V_{c0}	design ultimate shear resistance of a prestressed section uncracked in flexure
V_{cr}	design ultimate shear resistance of a prestressed concrete section cracked in flexure
V_{eff}	effective shear force including allowance for moment transfer
V_t	design shear transferred to the column
V_u	design ultimate punching shear resistance of a concrete section
V_x, V_y	design shear force on critical sections of a pad foundation
v	shear stress

v_b	design shear stress resistance of bent-up bars
v_c	design ultimate shear stress resistance of a singly reinforced concrete beam
v_c'	design concrete shear stress corrected to allow for axial forces
v_{c0}	design ultimate shear stress resistance of prestressed section uncracked in flexure
v_{cr}	design ultimate shear stress resistance of a prestressed section cracked in flexure
v_t	torsional shear stress
$v_{t, min}$	torsional shear stress without torsion reinforcement at ultimate load
v_{tu}	design ultimate torsional shear stress
v_u	design ultimate punching shear stress resistance of a concrete section
W	total load on a beam
W_k	characteristic wind load
W_{sw}	self weight of beam
w	deflection
	loading per unit length
	width of a support
w_d	dead load per unit length
	design crack width
w_i	imposed load per unit length
w_m	average crack width
x	neutral axis depth
	a statistic, e.g. cube strength
	general dimension
$\bar{x}$	mean
x_{bal}	depth of neutral axis in a balanced section
x_1	smaller dimension of a link, centre to centre of bars
y	deformation
	general dimension
y_0	half the length of the side of an end block in a prestressed beam
y_{p0}	half the length of the side of an end plate in a prestressed beam
y_1	larger dimension of a link, centre to centre of bars
	distance from neutral axis to tension fibres
y_2	distance from neutral axis to compression fibres
$\bar{y}$	distance to the centre of area, or centroid, of a cross-section
Z	elastic section modulus
Z_x, Z_y	section modulus relative to major and minor axis
z	elastic section modulus
	length
	lever arm
z'	theoretical optimum elastic section modulus
z_1	elastic section modulus for tension fibres in a prestressed beam
z_2	elastic section modulus for compression fibres in a prestressed beam
z_1'	optimum elastic section modulus for tension fibres in a prestressed beam

z_2'	optimum elastic section modulus for compression fibres in a prestressed beam
α	angle between a bent-up bar and the axis of a beam
	coefficient used in the design of pad foundations
	$A_{sc}f_y/(bh^2f_{cu})$ in column design graphs
	load distribution factor for the Hillerborg strip method
α_c	ratio of the sum of column stiffnesses to the sum of beam stiffnesses
	coefficient of thermal expansion of concrete
α_{c1}	value of α_c at lower end of column
α_{c2}	value of α_c at upper end of column
$\alpha_{c,\,min}$	minimum value of α_{c1} and α_{c2}
α_e	modular ratio
α_{sx}, α_{sy}	bending-moment coefficients for slabs with no provision to resist torsion at the corners or to prevent the corners from lifting
β	bond coefficient
	angle of tilt
	St Venant torsion factor
	angle between the 'compression strut' of a system of bent-up bars and the axis of a beam
	coefficient used in the design of pad foundations
	effective height factor for a column
	moment factor for a biaxially bent column
	non-dimensional length
β_b	ratio of moment after to moment before redistribution
β_{red}	ratio of the reduction in resistance moment
β_{sx}, β_{sy}	bending-moment coefficients for slabs with provision to resist torsion and to prevent corners from lifting
β_y	bending-moment coefficient
β_1	ratio of the longer to shorter base sides
γ	bending-moment coefficient
	specific weight of soil
γ_c	specific weight of concrete
γ_f	partial safety factor for load
γ_m	partial safety factor for material strength
Δ	stiffness determinant
	deflection
	large increment
δ	angle of friction for a soil
	small increment
ε_c	concrete strain
ε_{cc}	final concrete creep strain
ε_{cs}	shrinkage strain of reinforced concrete
ε_m	net strain in reinforcement

ε_s	strain in tension steel
ε_s'	strain in compression steel
ε_{sb}	strain in the steel due to bending
ε_{sh}	shrinkage strain of plain concrete
ε_{sp}	strain in the steel due to the prestress force
ε_t	strain due to tension stiffening
ε_{th}	thermal strain
$\varepsilon_1, \varepsilon_2$	strains at level 1 and 2 in a column section
η	loss of prestress ratio (P_s/P_t)
η_s	loss of prestress ratio (P_s/P_0)
η_t	loss of prestress ratio (P_t/P_0)
θ	angle
λ	thermal conductivity
μ	coefficient of friction
	ratio of moments of resistance in orthogonal directions
	roof shape factor for snow loading
ν	Poisson's ratio
ρ	density of a material
	area of steel relative to concrete in a section
σ	direct stress
	standard deviation
	bearing pressure
τ	shear stress
ϕ	angle
	bar diameter, or bar size
	creep coefficient
	diameter of a pile
ϕ'	angle of shear for a drained soil
ϕ_e	effective bar size in bond
$\psi_{T,c}$	reduction factor for strength loss in concrete at temperature T
$\psi_{T,s}$	reduction factor for strength loss in steel at temperature T
ω	statistical risk factor for snow loads

1

Introduction

1.1 The design process

The aim of structural design is to achieve structures that satisfy the requirements of the client at an acceptable cost. They should carry all normal loads safely, both during construction and in service, and should have adequate durability. They should also be able to resist the effects of accident and misuse, and in the case of fire should be sufficiently resistant to allow time for the occupants to escape, for the fire to be fought, and to minimise damage.

The design process consists of three main stages.

1 *Planning and overall structural design* At this stage the size and shape of the structure are decided; materials for construction are selected; and an investigation is made into the load-carrying capacity of the soil at the chosen site. The disposition and approximate sizes of the structural members, i.e. beams, columns, walls, floor slabs, foundations, etc., required to give stability to the structure, are determined; and estimates of the costs of design, construction, and maintenance are made. At this stage also it is necessary to establish a system of communication between all the personnel responsible for the design and construction, and to specify procedures for inspection during construction.

2 *Structural analysis* Generally an elastic method is used, allowing for some redistribution of moments due to the formation of plastic hinges in statically indeterminate structures. As an alternative a plastic method such as the yield line method for the analysis of slabs can be used where appropriate.

3 *Design of members* With the forces and moments obtained from the structural analysis stage each member is designed separately, using stress analysis to determine the required section properties. The earlier *elastic* method of design, as specified in CP 114, contained a number of illogicalities and has been superseded by the *limit state method*. Limit state design was introduced in the previous standard CP 110 and has been retained in BS 8110.

1.2 Limit state design

1.2.1 Introduction

Since a structure must be capable of carrying any combination of loads that can reasonably be expected to be applied during its intended life, it must be designed for the combination that will produce the worst effects. This combination is referred to as the *service load* or *working load*. However, owing to the uncertainties inherent in structural design, an adequate margin must be provided between the conditions produced by the service loads and those which would exist if the structure were about to collapse or become unserviceable for any other reason. In earlier methods of design this margin was provided by applying a global factor of safety, either to reduce the material strengths or to increase the loads. In limit state design partial safety factors are defined for each material and for each type of load. This is a more logical approach, which enables a more realistic design model of the structure to be derived.

A limit state can be defined as the state of a structure which represents the acceptable limit of an aspect of structural behaviour. The general criterion for limit state design is that the probability of any of the limit states being exceeded during the intended life of the structure should be acceptably low. Limit states are divided into two classes: *ultimate limit states* are those which, when exceeded, result in a partial or total collapse of the structure; *serviceability limit states* are those which, when exceeded, do not cause collapse, but leave the structure in an unserviceable condition. BS 8110 defines the following limit states.

1.2.2 Ultimate limit states (cl 2.2.2, Pt 1)

Structural stability Structures should be designed so that the loads are safely transmitted from the highest supported level down to the foundations. Possible causes of collapse are: overturning, elastic or plastic instability of the whole structure, or the collapse of one or more individual members.

Robustness Structures should be planned and designed so that they are not unreasonably susceptible to the effects of accidents. In particular, means such as horizontal and vertical ties should be provided so that local damage involving the loss of a key structural member does not cause collapse of the whole, or a major part of the structure. A typical instance of this type of collapse occurred in the early morning of 16 May 1968, in a tower block at Ronan Point in Canning Town in the London Borough of Newham, when a gas explosion in one flat caused the progressive collapse of all the flats on one corner of the building. The recommendations given in BS 8110 for robustness stem from the subsequent enquiry into that accident.

Special hazards Factors of safety against collapse greater than those normally recommended may be required in the design of structures intended to house hazardous processes such as flour milling or the manufacture of unstable chemicals.

1.2.3 Serviceability limit states (cl 2.2.3, Pt 1)

Deflection due to vertical loading Deflections should not adversely affect the appearance of the structure or cause damage to non-structural members such as partitions, finishes, etc. The recommended maximum deflection in a beam is $\frac{1}{250}$ of the span.

Response to wind loads The lateral deflections or lateral accelerations should not cause damage or, in a tall building, cause alarm or discomfort to the occupants. Normally, to avoid damage to non-structural members, the relative lateral deflection in any one storey should not exceed $\frac{1}{500}$ of the storey height.

Cracking It is necessary to limit the width of cracks, which occur normally in a concrete structure, so that the appearance or durability of the structure is not adversely affected. Excessively wide cracks allow ingress of water, with subsequent corrosion or frost damage.

Vibration Vibration should not be sufficient to cause alarm or discomfort to the occupants, or structural damage.

1.3 Statistical basis for design

When a material such as concrete is manufactured to a specified mean strength, tests on samples show that the actual strength deviates from the mean to a varying degree depending on how closely the process is controlled and on the variation in strength of the component materials. It is found that the spread of results approximates to a *normal distribution curve*, as shown in Fig. 1.1.

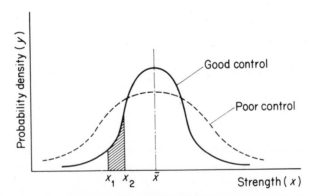

Fig. 1.1 Normal distribution curve.

The probability of a test result falling between two values of strength such as x_1 and x_2 is given by the area under the curve between the two values, i.e. the shaded area in the figure. The area under the whole curve is thus equal to unity.

The effect of quality control is as shown, poor control producing a flatter curve. The probability of a test result falling below a specified value is clearly greater when the quality of control is reduced.

The equation of the normal distribution curve is

$$y = \frac{1}{\sigma\sqrt{2\pi}} \exp\left[-(x-\bar{x})^2/2\sigma^2\right] \tag{1.1}$$

which shows that the curve is fully defined by the mean $\bar{x}$ and the standard deviation σ of the variable x.

For a set of n values of x the mean is given by

$$\bar{x} = (\Sigma x)/n \tag{1.2}$$

The standard deviation, which is a measure of the dispersion, is the root mean square of the deviations of x from the mean, given by

$$\sigma = \left[\frac{\Sigma(x - \bar{x})^2}{n} \right]^{1/2} \tag{1.3}$$

In practice it is not usually possible to obtain all the values of x that would theoretically be available. For example, it would not be possible to test all the concrete in a structure and it is therefore necessary to obtain estimates of $\bar{x}$ and σ by sampling. In this case the best estimate of the mean is still that given by Equation (1.2), but the best estimate for the standard deviation is given by

$$\sigma = \left[\frac{\Sigma(x - \bar{x})^2}{n - 1} \right]^{1/2} \tag{1.4}$$

where n is the number of test results in the sample.

Many electronic calculators have built-in functions which enable $\bar{x}$ and σ to be determined. However, if the results are obtained from samples it is advisable to check that the function which evaluates Equation (1.4) is used.

For hand calculations a more convenient form of Equation (1.4) is

$$\sigma = \left[\frac{\Sigma x^2 - n\bar{x}^2}{n - 1} \right]^{1/2} \tag{1.5}$$

Statistical distributions can also be obtained to show the variation in strength of other structural materials such as steel reinforcement and prestressing tendons. It is also reasonable to presume that if sufficient statistical data were available, distributions could be defined for the loads carried by a structure. It follows that it is impossible to predict with certainty that the strength of a structural member will always be greater than the load applied to it, or that failure will not occur in some other way during the life of the structure. The philosophy of limit state design is to establish limits, based on statistical data, experimental results, and engineering experience and judgement, that will ensure an acceptably low probability of failure. At present there is insufficient information to enable distributions of all the structural variables to be defined and it is unlikely that it will ever be possible to formulate general rules for the construction of a statistical model of anything so complicated as a real structure.

EXAMPLE 1.1   Mean and standard deviation (small sample)

Cube strengths of samples from a batch of concrete have the following values in N/mm^2: 34, 40, 42, 44, 50, 56, 60, 66. Find the mean and standard deviation for the sample and the best estimates for the batch.

Sample

$$n = 8$$
$$\bar{x} = (\Sigma x)/n$$
$$= (34 + 40 + \cdots + 66)/8 = 392/8 = 49 \ N/mm^2$$

$$\sigma = \left[\frac{\Sigma(x - \bar{x})^2}{n}\right]^{1/2}$$

which can be written as

$$\sigma = [(\Sigma x^2)/n - \bar{x}^2]^{1/2}$$
$$\Sigma x^2 = 34^2 + 40^2 + \cdots + 66^2 = 20\,048$$

Hence

$$\sigma = [20\,048/8 - 49^2]^{1/2} = 10.25 \ N/mm^2$$

Batch

$$x = 49 \ N/mm^2 \text{ as before}$$
$$\sigma = [(\Sigma x^2 - n\bar{x}^2)/(n - 1)]^{1/2}$$
$$= [(20\,048 - 8 \times 49^2)/7]^{1/2} = 10.95 \ N/mm^2$$

Summarising:

$$\bar{x} = 49 \ N/mm^2$$
$$\sigma = 10.25 \ N/mm^2 \text{ (sample)}, \ 10.95 \ N/mm^2 \text{ (batch)}$$

EXAMPLE 1.2 *Mean and standard deviation (large sample)*

The results of 100 cube tests representing a concrete mix are tabulated below. Calculate the mean and standard deviation for the sample and the mix.

32.9	33.2	32.2	35.2	32.0	35.6	33.8	33.1	37.4	38.6
28.6	29.3	34.5	30.1	35.5	29.3	32.0	33.9	32.3	30.8
31.3	33.2	27.8	35.3	30.0	36.3	33.3	28.3	30.9	40.1
32.5	31.7	34.5	32.8	36.4	33.3	30.4	33.4	36.6	40.5
25.1	33.0	31.7	32.1	26.2	35.9	33.4	32.3	32.9	29.9
32.8	33.5	34.9	33.1	32.7	28.7	31.6	32.8	36.8	40.8
31.6	33.8	27.3	30.3	35.8	33.4	34.3	26.9	31.2	31.4
29.1	29.6	35.3	34.9	32.1	35.9	33.2	32.6	37.6	37.8
32.0	34.2	30.0	32.6	36.2	29.2	33.7	31.9	38.4	30.1
33.9	34.4	34.6	34.0	36.3	36.5	34.1	34.2	38.2	38.3

With such a large number of tests it is convenient to group the data into class intervals of 1 N/mm^2 as follows. There is not much loss of accuracy if the class interval is fairly small.

Cube strength (x)	Class interval	Frequency (f)
25	24.5–25.4	1
26	25.5–26.4	1
27	26.5–27.4	2
28	27.5–28.4	2
29	28.5–29.4	5
30	29.5–30.4	8
31	30.5–31.4	4
32	31.5–32.4	15
33	32.5–33.4	20
34	33.5–34.4	12
35	34.5–35.4	8
36	35.5–36.4	9
37	36.5–37.4	4
38	37.5–38.4	5
39	38.5–39.4	1
40	39.5–40.4	1
41	40.5–41.4	2

The frequency f indicates the number of times that a result falls within the class interval whose mid-value is x. The sum Σx therefore becomes Σfx and Σx^2 becomes Σfx^2, i.e.

$$\Sigma x = 1 \times 25 + 1 \times 26 + 2 \times 27 + \cdots + 2 \times 41 = 3321$$
$$\Sigma x^2 = 1 \times 25^2 + 1 \times 26^2 + 2 \times 27^2 + \cdots + 2 \times 41^2 = 111\,231$$

Hence

$$\bar{x} = 3321/100 = 33.21 \text{ N/mm}^2$$
$$\sigma(\text{sample}) = [111\,231/100 - (33.21)^2]^{1/2} = 3.07 \text{ N/mm}^2$$
$$\sigma(\text{mix}) = \{[111\,231 - 100 \times (33.21)^2]/99\}^{1/2} = 3.08 \text{ N/mm}^2$$

Note that with such a large sample there is little difference between $\sigma(\text{sample})$ and $\sigma(\text{mix})$.

1.4   BS 8110 (1985)

BS 8110 gives recommendations for the design and construction of concrete structures excluding bridges, water-retaining structures, and concrete containing high-alumina cement. The standard is in three parts.

Part 1 covers the structural use of reinforced and prestressed concrete, both cast-in-situ and pre-cast. Recommendations for the design of members to the ultimate limit state are given in detail. The serviceability requirements for deflection and cracking are deemed to be satisfied if simple rules concerning the span/depth ratio of beams and the spacing of reinforcement are observed. The recommendations in Part 1 give designs that are safe and reasonably economical for most normal situations.

Part 2 contains additional information and recommendations which enable more rigorous analyses to be performed in situations where the methods of Part 1 are not directly applicable or where a significant advantage could be achieved.

Part 3 contains design graphs for the ultimate limit state in reinforced concrete beams and columns, based on the recommendations of Part 1. Design graphs for prestressed concrete are not included in the standard, but are provided in Appendix B1 in this book.

1.5 Drawings for reinforced concrete designs

1.5.1 Introduction

When a design is completed the results are communicated by means of drawings to those responsible for construction. The overall arrangement and external dimensions of the members of a structure or a major part of a structure are given in a *general arrangement drawing*, frequently accompanied by one or more *detail drawings* which show enlarged views of any parts that are too complicated to be included on a general arrangement drawing. Both of the above are outline drawings which do not show any reinforcement, but provide sufficient information to enable all other work such as setting out, excavation, and the design and erection of formwork to be undertaken. Work on the reinforcement is usually dealt with by specialist subcontractors, namely the bar bender and the steel fixer, who are responsible respectively for producing bars of the required shape and size and for fixing the bars in position prior to pouring the concrete into the moulds.

1.5.2 Bar-bending schedules

Specifications for the bending of bars and the preparation of bar-bending schedules are set out in BS 4466. Bars should be designed to have as few bends as possible and wherever practicable should conform to one of the *preferred shapes*, which can be defined simply by a shape code and certain basic dimensions. The bar-bending schedule is a table which provides the following information about each bar.

Member   A reference identifying a particular structural member or group of identical members.
Bar mark   An identifying number which is unique to each bar in the schedule.
Type and size   A code letter: T for high yield steel, R for mild steel (see Chapter 2), followed by the size of the bar in mm. For example R16 denotes a mild steel bar 16 mm in diameter.
Number of members   The number of identical members in the group.
Number of bars in each
Total number
Length of each bar (mm)
Shape code
Dimensions required for bending   Five columns specifying the standard dimensions corresponding to the particular shape code. These dimensions contain allowances for

tolerances. If a bar does not conform to one of the preferred shapes a dimensioned drawing is supplied.

Bars are delivered to the site in bundles, each of which is labelled with the reference number of the bar schedule and the bar mark. These two numbers uniquely identify every bar in the structure.

1.5.3   Drawings for reinforced concrete designs

Reinforcement drawings are prepared primarily for the steel fixer and should conform to the *Standard method of detailing reinforced concrete* issued jointly by the Concrete Society and the Institution of Structural Engineers. The main points to be noted are as follows:

1   The outlines of the concrete should be slightly finer than the reinforcement.

2   In walls, slabs, and columns a series of bars of a particular mark is indicated by the end bars and only one bar in the series is shown in full; the other bar is shown as a short line. In Fig. 1.2(a), for example, the reinforcement consists of two series of bars forming a rectangular grid in plan.

3   Each series is identified by a code which has the following form:

Number, type, diameter – bar mark – spacing, comment

For example, in Fig. 1.2(a) 25T20-1-250 indicates that the series contains 25 bars in high-yield steel (T), 20 mm diameter, with bar mark 1, spaced at 250 mm between centres. The complete code is used once only for a particular series and wherever possible should appear in the plan or elevation of the member. In sections the bars are identified simply by their bar mark; and again only the end bars need to be shown.

4   Since the bars are delivered on site bent to the correct radii, bends do not need to be detailed, and may be drawn as sharp angles.

5   Dimensions should be in mm rounded to a multiple of 5 mm. There is no need to write mm on the drawing.

6   Except in the case of very simple structures the dimensions should refer only to the reinforcement and should be given only when the steel fixer could not reasonably be expected to locate the reinforcement properly without them. In many cases, since the bars are supplied to the correct length and shape, no dimensions are necessary, as for example in Fig. 1.2(a). Dimensions should be given from some existing reference point, preferably the face of concrete that has already been cast. For example in Fig. 1.2(b) the dimension to the first link is given from the surface of the *kicker*, which would have been cast with the floor slab and is used to locate the column to be constructed. The formwork for the column is attached to the kicker and the vertical reinforcement starts from the kicker.

7   Cover to the ends and sides of bars is usually given in the form of notes on the drawing.

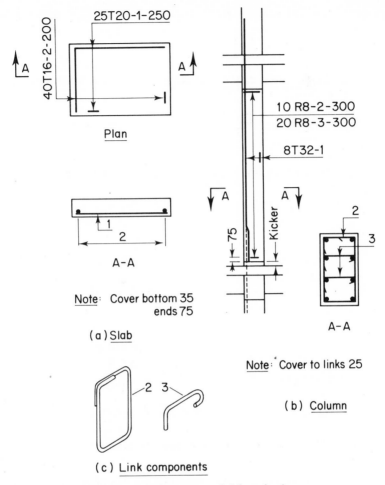

Fig. 1.2 Reinforcement of slab and column.

8   Only part of the outlines of adjoining members is shown and in sections only the outlines of the concrete which has been cut through are shown; any concrete beyond the section is generally omitted. The reinforcement in adjoining members is also omitted except where it is necessary to show the relative positions of intersecting or lapping bars. In such cases it is shown as broken lines. In Fig. 1.2(b), for example, it can be seen that the reinforcement of the lower column is to be left protruding from the kicker to form the lap with the reinforcement of the column to be constructed. Bars with diameters less than or equal to 12 mm need not be cranked at laps.

9   Sections are drawn to show the relative positions of bars and the shape of links. In the case of beams and columns they are usually drawn to a larger scale than the elevation.

10   The ends of overlapping bars in the same plane are shown as ticks. For example, the conventional representation of the links is shown in the section of the column in Fig. 1.2(b). The actual shapes of the link components are shown in Fig. 1.2(c). There is not really any need to indicate overlapping in links except when the separate components are

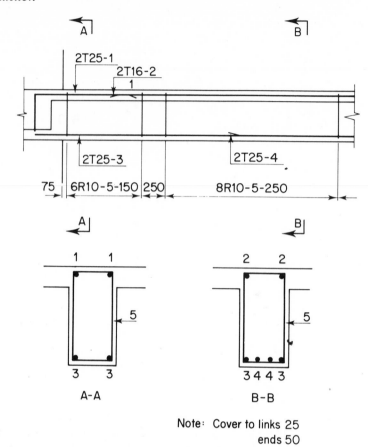

Fig. 1.3   Reinforcement of a beam.

to be fixed on site, as in this case. Where the links are supplied in one piece, as for the beam in Fig. 1.3, the ticks are frequently omitted.

11   Section arrows for beams and columns should always be in the same direction, i.e. left facing for beams, downwards for columns. The section letters (numbers are not recommended) should always be between the arrows and should be written in the upright position.

12   When detailing beams all the bars are shown in full. In elevations the start and finish of bars in the same plane are indicated by ticks. The start is identified by the full bar code, the end simply by the bar mark – see Fig. 1.3 which shows the elevation and sections of part of a beam. Note that the reinforcement in the adjoining column and integral floor slab is not shown; separate drawings would be provided for these. Note also that the dimension to the start of the first series of links is given from the face of the column already constructed and that a dimension is given between each series of links.

13   Although the reinforcement in adjoining members is not shown it is important for the designer to ensure that it will not obstruct the reinforcement of the detailed member. Thus it is especially important in beam–column construction to ensure that the reinforcements of a beam and a column do not intersect in the same plane.

1.6 Tutorial problems

1.6.1 Mean and standard deviation

Tests on samples of batches of concrete from two plants A and B yield the following strengths in N/mm^2.

> A: 30, 35, 25, 36, 42, 45, 28
> B: 35, 24, 40, 31, 36, 42, 35

For each batch determine the mean and standard deviation of the sample and estimate the mean and standard deviation for the batch.

Answer

	Mean	σ(sample)	σ(batch)
A:	34.4	6.78	7.32
B:	34.7	5.50	5.94

1.6.2 General questions

Use the results of the previous problem to answer the following questions.

(a)   Which plant exhibits the better control of the concrete strength?
(b)   What is the effect on the mean and standard deviation of
  (i)   adding $5 N/mm^2$ to each test result?
  (ii)   multiplying each test result by 1.5?
(c)   What strength corresponds to 1.64 standard deviations below the mean of the batch? How is this value related to the level of control over the strength?
(d)   If the whole batch could be tested, what proportion of the test results would be expected to fall below the mean?

Answers
(a)   Plant B – the means are approximately the same, but the standard deviation for Plant B is lower, indicating a smaller spread of results.
(b)   (i)   The mean is increased by $5 N/mm^2$; the standard deviation is not affected.
  (ii)   Both the mean and the standard deviation are multiplied by 1.5.
(c)   A: 22.4, B: 25.0. The strength at any specified number of standard deviations below the mean will be lower when the control is poorer.
(d)   50%

References

Report of the enquiry into the collapse of flats at Ronan Point, Canning Town. Ministry of Housing and Local Government, 14 October 1968.
BS 4466 (1981) *Bending dimensions and scheduling of bars for the reinforcement of concrete*. British Standards Institution, London.
Standard methods of detailing reinforced concrete. Report of the Joint Committee, The Concrete Society and the Institution of Structural Engineers.

2

Properties of Materials

2.1 Characteristic strength

2.1.1 Concrete

It follows from Section 1.3 that the mean strength of a material is unsuitable as the basis for design because 50% of all test results would be expected to fall below it. The design strength is derived from the *characteristic strength*, which is defined as the strength below which only 5% of all test results would be expected to fall (cl 2.4.2.1, Pt 1). The characteristic strength is therefore represented by the upper boundary of an area of 0.05 under the tail of the probability density curve, as shown in Fig. 2.1. If normal distribution is assumed it is 1.64 standard deviations below the mean strength.

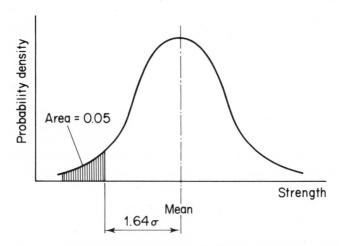

Fig. 2.1 Relationship between mean and characteristic strength.

The mean strength that must be aimed at can thus be determined if the standard deviation is known from previous experience of the particular manufacturing process. For example, to produce a concrete with a characteristic strength of 30 N/mm^2 in a plant for which a standard deviation of 5 N/mm^2 is expected,

$$\text{required mean strength} = 30 + 5 \times 1.64 = 38.2 \text{ N/mm}^2$$

The strength of concrete increases with age, as shown in Table 2.1.

Table 2.1 Effect of age on strength of concrete (from Table 7.1, Pt 2)

Characteristic strength (N/mm^2) f_{cu}	Cube strength (N/mm^2) at age of:				
	7 days	2 months	3 months	6 months	1 year
20	13.5	22	23	24	25
25	16.5	27.5	29	30	31
30	20	33	35	36	37
40	28	44	45.5	47.5	50
50	36	54	55.5	57.5	60

The characteristic strength f_{cu} is the 28-day cube strength, i.e. the crushing strength of a standard cube cured under standard conditions for 28 days. The 28-day strength is approximately 80% of the strength at one year, after which there is very little increase in strength. Strengths higher than the 28-day strength are not used for design unless there is evidence to justify the higher strength for a particular concrete (cl 3.1.7.3, Pt 1).

Specifications for the production and testing of concrete are given in BS 5328 and BS 1881 respectively. BS 5328 also covers the grading of concrete. Concrete mixes are either *prescribed*, i.e. specified by mix proportions, or *designed*, i.e. specified by characteristic strength. For example, grade C30P denotes a prescribed mix which would normally give a strength of 30 N/mm^2; grade C30 denotes a designed mix for which a strength of 30 N/mm^2 would be guaranteed. The grades recommended by BS 8110 are from 25 to 50 in steps of 5 N/mm^2 for normal-weight aggregates; C15 is the lowest grade recommended for lightweight aggregates. The lowest grades recommended for pre-stressed concrete are C30 for post-tensioning and C40 for pretensioning.

Although the definition of characteristic strength theoretically allows that a random test result could have any value, however low, a practical specification for concrete in accordance with BS 5328 would require both of the following conditions for compliance with the characteristic strength, thus excluding very low values:

(a)   the average strength determined from any group of four consecutive test results exceeds the specified characteristic strength by 3 N/mm^2 for concretes of grade C20 and higher, or 2 N/mm^2 for concretes of grade C7.5–C15.

(b)   the strength determined from any test result is not less than the specified characteristic strength minus 3 N/mm^2 for concretes of grade C20 and above, or 2 N/mm^2 for concretes of grade C7.5–C15.

Concrete not complying with the above conditions would be rejected.

2.1.2   Steel

The characteristic strength of steel reinforcement is denoted by f_y. For hot-rolled steel it is the yield stress; for cold-worked steel it is the 0.2% proof stress (see Fig. 2.5). The following values are recommended by BS 8110 (cl 3.1.7.4, Pt 1).

Hot-rolled mild steel	250 N/mm^2
High-yield steel (hot-rolled or cold-worked)	460 N/mm^2

For prestressing tendons the characteristic strength is the ultimate strength f_{pu} (see Fig. 2.5). Recommended values are given in Appendix A3.

2.2   Design strength

The characteristic strength allows for variation up the point of delivery at the manufacturing plant. It is determined from tests on samples of material that have been processed under strictly controlled standard conditions in a laboratory. Conditions on site, however, cannot be as ideal, or so strictly controlled, as in the laboratory. In the case of concrete some segregation may occur while it is being transported; conditions for casting and compaction vary; there may be contamination by rain; and curing is usually less than ideal, especially in very hot or very cold weather. The strength of concrete in an actual structure is consequently found to be less than the characteristic strength, and the variation in strength to be greater than in the laboratory.

The design strength of a material must therefore be lower than its characteristic strength and is obtained by dividing the characteristic strength by a *partial safety factor* γ_m. The value chosen for γ_m depends upon the susceptibility of the material to variation in strength – steel reinforcement is considerably less affected by site conditions than concrete. It also takes into account the probability of inaccuracies in the assessment of the resistance of sections and the importance of the limit state being considered.

Recommended values of γ_m for the ultimate limit state, which have been found by experience to give an acceptable level of safety for normal structures, are listed below (Table 2.2, Pt 1).

Reinforcement	1.15
Concrete in flexure or axially loaded	1.50
Shear strength without shear reinforcement	1.25
Bond strength	1.40
Others (e.g. bearing stress)	$\geqslant 1.50$

The same factors are implied when the serviceability limit states of deflection and cracking are dealt with by the 'deemed to satisfy' rules given in BS 8110, Pt 1 (see Chapter 5 in this book). Alternative partial safety factors may be applied when more rigorous methods of analysis are used, as described in BS 8110, Pt 2.

When the effects of exceptional loads, fire, or local damage are being considered γ_m may be reduced to 1.3 for concrete and 1.0 for steel (cl 2.4.4.2, Pt 1).

2.3   Modulus of elasticity of concrete (cl 7.2, Pt 2)

The modulus of elasticity of concrete does not need to be considered in the design of reinforced concrete members unless the actual values of deflection or crack widths have to be calculated, which is not normally necessary. However, it is required in the design of prestressed concrete members (see Chapter 12) and for the analysis of statically indeterminate structures (see Chapter 4).

The value of the modulus of elasticity is related to the type of aggregate and the strength of the concrete. Since the stress–strain curve for concrete is non-linear, a secant, or static modulus is used, based on the 28-day characteristic strength. BS 8110 gives the following formulae for normal-weight concrete:

$$E_{c,28} = K_0 + 0.2f_{cu,28} \tag{2.1}$$

where

$E_{c,28}$ is the modulus of elasticity (in kN/mm^2) at the age of 28 days.
$f_{cu,28}$ is the 28-day characteristic strength (in N/mm^2)
K_0 is a constant closely related to the modulus of elasticity of the aggregate.

For guidance it is recommended that a typical range of values of K_0 from 14 kN/mm^2 to 26 kN/mm^2 be considered, using the mean value of 20 kN/mm^2 for general design purposes.

For concrete at ages other than 28 days, the modulus of elasticity can be obtained from

$$E_{c,t} = E_{c,28}(0.4 + 0.6f_{cu,t}/f_{cu,28}) \tag{2.2}$$

where

$E_{c,t}$ is the modulus of elasticity of the concrete (in kN/mm^2) at age $t \geqslant 3$ days
$f_{cu,t}$ is the strength of the concrete at age t, from Table 2.1.

Alternatively the modulus of elasticity can be determined from tests, as specified in BS 1881.

2.4   Creep, shrinkage, and thermal strains

2.4.1   Introduction

This section gives a brief description of the properties of creep, drying shrinkage, and thermal expansion and contraction in concrete based on extracts from Section 7, Pt 2 of BS 8110. It is stated that while the information is based primarily on laboratory data and is provided for general guidance, it is, however, intended for general use in design offices and should be satisfactory for the majority of structures. In general these properties affect the deformation of concrete and must therefore be taken into account in the design of reinforced concrete at the serviceability limit states of deflection and cracking (see Chapter 5). They have little effect on the strength of reinforced concrete at the ultimate limit state. In prestressed concrete, however, since the ultimate strength and deformation are related, creep and shrinkage must be considered at both the serviceability and ultimate limit states (see Chapter 12).

For accurate prediction of time-dependent strains in concrete considerable experience is necessary, including the ability to predict changes in stress, the ambient temperature, and the relative humidity during the intended life of the structure. It is also necessary to carry out tests on the particular concrete that is to be used in the structure.

2.4.2   Creep (cl 7.3, Pt 2)

When a specimen of material is subjected to a stress below the elastic limit, an immediate elastic deformation occurs. In some materials the initial deformation is followed, if the load is maintained, by further deformation over a period of time. This is the phenomenon of *creep*. In concrete creep is thought to be due to the internal movement of

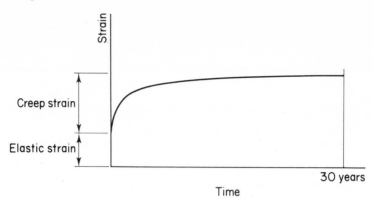

Fig. 2.2   Rate of creep.

free or loosely bound water and to the change in shape of minute voids in the cement paste. The rate of creep varies with time, as shown in Fig. 2.2.

It may be assumed that under constant conditions 40% of the total creep occurs in the first month, 60% in 6 months, and 80% in 30 months. For design purposes creep is assumed to be complete in 30 years. Creep is partly recoverable when the load is reduced. The final creep recovery after one year is given approximately by

$$\text{Reduction in final creep strain} = (0.3 \times \text{stress reduction})/E_u \qquad (2.3)$$

where E_u is the value of the modulus of elasticity at the age of unloading.

The *creep coefficient* ϕ is a coefficient which, when multiplied by the elastic strain, gives the final creep strain, i.e.

$$\varepsilon_{cc} = \text{stress}/E_t \times \phi \qquad (2.4)$$

where E_t is the elastic modulus of the concrete at the age of loading.

It follows that the effective modulus of elasticity, taking creep into account, may be expressed as

$$E_c = E_t/(1 + \phi) \qquad (2.5)$$

The *specific creep strain* is the strain per unit of stress, given by ϕ/E_t.

For design purposes it may be assumed that creep strain is directly proportional to stress, as implied in the above equations. Values of the 30-year creep coefficient for general use in the design of prestressed concrete members are given in Chapter 12. For more accurate prediction of creep strains the coefficient may be obtained from Table 2.2, which is derived from Fig. 7.1, Pt 2.

Table 2.2   Final (30-year) creep coefficient

Exposure	Effective section thickness (mm)	Age at loading (days)					
		1	3	7	28	90	365
Indoor	150	—	4.1	3.6	3.0	2.3	1.5
	300	—	3.3	2.8	2.3	1.8	1.2
	600	—	2.9	2.5	2.1	1.6	1.1
Outdoor	150	2.8	2.5	2.1	1.8	1.4	0.9
	300	2.2	1.9	1.6	1.4	1.1	0.6
	600	2.0	1.8	1.5	1.3	0.9	0.6

Indoor and outdoor exposure refer to normal conditions in the United Kingdom and correspond to relative humidities of 45% and 85% respectively. For other exposure conditions refer to BS 8110.

The effective section thickness is related to the ratio of the volume to the exposed surface area from which water can evaporate. For uniform sections the effective section thickness is defined as twice the cross sectional area divided by the exposed perimeter. If drying is prevented by immersing in water, or by sealing, the effective section thickness should be taken as 600 mm.

2.4.3   Drying shrinkage (cl 7.4, Pt 2)

Drying shrinkage, often referred to simply as *shrinkage*, is caused by the evaporation of water from the concrete. Shrinkage can occur both before and after the hydration of the cement is complete. It is most important, however, to minimise it during the early stages of hydration in order to prevent cracking and to improve the durability of the concrete. Shrinkage cracks in reinforced concrete are due to the differential shrinkage between the cement paste, the aggregate, and the reinforcement. Its effect can be reduced by prolonged curing, which allows the tensile strength of the concrete to develop before evaporation occurs.

In prestressed concrete shrinkage causes loss of prestress; and average values of shrinkage strain, for general use in the design of prestressed concrete, are given in Chapter 12. Table 2.3 is derived from Fig. 7.2, Pt 2 and may be used to obtain more accurate predictions of shrinkage strain in the United Kingdom. The conditions of exposure and the definition of effective section thickness are the same as those applying to Table 2.2 for creep strain. For other exposure conditions refer to BS 8110.

Table 2.3   Shrinkage strains in concrete

Exposure	Effective section thickness (mm)	30-year shrinkage microstrains	6-month shrinkage microstrains
Indoor	150	411	188
	300	360	101
	600	298	44
Outdoor.	150	123	56
	300	104	30
	600	88	13

The strains in the table relate to concretes of normal workability without water reducing additives, i.e. with an original water content of about 190 litres/m^3. For water contents between 150 litres/m^3 and 230 litres/m^3 they can be adjusted by simple proportion.

The following factors should also be taken into account when assessing shrinkage strain.

(a) The *type of aggregate* Aggregates which have a high moisture movement or a low modulus of elasticity produce higher shrinkages than are normally expected. For further information see BRE Digest No. 35.

(b) *Seasonal fluctuation* An increase in ambient humidity causes the concrete to expand. In concrete subject to outside exposure the maximum shrinkage occurs at the end of the summer. A typical seasonal fluctuation is ±0.4 times the 30-year shrinkage strain.

(c)   *Reinforcement*   Shrinkage is restrained by reinforcement. An estimate of the shrinkage strain on a member with a symmetrically reinforced section is given by

$$\varepsilon_{cs} = \varepsilon_{sh}/(1 + K\rho) \tag{2.6}$$

where

> ε_{sh} is the shrinkage of the plain concrete
> ρ is the area of steel relative to the concrete
> K is a coefficient taken as 25 for indoor exposure and 15 for outdoor exposure.

2.4.4   Thermal strains (cl 7.5, Pt 2)

Thermal strains are given by

$$\varepsilon_{ct} = \alpha_c t \tag{2.7}$$

where

> α_c is the coefficient of thermal expansion
> t is the rise in temperature.

The coefficient of thermal expansion depends upon the type of aggregate and the degree of saturation of the concrete. Typical values for partially dry concrete, corresponding to an ambient relative humidity of 60%, range from $7E-6/°C$ to $12E-6/°C$ depending on the aggregate. For saturated and dry concrete these values can be reduced by approximately $2E-6/°C$ and $1E-6/°C$ respectively.

2.5   Stress–strain curves for design

2.5.1   Introduction

Stress–strain curves are used primarily for the design of members in the ultimate limit state. In this state time-dependent effects such as creep and shrinkage have little effect, so it is only necessary to consider short-term loading. In reinforced concrete it is usually assumed that at the ultimate limit state the tensile strength of the concrete will have been exceeded, so that only the effects of compression need be considered. Both tensile and compressive effects must be considered, however, for reinforcement. In the case of prestressing tendons it is only necessary to consider tension.

2.5.2   Stress–strain curves for concrete

A curve representative of the actual conditions in a structure at the ultimate limit state has the shape shown in Fig. 2.3.

The maximum stress is reached at a strain of about 0.002, after which the stress starts to fall. Disintegration of the concrete does not commence, however, until the strain reaches 0.0035, which is therefore taken as the limiting strain for concrete in the ultimate limit state. The maximum stress is seen to be only 80% of the characteristic strength f_{cu}. The reason for this is that the standard cube test gives an artificially high result because of the lateral restraints produced by friction between the pressure plates and the faces of the cube.

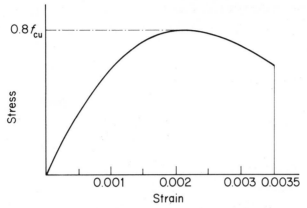

Fig. 2.3 Actual short-term stress–strain curve for concrete.

A curve having the general shape of Fig. 2.3 is fully defined in Fig. 2.1, Pt 2 for use when a rigorous analysis is required. For normal design purposes, however, BS 8110 recommends an idealised curve (Fig. 2.1, Pt 1). This curve is reproduced in Fig. 2.4. The rigorous analysis of sections is not considered in this book.

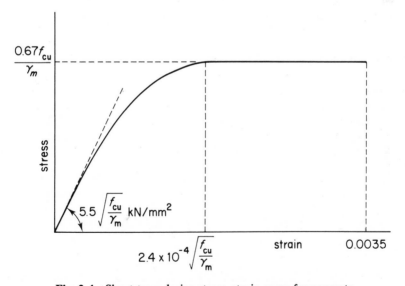

Fig. 2.4 Short-term design stress–strain curve for concrete.

The maximum stress is reduced to $0.67f_{cu}/\gamma_m$, where $\gamma_m = 1.5$, the partial safety factor for concrete. If the effect of γ_m is ignored the area under the idealised curve and the distance of its centroid from the stress axis is approximately the same as for the actual curve. The reduction of the stress from $0.8f_{cu}$ to $0.67f_{cu}$ is to compensate for the levelling out of the idealised curve and does not constitute an additional safety factor.

2.5.3   Stress–strain curves for steel

The shape of the stress–strain curve for steel depends upon the type of steel and the treatment given to it in manufacture. For the types of steel used for reinforcement actual curves produced by short-term tensile loading have the typical shapes shown in Fig. 2.5. Curves for compression are similar.

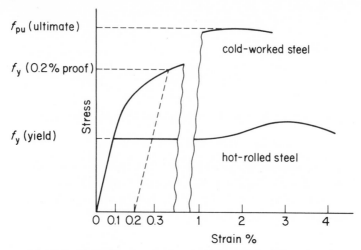

Fig. 2.5 Typical stress–strain curves for steel reinforcement.

From the figure it can be seen that reinforcing steels yield, or become significantly plastic, at stresses well below the failure stress and at strains well below the limiting strain for concrete (0.0035). In a reinforced concrete member, therefore, the steel reinforcement may undergo considerable plastic deformation before the ultimate limit state is reached, but will not fracture. However, large steel strains are accompanied by the formation of cracks in the concrete in the tensile zone, and these may become excessive and result in a serviceability failure at loads below the ultimate limit state.

For normal design purposes BS 8110 recommends a single, generalised stress–strain curve (Fig. 2.2, Pt 1) for both hot-rolled and cold-worked reinforcement. This curve is reproduced in Fig. 2.6. It is assumed that yielding commences at the design strength f_y/γ_m, where $\gamma_m = 1.15$, the partial safety factor for reinforcement. The modulus of elasticity is 200 kN/mm^2 for all types of reinforcement.

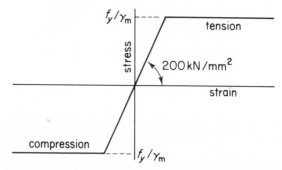

Fig. 2.6 Short-term design stress–strain curve for reinforcement.

Steels used for prestressing tendons have stress–strain curves similar to the curve for cold-worked steel in Fig. 2.5. Since prestressing tendons are subjected to stresses approaching the ultimate stress f_{pu} it is necessary to take a greater portion of the curve into account, and the generalised curve recommended by BS 8110 is trilinear (Fig. 2.3, Pt 1). This curve is reproduced in Fig. 2.7. The maximum stress is the design ultimate stress f_{pu}/γ_m, where $\gamma_m = 1.15$. The modulus of elasticity varies with the type of steel from 165 to 205 kN/mm^2, as shown.

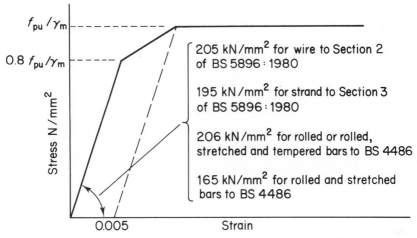

Fig. 2.7 Design stress–strain curve for prestressing tendons.

2.6 Tutorial problems

2.6.1 Mean and characteristic strength

Cubes made from samples of concrete from two different plants A and B have the following strengths in N/mm^2

A: 25, 30, 34, 40, 47, 49, 55
B: 30, 35, 37, 40, 42, 46, 50

Estimate the mean and characteristic strengths from each plant.

Answer
A: 40, 22.1 N/mm^2;   B: 40, 28.9 N/mm^2

2.6.2 Target mean strength

Assuming that there is no change in standard deviation, estimate the mean strength to which the mix would need to be designed in order to produce concrete with a characteristic strength of 25 N/mm^2 with plants A and B in Problem 2.6.1.

Answer
A: 42.9 N/mm^2;   B: 36.1 N/mm^2

2.6.3   Creep and shrinkage strains

A member with a 300 mm square section made in C45 concrete is exposed on all four sides to outdoor conditions. The load is applied when the concrete is three months old. The concrete is of normal workability and contains no additives. Determine:

(a)   the effective section thickness
(b)   the final creep coefficient
(c)   the modulus of elasticity at loading
(d)   the effective modulus of elasticity, taking creep into account.

Answers
(a) 150 mm; (b) 1.4; (c) 31.1 kN/mm^2; (d) 13.0 kN/mm^2

2.6.4   Shrinkage strain in a reinforced member

A 250 mm square column is symmetrically reinforced with 4T25 bars. It is built in to the structure so that half the perimeter is exposed to indoor conditions. Calculate the shrinkage strain after a period of 30 years. The original water content of the concrete is known to have been 220 litres/m^3.

Answer
245E−6

References

BS 1881 *Methods of testing concrete* (in several parts with different dates of issue), British Standards Institution, London.

BS 5328 (1981) *Methods of specifying concrete, including ready-mixed concrete*, British Standards Institution, London.

BRE Digest No. 35 (1983) *Shrinkage of natural aggregates in concrete*, Building Research Establishment, HMSO, London.

3

Loads

3.1 Characteristic loads

In general the loads applied to a structure are of the following types: dead loads, G_k, imposed loads, Q_k, wind loads, W_k, nominal earth loads, E_n, snow loads, and water pressure. Unlike material strengths, there is insufficient evidence to enable characteristic loads to be defined statistically.

Dead loads are loads due to the weight of the structure, i.e. the weight of all walls, permanent partitions, floors, roofs, finishes, and services. The actual weights of the materials used for construction should be used in the design, if known, otherwise average values may be obtained from BS 648, an extract from which is given in Appendix C1. An average value of the density of reinforced concrete is 2400 kg/m³, which is approximately equivalent to a specific weight of 24 kN/m³. The weights of tanks and other receptacles should be considered in both the full and empty conditions. The empty condition usually produces the worse effect when wind loads are acting.

Imposed loads are due to movable items such as furniture, occupants, machinery, vehicles, stored materials, etc., including inertia forces from the dynamic effects of movement. BS 6399, Pt 1 contains schedules of imposed floor loads that would normally be expected for different classes of occupancy. These loads include a small allowance for impact and other dynamic effects that may occur during normal use, but do not include forces resulting from the acceleration and braking of vehicles, movement of crowds, etc. The loads are usually given in the form of a distributed load and an alternative concentrated load. The alternative which produces the higher stresses is used for design, the concentrated load being placed in the position that will result in the most severe effect. Some examples showing the range of scheduled floor loadings are given in Table 3.1. A more complete list is given in Appendix C2.

Table 3.1

	Distributed kN/m²	Concentrated kN
Dwelling units (self-contained)	1.5	1.4
Boiler rooms (including machinery)	7.5	4.5
Assembly halls without fixed seating	5.0	3.6
Assembly halls with fixed seating	4.0	—
School classrooms, chapels	3.0	2.7
Industrial foundries	20.0	—

When designing a floor it is not necessary to consider the concentrated load if the floor is capable of effectively distributing the load. For the design of supporting beams the distributed load is always used. The actual values of loads, rather than those obtained from BS 6399, should be used when it is known that mechanical stacking of goods is intended or other abnormal loads are to be applied.

In multistorey buildings the probability of all the floors being simultaneously required to carry the full imposed load is less than that of an individual floor. Reductions in the loads transmitted to the supporting columns may therefore be made. For similar reasons the load to be carried by a single beam supporting a large floor area may also be reduced. These reductions are summarised in Chapter 4 (Fig. 4.28).

Wind loads are the static equivalent of the dynamic effects of wind on a structure. Methods of calculation may be obtained from CP3 Chapter 5, Pt 2 or BRE Digest No. 119. A brief description is also given in Appendix C4. The methods include an allowance for the increased stresses produced by the dynamic effects on buildings and objects of various shapes, sizes, and height. They also take into account such factors as the climatic conditions prevailing in various localities in the United Kingdom and the general roughness of the surrounding ground. The effects of vibration, such as resonance in tall chimneys, cooling towers, etc. must be considered separately, however.

Snow loads may be obtained from BS 6399, Pt 3. The effects of drifting, regional variations, altitude, roof shapes, and access are taken into account. A summary is given in Appendix C3. Snow load is considered as an imposed load.

Nominal earth loads may be due either to the action of earth on the structure, as for example on the vertical face of a retaining wall, or to the reaction of the earth to forces transmitted from the structure, as for example the bearing pressure beneath a foundation. Methods of calculation are not considered in general in this book, but see Chapter 11 and Design Studies 13.3 and 13.6.

3.2   Adverse and beneficial loads

An adverse load is one which increases the severity of the condition, i.e. stress resultant or deflection, under consideration. A beneficial load has the opposite effect. Consider, for example, the balanced cantilever beam in Fig. 3.1.

Assume that the maximum positive bending moment in span AB is to be determined. Its value is increased when w_1 is increased, but reduced when w_2 is increased. Therefore, w_1 is adverse and w_2 is beneficial. For other conditions the adverse and beneficial loads are as follows.

Condition	Adverse	Beneficial
Downward deflection at C	w_2	w_1
Downward deflection in AB	w_1	w_2
Negative moment at B	w_2	—
Spread of negative moment along AB	w_2	w_1
Shear at A	w_1	w_2
Shear at B in AB	w_1 and w_2	—
Shear at B in BC	w_2	—

Fig. 3.1

It follows that the worst conditions result when the adverse loads are at the maximum expected value and the beneficial loads are at the minimum. This is demonstrated in the next example.

EXAMPLE 3.1 The effect of adverse and beneficial loads

The symmetrical two-span continuous beam ABC in Fig. 3.2(a) is loaded by two distributed loads w_1 and w_2, as shown, which can each vary randomly from 10 kN/m to 20 kN/m. Calculate the maximum positive and negative bending moments and the maximum shear values.

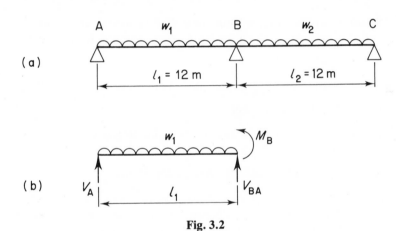

Fig. 3.2

It can be shown, by the theorem of three moments for example, that for equal spans of length l the bending moment at the support B is given by

$$M_B = -(w_1 + w_2)l^2/16 \tag{1}$$

Since both w_1 and w_2 are adverse in this case their maximum values must be used, giving

$$M_B = -(20 + 20) \times 12^2/16 = \underline{-360 \text{ kNm}}$$

Considering span AB as a free body – see Fig. 3.2(b) – and taking moments about B, the reaction at A is given by

$$V_A = w_1 l/2 + M_B/l$$

Clearly, since M_B is negative, the maximum value of V_A will not be obtained by using the value of M_B just calculated. However, by substituting for M_B from Equation (1),

$$V_A = (7w_1 - w_2)l/16,$$

which confirms what is obvious from inspection, namely that w_1 is adverse and w_2 is beneficial; and in order to obtain the maximum value of V_A, $w_1 = 20$ kN/m and $w_2 = 10$ kN/m must be used. Hence

$$V_A = (7 \times 20 - 10) \times 12/16 = \underline{97.5 \text{ kN}}$$

This is the maximum shear force at A.

By inspection the same values of w_1 and w_2 produce the maximum bending moment in span AB. The maximum bending moment occurs at the point of zero shear force. Assuming that this occurs at distance x from A

$$V_A - w_1 x = 0$$

Hence

$$x = V_A/w_1 = 97.5/20 = 4.875 \text{ m}$$

The maximum bending moment is therefore

$$V_A x - w_1 x^2/2 = 97.5 \times 4.875 - 20 \times (4.875)^2 = \underline{237.7 \text{ kNm}}$$

Since the beam is symmetrical the same maximum values occur in span BC.

Ignoring sign conventions for shear force, the shear force at B in AB is given by

$$V_{BA} = w_1 l/2 - M_B/l = (9w_1 + w_2)l/16$$

Therefore w_1 and w_2 are both adverse and the maximum value is given by

$$V_{BA} = 10 \times 20 \times 12/16 = \underline{150 \text{ kN}}$$

The maximum shear force at B in BC has the same numerical value.

3.3   Design load, partial safety factor for load

The design load is obtained for each type of load by multiplying the characteristic load by a partial safety factor γ_f. The value chosen for γ_f allows for unconsidered possible increases in load, inaccurate assessment of load effects, unforeseen stress redistribution, variations in dimensional accuracy, and the importance of the limit state being considered (cl 2.4.1.3, Pt 1).

Values of γ_f for the ultimate limit state are given in Table 3.2 (Table 2.1 in BS 8110, Pt 1).

The partial safety factors in the table may be assumed to provide an acceptable level of safety for normal structures. Their use also ensures that when a structure is designed for the ultimate limit state, the serviceability requirements will be met by observing the 'deemed to satisfy' rules in BS 8110, Pt 1 (see Chapter 5). An alternative approach allowed by BS 8110, but which will not be discussed in detail here, is to assess from experience, or by a more detailed analysis, the worst credible loads that may occur. It may then be possible to use values of γ_f lower than those in the table. However, if such an approach is adopted it may be necessary to carry out rigorous analyses for the serviceability limit states. For further information see cl 2.4.3.1.2, Pt 1 and Sections 2 and 3, Pt 2 of BS 8110.

In order to produce the most severe effect in the structure the adverse load must be as high and the beneficial load as low as may reasonably be expected. In combination 3 it is considered that there is less likelihood of the maximum adverse and the minimum

Table 3.2 Partial safety factors for load

Load combination	Load type					
	Dead Adverse	Dead Beneficial	Imposed Adverse	Imposed Beneficial	Earth and water pressure	Wind
1. Dead and imposed (and earth and water pressure)	1.4	1.0	1.6	0	1.4	—
2. Dead and wind (and earth and water pressure)	1.4	1.0	—	—	1.4	1.4
3. Dead and wind and imposed (and earth and water pressure)	1.2	1.2	1.2	1.2	1.2	1.2

beneficial loads being applied simultaneously, or for the maximum values of all three loads being reached at the same time. There is therefore no discrimination between adverse and beneficial loads and the values of the partial safety factors are lower than in combinations 1 and 2.

The values of γ_f for earth and water pressure should be applied in all cases except when the pressures are derived from loads that have already been factored, e.g. in the design of pad foundations (see Chapter 11).

3.4 Design envelopes

A design envelope is a graph showing, at any point on a structural member, the worst effects that result from the various load combinations considered in the design. The section dimensions and the reinforcement of the member are determined from the design envelope.

EXAMPLE 3.2 Design envelope for a balanced cantilever

The beam ABC in Fig. 3.3 carries the following characteristic loads:

Dead load 10 kN/m on both spans.
Imposed load 15 kN/m on span AB, 12 kN/m on span BC.

Sketch the design envelope for bending moment and shear force at the ultimate limit state. Indicate all maximum values and positions of zero bending moment (points of contraflexure).

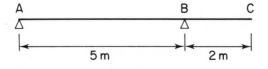

Fig. 3.3

Using the values of γ_f from Table 3.2 for dead and imposed load combination the maximum and minimum loads on the spans are as follows.

Maximum on AB $= 10 \times 1.4 + 15 \times 1.6 = 38$ kN/m
Maximum on BC $= 10 \times 1.4 + 12 \times 1.6 = 33.2$ kN/m
Minimum on AB or BC $= 10 \times 1.0 = 10$ kN/m

From the examples in Section 3.2 it may be deduced that the following load cases should be considered.

1.   Maximum on AB and BC
2.   Maximum on AB, minimum on BC
3.   Minimum on AB, maximum on BC

Plotting the resulting bending-moments and shear forces the diagrams in Fig. 3.4 are obtained.

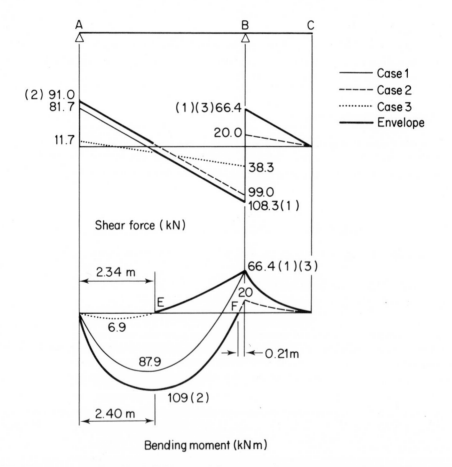

Fig. 3.4   Design envelope for clear and imposed loads.

Comments

(a) Only the numerical value of the shear force is required in design – the sign may, however, be important in the analysis of the structure.

(b) Positive (sagging) bending moments indicate that the bottom of a beam will be in tension; negative (hogging) moments indicate that the top will be in tension. Since beams need to be reinforced in the tension zone, it is conventional to draw the bending-moment diagram on the tension side, as shown.

(c) The envelope, shown as a heavy line, indicates the maximum values produced by any of the load cases. Note that on AB the envelope for shear force changes from case (2) to case (1) at the point where the numerical values of the shear force are equal.

(d) From the bending-moment envelope it is evident that tension reinforcement in the top of the beam is governed by case (3) and in the bottom of the beam by case (2). Note that in some regions tension reinforcement is required in both the top and the bottom of the beam.

(e) The points of contraflexure indicate theoretical points where the reinforcement may be curtailed, i.e. at points E and F on the bending-moment envelope.

In this problem it was only necessary to consider load combination (1) in Table 3.2. When wind loads are also acting additional load cases arising from combinations (2) and (3) must be considered; otherwise the procedure is exactly the same. It is frequently possible to decide which load cases will govern the design, and hence construct the envelope, without actually having to draw the complete diagrams for all the possible load cases.

3.5 Tutorial problems

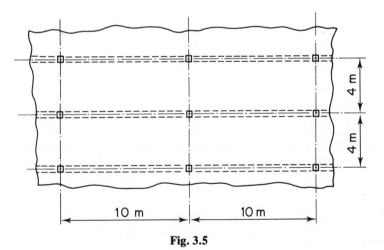

Fig. 3.5

3.5.1 Loads from a floor slab

Figure 3.5 shows part of a floor slab for a school supported by beams and columns. The slab is 150 mm thick; and the beams have a width of 250 mm and an overall depth (measured from the top of the slab) of 450 mm. Allowing 1 kN/m² for permanent floor covering and partition walls and assuming that each beam supports half the load carried by the slab on each side,

(a) determine for a typical beam the total dead and imposed characteristic loads and the total design adverse and beneficial loads,
(b) determine the maximum design axial load carried by a typical column (calculated by assuming that the beams are simply supported).

Answers
(kN) (a) 186, 120; 452, 186
      (b) 452

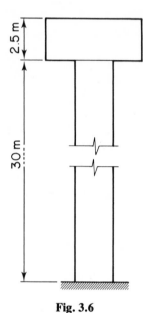

Fig. 3.6

3.5.2 Loads on a tower

A proposed design for an observation tower consists of a hollow concrete cylinder superimposed by a circular observatory as shown in Fig. 3.6. The characteristic loads are as follows:

Dead loads:
    Tower   900 kN
    Observatory 250 kN

Imposed loads:
    Tower   50 kN
    Observatory 325 kN distributed, with an additional concentrated load of 60 kN acting at a radius of 2.5 m

Wind loads (per metre of height):
Tower   1.5 kN
Observatory   6.0 kN

For each load combination in Table 3.2 determine the reactions (i.e. the vertical axial force, horizontal shear force, and moment) at the base of the tower,

(a) from the characteristic loads
(b) from the design loads for the ultimate limit state.

Answer

Load combination	Vertical (kN)	Horizontal (kN)	Moment (kNm)
Characteristic loads			
1. Dead and imposed	1585	0	150
2. Dead and wind	1150	60	1144
3. Dead and imposed and wind	1585	60	1294
Design ultimate loads			
1. Dead and imposed (max)	2306	0	240
(min)	1150	0	0
2. Dead and wind (max)	1610	84	1602
(min)	1150	84	1602
3. Dead and imposed and wind	1902	72	1553

Notes
1. For the design of the tower only the design loads would normally be considered, but for the foundation it may be necessary to consider both characteristic and design loads in separate stages of the design.
2. The (max) and (min) values of the design loads are obtained by the use of the load factors for adverse and beneficial loads respectively. The (min) reactions in combination (1) are the lowest possible and would not normally need to be considered. However both (max) and (min) need to be considered in combination (2). Generally the most severe effects are produced either by a combination of high axial force with high moment or low axial force with high moment.

3.5.3   Design envelope for a continuous beam

A continuous beam ABC has spans AB 6 m and BC 8 m. It has a uniform cross section and is simply supported at A, B, and C. Characteristic loads on both spans are: dead 25 kN/m, imposed 15 kN/m.

(a) What are the maximum and minimum design loads?
(b) What load combinations will produce maximum values of:
     (i)   shear force at A?
     (ii)   negative bending moment over the support B?
     (iii) positive bending moment in the span BC?
     (iv)   reaction at B?
(c) Sketch the design envelopes for shear force and bending moment, showing maximum values and the positions of zero bending moment.

Hints

For a uniform cross section the bending moment at B is given by

$$M_B = -(w_1 l_1^3 + w_2 l_2^3)/8(l_1 + l_2)$$

Plotting the maximum values on graph paper usually helps in constructing the shear-force envelope and in deciding which positions of zero moment need to be calculated.

Answers

(a)   max 59 kN/m, min 25 kN/m
(b)   (i)   max on AB, min on BC – i.e. load case (1)
      (ii)   max on AB, max on BC – i.e. load case (2)
      (iii)   min on AB, max on BC – i.e. load case (3)
      (iv)   load case (2)
(c)   see Fig. 3.7 (the load cases are shown in brackets)

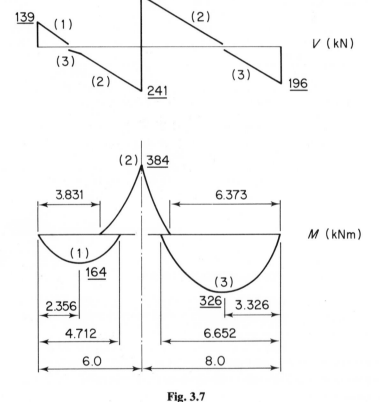

Fig. 3.7

References

BS 648 (1964) *Schedule of weights of building materials*, British Standards Institution, London.

BS 6399 (1988) *Loading for buildings* – Pt 1 *Code of practice for dead and imposed loads*, *Pt 3 Code of practice for imposed roof loads*, British Standards Institution, London.

CP3 (1986) *Code of basic data for the design of buildings* – Chapter 5 *Loading* – Pt 2 *Wind loads*, British Standards Institution, London.

Building Research Establishment Digest No. 119 (1983) *The assessment of wind loads*, Building Research Establishment, HMSO, London.

4

Analysis of the Structure

4.1 Introduction

The previous chapter has dealt with the calculation of loads – dead, live and wind – together with the concepts of limit states – serviceability and ultimate. The function of this chapter is to consider methods whereby the structure, or parts thereof, may be analysed under the applied loading at each of the limit states in order to determine the forces on the members and consequently to allow the member to be designed.

4.2 Design philosophies

4.2.1 Serviceability limit state

In this limit state, working or service loading is applied to the structure and thus an elastic analysis is appropriate. It should be pointed out that, in general, for reinforced concrete a full serviceability limit state analysis need not be carried out since the limit states concerning crack widths and deflection control can be carried out using 'deemed to satisfy' approaches. Only rarely is it necessary to employ full calculations for the above controls, most notably for highway structures and water-retaining structures for critical crack widths. It is essential that a serviceability analysis be carried out for prestressed concrete. This is, however, complex for hyperstatic structures due to the additional forces that will be introduced owing to the long-term effects of creep and shrinkage.

4.2.2 Ultimate limit state

At this limit state the concern is with incipient failure or collapse and thus factored loading is to be applied. The initial response is to consider allowing the use of 'plastic' methods of analysis. However, the use of such methods implies that the structural material will exhibit a large degree of ductility after the attainment of the yield or ultimate moment as in Fig. 4.1.

This in general will apply only to members which are predominantly in flexure, i.e. beams or slabs. The presence of shear forces will not significantly affect the assumption of ductility. The imposition of axial forces will, however, significantly reduce such ductility especially if the axial force is high enough to put the entire section into compression. Thus 'plastic' methods should not be used for frame structures.

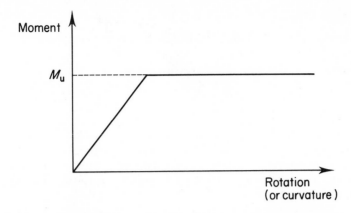

Fig. 4.1   Idealised moment–rotation relationship for plastic collapse.

It is permissible to use 'plastic' methods (yield-line approach) for slabs provided that any membrane forces are low. This will usually rule out the use of yield-line methods for multibay flat slabs, except that yield-line methods may give valuable insights into flat-slab behaviour around column heads (Reagan).

It is, however, possible to simulate the 'plastic' collapse approach for framed structures by carrying out what may be described as a 'pseudo-plastic' analysis by analysing the structure under the imposition of ultimate loading and then allowing a redistribution of the moments such that the resulting moment field is still in equilibrium with the applied loading. The amount of redistribution will be limited to ensure sufficient ductility in the members. This will effectively mean that redistribution can be carried out only on flexural members (Section 4.7).

Before considering further aspects of analysis, it is necessary to consider stability both of the structure and of the component members.

4.3 Stability

4.3.1 Member stability

Compared with structural steel work, this is not usually significant and is counteracted by placing limiting dimensions on structural elements.

(a) *Beams* (cl 3.4.1.6, Pt 1)
For beams the clear distance between restraints should not exceed the lesser of $60b_c$ or $250b_c^2/d$; for cantilevers with lateral restraint at the support only, $25b_c$ or $100b_c^2/d$, where b_c is the breadth of the compression face measured for beams midway between restraints and for cantilevers at the support, and d is the effective depth.

(b) *Columns* (cl 3.8.1.7 and 3.8.1.8, Pt 1)
For any column the clear distance between restraints, l_0, should not exceed 60 times the minimum thickness. If, however, one end of an unbraced column is unrestrained   (e.g. a cantilever column)   its clear height should not exceed the lesser of $60b$ or $100b^2/h$, where b and h are the smaller and larger dimensions of the column.

4.3.2   Structure stability

There are two basic concerns here. The first is that the structural elements are sufficiently tied together to avoid premature collapse caused by the removal of a member and the second concerns the possibility of the overturning of the structure under large horizontal loadings.

(a) *Tying forces*

Cl 3.1.4.2, Pt 1 states that   all structures (braced or unbraced) shall be capable of resisting at any floor level a horizontal force at ultimate limit state equal to 1.5% of the dead load of that storey (including the half height of the columns above and below).   This force is instead of and not additional to the wind loading. If the wind loading be larger, then it shall be considered instead of the additional force.

It is necessary to provide peripheral, internal, horizontal (and, for structures of five or more storeys, vertical) ties. Where expansion joints exist within the structure, each part shall be considered separately (cl 3.12.3, Pt 1). For design the reinforcement may be considered to act at its characteristic strength (f_y/γ_m). Reinforcement required to resist bending or shear, provided it is properly anchored, may be considered for resisting tying forces.

(i) **Peripheral ties**   (cl 3.12.3.5, Pt 1),

Peripheral ties at each floor and roof level shall be provided to resist a force of F_t, where F_t is the lesser of 60 kN or $(20 + 4n_0)$ kN where n_0 is the number of storeys in the structure. The tie must be placed within 1.2 m of the perimeter.

(ii) **Internal ties**   (cl 3.12.3.4, Pt 1),

In each direction the ties shall be capable of resisting the lesser of

F_t (kN/m width)

or

$(((g_k + q_k)/7.5) \times (l_r/5) \times F_t)$ (kN/m width),

where $(g_k + q_k)$ is the average characteristic applied load (kN/m) and l_r is the largest distance between the centre lines of supports in the direction being considered. The ties may be either uniformly distributed over the structure or grouped in the beams. The internal ties must be anchored adequately around the peripheral ties.

(iii) **Horizontal ties to columns and walls**   (cl 3.12.3.6, Pt 1),

These must resist the greater of
the lesser of $2F_t$ and $(l_s F_t)/2.5$, where l_s is the floor to ceiling height, and

3% of the total vertical design ultimate load at that level.

For corner columns, ties must be provided in both directions with each set of ties resisting the above forces.

(iv) **Vertical ties**   (cl 3.12.3.7),

These are to be designed to resist a tensile force equal to that of the maximum design vertical ultimate dead and imposed loading at that level.

EXAMPLE 4.1 Tying forces

For the structure shown in Fig. 4.2, design suitable ties using reinforcement of grade 460. Service loading for the structure is $q_k = 35$ kN/m and $g_k = 50$ kN/m.

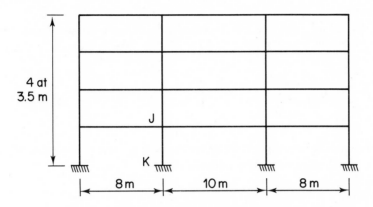

Fig. 4.2 Frame details for tying force calculations.

(i) Peripheral ties
No. of storeys $(n_0) = 4$,
so $20 + 4n_0 = 20 + 4 \times 4 = 36$,
so F_t is the lesser of 60 or 36,
$F_t = 36$ kN
Area of tie $= F_t/(f_y/\gamma_m)$
$\qquad\qquad = 36E3/(460/1.15)$
$\qquad\qquad = 90$ mm^2
Supply 2T8 (101 mm^2)

(ii) Internal ties
Consider point J,
calculate $(((g_k + q_k)/7.5) \times (l_r/5))$
$(((35 + 50)/7.5) \times (10/5)) = 22.6$
l_r must be taken as the higher of 8 and 10.
The tying force here is the value of F_t, i.e. 36 kN, and gives 2T8 bars.

(iii) Horizontal ties
Take the floor to ceiling height as 2.5 m,
thus $l_s/2.5 = 1$,
thus lesser of $2F_t$ and $(l_s/2.5) \times F_t$ is F_t.
Considering column KJ, the design vertical load is given by
$4 \times (1.6q_k + 1.4g_k) \times (8/2 + 10/2)$
$= 4 \times (1.6 \times 35 + 1.4 \times 50) \times (4 + 5)$
$= 4536$ kN
3% of the vertical force equals
$3 \times 4536/100 = 136$ kN,

thus the design force is 136 kN
Area of steel = 136E3/(460/1.15)
= 340 mm^2
Supply 3T12 (339 mm^2)

(iv) Vertical ties

Although they are not required for this structure, the calculation will still be performed. From above maximum design force at J is 4536 kN. This is then the design force for the tie, so

Area of steel = 4536E3/(460/1.15)
= 11 340 mm^2

Supply 14T32 (11 260 mm^2).

Although this area is substantial, the reinforcement for the column will be of this order owing to the bending moment acting on the column.

(b) *Overturning*

In general the critical case for overturning occurs when the maximum horizontal loading acts together with the minimum vertical loading. This will in general be given by the loading combination $1.4W_k + 1.0G_k$. Most structures are not susceptible to overturning, the exceptions being structures such as water towers where the wind force acts high up or where a large portion of the structure cantilevers beyond the foundations.

EXAMPLE 4.2　Overturning

Examine the two structures in Fig. 4.3 for overturning.

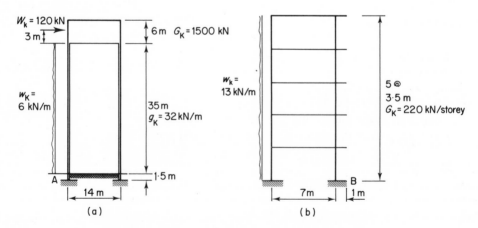

Fig. 4.3　Frame details for overturning calculations.

(a) *Taking moments about A*

$$M(A): 120 \times (6/2 + 35 + 1.5) \times 1.4 + 6 \times 35 \times (35/2 + 1.5) \times 1.4 + \cdots$$
$$- (1500 \times 7 + 32 \times 35 \times 7 + 400 \times 7) \times 1.0 = -8918 \text{ kN m}$$

The negative sign indicates that the restoring moment is greater than the overturning moment.

(b) *Taking moments about B*

$$M(B): 13 \times (5 \times 3.5)^2 \times 1.4/2 - 5 \times 200 \times (6.5 - 7.5/2) \times 1.0 = 36.9 \text{ kN m}$$

The positive sign indicates that overturning will occur.

4.4   Braced and unbraced frames

Essentially an unbraced frame is where the sway due to the imposition of horizontal loading is not limited (except by the inherent stiffness of the columns and beams) and the beam–column connection is required to resist the moment induced by sway. A braced frame is where the sway deflection is reduced substantially by the presence of cross bracing (rare in reinforced concrete construction), shear walls or a stiff core carrying the lifts, staircases or services. The bracing must be designed to take the action of the applied horizontal forces. Guidance on the design of cores to take such forces is given in a CIRIA Report (No. 112).

4.5   Frame analysis (cl 3.2.1, Pt 1)

4.5.1   General discussion

For a large frame structure, even with the availability of computer packages, an analysis of the whole structure is expensive and time consuming, and also probably unnecessary if only preliminary design is required. It should be remembered that an estimate of section properties will be needed to carry out the analysis of a hyperstatic structure. An analysis which takes account only of flexural effects should be sufficient.

To enable the analysis to be simplified BS 8110 allows the use of subframes. An example of this procedure is given in Fig. 4.4, where a 3-bay 4-storey frame together with all its possible subframes is illustrated, for both the braced and unbraced cases. It will not be necessary, in practice, to analyse all the possible subframes.

4.5.2   Subframes

The cases for braced and unbraced frames must be considered separately.

(a) *Braced frames*
All columns take full stiffness as do all beams spanning between joints which allow rotation (i.e. attached to columns).   Beams having one end fixed take a reduced stiffness of 50%   (cl 3.2.1.2.3) to allow for the fact that the remote end of the beam is fixed against rotation.

The structure (or substructure) will be subjected to the following loading cases (cl 3.2.1.2.2 Pt 1):

1.   *All spans with full loading* $(1.6Q_k + 1.4G_k)$, and

2.   *Alternate spans full load and the remainder with* $1.0G_k$ *only*
Note that the first loading case replaces the adjacent spans loaded case from CP 110 and

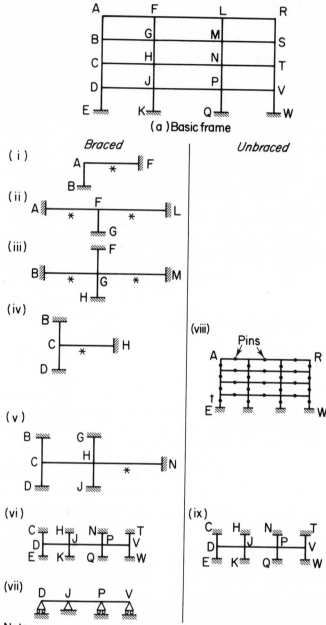

(a) Basic frame

(b) Subframes

Notes

(1) All members marked (∗) take reduced stiffness of half full value
(2) Ends of beams or columns may be taken as pinned as against
     encastré if more appropriate
(3) Not all subframes will need to be considered
(4) If the feet of the columns at foundation level are considered to be
     pinned then the pins marked (↑) should be omitted

Fig. 4.4   Basic frame with typical subframes for both the braced and unbraced case.

is to be used to determine the hogging moments over the supports. The all spans loaded case will slightly under estimate the maximum hogging moments. The second loading case will produce two loading patterns (this is illustrated in Example 4.3).

(b)   *Unbraced frames* (cl 3.2.1.3.2, Pt 1)
Only the two frames shown in Fig. 4.4(b) can be considered. The first (subframe(ix)) is similar to that for the unbraced case (subframe(vi)) except that all spans are to be loaded with $1.2(Q_k + G_k)$. The second (subframe(viii)) is to be analysed under the effect of wind loading $(1.2W_k)$, and is carried out by assuming points of contraflexure at the midpsans of all the beams and mid-storey heights for all the columns, including the bottom storey if the frame is considered to have fixed feet. If the frame has pinned feet, then a point of contraflexure already exists in the lower storey. It is thus possible to place hypothetical hinges at these positions and analyse the frame as isostatic. The horizontal reactions from the wind loading should be apportioned in the ratio of the column stiffnesses.

4.5.3   Sign conventions

In this text the following sign conventions have been adopted:

1.   Clockwise moments and rotations at the ends of members have been taken as positive,
2.   Hogging bending moments are negative and sagging bending moments positive,
3.   The sign of the shear force has been determined from the following relationship:

$$V = dM/dx \qquad\qquad (4.1)$$

All bending moment diagrams have been plotted on the tension face of the member in accordance with normal practice.

EXAMPLE 4.3   Frame analysis

Consider the frame shown in Fig. 4.5, which carries the following loading:

$$q_k = 35 \text{ kN/m}, \quad g_k = 50 \text{ kN/m} \quad \text{and} \quad w_k = 74 \text{ kN/m}$$

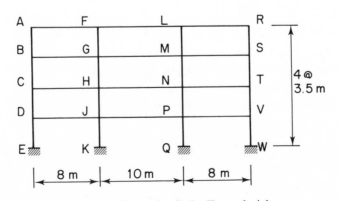

Fig. 4.5   Frame details for Example 4.1.

and has the following section properties:

$I_c = 2.13\text{E}11 \text{ mm}^4$, $I_{b8} = 1\text{E}12 \text{ mm}^4$, $I_{b10} = 4.35\text{E}12 \text{ mm}^4$ and $E_c = 26 \text{ kN/}$
mm^2

Analyse all the possible subframes for both the braced and the unbraced case and sketch the bending moment and shear force diagrams.

Note: in this example the analysis has been undertaken using slope deflection (see Section 4.5.5)

Member stiffnesses ($k = EI/L$)

8 m beam: $k_8 = 26 \times 1\text{E}12/8000\text{E}3 = 3.25\text{E}6 \text{ kN m}$
10 m beam: $k_{10} = 26 \times 4.35\text{E}12/10\,000\text{E}3 = 11.31\text{E}9 \text{ kN m}$
Column: $k_c = 26 \times 2.13\text{E}11/3500\text{E}3 = 1.58\text{E}6 \text{ kN m}$.

Loading:
1.   Dead load only ($1.0G_k$) = 50 kN/m
2.   Dead and live load ($1.6Q_k + 1.4G_k$) = $1.6 \times 35 + 1.4 \times 50 = 126$ kN/m
3.   Wind loading case ($1.2(Q_k + G_k)$) = $1.2(35 + 50) = 102$ kN/m

Table 4.1 gives the free and fixed moment data for all the load cases.

Table 4.1   Bending-moment data

Free bending moments ($ql^2/8$)

Load case	Span 8 m	10 m
$1.0G_k$	400	625
$1.6Q_k + 1.4G_k$	1008	1575
$1.2(Q_k + G_k)$	816	1275

Fixed end moments ($ql^2/12$ numerically)

Load case	Span 8 m	10 m
$1.0G_k$	267	417
$1.6Q_k + 1.4G_k$	672	1050
$1.2(Q_k + G_k)$	544	850 kN m

Braced
(i) *Single beam and column* (Fig. 4.6)

$M_{AB} = -M_{AF} = -k_{CL}M_{11}/(k_{CL} + k_{B1}/2)$
$M_{BA} = M_{AB}/2$
$M_{FA} = (4k_{CL}M_{12} + k_{B1}(2M_{12} - M_{11}))/(4k_{CL} + 2k_{B1})$
$M_{11} = -672 \text{ kN m}, M_{12} = 672 \text{ kN m}$
$k_{B1} = 3.25\text{E}6 \text{ kN m}, k_{CL} = 1.58\text{E}6 \text{ kN m},$

thus

$M_{AB} = 331 \text{ kN m and } M_{FA} = 842 \text{ kN m}.$

Reaction at A,

$R_A = q \times L_{AF}/2 - (M_{AF} + M_{FA})/L_{AF},$

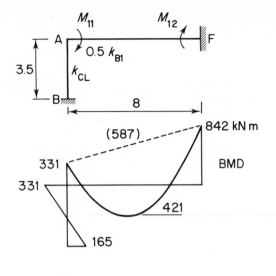

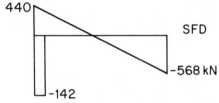

Fig. 4.6   Subframe (i).

Reaction at F,

$$R_F = q \times L_{AF}/2 + (M_{AF} + M_{FA})/L_{AF}$$

so,

$$R_A = 440 \text{ kN and } R_F = 568 \text{ kN}.$$

(ii) *Two beams and one column* (Fig. 4.7)

$$\Delta = 2(k_{B1} + k_{B2}) + 4k_{CL}$$
$$M_{AF} = (k_{B1}(2M_{11} - M_{12} - M_{21}) + 2(k_{B2} + 2k_{CL})M_{11})/\Delta$$
$$M_{FA} = (2(k_{B2}M_{11} - k_{B1}M_{21}) + 4k_{CL}M_{12})/\Delta$$
$$M_{FL} = (2(k_{B1}M_{21} - k_{B2}M_{21}) + 4k_{CL}M_{21})/\Delta$$
$$M_{MF} = (k_{B2}(2M_{22} - M_{21} - M_{12}) + 2(k_{B1} + 2k_{CL})M_{22})/\Delta$$
$$M_{FG} = 2M_{GF} = -4k_{CL}(M_{21} + M_{12})/\Delta$$

Reactions:

$$R_{AF} = q_{AF}L_{AF}/2 - (M_{FA} + M_{AF})/L_{AF}$$
$$R_{FA} = q_{AF}L_{AF}/2 + (M_{FA} + M_{AF})/L_{AF}$$
$$R_{FL} = q_{FL}L_{FL}/2 - (M_{LF} + M_{FL})/L_{FL}$$
$$R_{LF} = q_{FL}L_{FL}/2 + (M_{FL} + M_{LF})/L_{FL}$$

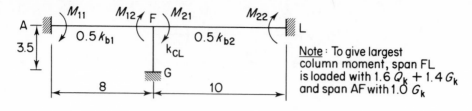

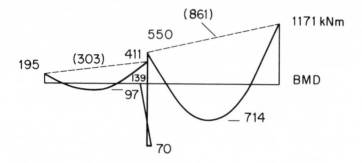

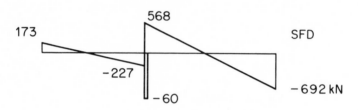

Fig. 4.7   Subframe (ii).

$M_{12} = -M_{11} = 267$ kN m
$M_{22} = -M_{21} = 1050$ kN m
$\Delta = 35.44\text{E}6$ kN m,

thus

$M_{AF} = -195$, $M_{FA} = 411$, $M_{FL} = -550$, $M_{LF} = 1171$, $M_{FG} = 139$ and
$M_{GF} = 70$ kN m respectively.

$R_{AF} = 173$, $R_{FA} = 227$, $R_{FL} = 568$, and $R_{LF} = 692$ kN respectively.

Note: a similar subframe can be set up at FLRM giving the same results.

(iii) *Two beams with columns above and below at centre* (Fig. 4.8)

$\Delta = 2(k_{B2} + k_{B1}) + 4(k_{CU} + k_{CL})$
$M_{HG} = 2M_{GH} = -4k_{CU}(M_{21} + M_{12})/\Delta$
$M_{HJ} = 2M_{JH} = -4k_{CL}(M_{12} + M_{21})/\Delta$
$M_{CH} = (k_{B1}(2M_{11} - M_{12} - M_{21}) + 2M_{11}(k_{B2} + 2k_{CU} + 2k_{CL}))/\Delta$
$M_{HC} = (2M_{12}(k_{B2} + 2(k_{CL} + k_{CU})) - 2k_{B1}M_{21})/\Delta$
$M_{HN} = (2M_{21}(k_{B1} + 2(k_{CU} + k_{CL})) - 2k_{B2}M_{12})/\Delta$
$M_{NH} = (k_{B2}(2M_{22} - M_{21} - M_{12}) + 2M_{22}(k_{B1} + 2(k_{CU} + k_{CL})))/\Delta$

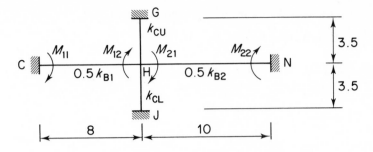

Note: Span HN carries maximum load and CH minimum

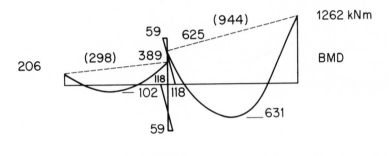

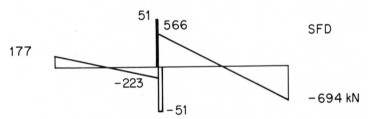

Fig. 4.8   Subframe (iii).

Reactions:

$$R_{CH} = q_{CH}L_{CH}/2 - (M_{CH} + M_{HC})/L_{CH}$$
$$R_{HC} = q_{CH}L_{CH}/2 + (M_{CH} + M_{HC})/L_{CH}$$
$$R_{HN} = q_{HN}L_{HN}/2 - (M_{HN} + M_{NH})/L_{HN}$$
$$R_{NH} = q_{HN}L_{HN}/2 + (M_{HN} + M_{NH})/L_{HN}$$
$$M_{12} = -M_{11} = 267 \text{ kN m}$$
$$M_{22} = -M_{21} = 1050 \text{ kN m}$$
$$\Delta = 417.6\text{E}8 \text{ kN m,}$$

thus

$$M_{HG} = M_{HJ} = 2M_{GH} = 2M_{JH} = 118 \text{ kNm}$$
$M_{HC} = 389$, $M_{CH} = -206$, $M_{HN} = -625$ and $M_{NH} = 1262$ kN m respectively.
$R_{CH} = 177$, $R_{HC} = 223$, $R_{HN} = 566$, and $R_{NH} = 694$ kN respectively.

The total load on the column from level CNH is given by

$$R_{HC} + R_{HN} = 789 \text{ kN}$$

(iv) *Single beam and one column above and below* (Fig. 4.9)

$$\Delta = 4(k_{CU} + k_{CL}) + 2k_{B1}$$
$$M_{CD} = 2M_{DC} = -4k_{CU}M_{11}/\Delta$$
$$M_{CB} = 2M_{BC} = -4k_{CL}M_{11}/\Delta$$
$$M_{CH} = 4(k_{CL} + k_{CU})M_{11}/\Delta$$
$$M_{HC} = (2k_{B1}(M_{12} - M_{11}) + 4(k_{CU} + k_{CL})M_{12})/\Delta$$
$$M_{12} = -M_{11} = 672 \text{ kN m}$$
$$\Delta = 19.12\text{E6 kN m,}$$

thus

$$M_{CD} = M_{CB} = 2M_{CD} = 2M_{BC} = 222 \text{ kN m}$$
$$M_{CH} = -444 \text{ and } M_{HC} = 900 \text{ kN m}$$
$$R_{CH} = 447 \text{ and } R_{HC} = 561 \text{ kN respectively.}$$

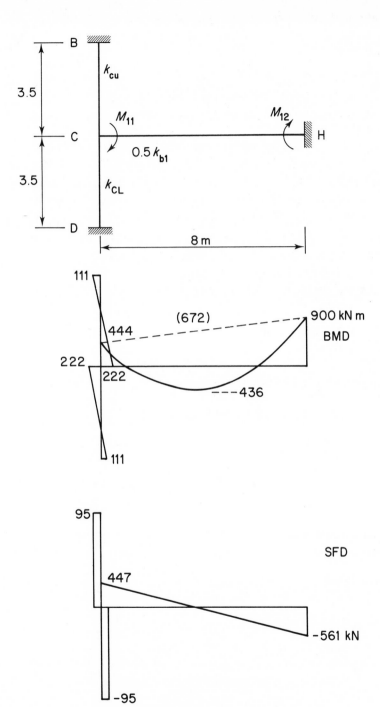

Fig. 4.9   Subframe (iv).

(v) *Two beams with two pairs of columns above and below* (Fig. 4.10)

There are three load cases:

1. all spans full load (126 kN m),
2. Span CH full load (126), HN dead load only (50), and
3. Span CH dead load only (50), HN full load (126)

$$\Delta = 16(k_{CU} + k_{CL} + k_{B1})(k_{CL} + k_{CU} + k_{B1} + 0.5k_{B2}) - 4k_{B1}^2.$$

$$M_{CB} = 2M_{BC} = 4k_{CU}(-4M_{11}(k_{CU} + k_{CL} + k_{B1} + 0.5k_{B2}) + 2(M_{12} + M_{21})k_{B1})/\Delta$$

$$M_{CD} = 2M_{DC} = 4k_{CL}(-4M_{11}(k_{CU} + k_{C1} + k_{B1} + 0.5k_{B2}) + 2(M_{12} + M_{21})k_{B1})/\Delta$$

$$M_{HG} = 2M_{GH} = 4k_{CU}(-4(M_{12} + M_{21})(k_{CU} + k_{CL} + k_{B1}) + 2k_{B1}M_{11})/\Delta$$

$$M_{HJ} = 2M_{JH} = 4k_{CL}(-4(M_{12} + M_{21})(k_{CU} + k_{CL} + k_{B1}) + 2k_{B1}M_{11})/\Delta$$

$$M_{HN} = 2k_{B2}(-4(M_{12} + M_{21})(k_{CU} + k_{CL} + k_{B1}) + 2k_{B1}M_{11})/\Delta + M_{21}$$

$$M_{CH} = -k_{B1}(-4M_{11}(4k_{CU} + 4k_{CL} + 2k_{B2} + 3k_{B1}) + \cdots$$
$$+ 8(M_{12} + M_{21})(k_{CL} + k_{CU}))/\Delta + M_{11}$$

$$M_{HC} = -k_{B1}(8M_{11}(k_{CU} + k_{CL} + 0.5k_{B2}) + \cdots$$
$$+ 4(M_{12} + M_{21})(4k_{CU} + 4k_{CL} + 3k_{B1}))/\Delta + M_{12}$$

$$M_{NH} = k_{B2}(-4(M_{12} + M_{21})(k_{CU} + k_{CL} + k_{B1}) + 2k_{B1}M_{11}))/\Delta + M_{22}$$
$$\Delta = 12E14 \text{ (kN m)}$$

Table 4.2 presents the results for each load case.

Table 4.2   Results for Subframe (iv)

	Load case		
	1	2	3
Moments (kN m)			
M_{11}	−672	−672	−267
M_{12}	672	672	267
M_{21}	−1050	−417	−1050
M_{22}	1050	417	1050
M_{CB} & M_{CD}	159	181	41
M_{HG} & M_{HJ}	29	−57	98
M_{HN}	−950	−624	−704
M_{CH}	−318	−362	−82
M_{HC}	892	738	508
M_{NH}	1100	314	1223
Reactions (kN)			
R_{CH}	432	457	147
R_{HC}	576	551	253
R_{HN}	615	219	578
R_{HN}	645	281	682

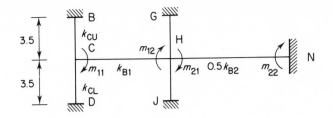

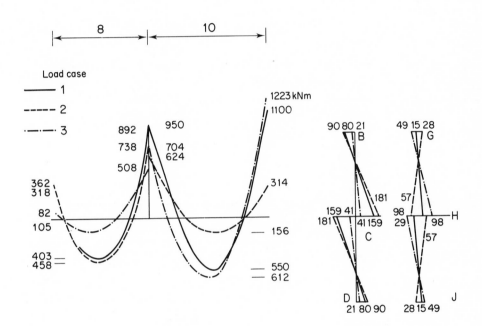

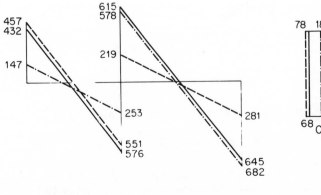

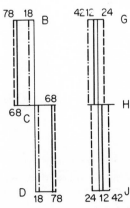

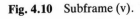

Fig. 4.10 Subframe (v).

(vi) *Complete storey* (Fig. 4.11)

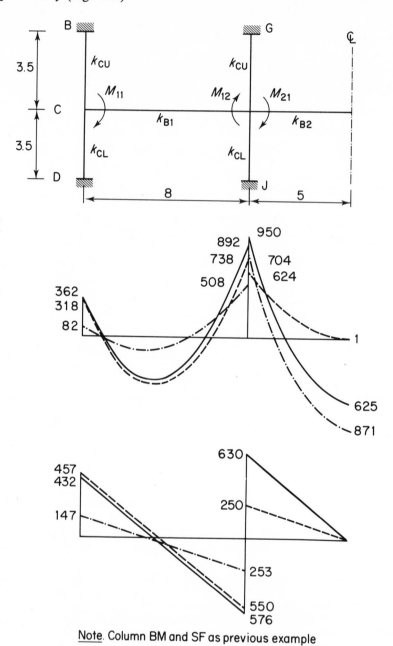

Note. Column BM and SF as previous example

Fig. 4.11   Subframe (vi).

There is structural symmetry about the centre line and there will also be symmetry of loading for all load cases, and consequently the stiffness of member HN may be reduced to $0.5k_{B2}$. This means that the solution given in (v) may be used (except that the moment at N for span NH is numerically equal to that at H).

(vii) *Continuous beam* (Fig. 4.12)

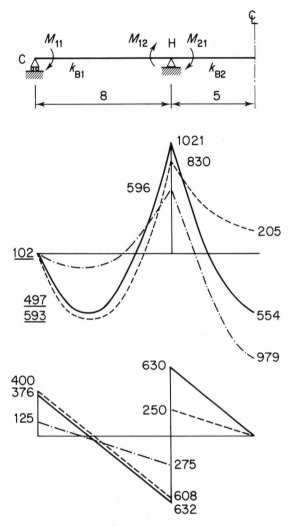

Fig. 4.12   Subframe (vii).

As in the previous case symmetry may be used to simplify the problem.

$$M_{CH} = 0$$
$$M_{HC} = -M_{HN} = -(k_{B2}(M_{11} - 2M_{12}) + 3k_{B1}M_{21})/(3k_{B1} + 2k_{B2})$$

The results of the analysis are presented in Table 4.3.

Table 4.3   Results for Subframe (vi)

	Load case		
	1	2	3
Moments (kN m)			
M_{11}	−672	−672	−267
M_{12}	672	672	267
M_{21}	−1050	−417	−1050
M_{HC}	1021	830	596
Reactions (kN)			
R_{CH}	376	400	125
R_{HC}	632	608	275
R_{HN}	630	250	630

Only one subframe may be considered – that comprising the whole of one storey loaded with $1.2(G_k + Q_k)$. The results for this may be obtained *pro rata* from load case 1 of subframe (vi).

So

$$M_{11} = -M_{12} = -554 \text{ kN m and } M_{21} = -M_{22} = -850 \text{ kN m giving}$$

$$M_{CB} = M_{CD} = 129, \quad M_{HG} = M_{HJ} = 23, \quad M_{HN} = -768, \quad M_{CH} = -258, \quad \text{and}$$

$$M_{HC} = 722 \text{ kN m respectively.}$$

Unbraced
(i)   *Vertical loading* (Fig. 4.13)

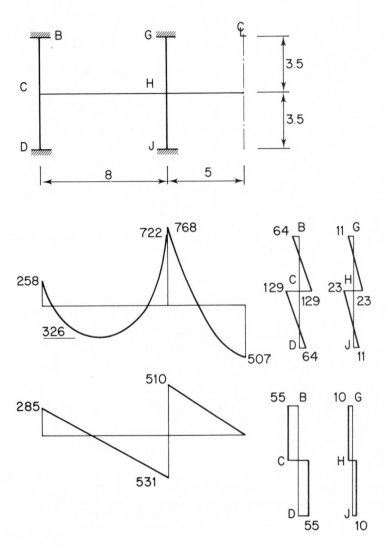

Fig. 4.13   Single-storey subframe for the 'braced' case.

(ii) *Horizontal loads* (Fig. 4.14)

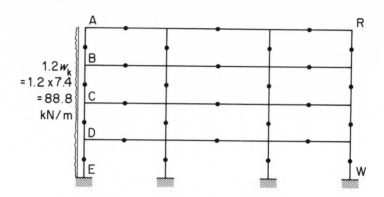

Fig. 4.14   Wind loading on frame.

Applied   force   at   A   and $E = 88.8 \times 3.5/2 = 155.4$ kN,   and   at   B,   C   and
$D = 155.4 \times 2 = 310.8$ kN

Top Storey

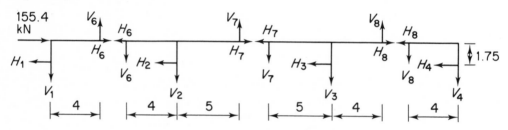

Fig. 4.15   Analysis of top storey.

The applied vertical force is resisted in proportion to the stiffnesses of the columns, thus
each of the horizontal reactions equals 155.4/4 or 38.85 kN. The remainder of the forces
can then be found by statics. The resulting forces are shown in Fig. 4.15.

3rd Storey

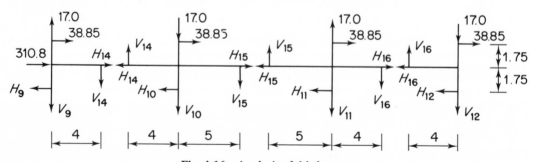

Fig. 4.16   Analysis of third storey.

The horizontal reactions are given by

$$(310.8 + 4 \times 38.85)/4 = 116.55 \text{ kN}.$$

The resultant forces are given in Fig. 4.16.

The 1st and 2nd storeys are analysed in similar fashion, and the complete bending-moment diagram is given in Fig. 4.17 for the wind blowing from A toward R. If the wind reverses, then the bending moments will change sign.

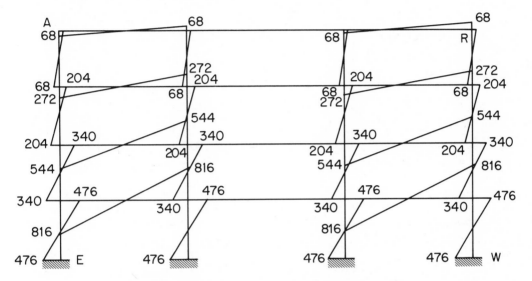

Fig. 4.17 Bending on the unbraced frame due to wind.

The combined bending-moment diagrams for the first storey under the total load $1.2(G_k + Q_k + W_k)$ are given in Fig. 4.18(a) and (b). Note that for this type of structure the combination $1.4G_k + 1.6Q_k$ still needs to be checked as it could produce the worse case.

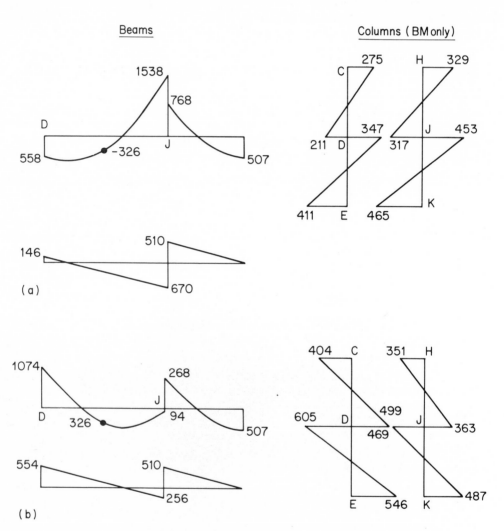

Fig. 4.18   Combined bending moments for the first storey of the unbraced frame.

4.5.4   Bending-moment and shear-force envelopes

Although the concept of bending-moment envelopes has already been introduced in Chapter 3, it is now necessary to develop the topic. Where multiple load cases have been analysed the bending-moment and shear-force diagrams have been superimposed. It is the extreme values (either positive or negative) which constitute the bending-moment or shear-force envelope, and it is for these values that the member must be designed.

The results from Fig. 4.12 have been replotted in Fig. 4.19 as an envelope. Note that in some cases it may well be found that a beam must be capable of withstanding both hogging and sagging bending moments within the span.

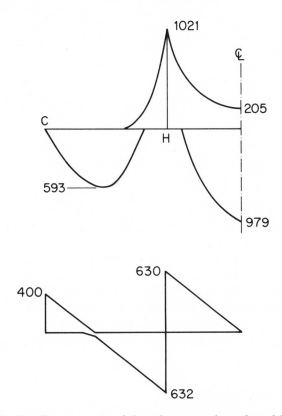

Fig. 4.19 Bending moment and shear forces envelopes for subframe (vii).

It should further be noted that all bending-moment diagrams have been drawn and labelled using the mid-span bending moments as key values. These are not, in general, however, necessarily the maximum values. For the beam shown in Fig. 4.20, the maximum value of the sagging bending moment, M_{max}, and the mid-span moment, M_{mid}, are given by Equations (4.2) and (4.3).

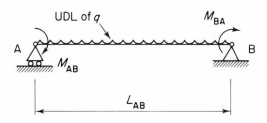

Fig. 4.20 Companrison between maximum and midspan moments.

$$M_{max} = qL_{AB}^2/8 + (M_{AB} - M_{BA})/2 + (M_{AB} + M_{AB})^2/(2qL_{AB}^2) \qquad (4.2)$$

$$M_{mid} = qL_{AB}^2/8 + (M_{AB} - M_{BA})/2 \qquad (4.3)$$

The values of M_{max} and M_{mid} are compared for the 8 m span in subframes (vi) and (vii) in Table 4.4.

Table 4.4   Comparison between maximum sagging and midspan moments

Subframe	q (kN/m)	M_{AB} (kN m)	M_{BA} (kN m)	M_{mid} (kN m)	M_{max} (kN m)	$\left(\dfrac{M_{max} - M_{mid}}{M_{max}}\right) \times 100$ (%)
(vi)	126	−318	892	403.0	423.4	4.8
	126	−362	738	458.0	466.8	1.9
	50	−82	508	105.0	133.4	21.3
	126	0	1021	497.5	562.1	11.5
(vii)	126	0	830	593.0	635.7	6.7
	50	0	596	102.0	157.5	35.2

There appears to be a large error for the $q = 50$ load case. This however is not the critical case for sagging moment design as it is the case with the minimum imposed load. The two remaining results for subframe (vi) are within 5% and thus are acceptable for design purposes. Greater care is needed when dealing with end spans of continuous beams on simple supports although it should be noted that even here the critical load case (second line of subframe (vi)) gives only a 6.7% error. As a general rule provided the numerical ratio of the end moments is less than three the mid-span moment may be used for design purposes. In other cases the maximum moment should preferably be used.

4.5.5   Choice of method of analysis

It is clear that since multiple load cases often need considering a method of analysis capable of handling these should be adopted. Whilst moment distribution may be fast, the process needs full repetition for each load case. If either slope–deflection or matrix methods are adopted, then multiple-load cases can be handled within one operation. For the analyses presented in Example 4.3 explicit formulations of the frame moments were derived using slope–deflection. For further details of these methods standard texts such as Coates *et al.* (1972) or Marshall and Nelson (1977) should be consulted.

4.5.6   Member stiffness

The flexural stiffness (k) of a member is defined as EI/L, where E is Young's modulus (for concrete), I the second moment of area of the section (in 'concrete' units) and L the length of the member between centre-lines.

BS 8110 (cl 2.5.2 Pt 1) indicates that the relative stiffness may be based on one of the following:

(i) *Concrete section alone*

Here the concrete section alone is taken, the reinforcement being ignored. Thus for a rectangular section (Fig. 4.21),

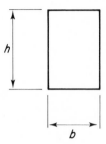

Fig. 4.21   Concrete section.

$$I_C = bh^3/12 \tag{4.4}$$

(ii) *Gross section*

Here the complete concrete section together with an allowance for the reinforcement on a modular ratio basis is made (Fig. 4.22)

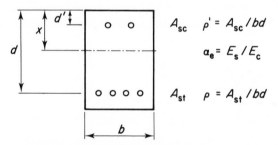

Concrete is considered cracked

Fig. 4.22   Gross section.

$$I_G/bd^3 = (x/d)^3/3 + (h/d - x/d)^3/3 + \rho'\alpha_e(x/d - d'/d)^2 + \cdots \tag{4.5}$$

$$+ \rho\alpha_e(1 - x/d)^2 \tag{4.6}$$

where

$$x/d = ((h/d)^2/2 + (\rho'\alpha_e(d'/d) + \rho\alpha_e)/((h/d + \alpha_e(\rho' + \rho)) \tag{4.7}$$

and

$$\rho = A_s/bd \quad \text{and} \quad \rho' = A'_s/bd$$

(iii) *Transformed section*

Here the compression zone only of the concrete is considered together with the reinforcement on a modular ratio basis (Fig. 4.23)

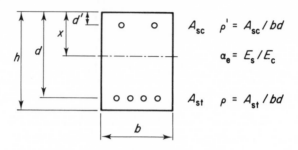

Concrete is considered uncracked

Fig. 4.23   Transformed section

$$I_T/bd^3 = (x/d)^3/3 + \rho'\alpha_e(x/d - d'/d)^2 + \rho\alpha_e(1 - x/d)^2 \tag{4.8}$$

where

$$x/d = -(\rho + \rho')\alpha_e + ((\rho + \rho')^2\alpha_e^2 + 2(\rho'd'/d + \rho)\alpha_e)^{0.5} \tag{4.9}$$

It is imperative that a consistent choice of the method used to calculate the second moments of area of the members is made throughout the structure.

The value of Young's modulus (E_s) for the reinforcement should be taken as $200\,\text{kN/mm}^2$ (cl 2.5.4, Pt 1). The short-term value of the concrete modulus $(E_{c,28})$ can be calculated from

$$E_{c,28} = K_0 + 0.2f_{cu,28} \tag{2.1}$$

(see Section 2.3).

Note however that a value of $\alpha_e = 15$ for an elastic analysis is allowed (cl 2.5.2, Pt 1).

It is usually sufficient to use the concrete section alone to calculate member stiffnesses, since either the gross section or transformed section requires knowledge of the quantity of reinforcement which can only be obtained after an analysis. Thus the use of the gross or transformed sections requires an iterative calculation.

EXAMPLE 4.4   Section properties

For the section shown in Fig. 4.24 calculate the values of the concrete, gross and transformed second moments of area using both the relevant value of $E_{c,28}$ and $\alpha_e = 15$.

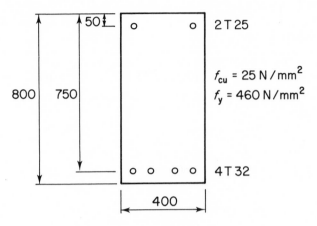

Fig. 4.24   Data for Example 4.4.

$$h/d = 800/750 = 1.067$$
$$d'/d = 50/750 = 0.067$$
$$A_{sc} = 2\text{T}25 = 982 \text{ mm}^2 \qquad \text{(Appendix A)}$$

$$\rho' = A_{sc}/bd = 982/(400 \times 750) = 3.3\text{E}-3$$
$$A_{st} = 5\text{T}32 = 4021 \text{ mm}^2 \text{ (Appendix A)}$$
$$\rho = A_{st}/bd = 4021/(400 \times 750) = 0.013$$
$$E_{c,28} = 20 + 0.2 \times 25 = 25 \text{ kN/mm}^2$$
$$\alpha_e = 200/25 = 8$$

(i) *Concrete section*

$$I_C = bh^3/12 = 400 \times 800^3/12 = 1.71\text{E}10 \text{ mm}^4$$
$$E_c I_C = 1.71\text{E}10 \times 25/1\text{E}6 = 0.427 \text{ kN m}^2$$

(ii) *Gross section*
Using Equation (4.7),

$$x/d = \frac{(1.067^2/2 + 8 \times 3.3\text{E}-3 \times 0.067 + 8 \times 0.013)}{(1.067 + 8 \times (3.3\text{E}-3 + 0.013))} = 0.564$$

using Equation (4.6),

$$I_G/bd^3 = (0.564)^3/3 + (1.067 - 0.564)^3/3 + 3.3\text{E}-3 \times 8(0.564 - 0.067)^2 +$$
$$\cdots + 0.013 \times 8(1 - 0.564)^2 = 0.129$$
$$I_G = 0.129 \times 400 \times 750^3 = 0.0218\text{E}12 \text{ mm}^4$$
$$E_c I_G = 25 \times 0.021\text{E}12/1\text{E}6 = 0.544\text{E}6 \text{ kN m}^2$$

with $\alpha_e = 15$,

$$x/d = 0.585 \text{ and } I_G/bd^3 = 0.151,$$

thus

$$E_c I_G = 0.34\text{E}6 \text{ kN m}^2$$

(iii) *Transformed section*
Using Equation (4.9),

$$x/d = -(0.013 + 3.3\text{E}-3) + ((0.013 + 3.3\text{E}-3)^2 \times 8^2 + 2(0.013 + 3.3\text{E}$$
$$-3 \times 0.067) \times 8)^{05}$$
$$= 0.348$$

Using Equation (4.8)

$$I_T/bd^3 = (0.348)^3/3 + 3.3\text{E}-3 \times 8(0.348 - 0.067)^2 + 0.013 \times 8(1 - 0.348)^2$$
$$= 0.0603$$

and

$$E_c/I_T = 25 \times 0.0605 \times 400 \times 750^3/1\text{E}6 = 0.254\text{E}6 \text{ kN m}^2.$$

Using $\alpha_e = 15$,

$$x/d = 0.431, I_T/bd^3 = 0.0964 \text{ and } E_c I_T = 0.0217\text{E}6 \text{ kN m}^2$$

4.5.7   Stiffness of non-rectangular sections and slabs,

There are three cases to be considered:

(i)   'T' beams and slabs,
(ii)   Flat slabs, and
(iii) Waffle slabs.

(i) *'T' beams and slabs*
Owing to the effect of shear lag in flanged beams (see Section 6.4), the full width of the flange cannot be used to resist the applied moment. Similarly the whole width of the

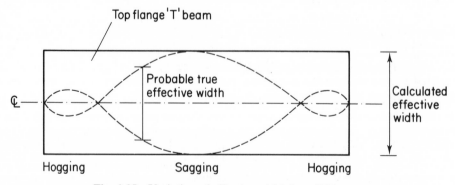

Fig. 4.25   Variation of effective width for a 'T' beam.

flange cannot be used for calculating the stiffness of a 'T' or 'L' beam. If a 'T' beam is under the action of both hogging and sagging bending moments, then in the regime of hogging moments the table of the 'T' is in tension and thus relatively ineffective owing to cracking and in the sagging moment regime the slab is in compression and thus contributing toward the stiffness, although not uniformly, as the moment is varying in magnitude along the beam. Figure 4.25 (after Beeby and Taylor 1978) sketches the likely variation of effective width along a 'T' beam under both sagging and hogging moments. It is also clear that the stiffness of the beam will vary along its length. It is, however, suggested that the concrete section defined in Fig. 4.26 can be taken over the whole length of the beam.

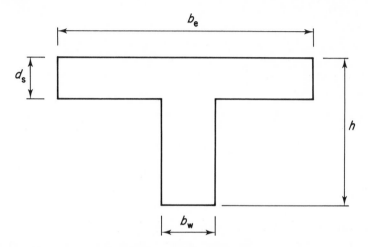

Fig. 4.26 'T' beam dimensions.

For the section shown in Fig. 4.26,

$$I/b_w h^3 = (b_e/b_w - 1)^3 (d_s/h)/12 + 1/12 +$$
$$\cdots + (b_e/b_w - 1)(d_s/h)(d_s/(2h) - x/h) + (0.5 - x/h)^2, \tag{4.10}$$

where

$$x/h = (0.5(b_e/b_w - 1)(d_s/h) + 0.5)/((b_e/b_w - 1)(d_s/h) - 1) \tag{4.11}$$

The effect of varying the stiffnesses of the members in an analysis is demonstrated in Fig. 4.27. Beeby and Taylor suggest that provided a consistent set of stiffnesses is used, then the exact distribution of bending moments is not overimportant provided that set of bending moments is in equilibrium with the applied loading.

With a 'T' beam and slab assembly it must be remembered that although the full width of the flange cannot be used in resisting the applied bending moments, the full width must be used in calculating the applied loading.

(ii) *Flat slabs*
For unbraced frames flat slab construction should be avoided unless substantial column drops or column heads are provided to resist the high bending moments induced by sway. Without column drops it will almost certainly be impossible to satisfactorily fix the reinforcement that will be needed.

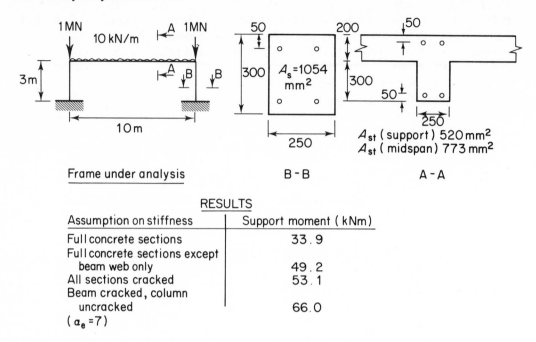

Frame under analysis   B–B   A–A

A_{st} (support) 520 mm^2
A_{st} (midspan) 773 mm^2

RESULTS

Assumption on stiffness	Support moment (kNm)
Full concrete sections	33.9
Full concrete sections except beam web only	49.2
All sections cracked	53.1
Beam cracked, column uncracked	66.0
(α_e =7)	

Fig. 4.27   Effect on analysis of variation in stiffness.

With braced frames flat slabs are perfectly satisfactory since, in general, moments will be lower. Provided that the slabs are of regular shape, a simple frame analysis may be used. Cl 3.7.2.4 Pt 1 indicates that   the full width of the slab may be used to calculate the flexural stiffness for an analysis under vertical loading.

For irregular-shaped flat slabs it will often be necessary to use finite element analysis (Zienkiewicz 1977, Rockey *et al.* 1983) to calculate the forces in the slabs.

(iii) *Waffle slabs*

Cl 3.6.2 Pt 1 indicates that   waffle slabs may be analysed either as solid slabs (using methods given in Section 10.8) or as flat slabs. Neither method appears to be entirely satisfactory since waffle slabs usually have a solid section around the column and discrete ribs in both directions elsewhere. It is almost certainly preferable to treat such slabs as flat slabs with substantial column drops. An alternative, and almost certainly preferable, method is to employ a grillage analysis whereby full account will be taken of the variation in stiffness between the solid portions and the ribs.

It should be noted that it is generally sufficient to design slabs with all spans carrying full design load. Slab design is covered in Chapter 10.

4.6   Column loads

The end forces (axial load and moment) are determined in the following fashion:

(a)   *End moments*   These are obtained from the appropriate frame or subframe analysis with maximum loading on one span and minimum on the other.

(b)   *Axial loads*   These are obtained by summing the reactions from the floor framing into the top of the column to the reactions from the floors above this. For the purpose of this calculation it is sufficiently accurate to assume the remaining floors are simply supported at their ends.

BS 6399 Pt 1 allows certain reductions in the imposed load to be taken by a column in a multistorey structure. It allows the greater reduction depending on either the number of storeys or the loaded area. These reductions are summarised in Fig. 4.28.

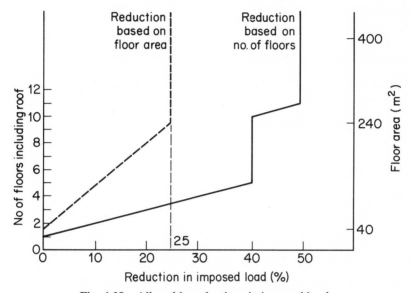

Fig. 4.28   Allowable reductions in imposed load.

It is recognised that there is a reduced probability of all floors being loaded to their respective maxima and that a large floor area will be less intensely loaded than a small area.

It should be remembered that the worst loading combination for a 'short' column is usually maximum moment and minimum axial load, although the combination of maximum axial load and moment should be checked. For a 'slender' column the worst case is likely to be maximum moment and maximum axial load owing to the additional moment induced by the slenderness effect (see Chapter 12).

EXAMPLE 4.5   Column loads

Determine the column loads for columns AE and FK for the braced frame in Example 4.3.

Column AE

Section AB
From subframe(i) $M = 331$ kN m and $N = 440$ kN

Section BC
From subframe(iv) $M = 222$ kN m

$$\text{Max } N = 447 + (0.9 \times 1.6 \times 35 + 1.4 \times 50) \times 4 = 927 \text{ kN}$$

The factor of 0.9 is for two storeys of live load.

$$\text{Min } N = 447 + 1.4 \times 50 \times 4 = 727 \text{ kN}$$

From subframe(v) $M = 181$ kN m

$$\text{Min } N = 432 + 1.4 \times 50 \times 4 = 712 \text{ kN}$$
$$\text{Max } N = 432 + (0.9 \times 1.6 \times 35 + 1.4 \times 50) \times 4 = 914 \text{ kN}$$

Section CD
From subframe(iv) $M = 222$ kN m

$$\text{Min } N = 447 + 2 \times 1.4 \times 50 \times 4 = 1007 \text{ kN}$$
$$\text{Max } N = 447 + 2 \times (0.8 \times 1.6 \times 35 + 1.4 \times 50) \times 4 = 1365 \text{ kN}$$

The factor of 0.8 is for three storeys loaded.

From subframe(v) $M = 181$ kN m

$$\text{Min } N = 432 + 2(1.4 \times 50) \times 4 = 992 \text{ kN}$$
$$\text{Max } N = 432 + 2(0.8 \times 1.6 \times 35 + 1.4 \times 50) \times 4 = 1350 \text{ kN}$$

Section DE
From subframe(iv) $M = 222$ kN m

$$\text{Min } N = 447 + 3(1.4 \times 50) \times 4 = 1287 \text{ kN}$$
$$\text{Max } N = 447 + 3(0.7 \times 1.6 \times 35 + 1.4 \times 50) \times 4 = 1757 \text{ kN}$$

From subframe(v) $M = 181$ kN m

$$\text{Min } N = 432 + 3(1.4 \times 50) \times 4 = 1272 \text{ kN}$$
$$\text{Max } N = 432 + 3(0.7 \times 1.6 \times 35 + 1.4 \times 50) \times 4 = 1742 \text{ kN}$$

Column FK

Section FG
From subframe(ii) $M = 140$ kN m and $N = 795$ kN.
The calculation for Max N would involve both spans AF and FL being fully loaded, which would reduce the moment applied to the column.

Section GH
From subframe(iii) $M = 140$ kN m

$$\text{Min } N = 789 + 1.4 \times 50 \times (4 + 5) = 1419 \text{ kN}$$
$$\text{Max } N = 789 + (0.9 \times 1.6 \times 35 + 1.4 \times 50)(4 + 5) = 1873 \text{ kN}$$

From subframe(v) $M = 98$ kN m

$$\text{Min } N = 831 + 1.4 \times 50 \times (4 + 5) = 1461 \text{ kN}$$
$$\text{Max } N = 831 + (0.9 \times 1.6 \times 35 + 1.4 \times 50) \times (4 + 5) = 1915 \text{ kN}$$

From subframe(vi) $M = 98$ kN m

$\quad$ Min $N = (253 + (1.4 \times 50 + 1.6 \times 35) \times 5) + 1.4 \times 50 \times 9 = 1513$ kN
$\quad$ Max $N = 883 + (1.4 \times 50 + 0.9 \times 1.6 \times 35) \times 9 = 1967$ kN

Section HJ
The results for this are presented in Table 4.5

Table 4.5   Loads on Column HJ

Subframe	(iii)	(v)	(vi)
M (kN m)	118	98	98
Max N (kN)	2855	2897	2949
Min N (kN)	2049	2091	2143

Section JK
The results for this are presented in Table 4.6

Table 4.6   Loads on Column JK

Subframe	(iii)	(v)	(vi)
M (kN m)	118	98	98
Min N (kN)	2679	2721	2773
Max N (kN)	3737	3779	3831

It will be seen from these results that the choice of subframe has only a slight effect on the forces on an interior column. For an exterior column this is not so. It will be apparent that the use of a subframe with only a single beam will tend to overestimate the column moment. The exact amount of this overestimation depends on the relative stiffnesses of the beam and column.

4.7   Redistribution of moments

In Section 4.2.2 it was indicated that after an elastic analysis has been performed it is permissible to redistribute these moments such that equilibrium is maintained with the applied loading to simulate plastic collapse provided that sufficient ductility exists within the members. It is suggested that Sections 6.1 and 6.2 should be read before the remainder of Section 4.7.

In Fig. 4.29 is presented some moment–curvature diagrams for the section given in the diagram, where it will be seen that low percentages of tensile reinforcement or high percentages of tensile reinforcement together with compression reinforcement will give large yield plateaux indicating high ductility. It is also significant that in all these cases the neutral axis depth is less than $0.5d$. Since the available rotation, or ductility, is a function of the neutral axis depth, it will be necessary to place restrictions on the amount of redistribution that can be allowed for a given neutral axis depth.

Cl 3.2.2, Pt 1 lays down three conditions for redistribution:

Condition 1.   Equilibrium must be maintained between the applied loading and the internal moments (and shears) at all times under all combinations of loading.

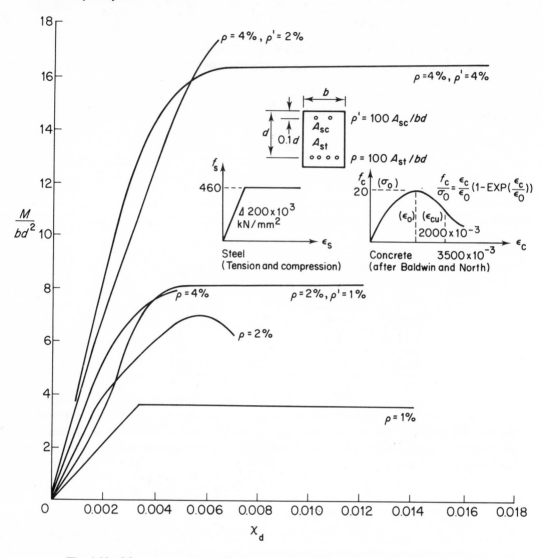

Fig. 4.29 Moment–curvature diagrams showing effect of reinforcement percentage.

Condition 2.   At the point of maximum moment the neutral axis depth (x) must satisfy

$$x/d < \beta_b - 0.4 \qquad (4.12)$$

where β_b is the ratio of the moment at the section after redistribution to that before redistribution, and is to be taken as not greater than unity.

Condition 3. The moment at any section should be at least 70% (or for unbraced structures over four storeys high – 90%) of the elastic moment envelope.

For a discussion of the effects of redistribution on the design process for elements in flexure reference should be made to Section 6.2.5.

The first condition is basically common sense but is equally something that many students (and for that matter experienced designers) can tend to ignore! Condition 2 ensures (a) that sufficient ductility is present at the section whose moment is being reduced, by restricting the neutral axis depth, and (b) that hinge formation could occur. It does not apply to the section to which moment is transferred as a result of redistribution at another section in order to satisfy Condition 1. Condition 2 also has the effect of not allowing any reduction in column moments unless the axial load is very small. Condition 3 effectively controls the amount of redistribution that may be carried out to 30% for all structures except for unbraced frames over four storeys, for which a value of 10% is imposed. The reason for this restriction is that the points of contraflexure will shift during the process of redistribution and the structure will for most of its life carry service loading. The positions of the points of contraflexure determined from this loading will be critical.

EXAMPLE 4.7   Redistribution on an encastré beam

Consider an encastré beam of 6 m span carrying a load of 30 kN/m at ultimate limit state; draw the bending moment diagram after 25% redistribution (Fig. 4.30).

The support moment is given by

$$qL^2/12 = 30 \times 6^2/12 = 90 \text{ kN m}$$

the central moment is given by

$$qL^2/24 = 45 \text{ kN m}$$

The point of contraflexure is given by the solution of

$$qLx/2 - qx^2/2 - qL^2/12 = 0$$

or

$$6(x/L)^2 - 6(x/L) + 1 = 0$$

or

$$x/L = 0.211$$

or

$$x = 0.211 \times 6 = 1.27 \text{ m}$$

The original bending moment diagram is plotted in Fig. 4.30(b).

A 25% reduction in the support bending moment will give a bending moment of

$$90 \times (1 - 25/100) = 67.5 \text{ kN m}$$

The free bending moment is

$$qL^2/8 = 135 \text{ kN m}$$

Thus the resultant sagging bending moment is $135 - 67.5 = 67.5$ kN m.

The bending-moment diagram resulting from this redistribution is plotted in Fig. 4.30(c).

The final diagram, plotted in Fig. 4.30(d), shows the diagram for 70% of the original elastic distribution superimposed on the redistributed diagram. It is seen that between points X1 and X2 the 70% rule determines the design moments. At the supports the neutral axis depth is restricted to

$$(0.75 - 0.4)d = 0.35d$$

Redistribution does not in general produce any significant savings in reinforcement since redistribution affects the amount of longitudinal (or bending) reinforcement only slightly and will increase the amount of shear steel (or links) since the shear capacity at the supports is reduced. It is generally accepted that the value of the shear force used to

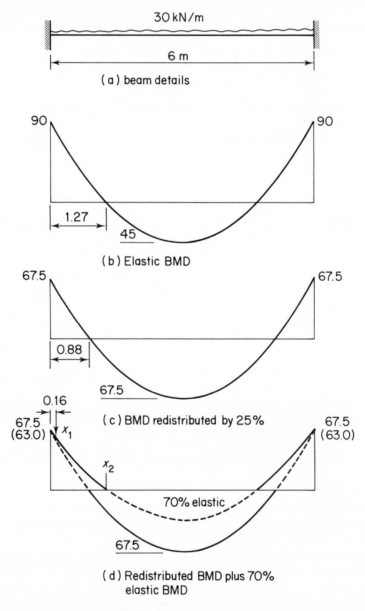

Fig. 4.30   Redistribution for an encastré beam.

design the section should be the greater of the two values calculated before and after redistribution. The only effect of redistribution in reducing the support moment will be to ease the placing of reinforcement in that the quantity in the upper face is reduced and will enable better compaction of the concrete to be achieved. The only case where redistribution will be beneficial is when the beam is in the form of a 'T' or 'L' section, since moment is transferred away from the portion where the flange is in tension to where it is in compression. It is therefore suggested that redistribution should be limited to this case. It is also possible that excessive redistribution may cause problems when fire engineering calculations are performed to determine the fire endurance of a concrete beam or slab (see Section 5.9).

EXAMPLE 4.7   Redistribution for a continuous beam

For the continuous beam analysed as subframe(vii) of Example 4.3, carry out a redistribution to obtain an optimum moment field.

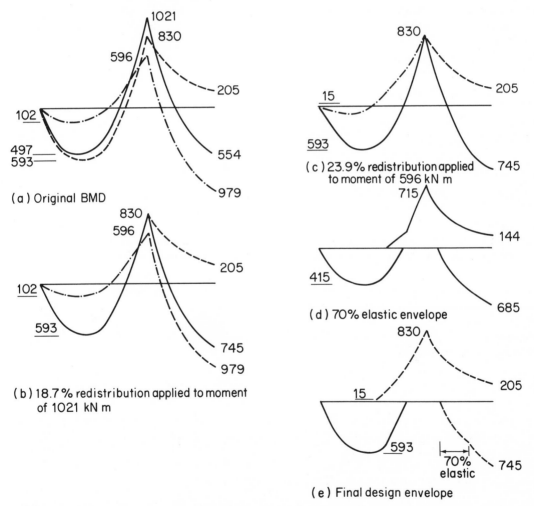

Fig. 4.31   Redistribution on subframe (vii).

Stage 1

Reduce the maximum hogging moment from 1021 to 830 kN m, i.e. a reduction of

$$(1021 - 830) \times 100/1021 = 18.7\%$$

The original bending moment is plotted in Fig. 4.31(a), and the first stage of redistribution in Fig. 4.31(b).

   Note it is not possible to reduce the bending moment to 596 kN m as this would mean a reduction of 41.6%.

Stage 2

Increase the hogging moment of 596 to 830 kN m. This will decrease the sagging moment of 979 to 745 kN m, i.e. a reduction of $(979 - 745) \times 100/979 = 23.9\%$. Stage 2 of the operation is plotted in Fig. 4.31(c).

Stage 3

Construct the bending-moment diagram produced by taking 70% of the original diagram. This is superimposed on the diagram obtained after Stage 2, and is plotted in Fig. 4.31(d).

   Note that since at all times in this example the 70% diagram is within the redistributed diagram, no further adjustments need be made and thus the diagram plotted in Fig. 4.31(e) is the final bending-moment envelope.

EXAMPLE 4.8   Redistribution in a subframe involving columns

Carry out a suitable redistribution for subframe(vi) of Example 4.3.

Stage 1

Reduce the 950 sagging moment to 704 kN m, i.e. a reduction of 25.9%. This has the effect of reducing the support moment in the adjacent span to

$$704 - (950 - 892) = 646 \text{ kN m}$$

with a corresponding sagging moment in the 8 m span of

$$(318 + 646)/2 - 1008 = -526 \text{ kN m}$$

and in the 10 m span

$$704 - 1575 = -871 \text{ kN m}$$

Stage 2

Decrease the 738 kN m moment to 646 kN m, i.e. a reduction of 12.5%, and thus increase the midspan bending moment in the 10 m span to -93 kN m as the support moment in the 10 m span has become

$$624 - (738 - 646) = 532 \text{ kN m}$$

These stages are plotted in Fig. 4.32(a)–(d), including the 70% diagram. The final bending-moment envelope is plotted in Fig. 4.32(e).

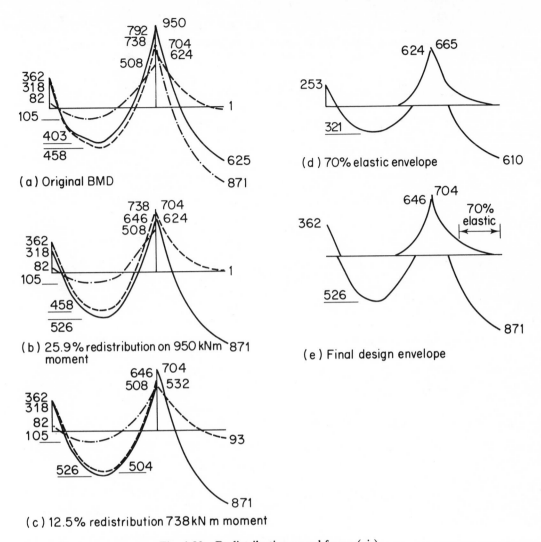

Fig. 4.32 Redistribution on subframe (vi.)

Note, no redistribution can occur at C since the beam at C is attached to two columns to which no redistribution may be taken.

4.8 Plastic analysis for continuous beams

For continuous beams it is possible to use plastic analysis methods as is illustrated in the following example.

EXAMPLE 4.9   Plastic analysis of a continuous beam

Design the continuous beam shown in Fig. 4.33 by plastic methods (note this beam is the same as subframe(vii) in Example 4.3). It may be assumed that sufficient ductility is present to allow full hinge rotation.

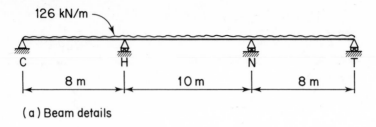

(a) Beam details

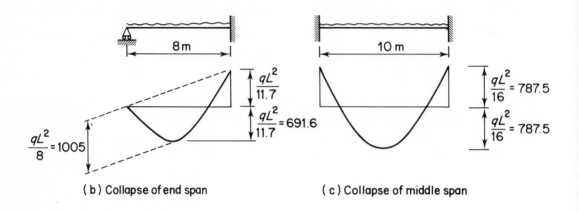

(b) Collapse of end span   (c) Collapse of middle span

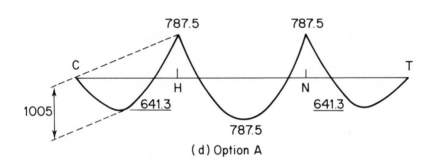

(d) Option A

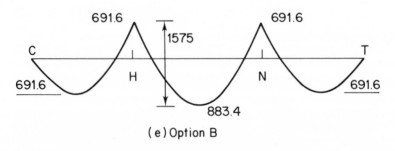

(e) Option B

Fig. 4.33   Plastic design of a continuous beam.

Assuming that the hogging and sagging moments of resistance are equal, then, for the end span (Fig. 4.33(b)),

$$M = qL^2/11.6 = 126 \times 8^2/11.6 = 691.6 \text{ kN m}$$

for the middle span (Fig. 4.33(c)),

$$M = qL^2/16 = 126 \times 10^2/16 = 787.5 \text{ kN m}$$

It is clear that the end span is critical, and therefore there are two solutions possible:

(a) A collapse moment of 787.5 over both supports, a sagging collapse moment of 787.5 for the centre span and a reduced sagging collapse moment in the end spans, or
(b) A collapse moment of 691.6 over both supports, a sagging collapse moment of 691.6 in the end spans and an increased sagging collapse moment in the centre span.

Option (a)
The solution to this is given in Fig. 4.33(d), where it is seen that the end span sagging moment is 614.3 kN m.

Option (b)
The solution to this is given in Fig. 4.33(e), where it is seen that the centre span sagging moment is given as 883.4 kN m.

Option (b) is almost certainly the better since it gives smaller hogging moments, which means that less tensile reinforcement will be required in the top face of the beam. It is also clear that this is a better solution than that given in Example 4.7 following redistribution, partly due to the limited redistribution carried out in that example.

4.9 Approximate analysis of continuous beams and one-way spanning slabs

For multi-span continuous beams (and one way spanning slabs), the bending moment and shear force coefficients given in Table 4.7 (from Tables 3.6 and 3.13, Pt 1) may be used.

Table 4.7 Design ultimate bending moments and shear forces for continuous beams and slabs

Action	Structure	Outer support	Middle of end span	First interior support	Middle of interior spans	Interior support
Moment ($\times FL$)	Beams	0	0.090	−0.110	0.070	−0.080
	Slab	0	0.086	−0.086	0.063	−0.063
Shear ($\times F$)	Beam	0.45		0.60		0.55
	Slab	0.40		0.60		0.50

Notes: L is the effective span
F is the total design ultimate load
No further redistribution is permitted.

There is an important series of restrictions on the use of this Table:

(1) The characteristic imposed load (Q_k) should not exceed the characteristic dead load (G_k).
(2) The loading should be uniformly distributed over at least three spans.
(3) The variation between the shortest and longest spans should not exceed 15% of the longest span.

There is also the implication that all spans are carrying the same total loading. The reason why the values for slabs are different to those for the beams is that 20% redistribution has been incorporated in the slab values whereas no redistribution is allowed on the beam values.

The analysis of the structure having been dealt with, the next chapter will deal in detail with the serviceability limit state.

4.10   Tutorial problems

4.10.1   Moments of area of a section

Determine the (a) concrete, (b) gross and (c) transformed second moments of area for the section given in Fig. 4.34.

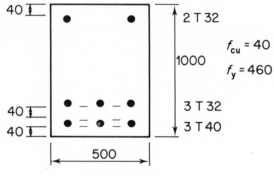

Fig. 4.34

Answers
(a)   4.17E10 mm⁴
(b)   5.11E10 mm⁴ ($d = 910$ mm, $\alpha_e = 7.14$, $x/d = 0.575$)
(c)   2.16E10 mm⁴ ($x/d = 0.338$).

4.10.2   Approximate analysis of a frame

Determine the bending moments, and sketch the bending moment diagram, using the approximate method of analysis for the frame given in Fig. 4.35.

(*Note*: the external columns have half the stiffness of the internal columns.)

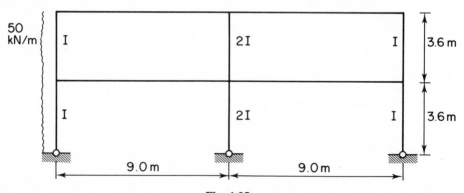

Fig. 4.35

Answer

The final BMD is given in Fig. 4.36 (nodal wind force at top = 108 kN, Top storey – reactions on pin in LH column 27 kN horizontal and 10.8 kN vertical (downwards). Bottom storey – reactions at base of LH column 81 kN horizontal and 86.4 kN vertical (downwards)).

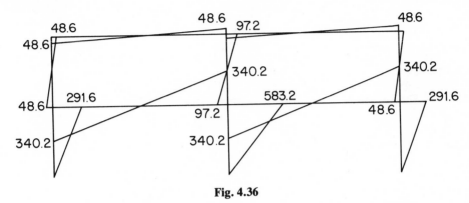

Fig. 4.36

4.10.3 Bending moment and shear force envelopes for a subframe

Draw the bending moment and shear force envelopes for the subframe shown in Fig. 4.37.

Stiffnesses = 10 m beam $10E6\,\mathrm{kNm}^2$ column $2\,\mathrm{kNm}^2$

12 m beam $12E6\,\mathrm{kNm}^2$

Loading (at service limit state) Dead $55\,\mathrm{kN/m}$ Live $40\,\mathrm{kN/m}$

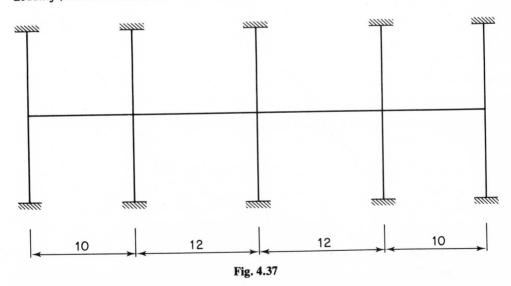

Fig. 4.37

Answer

The final bending moment and shear force envelopes are given in Fig 4.38(a) and (b).

BMD (beams only)

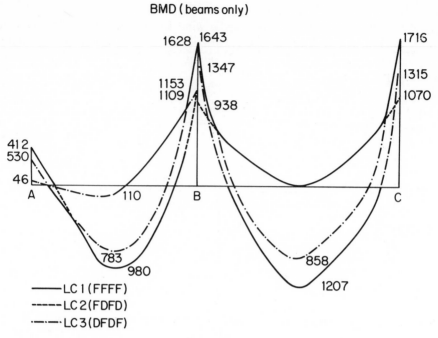

Fig. 4.38(a)

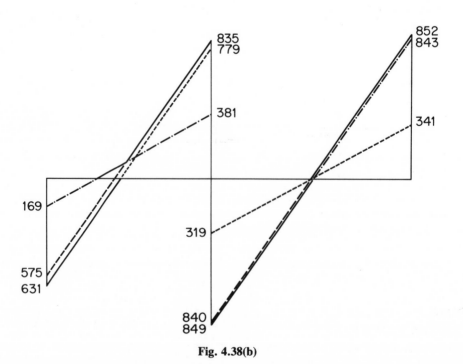

Fig. 4.38(b)

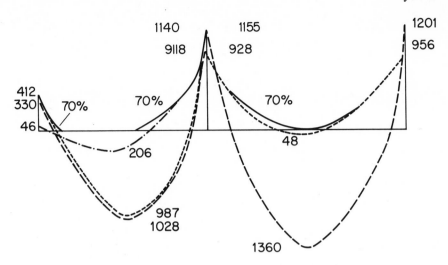

Fig. 4.39

There are three load cases:

all spans fully loaded (note symmetry)

alternate spans full and dead (since the frame is symmetric only one analysis is needed for the two load patterns).

4.10.4 Redistribution of moments

Carry out the maximum possible redistribution on the frame in Problem 4.10.3.

Answers
At C, reduce moment of 1716 by 30% to 1201, and reduce moment of 1315 to 1201 (8.7%).
At B, reduce moment of 1628 by 30% to 1140 and moment of 1153 to 1140.
At A no redistribution is allowed.
Check 70% rule in hogging areas!
Final redistributed envelope is plotted in Fig. 4.39.

References

Beeby A. W. and Taylor H. P. J. (1978). The use of simplified methods in CP110 – is rigour necessary? *Structural Engineer* **56A**(8), 209–15.
BS 6399 (1984). *Design loading for buildings* – Part 1 *Code of practice for dead and imposed loads*, British Standards Institution, London.
Coates R. C., Coutie M. G. and Kong F. K. (1972), *Structural Analysis*, Nelson, London.
Irwin A. W. (1984). *Design of shear wall buildings*. Report No. 112. Construction Industry Research and Information Association.
Marshall W. T. and Nelson H. M. (1977). *Structures*, Pitman, London.
Reagan P. E. (1981). *Behaviour of reinforced concrete flat slabs*. Report No. 89, Construction Industry Research and Information Association.
Rockey K. C. *et al.* (1983). *The finite element method – a basic introduction*, Granada, London.
Zienkiewicz O. C. (1977). *The finite element method*, McGraw-Hill.

5

Durability, Serviceability and Fire

5.1 Introduction

In the past engineers have been content to consider durability with respect only to satisfying certain serviceability limit states, e.g. crack control or deflection, using simplified methods or by the use of standard tables for, say, cover. It has become apparent in recent years that a more fundamental approach is necessary to deal with the whole concept of durability. Controlling cover or crack widths (both locally using bar-spacing rules and globally by span/effective depth ratio calculations for deflection) is only a part of the design process. Although design for durability using a service life prediction approach is not yet possible, it is clear that the designer ought to possess some knowledge of how loss in durability may occur. Essentially there are three mechanisms whereby durability may be lost:

(i)   Corrosion of the reinforcement,
(ii) Akali–aggregate reaction, and
(iii) Sulphate attack.

Each of these will now be discussed in turn.

5.2 Corrosion of the reinforcement

Corrosion will, at an extreme, lead to spalling of the concrete cover and exposure of the corroded reinforcement, if any remains, since the products of corrosion occupy a larger volume than the original steel. By the time all this has happened it will be far too late to combat corrosion.

Corrosion is an extremely complex phenomenon which is still not completely understood. Essentially corrosion will occur when the pH value of the concrete reduces from a high value of around 13 during placing to a value of below 9 at a later stage (Page and Treadaway 1982). This change is known as a loss in passivity and is due to two causes:

(a)   Carbonation, and
(b)   Chloride attack.

5.2.1 Carbonation

This is a gradually advancing attack caused by the penetration of acidic gases (most notably carbon dioxide) which react with any free alkali present, causing a loss in pH. Being a diffusion process the depth of carbonation is proportional to the square root of time. The constant of proportionality is a function of the concrete quality and the environment in which the concrete is situated. In general the concrete covers specified in Table 3.4, Pt 1 (summarized as Table 5.1) are adequate to ensure that the carbonation will not reach the reinforcement. The effects of corrosion resulting from carbonation on reinforcement are illustrated in Fig. 5.1.

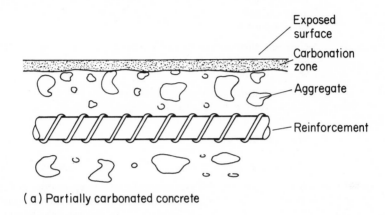

(a) Partially carbonated concrete

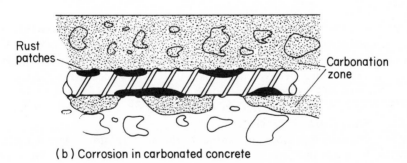

(b) Corrosion in carbonated concrete

Fig. 5.1 Corrosion due to carbonation.

However, the covers specified in Table 5.1 are adequate only if the concrete has a low coefficient of permeability which will be ensured by making certain that the concrete is sufficiently workable and can be correctly placed and vibrated. This should place an onus on the designer for the need to consider very carefully the construction techniques to be used. Thus around areas of reinforcement congestion the selection may need thickening locally to ensure the concrete can flow adequately. Another common source of high permeability concrete is at construction joints. Whilst these cannot be avoided, it may be

Table 5.1 Nominal covers to all reinforcement to meet durability requirements

Exposure	Position	Nominal cover (mm)				
Mild	Concrete surfaces protected against weather or aggressive environments, e.g. internal	25[3]	20	20[1]	20[1]	20[1]
Moderate	Concrete surfaces sheltered from severe rain or freezing whilst wet, subject to condensation, continuously under water, or in contact with non-aggressive soil conditions	—	35[3]	30	25	20
Severe	Concrete surfaces exposed to severe rain, alternate wetting and drying or occasional freezing or severe condensation	—	—	40	30	25
Very severe	Concrete surfaces exposed to sea water spray, de-icing salts, corrosive fumes or severe freezing whilst wet	—	—	50[2]	40[2]	30
Extreme	Concrete surfaces exposed to abrasive action, flowing water with pH $\leqslant$ 4.5, or machinery or vehicles	—	—	—	60[2]	50
	Minimum free w/c ratio	0.65	0.60	0.55	0.50	0.45
	Minimum cement content (kg/m³)	275	300	325	350	400
	Minimum concrete grade	C30	C35	C40	C45	C50

Notes: (1) Cover may be reduced to 15 if maximum size of aggregate does not exceed 15 mm
(2) Where concrete is subject to freezing whilst wet, air entrainment must be used.
(3) For prestressed concrete, grade C30 may not be used in any circumstance and grade C35 may only be used where the exposure condition is MILD.

preferable to ensure that these do not occur at points of high local stresses. Construction joints can in some cases be avoided by the use of retarding agents or the workability improved by the use of superplasticisers.

Another factor in ensuring low permeability is the curing of the concrete. Concrete must be adequately cured. The modern trend of relating the striking times of shuttering to the concrete strength is somewhat disturbing since the cement manufacturers are now producing an OPC which behaves more like an RHC by increasing the C_3A content. Thus most modern OPCs show little strength increase after 28 days. An adverse feature of rapid hydration is the increased heat of hydration which leads to an increased occurrence of early thermal cracking.

Beeby has indicated that cracking parallel to the main reinforcement is more harmful in corrosive conditions than cracks normal to the main reinforcement. These cracks are usually due to shrinkage and early thermal strains and are exacerbated by poor detailing and quantity of secondary reinforcement. It is therefore recommended that for all structures some estimate should be made of the extent of early thermal cracking and measures taken to mitigate its effect (see Section 5.8).

5.2.2 Chloride attack

Some free chloride ions will exist in the hydrating cement, but this will generally be a low proportion. The use of admixtures containing calcium chloride is no longer permitted, but it is still possible to introduce chlorides as contaminants in either the aggregate or the mixing water. Thus, the use of, say, sea dredged sands is to be deprecated. An additional source of chloride attack from the environment is due to sea water or de-icing salts. Here the chloride attack is along cracks in the concrete cover (Fig. 5.2), and thus for both these incidences a very rigorous control is made on cracking (BS 5337 or BS 5400 Pt 4). The existence of cracking also increases the surface open to carbonation attack, but the magnitude of this effect is not known.

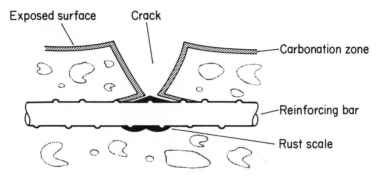

Fig. 5.2   Corrosion in cracked concrete.

5.3   Alkali–aggregate reaction

Here a reaction occurs between the alkalinity of the pore water caused by either alkaline elements in the cement or an external source such as sea water or de-icing salts and certain types of silica within the aggregate, usually opal. Most British aggregates are low in opal, but as yet there is no sufficient test for this. The effect of the alkali–aggregate reaction is to cause a positive volume change with the associated macrocracking, which will probably exacerbate the situation as more water will seep into the concrete and speed up the reaction.

   Alkali–aggregate reaction is likely if:

(a)   the concrete is subjected to an external source of water (a wetting and drying cycle may be more critical than total permanent immersion);
(b)   the total alkali content in the cement exceeds the equivalent of 3 kg of Na_2O per cubic metre or if the concrete is in an alkali aggressive environment, or
(c)   the aggregate is potentially reactive (this will have to be based on previous experience).

Alkali–aggregate reaction can be avoided if:

(a)   the concrete can be kept dry and the minimum possible mixing water used;
(b)   either a low alkali cement is used, or normal cements with some of the cement replaced by pfa or blast-furnace slag (this latter reduces the inherent alkalinity);
(c)   the aggregate used is not susceptible to such a reaction.

5.4   Sulphate attack

This will occur from free sulphates, in either the soil or groundwater, thus sulphate attack is usually only important for buried structures including piles, foundations and retaining walls. It is usually sufficient to counteract sulphate attack by using sulphate resisting cements (SRC) as laid down in Table 6.1 of Pt 1 (summarised here as Table 5.2).

Table 5.2   Concrete exposed to sulphate attack

	Concentration of sulphate (SO_3)				For dense (normal weight) 20 mm aggregate concrete	
	Soil					
Class	Total SO_3	SO_3 in 2:1 soil/water extract	Ground water	Type of cement	Minimum cement content (inc. of pfa or ggbfs)	Maximum free w/c ratio
1	<0.2	<1.0	<0.3	All cements except OPC and RHC should be combined with pfa or ggbfs	—	—
2	0.2–0.5	1.0–1.9	0.3–1.2	All cements except OPC & RHC with pfa or ggbfs	330	0.50
				OPC & RHC with 25–40% pfa or 70–90% ggbfs	310	0.55
				SRPC or SSC	280	0.55
3	0.5–1.0	1.9–3.1	1.2–2.5	OPC & RHC with 25–40% pfa or 70–90% ggbfs	380	0.45
				SRPC or SSC	330	0.50
4	1.0–2.0	3.1–5.6	2.5–5.0	SRPC or SSC	370	0.45
5	>2.0	>5.6	>5.0	SRPC or SSC (with protective coating)	370	0.45
	%	g/L	g/L		kg/m³	

Key: OPC   Ordinary Portland cement   SRPC   Sulphate resisting Portland cement
RHC   Rapid hardening cement   SSC   Super sulphated cement
pfa   Pulverized fuel ash   ggbfs   Ground granulated blast furnace slag

However, not even sulphate-resisting cement will cure the problem if insufficient care is taken in placing, vibrating and curing the concrete.

Having discussed the basis of the need for design for durability attention can now be given to the consideration of design to satisfy serviceability limit states.

5.5   Serviceability limit states

These are criteria which are applied to the structure or structural element whilst carrying the design working, or service, loading. Although serviceability limit states have already been discussed in Chapter 1, it is worthwhile to recapitulate the essential ones here.

5.5.1   Deflection

This may be considered either by using span/effective depth ratios or by explicit calculations. The following deflection limits are applied (cl 3.2, Pt 2):

For visible structural members span/250
For members carrying brittle finishes lesser of span/500 or 20 mm
For members carrying non-brittle finishes lesser of span/350 or 20 mm.

For cantilevers the span must be taken as the effective span to allow for some rotation at the root. Special consideration will need to be given if the supporting structure for a cantilever is relatively flexible and therefore susceptible to large rotations. These rotations must be allowed for in the total deflection of the cantilever.

5.5.2   Crack widths

In normal reinforced concrete (not including bridge decks or water retaining structures) an average crack width of 0.3 mm is considered acceptable (cl 3.11.12.2.1, Pt 1). For cracking in prestressed concrete reference should be made to Section 12.2. Two methods are available for handling crack-width calculations. The first is by considering the spacing of the flexural reinforcement and should only be used if early thermal strains and shrinkage can be considered negligible. The second is by performing an elastic crack-width calculation on the section including the effects of shrinkage and early thermal cracking.

5.5.3   Vibration or dynamic response

This is, in general, not usually critical for most reinforced concrete structures, but may need considering in special circumstances, e.g. the design of a support system for heavy vibrating or oscillating machinery or the design of cooling towers under the effect of wind vortices.

5.5.4   Fire

This will be dealt with in Section 5.9.

For crack control, deflections and fire, BS 8110 allows either a 'deemed to satisfy' approach or an approach using full calculations.

For crack control and deflections the 'deemed to satisfy' approach is in general very conservative, but is adequate for normal routine designs.

However, where in the case of deflections it is required to know the exact deflection or where shrinkage and creep strains may be abnormally high, then the explicit method must be used. If either substantial early thermal cracking is likely to occur either parallel to or transverse to the main reinforcement or the concrete is to be subjected to a hostile environment, then crack-width calculations must be performed. The use of 'deemed to satisfy' approaches for fire are covered in Section 5.9.

It should be noted that it is possible to omit Sections 5.6.3, 5.7.1 (a) and 5.9.3 on a first reading of the text.

5.6 Deflections

5.6.1 Span/effective depth ratio method (cl 3.4.6 Pt 1) – Theoretical justification

For any beam the midspan deflection, Δ, may be written as

$$\Delta = k_1 W L^3 / E_s I_s \tag{5.1}$$

where

k_1 = coefficient dependent on the load pattern and support conditions
W = total service load
L = the effective span
E_s = Young's modulus for the reinforcement, and
I_s = the second moment of area of the section in 'steel' units considered for the cracked case and taken as a mean value for the whole span. In practice, the value at midspan is used, hence overestimating the deflection.

The midspan bending moment, M_s, is given by

$$M_s = k_2 W L \tag{5.2}$$

where

k_2 = a further coefficient depending on the load pattern. Substituting Equation (5.2) into Equation (5.1) gives

$$\Delta = (k_1/k_2) M_s L^2 / E_s I_s \tag{5.3}$$

or

$$(\Delta/L) = (k_1/k_2) M_s L / E_s I_s \tag{5.4}$$

Using the Bernoulli theory of simple bending,

$$f_s = M_s (d - x) / I_s \tag{5.5}$$

where

d = effective depth,
x = the depth of the neutral axis from the extreme compression fibre.

Substituting Equation (5.5) into Equation (5.4) gives

$$(\Delta/L) = ((k_1/k_2) f_s / (1 - x/d))(L/d) \tag{5.6}$$

It may thus be seen from Equation (5.6) that if the allowable deflection is expressed as a proportion of the span (e.g. span/250), then this ratio may be directly related to the span to effective depth ratio (L/d).

In practice the term modifying the span/effective depth ratio in Equation (5.6) cannot be evaluated as it stands and certain modifications need to be made for this approach to be used.

5.6.2 BS 8110 Provisions

This is done by specifying:

(i)   a basic span/effective depth ratio,
(ii)   a modification factor to allow for the effect of the tensile reinforcement, and
(iii) a modification factor for the compressive reinforcement.

(i) *Basic span/effective depth ratios*
These are given in Table 5.3 (reproduced from Table 3.10 Pt 1)

Table 5.3   Basic span/effective depth ratios

Support conditions	Rectangular beams	Flaned beams $b_w/b < 0.3$
Cantilever	7.0	5.6
Simply supported	20.0	16.0
Continuous	26.0	20.8

For flanged beams with a b_w/b ratio greater than 0.3 (b_w is the web width and b the effective flange width), linear interpolation between the two columns in Table 5.3 should be made.   The reduction factor for 'T' and 'L' beams is given by

$$0.8 + 2(b_w/b - 0.3)/7$$

This procedure is necessary to allow for the loss in stiffness caused by the loss of concrete adjacent to the web.
   For simply supported or continuous beams having spans greater than 10 m, Table 5.3 may still be used except that if it is necessary to limit the deflections after the construction of finishes or partitions, the values in Table 5.3 should be multiplied by 10/span. For cantilevers with spans exceeding 10 m full calculations must be performed using the method described in Section 5.6.3.

(ii) *Modification factor for tensile reinforcement*
The modification factor, F_1, is given by

$$F_1 = 0.55 + (477 - f_s)/(120 \times (0.9 + M/bd^2)) \tag{5.7}$$

The value   of F_1 shall not exceed 2.

M is the design ultimate moment of the section, b and d are the breadth and effective depth of the section respectively and f_s the service stress in the reinforcement.
   This last can either be obtained from a full service stress analysis or from

$$f_s = \tfrac{5}{8}f_y(A_{s,\,req}/A_{s,\,prov})/\beta_b \tag{5.8}$$

where the $\tfrac{5}{8}$ factor is introduced as an approximate ratio between the service and ultimate bending moments, the ratio $(A_{s,\,req}/A_{s,\,prov})$ to allow for the effect of the actual reinforcement placed

$(A_{s,\,prov})$ being greater than that from design calculations $(A_{s,\,req})$, and

β_b, the ratio of the moment at the section after redistribution to that before.

   If either the amount of redistribution is unknown or the design moment is greater than the elastic ultimate moment β_b is taken as unity.

(iii) *Modification factor for compression reinforcement* (F_2)

$$F_2 = 1 + \rho'/(3 + \rho') \qquad (5.9)$$

The factor F_2 should be taken as not greater than 1.5.

$$\rho' = 100A'_{s,\,prov}/bd$$

The final span/effective depth ratio is given by

(basic span/effective depth ratio) $\times F_1 \times F_2$ $\qquad (5.10)$

EXAMPLE 5.1   *Deflection control using span/effective depth ratios*

Check that the design of the cantilever beam shown in Fig. 5.3 is suitable for the serviceability limit state of deflection.

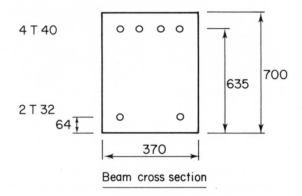

Beam cross section

Beam data : Transient load 40 kN/m
Permanent load 30 kN/m
Span (Cantilever) 4 m
f_{cu} 30 N/mm^2
f_y 460 N/mm^2

Fig. 5.3   Beam data for Examples 5.11 and 5.12.

(i)   From Table 5.3, the basic span/effective depth ratio = 7
(ii)   Factor F_1 – tension reinforcement.
Assuming $A_{s,\,req} = A_{s,\,prov}$ and $\beta_b = 1.0$, then

$$f_s = \tfrac{5}{8}f_y = \tfrac{5}{8} \times 460 = 287.5 \text{ N/mm}^2.$$

Loading at ULS = $(1.4 \times 30 + 1.6 \times 40) = 106$ kN/m,
Maximum bending moment, $M = qL^2/2 = 106 \times 4^2/2 = 848$ kN/m,
$b = 370$, $d = 635$ so $M/bd^2 = 848\text{E}6/(370 \times 635^2) = 5.68$ N/mm^2
$F_1 = 0.55 + (477 - 287.5)/(120(0.9 + 5.68)) = 0.79$.

(iii)   Factor F_2 – compression reinforcement.

$$\rho' = 100 \times 1608/(635 \times 370) = 0.684\%$$
$$F_2 = 1 + 0.684/(3 + 0.684) = 1.19.$$

Thus final span/effective depth ratio is given as

$$7 \times 0.79 \times 1.19 = 6.58.$$

Since the span is 4 m, the minimum effective depth is given as $4000/6.58 = 608$ mm.

This is less than the actual effective depth of 635 mm, thus the design is satisfactory.

5.6.3 Explicit method

This comprises two stages:
(i)   Calculation of the curvatures at discrete points along the beam, and
(ii) Calculation of the deflections from these curvatures.

(i) *Calculation of curvatures*
It is required to calculate the instantaneous curvatures under both the total load $(1/r_{it})$ and the permanent load $(1/r_{ip})$, the long-term curvature under the permanent load $(1/r_{lp})$ together with the curvature due to shrinkage $(1/r_{cs})$.
   The total curvature $(1/r_x)$ is then given by

$$1/r_x = 1/r_{lp} + (1/r_{it} - 1/r_{ip}) + 1/r_{cs} \tag{5.11}$$

   The permanent loading is that portion of the live load which may be considered as always being present together with the dead load. Cl 3.3.3, Pt 2 suggests that for offices or domestic usage 25% of the live load be considered permanent and for storage areas 75%. Other cases should be given intermediate values.
   Curvatures are to be calculated on the assumption that either the concrete is uncracked or is cracked and carries a limited tensile strength (1 N/mm² under instantaneous loading or 0.55 N/mm² under permanent loading). The larger of the two curvature values is to be used.   The value of Young's modulus for the concrete will need modifying for creep in the long-term loading case (see Section 2.3).
   The shrinkage curvature, $1/r_{cs}$, is given by

$$1/r_{cs} = \varepsilon_{cs} \alpha_e S_s / I \tag{5.12}$$

where S_s is the first moment of area of the reinforcement about the neutral axis calculated for the long-term loading case and is given by Equation (5.2), and

   I is the second moment of area.

The shrinkage strain, ε_{cs}, is obtained using data in Section 2.6.

(ii) *Calculation of deflections*
This may be carried out in two ways by either (a) double integration of the curvature or (b) an approximate method.

(a) *Double integration of the curvatures*
Using small-deflection theory,

$$1/r_x = d^2w/dx^2 \tag{5.12}$$

where w is the vertical deflection at any point and x a co-ordinate. Replacing the second differential by its finite difference equivalent gives

$$1/r_x = (w_{x+} w_{x+1} - 2w_{x-1})/(\Delta x)^2 \tag{5.13}$$

Loading	BMD	K
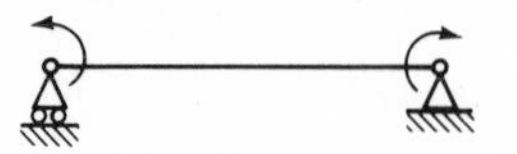	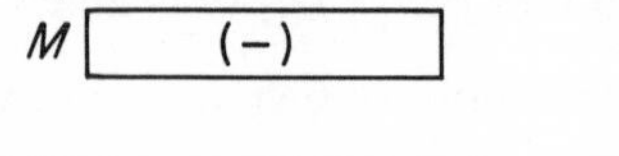 M $(-)$	0.125
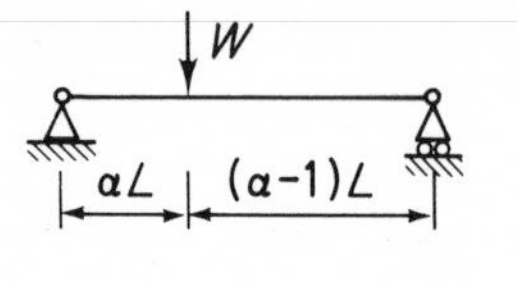 αL $(\alpha-1)L$	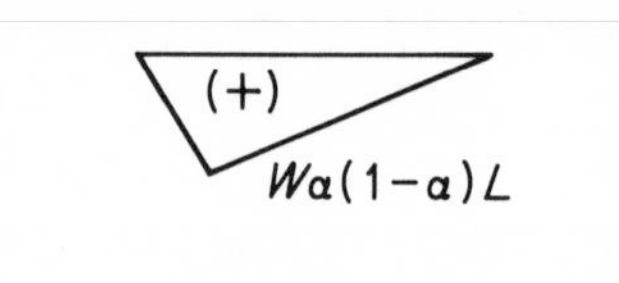 $(+)$ $W\alpha(1-\alpha)L$	$(3-4\alpha^2)/48(1-\alpha)$
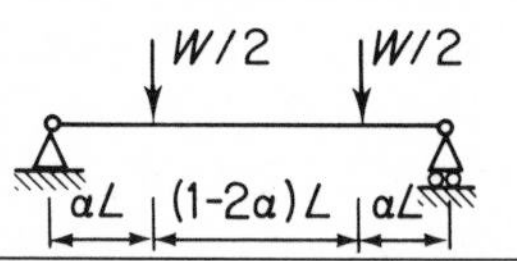 $W/2$ $W/2$ αL $(1-2\alpha)L$ αL	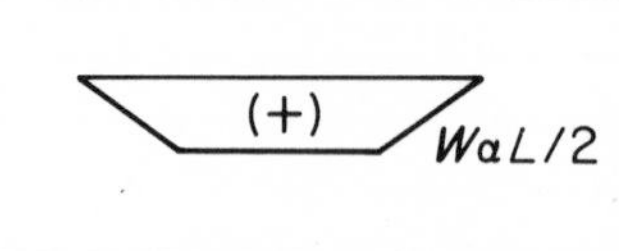 $(+)$ $W\alpha L/2$	$0.125-\alpha^2/6$
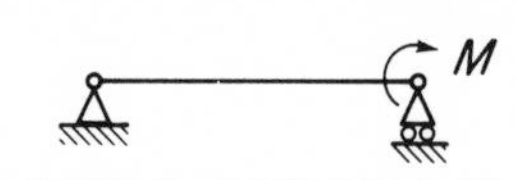	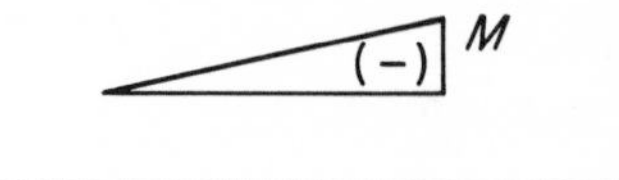 $(-)$ M	0.0625
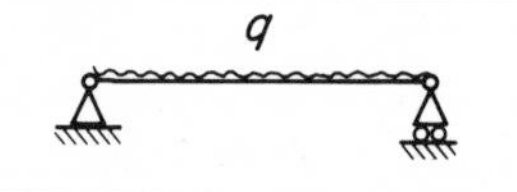 q	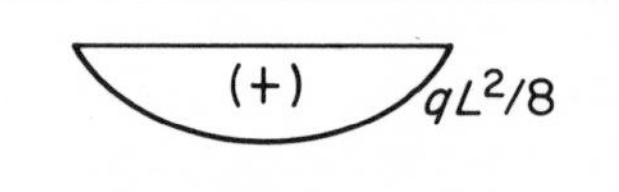 $(+)$ $qL^2/8$	5/48
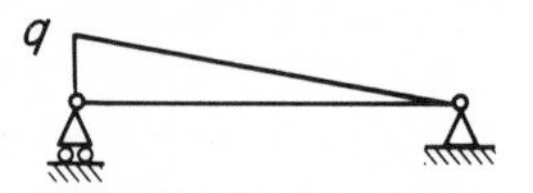 q	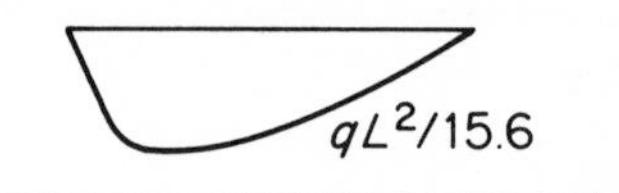 $qL^2/15.6$	0.102
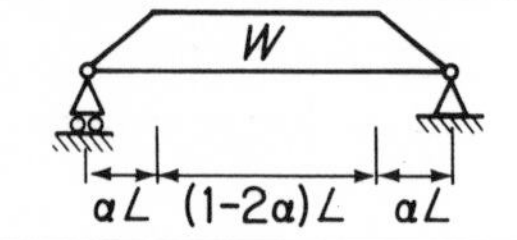 W αL $(1-2\alpha)L$ αL	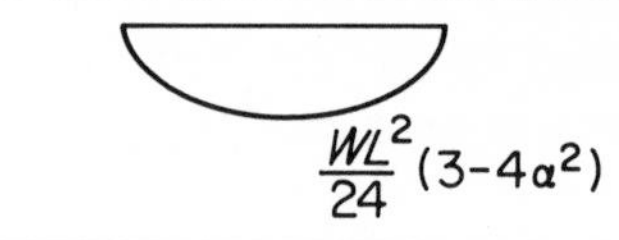 $\frac{WL^2}{24}(3-4\alpha^2)$	$(5-4\alpha^2)^2/80(3-4\alpha^2)$
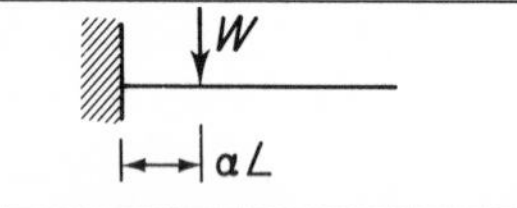 W αL	 $W\alpha L$	$\alpha(3-\alpha)/6$
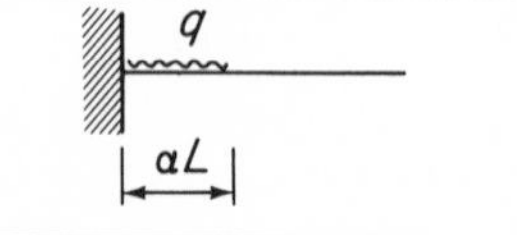 q αL	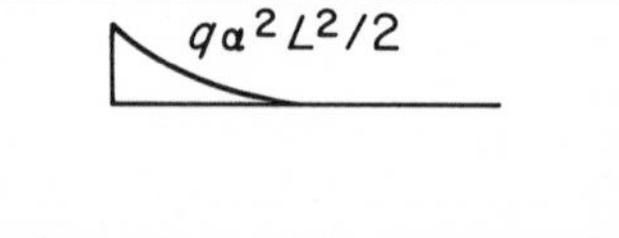 $qa^2L^2/2$	$\alpha(4-\alpha)/12$
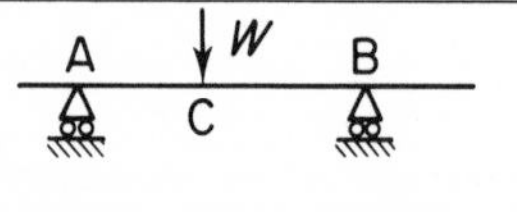 A W B C	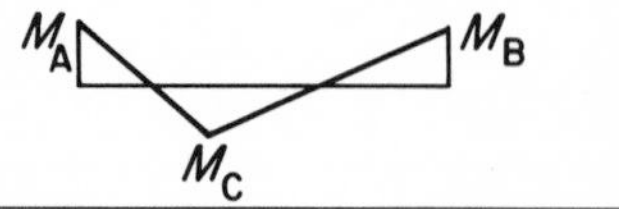 M_A M_B M_C	$k=0.083(1-\beta/4)$ $\beta=(M_A+M_B)/M_C$ numerical values of M_A etc. are used
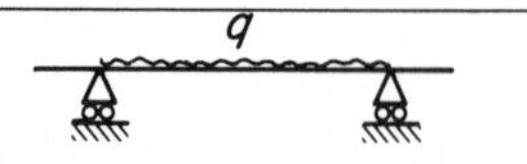 q	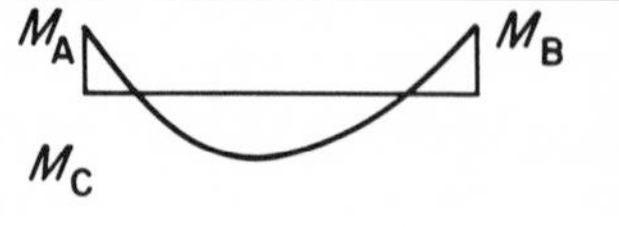 M_A M_B M_C	$k=0.104(1-\beta/10)$ $\beta=(M_A+M_B)/M_C$ M_C may be either the midspan or maximum value, any error will be small

Fig. 5.4   Values of coefficient K.

where Δx is a distance increment along the beam and the deflections, w, are taken at point x and on either side of it.

For a simply supported (or continuous) beam the deflections are zero at the supports and for a cantilever both the deflection and slope are zero at the support.

(b) *Approximate method*

Here, the maximum deflection, w_{max}, is related to the maximum curvature $(1/r_{x,max})$ by

$$w_{max} = KL^2(1/r_{x,max}) \tag{5.14}$$

where L is the effective span and K is a parameter depending on the shape of the bending-moment diagram. Values of K for common load cases are given in Fig. 5.4.

Note that since this method is non-linear the deflection obtained under complex loading cases cannot be obtained as the sum of the deflections under the individual load cases. Instead, a value of K should be selected from the one most closely resembling the case for the total bending-moment diagram.

EXAMPLE 5.2   *Deflection calculations*

For the cantilever shown in Fig. 5.3, find the deflection of the free end.

Young's modulus for the concrete is 25 kN/mm^2 the creep coefficient (ϕ) will be taken as 2.0 and the shrinkage strain (ε_{cs}) as 300 microstrain.

Divide the beam into five length increments each of 1 m. For each slice calculate the uncracked and cracked second moments of area.

Uncracked (gross section)

This is covered in Section 4.5.6, to which reference should be made.

Cracked

The strain and stesss profiles to calculate these are given in Fig. 5.5.

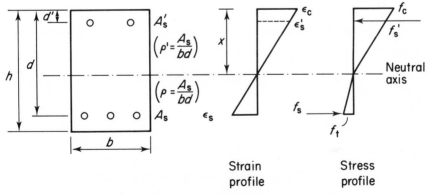

Strain profile   Stress profile

Fig. 5.5   Stress and strain profiles for cracked section.

For horizontal equilibrium,

$$bxf_c/2 + A_s'f_s' = bf_t(d-x)/2 + A_sf_s \tag{5.16}$$

Substituting the values of the stresses given in Fig. 5.6 in terms of the concrete strain ε_c gives

$$x/(2d)+\rho'\alpha_e(1-(d'/d)(d/x)) = f_t(1-x/d)/(2E_c\varepsilon_c)+\rho\alpha_e(d/x-1) \tag{5.17}$$

Taking moments about the tension steel and rearranging gives

$$M/bd^2E_c\varepsilon_c = \alpha_e(1-(d'/d)(d/x))\rho'(1-d'/d)+$$
$$(x/2d)(1-x/(3d))-f_t(1-x/d)^2/(6E_c\varepsilon_c) \tag{5.18}$$

Eliminating $E_c\varepsilon_c$ between Equations (5.17) and (5.18) gives

$$\frac{\dfrac{x}{2d}+\rho'\alpha_e\left[1-\left(\dfrac{d'}{d}\right)\left(\dfrac{d}{x}\right)\right]-\rho\alpha_e\left(\dfrac{d}{x}-1\right)}{\alpha_e\left[1-\left(\dfrac{d'}{d}\right)\left(\dfrac{d}{x}\right)\right]\rho'\left(1-\dfrac{d'}{d}\right)+\dfrac{x}{2d}\left(1-\dfrac{x}{3d}\right)} = \frac{\dfrac{f_t}{2}\left(1-\dfrac{x}{d}\right)}{\dfrac{f_t}{6}\left(1-\dfrac{x}{d}\right)^2+\dfrac{M}{bd^2}} \tag{5.19}$$

Equation (5.19) can only be solved iteratively using a computer as was done for this example. The cracked second moment of area is then given by

$$I_c/bd^3 = (x/d)^3/3+\alpha_e\rho'(d'/d-x/d)^2+\rho\alpha_e(1-x/d)^2 \tag{5.20}$$

To calculate the effect of the shrinkage the first moment of area of the reinforcement, S_s, must be calculated using Equation (5.21):

$$S_s/bd^2 = \rho(1-x/d)-\rho'(d'/d-x/d) \tag{5.21}$$

At all points the lesser of the cracked and uncracked values of the second moments of area are taken.

The results for this example are given in Table 5.4.

To allow the boundary conditions to be evaluated at point 5 in the beam it is necessary to introduce a fictitious point 6 as in Fig. 5.6.

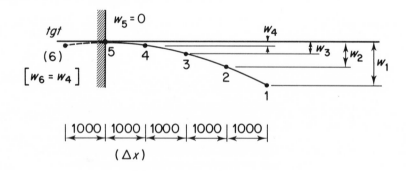

Fig. 5.6 Deflection profile.

The boundary conditions are,
(1) Deflection at point 5 is zero, or

$$w_5 = 0$$

Table 5.4 Details of deflection calculations for Example 5.2

Point	Distance from free end (m)	α_e	M (kN m)	f_t (N/mm²)	I/bd^3	S/bd^2 (×10⁻³)	$-1/r_{1p}$ (×10⁻⁸) (m⁻¹)	$-1/r_{1t}$ (×10⁻⁸) (m⁻¹)	$-1/r_{1p}$ (×10⁻⁸) (m⁻¹)	$-1/r_{cs}$ (×10⁻⁸) (m⁻¹)	$-1/r_t$ (×10⁻⁸) (m⁻¹)	$(\Delta x)^2$ $(1/r_t)$ (mm)
1	0	—	0									—
2	1.0	24	15	0.55	0.225	1.05	−3.56	11.55	8.44	5.29	21.72	0.2172
		8	15	1.00	0.178							
		8	35	1.00	0.128							
3	2.0	24	60	0.55	0.204	4.28	−19.79	42.83	37.25	29.35	89.64	0.8964
		8	60	1.00	0.128							
		8	140	1.00	0.138							
4	3.0	24	135	0.55	0.207	5.02	−41.30	90.48	82.61	27.50	159.29	1.5929
		8	135	1.00	0.138							
		8	315	1.00	0.147							
5	4	24	240	0.55	0.208	5.27	−70.37	157.63	146.15	28.74	262.15	2.6215
		8	240	1.00	0.144							
		8	560	1.00	0.150							

(2) The slope at point 5 is zero, or

$$(w_6 - w_4)/(2\Delta x) = 0,$$

or

$$w_6 = w_4.$$

Applying Equation (5.14) at each of the points 2–5 in the beam gives

$$
\begin{aligned}
2w_4 &= 2.6215 \\
w_3 - 2w_4 &= 1.5929 \\
w_2 - 2w_3 + w_4 &= 0.8964 \\
w_1 - 2w_2 + w_3 &= 0.2172
\end{aligned}
\tag{5.22}
$$

Hence solving Equation (5.22) gives the deflection at the free end, w_1, as

$$w_1 = 12.0 \text{ mm}$$

If the approximate method is used to calculate the deflections using Equation (5.15), then from Fig. 5.4, $K = 0.25$ for the cantilever udl loading case

$$L = 4000 \text{ mm}$$

$1/r_{x,\text{max}} = 262.15\text{E} - 8 \text{ mm}^{-1}$ (from Table 5.4),

thus,

$$w_{\text{max}} = KL^2(1/r_{x,\text{max}}) = 0.25 \times (4000)^2 \times 262.15\text{E} - 8 = 10.5 \text{ mm}$$

Note that this has underestimated the deflection by 1.5 mm (or 12.5%).

5.7 Crack widths (cl 3.12.11.2.1, Pt 1)

5.7.1 Flexural cracking

For the majority of cases, provided that the cover is not greater than 50 mm and the exposure is normal internal or external, then a crack-width limitation of 0.3 mm is acceptable. In other circumstances reference should be made to either BS 5400 or BS 5337. The crack widths can be checked either using bar-spacing rules, which will usually be satisfactory, or by explicit calculation. The latter method will be covered first.

(a) *Explicit calculation of crack widths*
The background to those in CP110 was given by Beeby in 1979, and remains, except for the tension stiffening equation, essentially the same for BS 8110.
    The theory developed starts from three basic assumptions:

(i) There is a limiting distance from a crack, S_0, at which the stress distribution is not affected by the crack, and thus the expected crack spacing, S, is limited by

$$S_0 < S < 2S_0 \tag{5.23}$$

(ii) The average crack widths, w_m, is related to the average crack spacing, S_m, and average strain, ε_m, by

$$w_m = S_m \varepsilon_m \tag{5.24}$$

There will be either breakdown of bond or slip between the reinforcement and the concrete at a crack since there is no longer deformation compatibility, so S_m is given by

$$S_m = k_1 c + k_2 \phi / \rho \tag{5.25}$$

where c is the cover to the reinforcement, ϕ the bar diameter and ρ the reinforcement ratio. This relationship has been found to hold for both plain and deformed bars, but was originally derived for the case of pure tension. Equation (5.25) thus needs modifying to allow for flexure, and in so doing takes the form

$$w = a_{cr} w_0 w_{lim} \varepsilon_m / (c w_{lim} + (a_{cr} - c) w_0) \tag{5.26}$$

where w is the calculated crack width,

w_0 the crack width given by Equations (5.24) and (5.25),

w_{lim} the maximum crack height ($= k_1 h_{cr} \varepsilon_m$),

h_{cr} is the crack height and

a_{cr} the distance from the point being considered to the nearest bar.

Equation (5.26), however, needs some simplification to allow it to be used generally. This is done by setting

$$w_{lim} = 1.5(h - x)\varepsilon_m$$

giving a 20% probability of the design crack width being exceeded, and also by setting

$$w_0 = 3c\varepsilon_m$$

If the two above simplifications are substituted into Equation (5.26), and some rearrangement is performed, the design surface crack width, w_d, is given by

$$w_d = 3a_{cr}\varepsilon_m / (1 + 2(a_{cr} - c_{min})/(h - x)) \tag{5.27}$$

where ε_m is the average steel strain at the level being considered,

c_{min} is the minimum cover to the reinforcing steel,

h is the overall depth of the section,

and x is the neutral axis depth.

ε_m may be calculated either by using the same assumptions as those used for calculating the cracked section properties for deflections, or by calculating the strain based on the assumption that the concrete has no strength in tension and then correcting the value by an allowance for tension stiffening, ε_t, given by

$$\varepsilon_t = -b_t(h - x)(a' - x)/(3E_s A_s(d - x)) \tag{5.28}$$

where a' is the distance from the compression face to the point at which cracking is being considered,

d is the effective depth,

and b_t the width of the section at the steel centroid.

The mean strain, ε_m, is given by

$$\varepsilon_m = \varepsilon_1 + \varepsilon_t$$

where ε_1 is the strain at the point being considered.

It may be calculated using similar triangles since the strain in the reinforcement and the depth of the neutral axis are known. So for cracking on the tension face of a beam or slab,

$$\varepsilon_1 = \varepsilon_s(h-x)/(d-x) \tag{5.29}$$

where ε_s is the strain in the reinforcement calculated on the assumption that the concrete below the neutral axis has no strength. If ε_m is negative the section is uncracked.

For crack-width calculations a creep coefficient of unity should be employed.

EXAMPLE 5.3   *Calculation of crack widths*

Check the crack widths at the support for the beam of Example 5.2. The critical points for cracking are either between two bars (A) or at the corner (B) (Fig. 5.7(a)).

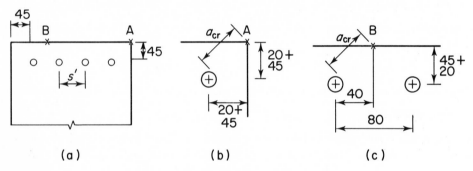

Fig. 5.7   Beam detailing for Example 5.3.

For point A (Fig. 5.7(b))

$$a_{cr} = (40^2 + 65^2)^{0.5} - 20 = 56 \text{ mm}$$

For point B (Fig. 5.7(c))

$$a_{cr} = 65 \times 2^{0.5} - 20 = 72 \text{ mm}$$

The neutral axis depth is calculated using Equation (4.9):

$$\rho = 4229/(370 \times 635) = 0.019,$$
$$\rho' = 1608/(370 \times 635) = 6.84\text{E} - 3,$$
$$d'/d = 64/635 = 0.10$$
$$(x/d) = -(\rho + \rho')\alpha_e + (((\rho + \rho')\alpha_e)^2 + 2(\rho'(d'/d) + \rho)\alpha_e)^{0.5}$$

$E_c = 25 \text{ kN/mm}^2$ (Example 5.1), $\phi = 1$ so value to be used for crack-width calculations is $25/2 = 12.5 \text{ kN/mm}^2$.

$$\alpha_e = E_s/E_c = 200/12.5 = 16$$

Thus

$$x/d = 0.482 \quad \text{or } x = 0.482 \times 635 = 306 \text{ mm}$$

From Equation (4.8) (in steel units)

$$
\begin{aligned}
I/bd^3 &= (x/d)^3/(3\alpha_e) + \rho'(d'/d - x/d)^2 + \rho(1 - x/d)^2 \\
&= 8.429\text{E}-3 \\
I &= 8.429\text{E}-3 \times 370 \times 635^3 = 7.985\text{E}8 \text{ mm}^3 \\
f_s &= M_s(d - x)/I \\
M_s &= 70 \times 4^2/2 = 560 \text{ kN mm},
\end{aligned}
$$

so

$$
\begin{aligned}
f_s &= 560\text{E}6(635 - 306)/7.985\text{E}8 = 231 \text{ N/mm}^2. \\
\varepsilon_s &= f_s/E_s = (231/200)\text{E}3 = 1155 \text{ microstrain.} \\
\varepsilon_1 &= (h - x)/(d - x) \\
&= 1155 \times (700 - 306)/(635 - 306) \\
&= 1383 \text{ microstrain}
\end{aligned}
$$

To allow for tension stiffening use Equation (5.28). Since the cracks are on the tension face $a' = h$,

so

$$\varepsilon_t = -b_t(h - x)^2/(3E_s A_s(d - x))$$

or

$$
\begin{aligned}
\varepsilon_m &= 1383 - (370(700 - 306)^2/(3 \times 200\text{E}3 \times 4229(635 - 306)))\text{E}6 \\
&= 1314 \text{ microstrain.}
\end{aligned}
$$

So for Point A the crack width, w_d, is given by,

$$
\begin{aligned}
w_d &= 3a_{cr}\varepsilon_m/(1 + 2(a_{cr} - c_{min})/(h - x)) \\
&= 3 \times 72 \times 1314\text{E}-6/(1 + 2(56 - 45)/(700 - 306)) \\
&= 0.21 \text{ mm}
\end{aligned}
$$

and for Point B,

$$
\begin{aligned}
w_d &= 3 \times 72 \times 1314\text{E}-6/(1 + 2(72 - 45)/(700 - 306)) \\
&= 0.25 \text{ mm}
\end{aligned}
$$

Both these crack widths are below 0.3 mm and therefore satisfactory.

(b) *Bar-spacing rules*
The starting point for the derivation of these is the crack-width equation (5.27). If a crack should occur over a bar, then

$$a_{cr} = c_{min},$$

or

$$w_d = 3a_{cr}\varepsilon_m.$$

From the span/effective depth method of calculating deflections it will be remembered that the service stress in the reinforcement was given approximately by

$$f_s = \tfrac{5}{8}f_y/\beta_b \tag{5.8(a)}$$

Since $\varepsilon_m = f_s/E_s$ and $w_d = 0.3$ mm,

a_{cr} is given by

$$a_{cr} = 32\,000\beta_b/f_y \tag{5.30}$$

Since, however, the maximum crack width occurs mid-way between bars, the value given by Equation (5.30) should be doubled. In practice a slightly higher value than this is adopted, so the clear distance between bars, s, is given by

$$s = 75\,000\beta_b/f_y \tag{5.31}$$

This equation forms the basis of Table 3.30, Pt 1. A maximum value of 300 mm is imposed on the spacing s. The distance to a corner bar should not exceed half the value predicted by Equation (5.31).

For slabs, in no case should the clear distance between bars exceed the lesser of three times the effective depth or 750 mm. Also unless full calculations are performed, the following rules may be applied (cl 3.12.11.2.7, Pt 1).

(a)   No further check is required on bar spacing if either:

   (1)   grade 250 steel is used and the slab depth does not exceed 250 mm; or
   (2)   grade 460 steel is used and the slab depth does not exceed 200 mm; or
         the reinforcement percentage ($100A_s/bd$) is less than 0.3%;

(b)   where none of the conditions (1), (2) and (3) apply the bar spacings should be limited to the values given by Equation (5.31), where the reinforcement percentage exceeds 1% or the values given by Equation (5.31) divided by the reinforcement percentage for lesser amounts.

In general bar spacing to restrict cracking in beams is seldom critical. This, however, is not the case in slabs.

EXAMPLE 5.4   Bar-spacing rules

Check the spacing of the bars in the beam of Example 5.2.
$\quad\quad\beta_b = 1.0, f_y = 460$ N/mm^2, so
$\quad\quad s = 75\,000\beta_b/f_y = 75\,000 \times 1.0/460 = 163$ mm.

Clearly this is not exceeded in this beam since there are four bars in a total width of 370 mm.

5.8   Early thermal cracking

5.8.1   BS 8110 approach

This is due to the generation of heat of hydration during the early period of setting of the concrete. Cracks may occur either due to internal temperature gradients in large pours or by restraint from the surrounding hardened concrete during subsequent cooling.

The strain due to early thermal cracking (ε_{th}) is given by

$$\varepsilon_{th} = \Delta T \alpha R \tag{5.32}$$

where ΔT is the temperature rise, α the coefficient of thermal expansion and R the degree of restraint offered by the surrounding structure, which is given in Table 5.5 (taken from Table 3.3, Pt 2).

Table 5.5   Degree of restraint

Type of pour	Value of restraint (R)
Thin wall on to massive base	0.6–0.8 at base
Massive pour on to blinding	0.1–0.2
Massive pour on to existing mass concrete	0.3–0.4 at base 0.1–0.2 at top
Suspended slabs	0.2–0.4
Infill bays	0.8–1.0

The values of α to be used are given in Table 5.6 together with the values of limiting tensile strains (from Table 3.2, Pt 2).

Table 5.6   Thermal expansion data

Aggregate type	Coefficient of thermal expansion (microstrain/deg C)	Tensile strain capacity (microstrain)
Gravel	12.0	70
Granite	10.0	80
Limestone	8.0	90

BS 8110 works in terms of limiting temperatures rises for given restraint parameters. This in practice may not be easy to use since it will need calculations (or data) to determine the temperature rise from knowledge of the heat of hydration, and it may be easier to use the approach given in BS 5337. Note that BS 5337 is being currently revised and will be issued as BS 8007. The approach in the new code is essentially similar to that of BS 5337, although it is likely that more data on temperature rises will be made available and should then be used in place of those given in Table 5.7. The BS 5337 approach is briefly outlined here.

5.8.2   BS 5337 approach

Here the temperature rise ΔT is divided into two components:

T_1 the temperature drop from a maximum value during hydration to ambient, and

T_2 which allows for the seasonal variations after hardening.

Typical values of T_1 and T_2 are given in Table 5.7 (after Anchor 1981).

Table 5.7   Values of T_1 and T_2

	T_1	T_2
Summer	30	20
Winter	20	10 (deg C)

Note, BS 5337 uses a coefficient of thermal expansion half that recommended by BS 8110, which in effect either implies a restraint factor (R) of 0.5 or is recognising that for immature concrete the thermal expansion is lower than that for mature concrete, for which the values are given in BS 8110. Note also that should the cement content exceed 340 kg/m^3 or the thickness of concrete exceed 400 mm when there are both surfaces exposed, the values of T_1 in Table 5.7 will need increasing.

EXAMPLE 5.5   Early thermal cracking

A 300 thick wall is to be cast using siliceous aggregate in summer. Calculate the likely crack width due to early thermal cracking if the wall is reinforced with T12–300. The restraint parameter may be taken as 0.5.
    From Table 5.7 $T_1 = 30$ and $T_2 = 20°C$

so

$$\varepsilon_{th} = (T_1 + T_2)\alpha R = (30 + 20) \times 12 \times 0.5 = 300 \text{ microstrain}$$

This is in excess of the tensile strain capacity of 70 microstrain, so cracking will ensue.
    For axial tension $h - x$ in the crack width equation (Equation (5.27)) is replaced by $2h$ (cl 3.8.3, Pt 2),

so

$$w_d = 3a_{cr}\varepsilon_m/(1 + 2(a_{cr} - c_{min})/(2h))$$

Figure 5.8 gives the dimensions needed in the above formula:

$$w_d = 3 \times 147 \times 300E - 6/(1 + 2(147 - 25)/(2 \times 300))$$
$$= 0.09 \text{ mm, which is acceptable}$$

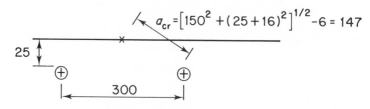

Fig. 5.8   Detailing for Example 5.5.

5.9   Fire design of structures

5.9.1   Introduction

In England and Wales the *Building Regulations* (1985) specify the period of fire resistance which the structure and its elements must be designed to endure. This period ranges from 0.5 to 4 hours and will depend on the use of the structure and its size both in terms of compartment area and volume. Certain parts of the structure may be designated as protected, i.e. must be capable of withstanding intact the full effects of a '4 hr' fire. The resistance period is to allow evacuation of the occupants, safety in fire fighting and minimization of structural damage.

Although concrete is a good insulator, fire causes a considerable build-up in temperature within the section which leads to reductions in strength and increases in ductility in both the reinforcement and the concrete. For flexural members it is essentially the behaviour of the reinforcement that dominates, thus making possible the use of relatively simple calculation methods. However, for members carrying a compressive load the situation is far more complex in that internal redistributions of stresses occur because time-dependent effects become operative.

Traditionally adequate fire resistance for concrete members has been attained by specifying cover to the reinforcement and minimum member thicknesses. This method relies on data from the standard fire test. Gradually this approach is being superseded by a fire engineering method in which rational design methods are coming into use.

BS 8110 allows three methods to be used to calculate fire resistance requirements:

(i)   cover and member size data,
(ii) fire test performance, and
(iii) fire engineering approach.

Since both the first two methods are derived from fire testing, the fire test will now be briefly described.

5.9.2   Standard fire test

In the standard fire test, an element from a structure is exposed to standard temperature time response in a furnace whilst being loaded with full service loading.

Slabs are heated on the soffit only and beams on the soffit and side faces. Traditionally columns have been tested by being heated on all four sides whilst under axial load only. Owing to sizes of available furnaces, there are often restrictions on the maximum size of member that can be tested. It has been recognised for some while that the effect of the surrounding structure on an element being exposed to a fire is to cause a substantial redistribution of forces within the element. The new fire test standard (BS 476 Pts 20–22) recognises this fact for slab and beam elements in that it allows the effect of continuity to be modelled in the actual test. For columns the situation is much more complex and reference should be made to Purkiss and Weeks (1987).

BS 476 recognizes three criteria for evaluating the fire test performance of an element:

(i)   that throughout the test the element should remain an effective flame barrier (this basically is to stop the spread of fire);

(ii)   that the temperature on an unexposed face should not exceed certain values (again this is to protect the compartment away from the fire);

(iii)   that the element should not fail nor its deflection or rate of deflection exceed terminal values.

The standard time–temperature response used in the fire test is compared with actual time–temperature responses measured in a compartment fire in Fig. 5.9, where it will be observed that a compartment response rises to a peak dependent on the fire load and the available ventilation before decaying, whereas the standard response continues rising.

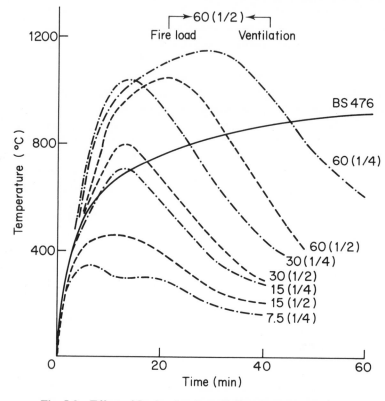

Fig. 5.9   Effect of fire load and ventilation on temperature.

This is one of the reasons why the fire test has gradually become discredited as a method for evaluating fire resistance. The others are a lack of recognition of more critical loading cases, e.g. a column heated on three sides under an axial load and a moment applied such that the thermal moment is in the same sense as the applied moment as at the periphery of a building, and the lack of ability to properly model structural restraint or continuity, which will have the effect of introducing additional loading caused by the deformation of the member under test. It has been established that a moderate degree of restraint may enhance the fire performance, whereas a high value will not, and may even lead to a severe reduction.

In spite of these criticisms the standard furnace test does remain a valid method of comparative testing to establish the relative merits of differing forms of construction.

Some of the data evolved from fire tests and included in BS 8110 Pt 2 Section 3 is summarised in Table 5.8, which is to be read in conjunction with Fig. 5.10.

Table 5.8 Fire resistance requirements

Member	Dimension concrete	type	Fire resistance (hours)					
			0.5	1	1.5	2	3	4
Plain soffit floor								
Reinforced simply supported	Thickness NW		75	95	110	125	150	170
	Cover		15	20	25	35	45	55
	Thickness LW		70	90	105	115	135	150
	Cover		15	15	20	25	35	45
Reinforced continuous	Thickness NW		75	95	110	125	150	170
	Cover		15	20	20	25	35	45
	Thickness LW		70	90	105	115	135	150
	Cover		15	15	20	20	25	35
Ribbed open soffit floor								
Reinforced simply supported	Thickness NW		70	90	105	115	135	150
	Width		75	90	110	125	150	175
	Cover		15	25	35	45	55	65
Reinforced continuous	Thickness NW		70	90	105	115	135	150
	Width		75	80	90	110	125	150
	Cover		15	20	25	35	45	55
Walls								
ρ>0.9% rft	Thickness		150	150	175	—	—	—
0.4%<ρ<1.0%	Thickness NW		100	120	140	160	200	240
	Cover		25	25	25	25	25	25
ρ>1.0%	Thickness		75	75	100	100	150	180
	Cover		15	15	25	25	25	25
0.4%<ρ<1.0%	Thickness LW		100	100	115	130	160	190
	Cover		10	20	20	25	25	25
Columns								
Fully exposed	Width	NW	150	200	250	300	400	450
	Cover		20	25	30	35	35	35
	Width	LW	150	160	200	240	320	360
	Cover		20	20	25	35	35	35
One face exposed	Thickness NW		100	120	140	160	200	240
	Cover		20	25	25	25	25	25
	Thickness LW		100	100	115	130	160	190
	Cover		10	20	20	25	25	25
Beams								
Reinforced simply supported	Width	NW	80	120	150	200	240	280
	Cover		20	30	40	50	70	80
	Width	LW	80	100	130	160	200	250
	Cover		15	20	35	45	55	65
Continuous	Width	NW	80	80	120	150	200	240
	Cover		20	20	35	50	60	70
	Width	LW	60	80	90	110	150	200
	Cover		15	20	25	35	45	55

Table 5.8 Ctd.   Fire resistance requirements

Member	Dimension concrete	type	Fire resistance (hours)					
			0.5	1	1.5	2	3	4
Prestressed								
simply supported	Width	NW	100	120	150	200	240	280
	Cover		25	40	55	70	80	90
continuous	Width	NW	80	100	120	155	200	240
	Cover		20	30	40	55	70	90

Notes
1. NW signifies normal weight or dense concrete and LW lightweight concrete.
2. Cover is the cover to the *main reinforcement* (or *tendons*).
3. For flat soffit slabs and columns the cover is the actual cover, whereas for beams and ribbed floors the weighted or mean cover may be taken (Fig. 5.10).

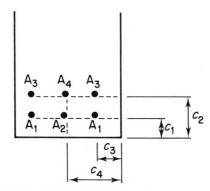

Average (or weighted) cover, $c_{eff} =$

$$\frac{c_1 A_2 + 2A_1 \begin{bmatrix} \text{Lesser of} \\ c_1 \text{ or } c_3 \end{bmatrix} + 2A_3 \begin{bmatrix} \text{Lesser of} \\ c_2 \text{ or } c_3 \end{bmatrix} + A_4 \begin{bmatrix} \text{Lesser of} \\ c_4 \text{ or } c_2 \end{bmatrix}}{2(A_1 + A_3) + A_2 + A_4}$$

(a) Definition of average cover for a beam or rib

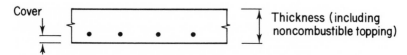

Note : For two-way spanning slabs the cover is the weighted cover for the reinforcement in both directions

(b) Plain soffit floors

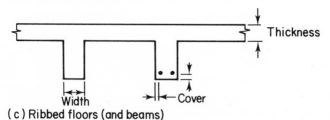

(c) Ribbed floors (and beams)

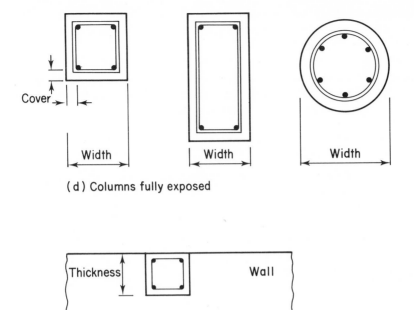

(d) Columns fully exposed

(e) Column with one face exposed

Fig. 5.10 Fire resistance requirements.

It should be noted that for covers greater than 40 mm supplementary reinforcement in the form of mesh is recommended by cls 4.1.7 and 4.3.4, Pt 2. However, it should be pointed out that such supplementary reinforcement is difficult to fix satisfactorily and in general should be avoided unless absolutely necessary. Where Table 5.8 indicates covers greater than 40 additional protection should be applied in the form of plaster to supplant part of the concrete cover in accordance with Table 5.9 (from cl 4.2.4, Pt 2).

Table 5.9 Equivalent protection thicknesses

Material	Factor (F_3)
Mortar or gypsum plaster	0.6
Lightweight plaster/ sprayed lightweight insulation	up to 2 h, 1.0 over 2 h, 2.0
Vermiculite slabs	up to 2 h, 1.0 over 2 h, 1.5

Notes
(i)   Equivalent thickness of replacement = $F_3 \times$ (reduction in concrete cover)
(ii) Maximum thickness of addition protection is 50 mm.

It should be noted that certain cases of fire resistance are not adequately covered by BS 8110, the prime example being edge columns in a structure which will be fire exposed on three sides and loaded by both a moment and axial load. There is regrettably no simple answer to this problem except to suggest that if the moment is high compared to the axial load, beam data might be more appropriate.

In general for fire resistance periods below 2 hours tabulated data should be adequate. Above 2 hours for flexural members a fire engineering approach should always be used in order to obtain what will normally be a less onerous solution than will be obtained from tabulated data. This may also be true below 2 hours.

5.9.3 Fire engineering approach

Currently BS 8110 only allows this for members which are predominantly subject to flexure. The reason for this is that whilst substantial research has been carried out on material behaviour at elevated temperatures, it is only possible to simulate the case, using finite element techniques, when high compressive stresses are present. There are not sufficient results to enable a simpler approach to be made available to design engineers.

There are two stages in this method:

(i)   Determination of temperatures within the element, and
(ii) Structural analysis.

(i) *Determination of temperatures*
The determination of temperatures involves the solution of the Fourier heat diffusion equation,

$$\dot{T} = \text{div}(\lambda \text{ grad } T) \tag{5.33}$$

where T is the temperature and λ is a space- and temperature-dependent thermal conductivity.

The boundary conditions imposed on Equation (5.33) must model the heat transfer from the fire to the structural element both by convection and by the more dominant radiation. No closed form solutions exist to Equation (5.33) and thus recourse must be had to finite or boundary element methods. Fortunately, however, for some standard cases graphical solutions have been produced for what might be described as average concretes. Some typical graphical solutions are given in Fig. 5.11.

(ii) *Structural analysis*
Essentially the same methods are used as at ambient conditions except that temperature-dependent materials strengths are used. The modification factors $\psi_{T,c}$ and $\psi_{T,s}$ for concrete and steel respectively are given in Fig. 5.12.

The principles involved are best illustrated by examples. A simply supported beam is covered in Example 5.6 and a continuous slab in Study 13.4.

During a fire substantial redistribution of the moment field occurs. Consider the internal span of a multispan one-way spanning slab shown in Fig. 5.13(a). At serviceability, i.e. effectively under the influence of working loads, assuming all spans fully loaded, the bending-moment distribution is as in Fig. 5.13(b), where it will be seen that a substantial reserve of strength appears to exist. During a fire the strengths of both the reinforcement and the concrete is reduced as the temperatures in the slab rise. The effect of this is to reduce the moment capacities at both mid-span and support as shown in Fig.

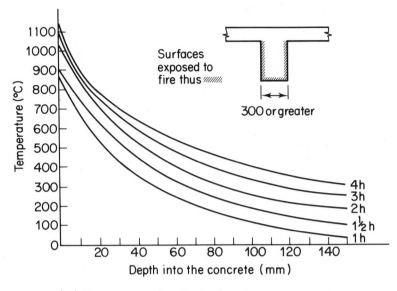

(a) Temperature distribution in a dense concrete beam

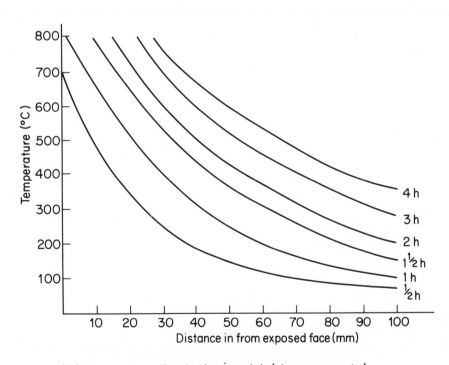

(b) Temperature distribution in a slab (dense concrete)

Fig. 5.11 (a) Temperature distribution in a dense concrete beam (b) Temperature distribution in a slab (dense concrete).

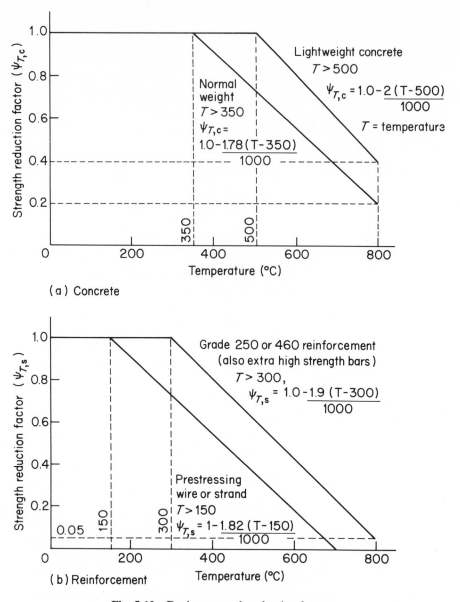

Fig. 5.12   Design strength reduction factors.

5.13(c). It will, however, be noted that this effect is more marked at mid-span, where it is possible that a zero strength plastic hinge may develop in as little as 2 hours, whereas the moment capacity at the support may reduce by only about 20% over a 4 hour period. This effect leads to a shift in the points of contraflexure towards mid-span, ultimately making the slab act as a pair of cantilevers.

It therefore becomes obvious that if a high fire-endurance period is required it is better, under ambient conditions, to maintain a high design moment at the support, where the reduction due to fire will be small, than to allow excessive redistribution at ambient to mid-span, where the reduction due to fire will be high and may reduce the moment capacity at mid-span to zero. In order to ensure adequate fire performance it may well be advisable to ensure that the ratio of the design moment at the support to that at mid-span exceeds about 1.3. This also enables 'deemed to satisfy clauses' to be employed in checking the fire response. Should the ratio of design moments drop below 1.3, then it is recommended that even for fire periods below 2 hours full fire engineering calculations should be employed. It may well be safe to use cover values for simply supported conditions in this case, but it is by no means certain.

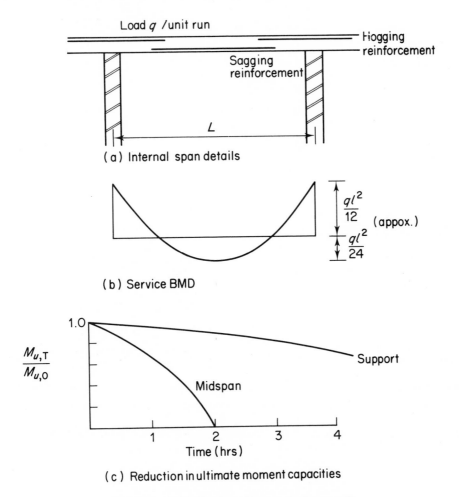

Fig. 5.13 Redistribution of moments during a fire.

EXAMPLE 5.6   Fire endurance of a simply supported beam

Determine the fire endurance of the beam for which data are given in Fig. 5.14.

Since the beam is simply supported the critical section will be mid-span, since there is little likelihood of shear failure.

The first stage is to determine the temperature in the reinforcement and the concrete.

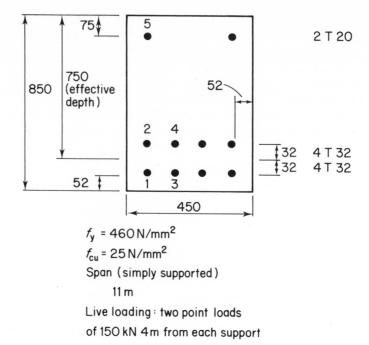

$f_y = 460 \, \text{N/mm}^2$

$f_{cu} = 25 \, \text{N/mm}^2$

Span (simply supported)

11 m

Live loading : two point loads

of 150 kN 4 m from each support

Fig. 5.14 Design data for Example 5.6.

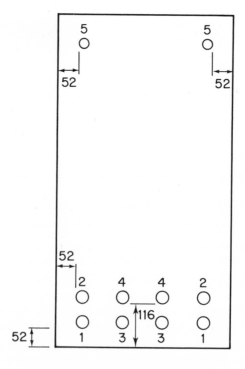

Fig. 5.15 Bar covers for Example 5.6.

To do this the minimum distance to the surface from each bar must be determined. The results (assuming uniform bar spacing) are given in Fig. 5.15, where it can be seen that bars 1, 2 and 3 have cover of 68 mm and bar 4 100 mm. Using Fig. 5.11(b) and Fig. 5.12(a) the temperatures and the strength reduction factors for each bar can be tabulated. This is done in Table 5.10 for fire periods of 1, 1.5, 2, 3 and 4 hours.

Table 5.10 Reinforcement temperatures and strength losses

| | Bar 1, 2, 3, 5 | | 4 | |
Time (h)	Temp (°C)	Strength loss ($\psi_{T,s}$)	Temp (°C)	Strength loss ($\psi_{T,s}$)
1.0	210	1.00	110	1.0
1.5	300	1.00	190	1.0
2.0	360	0.89	260	1.0
3.0	440	0.73	330	0.94
4.0	530	0.56	400	0.81

For the concrete a mean temperature is required at these times also. It will be sufficiently accurate to evaluate temperatures at the face, at quarter width and in the centre and then take the mean. The temperatures are found using Fig. 5.11(a) and the strength reduction factors using Fig. 5.12(b). The results are summarised in Table 5.11.

Table 5.11 Concrete temperatures and strength loss

| | | Position | | Weighted | |
Time (h)	Face T_1 (°C)	Quarter depth T_2 (°C)	Centre T_3* (°C)	mean $(2T_1 + 2T_2 + T_3)/5$ (°C)	Strength loss ($\psi_{T,c}$)
1.0	860	90	20	384	0.94
1.5	920	160	80	448	0.83
2.0	1000	230	180	528	0.68
3.0	1020	360	290	634	0.49

* These values have been extrapolated from Fig. 5.11(a).

From horizontal equilibrium the net tensile and compression forces must balance, so

$$\Sigma A_{st,i}\psi_{T,s_i}f_y - A_{sc}\psi_{T,s}f_y - 0.9 \times b(0.67\psi_{T,c}f_{cu}/\gamma_m) = 0$$

or

$$T_s - C_s - xC = 0$$

The values of T_s, C_s and C are given in Table 5.12. For concrete γ_m is taken as 1.3 (for the reinforcement the value is unity).

The moment capable of being resisted by the section is given by

$$M = (0.9 \times b(0.67f_{cu}\psi_{T,c}/\gamma_m)(0.45x)) + A_{sc}\psi_{T,s}f_yd' - \Sigma A_{st,i}\psi_{T,s_i}f_yd$$

or

$$M = M_c + M_{cs} - M_{ts}.$$

This calculation is also carried out in Table 5.12.
  The applied load on the beam is calculated as follows:

Dead load

$$1.05 \times (0.85 \times 0.45 \times 25) \times 11^2/8 = 152 \text{ kN m.}$$

Live load

$$150 \times 4 = 600 \text{ kN m.}$$

Total moment is 752 kN m.

Table 5.12   Calculation of moment capacity

Time (h)	T (MN)	C_s (MN)	C_c (kN/mm)	x (mm)	M_c (kN m)	M_{cs} (kN m)	M_{ts} (kN m)	M (kN m)
1.0	2.96	0.28	4.91	546	658.7	21.0	2313.8	1634.1
1.5	2.96	0.28	4.33	619	746.6	21.0	2313.8	1546.2
2.0	2.71	0.26	3.55	690	760.6	19.5	2160.7	1380.6
3.0	2.32	0.21	3.13	674	639.8	15.8	1731.5	1075.9
4.0	1.84	0.16	2.56	656	495.7	12.0	1375.7	867.8

  At no time does the moment of resistance calculated in Table 5.12 decrease below the applied moment. However, calculating the average cover in accordance with Fig. 5.10 and arriving at a figure of 60 mm, Table 5.8 indicates a fire resistance of around 2.5 hours. Part of the reason for the discrepancy is due to the tabular approach being conservative; the other is due to some of the assumptions made in the calculations. The least acceptable assumption is that the tensile steel has yielded. This is probably unlikely given the high neutral axis depths, and will as a result probably overestimate the resistance moment except that the concrete temperatures, and thus strengths, may have been underestimated. Thus the calculations should only be taken as a guide, and as such indicate a substantial reserve of strength at 2 hours and some reserve at 4 hours.

5.10 Tutorial problems

5.10.1   Crack widths and deflections

For the beam shown in Fig. 5.16,

(a) calculate, at mid-span, the maximum crack width;
(b) check that the beam satisfies the serviceability limit state of deflection by considering the span/effective depth ratio method;
(c) by considering the mid-span curvature, calculate the mid-span deflection.

Answers
(a) At both A and B, $w_d = 0.21$ mm ($M_s = 173.8$ kN m, $x/d = 0.405$, $I = 226.8E6$ mm^4, $\varepsilon_t = -149$ microstrain, $\varepsilon_m = 1301$ microstrain).
(b) Minimum effective depth = 521 mm ($M/bd^2 = 266.8$ N/mm^2, $f_s = 287.5$ N/mm^2, $F_1 = 0.96$).

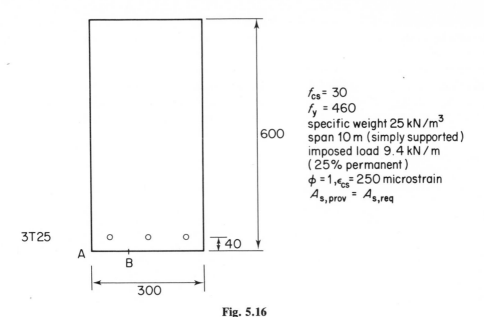

$f_{cs} = 30$
$f_y = 460$
specific weight 25 kN/m³
span 10 m (simply supported)
imposed load 9.4 kN/m
(25% permanent)
$\phi = 1, \epsilon_{cs} = 250$ microstrain
$A_{s,prov} = A_{s,req}$

Fig. 5.16

(c) Maximum deflection = 31.5 mm (moment under total load = 173.5 kN m, moment under permanent load = 85.6 kN m, for long-term permanent loading $x/d = 0.428$, for instantaneous total loading 0.534, and for instantaneous permanent loading 0.551, $S_s/bd^2 = 5.14E - 3$, $1/r_x = 3.02E - 6$ mm^{-1}, $K = \frac{5}{8}$).

5.10.2 One-way spanning slab

A multispan one-way spanning slab was designed using Table 4.7. The slab is 200 mm thick over a span of 6 m and carries an imposed load of 2.5 kN/m². The reinforcement fixed was T12-250 at an internal support and T12-250 at mid-span of an interior support. The cover to the reinforcement is 25 mm. The concrete is grade 25 with a specific weight of 25 kN/m³ and the reinforcement grade 460.

(a) Check that the bar spacing is satisfactory,
(b) Check the serviceability limit state of deflection using the span/effective depth ratio method,
(c) For how long could the slab be expected to endure in a fire?

Comment on your answer to part (c).

Answers
(a) Satisfactory (since slab depth not greater than 200 with grade 460 reinforcement and spacing less than 3d).
(b) Minimum effective depth = 127 mm ($A_{s,req} = 397$ mm², $f_s = 210$ N/mm² (note comment below Table 4.7), $F_1 = 1.81$.)
(c) Approximately 1 h 40 mins.

Table 5.8 indicates that a cover of 25 mm is adequate for a 2 h fire resistance for a continuous slab. The reason why this slab fails to satisfy a 2 h rating when a fire engineering calculation is performed is that the ratio of the support to mid-span design moment is as low as unity and thus too much of the moment capacity is exposed to the full effects of the fire at mid-span. Less redistribution would improve the result.

(Total load on the slab under fire conditions = 7.75 kN/m^2, moment required to be resisted = 34.9 kN m/m. The remaining calculations are summarised in Table 5.13.)

Table 5.13

Midspan					Support					
Time T_s (h) ($^\circ$C)		$\psi_{T,s}$	x (mm)	$M_{u,m}$ (kN m/m)	T_c ($^\circ$C)	$\psi_{T,c}$	x (mm)	$\psi_{T,s}$	$M_{u,s}$ (kN m/m)	$M_{u,t}$ (kN m/m)
0.5	400	0.81	12.1	27.0	500	0.73	20	1.0	33.2	60.2
1.0	590	0.45	6.7	15.0	600	0.54	28	1.0	32.6	47.0
1.5	750	0.14	2.1	4.7	700	0.38	38	1.0	31.6	36.3
2.0	810	0.03	0.4	1.0	720	0.34	44	1.0	31.0	32.0
3.0	850	0		0	760	0.27	56	1.0	29.9	29.9
4.0	850	0		0	780	0.23	58	0.9	26.8	26.8

References

Anchor R. D. (1981). *Design of liquid retaining concrete structures*, Surrey University Press.

Anchor R. D., Malhotra H. L. and Purkiss J. A. (1986). *Design of structures against fire*, Elsevier Applied Science.

Anderberg Y. (ed.) (1986). *Properties of materials at high temperatures* – Steel, RILEM reports, Lund Institute of Technology.

Beeby A. W. (1978). Corrosion of reinforcing steel in concrete and its relation to cracking, *Structural Engineer*, **56A** (3), 77–81.

Beeby A. W. (1979). The prediction of crack widths in hardened concrete. *Structural Engineer*, **57A** (1), 9–17.

BRE Digest 250 (1981). *Concrete in sulphate bearing soils and groundwaters*, Building Research Establishment, Garston.

BRE Digest 258 (1982). *Alkali–aggregate reactions in concrete*, Building Research Establishment, Garston.

BRE Digest 263 (1982). *The durability of steel in concrete – Part 1 – Mechanism of protection and corrosion*, Building Research Establishment, Garston.

BS 476 Part 8 (1972). *Test methods and criteria for the fire resistance of elements of building construction*, British Standards Institution, London.

BS 476 Parts 20–22 (1986). *Method for the determination of the fire resistance of loadbearing elements of construction*, British Standards Institution, London.

BS 5337 (1976). *Code of practice for the structural use of concrete for retaining aqueous liquids*, British Standards Institution, London.

BS 5400 Part 4 (1984). *Steel, concrete and composite bridges – Part 4 – Code of practice for design of concrete bridges.* British Standards Institution, London.

BS 8007 (1987) *Code of practice for the structural use of concrete for retaining aqueous liquids*, British Standards Institution, London.

FIP/CEB (1978). *Report on methods of assessment of the fire resistance of concrete structural members*, Cement and Concrete Association.

I. Struct. E/ Concrete Society (1975). *Fire resistance of concrete structures*, Institution of Structural Engineers.

I. Struct. E/ Concrete Society (1978). *Design and detailing of concrete structures for fire resistance*, Institution of Structural Engineers.

Malhotra H. L. (1982). *Design of fire-resisting structures*, Surrey University Press.

Malhotra H. L. (1984). *Spalling of concrete in fires*, Technical Note No. 118, Construction Industry Research and Information Association.

Page C. L. and Treadaway K. W. J. (1982). Aspects of the electrochemistry of steel in concrete. *Nature*, **297** (5862), 109–15.

Pomeroy C. D. (1982). *Requirements for durable concrete*, C & CA Reprint No. 3/85, Cement and Concrete Association.

Purkiss J. A. (1985). Design of concrete structures under fire conditions using rational approaches. *10th Conference Our world in concrete and concrete structures, Singapore*. Premier Conference Pte. pp. 64–95.

Purkiss J. A. and Weeks N. J. (1987). A computer study of the behaviour of rc columns in a fire. *The Structural Engineer*, **65B**, 22–8.

Schneider U. (ed.) (1985). *Properties of materials at high temperatures – Concrete*, RILEM report, Department of Civil Engineering, Gesamthochschule, Kassel.

6

Reinforced Concrete Beams

6.1 Introduction

6.1.1 Scope

This chapter, which is based on cl 3.4.4, Pt 1, deals with the analysis and design of sections for the ultimate moment of resistance. The procedures described are suitable for most structures. Recommendations for more rigorous analysis, which may be desirable in special cases, are given in Pt 2 of BS 8110. Only rectangular and flanged sections, which for reasons of economy and convenience are by far the most common, are discussed. The same principles may, however, be applied to sections of any shape.

6.1.2 Ultimate moment of resistance

The ultimate moment of resistance of a section is the greatest bending moment that can be resisted by the section, assuming the beam to be in pure flexure. It is defined as the moment of resistance when the maximum compressive strain in the concrete reaches the limiting value of 0.0035, i.e. the strain at which concrete starts to distintegrate in compression.

6.1.3 Longitudinal reinforcement

Since the tensile strength of concrete is low, it is normally assumed that on the tension side of the neutral axis the concrete is cracked, and makes no contribution to the ultimate moment of resistance, all tensile forces in this zone being carried by steel reinforcement. In some cases it is also necessary to provide longitudinal reinforcement in the compression zone. Beams are thus said to be either *singly* or *doubly* reinforced. Reinforcement is also required in the sides of beams with an overall depth of more than 750 mm to prevent excessive cracking.

6.1.4 Shear reinforcement

In practice, since a state of pure flexure occurs rarely, if ever, a beam is required additionally to resist the effects of shear stresses arising from the transverse loads and torsion. The combined effects of bending and shear may cause premature failure, and in

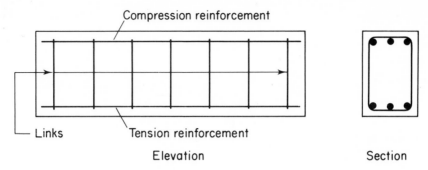

Fig. 6.1   Arrangement of reinforcement in a beam.

order to ensure that the ultimate moment of resistance is reached, shear reinforcement is provided in the form of bent-up bars or links at right angles to the longitudinal reinforcement, as shown in Fig. 6.1. A fuller description of shear reinforcement and rules for its design are given in Chapter 7.

6.1.5   Links for the containment of compression reinforcement

In a doubly reinforced beam, or a column, the links also serve to contain the compression reinforcement and prevent it from buckling. Rules for the detailing and spacing of such links are given in Appendix A2. During construction the main longitudinal reinforcement and the links are wired together in the form of a cage before casting the concrete. For maximum efficiency the main reinforcement is located as close as possible to the tension and compression faces of the beam, consistent with the requirements for cover.

6.1.6   Maximum and minimum reinforcement

The recommended maximum and minimum areas of reinforcement and rules for the spacing of bars and links are given in Appendix A2.

6.2   General principles – singly reinforced beams

6.2.1   Strains in concrete and steel

Consider the section in Fig. 6.2. In both the serviceability and ultimate limit states it is assumed that sections which were plane before bending remain plane after bending, giving a linear distribution of strain over the section as shown. In the ultimate limit state the maximum strain in the concrete is fixed at 0.0035. The corresponding strain in the tension reinforcement can be obtained from the strain diagram by simple proportion, thus

$$\varepsilon_s = 0.0035(d - x)/x \tag{6.1}$$

where x is the depth of the neutral axis and d is the depth to the centroid of the tension reinforcement, i.e. the effective depth of the section.

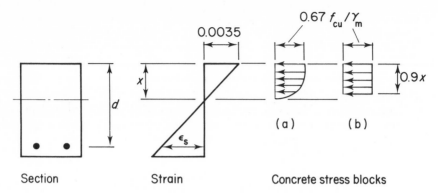

Fig. 6.2   Distribution of stress and strain.

6.2.2   The concrete stress block

The distribution of compressive stress is referred to as the *stress block*. Experiments have shown that the shape of the stress block at the ultimate limit state is similar to the short-term stress–strain curve for concrete. BS 8110 recommends two alternative stress blocks for normal design purposes. These are shown as blocks (a) and (b) in Fig. 6.2. In block (a) the stresses are derived from the idealised stress–strain curve in Fig. 2.4. Block (b) is rectangular and yields simpler design formulae than block (a), but there is very little difference in the results obtained, whichever block is assumed. BS 8110 uses block (b) for the derivation of design formulae for beams in Pt 1, but the design graphs for beams and columns in Pt 3 are derived from block (a). In this book the design graphs in Appendix B1 are derived from block (b), which enables graphs to be produced which are independent of the concrete strength, thus reducing the total number of graphs required.

6.2.3   Depth of the neutral axis

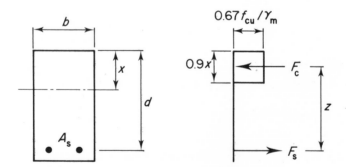

Fig. 6.3   Forces on a singly reinforced section.

Consider the section in Fig. 6.3, and assume that at the ultimate limit state the resultant forces in the concrete and steel are F_c and F_s, as shown. The ultimate moment of resistance is the couple produced by these forces. From the figure,

$$F_c = 0.67(f_{cu}/\gamma_m) \times 0.9bx$$

Putting $\gamma_m = 1.5$,

$$F_c = 0.402f_{cu}bx \qquad\qquad (6.2)$$
$$F_s = f_s A_s \qquad\qquad (6.3)$$

where f_s is the stress in the steel and A_s is the cross-sectional area of the steel.

Provided that the beam is not subjected to any axial force, F_c and F_s must be equal and opposite. Hence, by combining the last two equations and tranposing,

$$x = f_s A_s / 0.402f_{cu}b \qquad\qquad (6.4)$$

6.2.4 Over-reinforced and under-reinforced sections

With small areas of tension reinforcement the steel stress reaches the design strength before the ultimate moment of resistance is attained. The addition of more tension reinforcement increases the ultimate moment of resistance by increasing the tensile force on the section; and equilibrium is maintained by an automatic corresponding increase in the depth of the compression zone. It is evident, however, from the strain diagram in Fig. 6.2, that as the depth of the neutral axis is increased the strain in the tension reinforcement is reduced until eventually the steel stress falls below the design strength and the steel is still elastic at the ultimate moment of resistance.

A section in which the tension reinforcement has reached the design strength before the ultimate moment of resistance is attained is said to be *under-reinforced*. Conversely a section in which the tension reinforcement is still elastic at the ultimate moment of resistance is said to be *over-reinforced*. If the design strength of the tension reinforcement and the limiting strain in the concrete are reached simultaneously the section is said to be *balanced*.

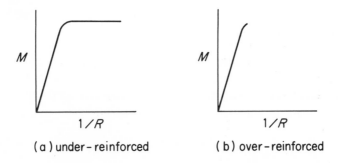

(a) under-reinforced   (b) over-reinforced

Fig. 6.4 Moment–curvature relationships.

The behaviour of under-reinforced and over-reinforced sections subject to a gradually increasing moment is shown by the moment–curvature relationships in Fig. 6.4. At an under-reinforced section a plastic hinge starts to develop when the bending moment reaches the ultimate moment of resistance. Some further rotation can then take place at constant moment before failure occurs. At an over-reinforced section, on the other hand, a plastic hinge does not develop and failure occurs by crushing of the concrete without prior yielding of the tension reinforcement. Failure tends to be sudden and catastrophic and is not preceded by evidence such as excessive cracking of the concrete and large deflections.

The depth of the neutral axis corresponding to the balanced condition can be obtained as follows. The design strength of the steel is f_y/γ_m. Putting $\gamma_m = 1.15$,

$$f_s = 0.87f_y \tag{6.5}$$

If the steel is elastic

$$f_s = E_s \varepsilon_s$$

where the modulus of elasticity E_s, from Fig. 2.6, is $200\,\text{kN/mm}^2$, and ε_s is given by Equation (6.1). Hence

$$f_s = 700(d-x)/x \tag{6.6}$$

On a balanced section the stresses given by Equations (6.5) and (6.6) are equal. Hence

$$x_{bal} = d/(1 + 0.87f_y/700) \tag{6.7}$$

Substituting appropriate values of f_y,

for high-yield steel ($f_y = 460\,\text{N/mm}^2$) $x_{bal} = 0.636d$
for mild steel ($f_y = 250\,\text{N/mm}^2$) $x_{bal} = 0.763d$

When $x < x_{bal}$ the section is under-reinforced; when $x > x_{bal}$ it is over-reinforced.

6.2.5   Limits to the depth of the neutral axis

In order to avoid the sudden type of failure exhibited by an over-reinforced section the ratio x/d (i.e. depth of neutral axis/effective depth) is restricted to a value which is less than x_{bal} by a safe margin.

When redistribution of moments is assumed during analysis (see Chapter 4) it is implied that where the elastic moments are reduced the beam must be sufficiently ductile to enable plastic hinges to develop and rotation to take place. Increased ductility is ensured, for a given strain in the concrete, by reducing further the limiting value of x/d. Ductility is not required where the elastic moments are increased because in these regions the beam does not reach the ultimate limit state until the full design load is applied. Failure of the beam is progressive, requiring rotation at the plastic hinges before collapse occurs. It is not necessary therefore to place such severe restrictions on the value of x/d where moments have been increased. BS 8110 implies the following recommendations (cls 3.2.2.1 and 3.4.4.3–4, Pt 1)

redistribution $\leqslant 10\%$ .... max. $x/d = 0.5$
redistribution between 10% and 30% .... max. $x/d = \beta_b - 0.4$ (6.8)

where $\beta_b = \dfrac{\text{moment after redistribution}}{\text{moment before redistribution}} \leqslant 1$ (6.9)

The above definition of β_b does not preclude values of x greater than $0.5d$ where the elastic moments have been increased. In such cases for amounts of redistribution greater than 10% β_b has the maximum value of 1.0, which gives max. $x/d = 0.6$.

By plotting Equation (6.4) in dimensionless form, as in Fig. 6.5, the effect on x/d of adding increasing amounts of tension reinforcement to a singly reinforced section is shown. The dotted lines indicate the limits imposed by redistribution when elastic moments are reduced.

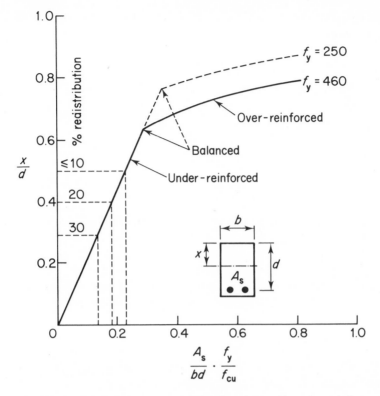

Fig. 6.5   Relationship between neutral axis depth and area of tension reinforcement.

6.3   Design formulae for rectangular sections

6.3.1   Introduction

When designing for the ultimate limit state it may be assumed that the dimensions of the section, or of a trial section, will have been chosen, and that the required ultimate moment of resistance is known. Design formulae are required to enable the cross-sectional area of the tension reinforcement, and compression reinforcement if needed, to be determined. In the remaining sections of this chapter the derivation and use of the design formulae given in cls 3.4.4.4 and 3.4.4.5, Pt 1 are described.

6.3.2   Singly reinforced beams

Referring back to Fig. 6.3, since the resultant forces in the steel and concrete are equal and opposite, either could be used to obtain an expression for the ultimate moment of resistance. However, since the area of the reinforcement is not known at this stage, it is better to start with the concrete force F_c, thus

$$M = F_c z \tag{6.10}$$

Substituting for F_c from Equation (6.2),

$$M = 0.402 f_{cu} bxz \tag{6.11}$$

The lever arm is given by

$$z = d - 0.45x \qquad (6.12)$$

Combining these two equations to eliminate x

$$M = 0.8933bf_{cu}zd - 0.8933bf_{cu}z^2$$

Since f_{cu}, b, and d are constant for a particular section, the ultimate moment of resistance may be represented in dimensionless form by

$$K = M/f_{cu}bd^2 \qquad (6.13)$$

Hence

$$K = 0.8933z/d - 0.8933(z/d)^2 \qquad (6.14)$$

This is a quadratic equation in z/d. Rounding 0.8933 to 0.9 and solving,

$$z = d\{0.5 + \sqrt{(0.25 - K/0.9)}\} \qquad (6.15)$$

An upper limt of $z = 0.95$ is specified (cl 3.4.4.1(e), Pt 1).

A formula for the neutral-axis depth, which does not include the area of the reinforcement, can now be obtained by transposing Equation (6.12):

$$x = (d - z)/0.45 \qquad (6.16)$$

The area of tension reinforcement can be determined by expressing the ultimate moment of resistance in terms of the steel force, i.e. $M = F_s z$. Now, assuming that the section is under-reinforced and using Equation (6.3),

$$M = 0.87f_y A_s z \qquad (6.17)$$

from which

$$A_s = M/0.87f_y z \qquad (6.18)$$

If z exceeds $0.95d$ it is replaced in the above equation by $0.95d$.

EXAMPLE 6.1   *Design of a singly reinforced section*

A singly reinforced beam has a rectangular section 300 mm wide, with an effective depth of 600 mm. The characteristic strengths are: concrete 30 N/mm², steel 460 N/mm².

(a) Determine the maximum ultimate moment of resistance of which the section is capable. Calculate the area of reinforcement and show how it could be arranged. If the maximum aggregate size is 20 mm, and the cover 40 mm, what is the minimum overall depth (rounding to 25 mm)?

(b) Determine the area of reinforcement to resist an ultimate bending moment of 350 kN m.

(a) *Maximum ultimate moment of resistance*

$$x_{max} = 0.5d$$
$$z = d - 0.45x = 0.775d$$

Hence, from Equation (6.14)

$$K_{max} = 0.156$$

But

$$M = Kf_{cu}bd^2$$

where

$$f_{cu}bd^2 = 30 \times 300 \times 600^2 = 3.24E9$$

Hence

$$M_{max} = 0.156 \times 3.24E9 = 505.4E6 \text{ N mm } \underline{(505.4 \text{ kN m})}$$

$$A_s = M/0.87f_yz = 505.4E6/(0.87 \times 460 \times 0.775 \times 600) = \underline{2716 \text{ mm}^2}$$

From the table of bar areas in Appendix A1 the nearest convenient arrangement of bars is 6T25 (2945 mm²) in two rows, as shown in Fig. 6.6. The vertical spacing between rows of bars is $\frac{2}{3}h_{agg}$ (see Appendix A2). Hence the overall depth is given by

$$h(\text{min.}) = 600 + 20/3 + 25 + 40 = 671.7 \text{ mm} - \text{say } \underline{675 \text{ mm}}$$

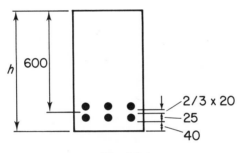

Fig. 6.6

Checking that the reinforcement does not exceed the maximum allowable, i.e. 4% of the gross cross-sectional area (see Appendix A2),

$$\text{max. } A_s = 0.04 \times 300 \times 675 = 8100 \text{ mm}^2$$

Hence the reinforcement (2945 mm²) does not exceed the maximum. It can be shown that the maximum cannot be exceeded in a singly reinforced section using high-yield steel if the neutral axis depth is limited to $0.5d$.

(b) *M = 350 kN m*

$$K = M/f_{cu}bd^2$$
$$= 350E6/3.24E9 = 0.1080$$

$$z = d\{0.5 + \sqrt{(0.25 - K/0.9)}\} = 0.860d$$

$$A_s = M/0.87f_yz$$
$$= 350E6/(0.87 \times 460 \times 0.86 \times 600)$$
$$= 1695 \text{ mm}^2, \text{ i.e. 6T20 (1885 mm}^2)$$

EXAMPLE 6.2   Moment of resistance of a given singly reinforced section

Determine the ultimate moment of resistance of a rectangular beam of width 200 mm and effective depth 450 mm singly reinforced with four 20 mm diameter high-yield bars (4T20). The characteristic concrete strength is 30 N/mm^2.

First find the depth of the neutral axis by considering the equilibrium of the section, i.e. using Equation (6.4)

$$x = f_s A_s / 0.402 f_{cu} b$$

From the bar area tables (Appendix A1) $A_s = 1257$ mm^2
Assuming the steel stress is at the design strength,

$$f_s A_s = 0.87 f_y A_s$$
$$= 0.87 \times 460 \times 1257 = 503.1E3 \text{ N}$$

Hence

$$x = 503.1E3/(0.402 \times 30 \times 200) = 208.6 \text{ mm}$$

Since $x < 0.5d$, the steel stress is at the design strength as assumed, and the moment of resistance is given by

$$M = F_s z = F_s (d - 0.45x)$$
$$= 503.1E3(450 - 0.45 \times 208.6) = 179.2E6 \text{ N mm, i.e. } \underline{179.2 \text{ kN m}}$$

6.3.3   Doubly reinforced beams

By combining Equations (6.11) and (6.12) to eliminate z, Equation (6.14) can be expressed in terms of the neutral-axis depth ratio:

$$K = 0.402 x/d - 0.18(x/d)^2 \tag{6.19}$$

If the upper limits of x/d from Section 6.2.5 are inserted, the maximum values of K for a singly reinforced section are obtained. Let these be denoted by K'.

When redistribution does not exceed 10%, x/d (max.) = 0.5, giving

$$K' = 0.156 \tag{6.20}$$

When redistribution is between 10% and 30%, x/d (max.) $= \beta_b - 0.4$, giving

$$K' = 0.402(\beta_b - 0.4) - 0.18(\beta_b - 0.4)^2 \tag{6.21}$$

Recapitulating, $K = M/f_{cu} b d^2$, where M is the ultimate moment of resistance required from the section. If K exceeds K' the ultimate moment of resistance cannot be obtained from the given section if it is singly reinforced. The solution is either to increase the effective depth, or the width, or the grade of concrete, or to reinforce the concrete in the compression zone.

BS 8110 recommends that the lever arm of a doubly reinforced section be obtained simply by substituting K' for K in Equation (6.15), thus

$$z = d\{0.5 + \surd(0.25 - K'/0.9)\} \tag{6.22}$$

The virtue of this expression is that it has exactly the same form as Equation (6.15), which could be advantageous in a computer program. However, the value of z may also be obtained directly from first principles by substituting the maximum values of x/d into Equation (6.12), thus

for redistribution $\leqslant 10\%$ $z = 0.775d$ (6.23)

for redistribution $> 10\%$ $z = d\{1 - 0.45(\beta_b - 0.4)\}$ (6.24)

The value of z is unaffected by the addition of compression reinforcement provided that equilibrium is maintained by increasing the amount of tension reinforcement correspondingly, as will be shown later.

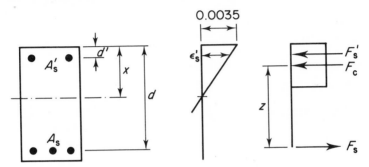

Fig. 6.7 Forces on a doubly reinforced section.

Formulae for the amount of compression and tension reinforcement required in a doubly reinforced section may be obtained by considering Fig. 6.7, which shows the forces acting on the section. Taking moments about the tension reinforcement, the ultimate moment of resistance is given by

$$M = F_c z + F_s'(d - d')$$ (6.25)

where F_c and F_s' are the resultant forces exerted respectively by the concrete stress block and the compression reinforcement.

Since $M = K f_{cu} b d^2$ and $F_c z = K' f_{cu} b d^2$

$$(K - K') f_{cu} b d^2 = F_s'(d - d')$$

Hence, assuming that the stress in the compression reinforcement is at the design strength, which will be shown to be the usual case,

$$(K - K') f_{cu} b d^2 = 0.87 f_y A_s'(d - d')$$

from which the required area of compression reinforcement may be obtained, thus

$$A_s' = (K - K') f_{cu} b d^2 / 0.87 f_y (d - d')$$ (6.26)

This is the area of compression reinforcement required to produce the additional moment of resistance over and above the maximum capacity of the singly reinforced section. The total area of tension reinforcement is therefore the sum of what is required for the singly reinforced section – from Equation (6.18) – and an additional area that will exert a tensile force equal to the force in the compression reinforcement, thus maintaining the equilibrium of the section. If the stresses in both reinforcements are at the design strength this additional area must be equal to the area of the compression reinforcement, and hence

$$A_s = K'f_{cu}bd^2/0.87f_yz + A_s' \tag{6.27}$$

The stress in the tension reinforcement must be at the design strength provided that $x < x_{bal}$, which is the normal condition. From the strain diagram in Fig. 6.7 the strain in the compression reinforcement is given by

$$\varepsilon_s' = 0.0035(x - d')/x \tag{6.28}$$

The stress in the compression reinforcement is obtained by multiplying by the modulus of elasticity, thus

$$f_s' = 700(1 - d'/x) \tag{6.29}$$

which is equal to the design strength provided that

$$d'/x \leqslant 1 - 0.87f_y/700 \tag{6.30}$$

Putting $f_y = 460$ N/mm^2 and 250 N/mm^2 respectively into this equation shows that the stress in the compression reinforcement will not reach the design strength if the ratio d'/x exceeds 0.43 for high-yield steel, or 0.69 for mild steel. This condition is likely to arise with high-yield steel when high percentages of redistribution have been used, as shown in Fig. 6.8. A typical case is solved from first principles in Example 6.4. The design graphs (Graphs 2–7, Appendix B1) take the condition into account where necessary.

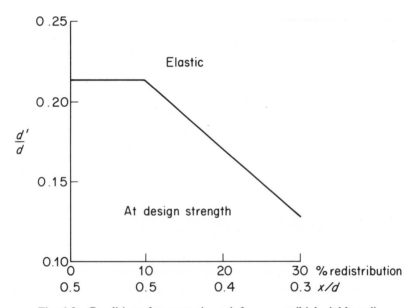

Fig. 6.8   Condition of compression reinforcement (high yield steel).

EXAMPLE 6.3   Maximum ultimate moment of resistance

A singly reinforced beam constructed from grade 30 concrete has a width of 200 mm and an effective depth of 450 mm. The characteristic steel strength is 460 N/mm². Calculate the maximum permissible ultimate moment of resistance and the corresponding area of reinforcement,

(i) with 10% redistribution
(ii) when the elastic bending moments have been reduced by 30% by redistribution,

$$\text{max. } K = K'$$
$$M = K'f_{cu}bd^2$$
$$= K' \times 30 \times 200 \times 450^2 = K' \times 1.215E9 \text{ N mm}$$

(i) *10% redistribution*

$$K' = 0.156$$
$$M = 0.156 \times 1.215E9 = 189.5E6 \text{ N mm, i.e. } \underline{189.5 \text{ kN m}}$$
$$z = 0.775d - \text{from Equation (6.23)}$$
$$A_s = M/0.87f_yz$$
$$= 189.5E6/(0.87 \times 460 \times 0.775 \times 450)$$
$$= 1358 \text{ mm}^2, \text{ say } \underline{3T25 \text{ (1473 mm}^2)}$$

(ii) *30% redistribution* $(\beta_b = 0.7)$

$$K' = 0.402(\beta_b - 0.4) - 0.18(\beta_b - 0.4)^2$$
$$= 0.402 \times 0.3 - 0.18 \times 0.3^2 = 0.1044$$
$$M = 0.1044 \times 1.215E9 = 126.9E6 \text{ N mm, i.e. } \underline{126.9 \text{ kN m}}$$

The lever arm can be obtained either from Equation (6.15), as recommended by BS 8110, i.e.

$$z = d\{0.5 + \sqrt{(0.25 - K'/0.9)}\}$$

or from Equation (6.24), i.e.

$$z = d\{1 - 0.45(\beta_b - 0.4)\}$$

Substituting for d, and either K' or β_b,

$$z = 389.3 \text{ mm}$$

and

$$A_s = 126.9E6/(0.87 \times 460 \times 389.3)$$
$$= \underline{815 \text{ mm}^2, \text{ say } 3T20 \text{ (942 mm}^2)}$$

There is a small difference between the values of z obtained from Equations (6.15) and (6.24). This is caused by the rounding of 0.8933 to 0.9 in the derivation of Equation (6.15) and is insignificant.

EXAMPLE 6.4   *Design of a doubly reinforced section*

A beam has a rectangular section 250 mm wide with an effective depth of 450 mm. Characteristic strengths are: concrete 30 N/mm², steel 460 N/mm². The depth of the compression reinforcement (if required) is to be 70 mm. Design suitable reinforcement for an ultimate moment of resistance of 220 kN m, assuming that redistribution has been used to reduce the elastic moments by: (a) 10%, (b) 20%, (c) 30%

Constants are:

$$f_{cu}bd^2 = 30 \times 250 \times 450^2 = 1.519E9$$
$$0.87f_y = 0.87 \times 460 = 400.2 \text{ N/mm}^2$$
$$K = 220E6/1.519E9 = 0.1448$$

(a)   *≤10% redistribution*

$K' = 0.156$, i.e. $K < K'$, so design as singly reinforced,

$$z = d\{0.5 - \sqrt{(0.25 - K/0.9)}\}$$

Putting $K = 0.1448$ gives $z = 0.7985d$, i.e. $z < 0.95d$, which is acceptable.

$$A_s = M/0.87f_yz$$
$$= 220E6/(400.2 \times 0.7985 \times 450)$$
$$= \underline{1530 \text{ mm}^2 - \text{say } 5T20 \ (1571 \text{ mm}^2)}$$

(b)   *20% redistribution ($\beta_b = 0.8$)*

$$K' = 0.402(\beta_b - 0.4) - 0.18(\beta_b - 0.4)^2 = 0.132$$
$$K = 0.1448$$

Hence $K > K'$, so design as doubly reinforced,

$$x = d(\beta_b - 0.4) = 0.4d = 0.4 \times 450 = 180 \text{ mm}$$
$$d'/x = 70/180 = 0.389 < 0.43$$

Hence the stress in the compression reinforcement is at the design strength and

$$A'_s = (K - K') f_{cu}bd^2/0.87f_y(d - d')$$
$$= (0.1488 - 0.132) \times 1.519E9/400.2(450 - 70)$$
$$= \underline{128 \text{ mm}^2 - \text{say } 2T10 \ (157 \text{ mm}^2)}$$

$$z = d - 0.45x$$
$$= 450 - 0.45 \times 180 = 369 \text{ mm}$$

$$A_s = K'f_{cu}bd^2/0.87f_yz + A'_s$$
$$= 0.132 \times 1.519E9/(400.2 \times 369) + 128$$
$$= \underline{1486 \text{ mm}^2 - \text{say } 5T20 \ (1571 \text{ mm}^2)}$$

(c)   *30% redistribution* ($\beta_b = 0.7$)

$$\beta_b = -0.4 = 0.3$$
$$K' = 0.402 \times 0.3 - 0.18 \times 0.3^2 = 0.104$$
$$x = 0.3d = 0.3 \times 450 = 135 \text{ mm}$$
$$d'/x = 70/135 = 0.5185 > 0.43$$

Hence the stress in the compression reinforcement has not reached the design strength and $0.87f_y$ in Equation (6.26) must be replaced with f'_s, the elastic stress in the steel, thus

$$A'_s = (K - K') f_{cu} bd^2 / f'_s (d - d')$$

From Equation (6.29)

$$f'_s = 700(1 - d'/x)$$
$$= 700(1 - 0.5185) = 337.1 \text{ N/mm}^2$$

and

$$A'_s = (0.1448 - 0.104) \times 1.519\text{E}9/337.1(450 - 70)$$
$$= 484 \text{ mm}^2 - \text{say } \underline{5\text{T}12 \ (565 \text{ mm}^2)}$$

To determine A_s, A'_s must be replaced in Equation (6.27) with $A'_s f'_s / 0.87 f_y$ to preserve equilibrium:

$$A_s = K' f_{cu} bd^2 / 0.87 f_y z + A'_s f'_s / 0.87 f_y$$

where

$$z = d - 0.45x$$
$$= 450 - 0.45 \times 135 = 389.3 \text{ mm}$$

Hence

$$A_s = 0.104 \times 1.519\text{E}9/(400.2 \times 389.3) + 484 \times 337.1/400.2$$
$$= 1422 \text{ mm}^2 - \text{say } \underline{3\text{T}25 \ (1473 \text{ mm}^2)}$$

EXAMPLE 6.5   Moment of resistance of a given doubly reinforced section

A doubly reinforced beam has the section shown in Fig. 6.9(a),

(a)   Determine the effective depth of the section.
(b)   Given that the characteristic strengths of the reinforcement and the concrete are 460 N/mm² and 30 N/mm² respectively, calculate the ultimate moment of resistance of the section, assuming there has been no redistribution of moments.

(a)   *Effective depth.*   The effective depth d is to the centroid of the tension reinforcement, and can be found by taking moments of area of the tension steel about the top of the section. As the bars are of equal size they can each be assumed to have unit area:

$$5d = 3(1000 - 60) + 2(1000 - 120)$$

from which $\underline{d = 916 \text{ mm}}$

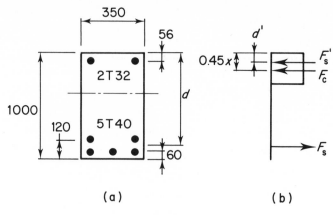

Fig. 6.9

(b) *Ultimate moment of resistance.* Obtaining areas of reinforcement from the bar area tables in Appendix A1, $A_s = 6283 \text{ mm}^2$, $A_s' = 1608 \text{ mm}^2$.

The dimensions required are:

$$d = 916 \text{ mm}, \ d' = 56 \text{ mm}, \ b = 350 \text{ mm}$$

The forces on the section are shown in Fig. 6.9(b). Assuming that all the reinforcement is at the design strength,

$$F_s' = 0.87 \times 460 \times 1608\text{E}-3 = 643.5 \text{ kN}$$
$$F_s = 0.87 \times 460 \times 6283\text{E}-3 = 2514 \text{ kN}$$
$$F_c = 0.402 f_{cu} bx$$
$$\quad = 0.402x \times 30 \times 350\text{E}-3 = 4.221x \text{ kN}$$

For equilibrium $F_s = F_s' + F_c$

Hence

$$x = (2514 - 643.5)/4.221 = 443.1 \text{ mm}$$

A check can now be made that both steel stresses are at the design strength, as assumed,

$$x/d = 443.1/916 = 0.484 < 0.5$$
$$d'/x = 56/443.1 = 0.126 < 0.43$$

Thus the assumption is confirmed and the ultimate moment of resistance can be obtained by taking moments about the tension reinforcement. From Fig. 6.9(b)

$$M = F_s'(d - d') + F_c(d - 0.45x)$$
$$\quad = [643.5(916 - 56) + 4.221 \times 443.1(916 - 0.45 \times 443.1)] \times 1\text{E}-3$$
$$\quad = \underline{1819 \text{ kN m}}$$

6.4   Flanged beams

6.4.1   Effective width

When a series of beams is used to support a concrete slab it is common practice to cast the slab *in situ* to form an integral structure, as shown in Fig. 6.10. For this type of construction each intermediate beam is assumed to carry the dead and imposed loads from half the slab on each side of the beam. End beams carry the loads from half the slab on one side only. Each individual beam may therefore be assumed to have either a 'T' or an inverted 'L' section consisting of a vertical *web* (or *rib*) surmounted by a *flange*.

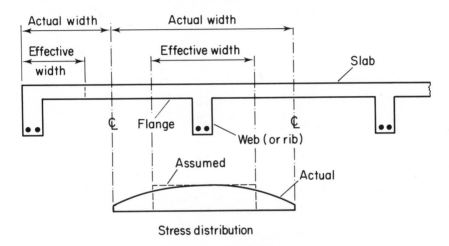

Fig. 6.10   Effective width of a flanged beam.

The distribution of compressive stress over the width of the flange is affected by the phenomenon of *shear lag* which causes a reduction in compression as the distance from the centre of the web increases, as shown. In order that the simple theory of bending may be used it is therefore necessary to define an *effective* width over which the stress may be considered to be uniform. In the absence of more accurate means of determination it is recommended (cl 3.4.1.5, Pt 1) that the effective width should be taken as the *lesser* of the following alternatives:

for 'T' beams – the actual width or the web width plus $l_z/5$
for 'L' beams – the actual width or the web width plus $l_z/10$

where l_z is the distance between points of zero moment (which, for a continuous beam, may be taken as 0.7 times the effective span).

EXAMPLE 6.6   Effective width of a flanged beam

The section of a beam-and-slab floor system is shown in Fig. 6.11. Determine the effective width of the flanges if the beams are

(a) continuous over supporting walls at 8 m centres
(b) simply supported over the same span.

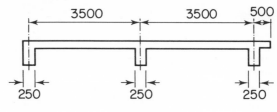

Fig. 6.11

'L' beam

Actual width $= (3500 + 250)/2 = 1875$ mm

$b = b_w + l_z/10$

(a) Continuous

$l_z = 0.7 \times 8000 = 5600$ mm

$b = 250 + 5600/10 = 810$ mm < 1875 mm

Hence effective width $= b = \underline{810 \text{ mm}}$

(b) Simply supported

$l_z = 8000$ mm

$b = 250 + 8000/10 = 1050$ mm < 1875 mm

Hence effective width $= b = \underline{1050 \text{ mm}}$

Middle 'T' beam

Actual width $= 3500$ mm

$b = b_w + l_z/5$

(a) Continuous

$l_z = 5600$ mm

$b = 250 + 5600/5 = 1370$ mm < 3500 mm

Hence effective width $= b = \underline{1370 \text{ mm}}$

(b) Simply supported

$l_z = 8000$ mm

$b = 250 + 8000/5 = 1850$ mm < 3500 mm

Hence effective width $= b = \underline{1850 \text{ mm}}$

Right-hand 'T' beam

Actual width = 3500/2 + 500 = 2250 mm
$b = b_w + l_z/10 +$ outstand (since outstand $< l_z/10$)
Outstand = 500 − 250/2 = 375 mm

(a) Continuous

$l_z = 5600$ mm
$b = 250 + 560 + 375 = 1185$ mm < 2250 mm

Hence effective width = $b = 1185$ mm

(b) Simply supported

$l_z = 8000$ mm
$b = 250 + 800 + 375 = 1425$ mm < 2250 mm

Hence effective width = $b = 1425$ mm

6.4.2   Design of sections – flange in compression

When the flange is in compression two cases must be considered:

(a)   neutral axis in the flange
(b)   neutral axis in the web.

The method of design is exactly the same for 'T' as for 'L' beams.

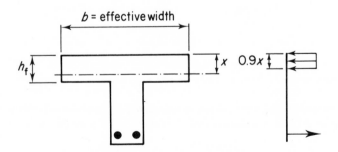

Fig. 6.12   Neutral axis in flange.

When the neutral axis is in the flange, it can be seen from Fig. 6.12 that since the concrete below the neutral axis is assumed to be cracked, and is ignored in design, the beam behaves like a rectangular beam whose width is equal to the effective width of the flange. All the design formulae derived for singly reinforced rectangular beams may therefore be used for flanged beams in this case.

If, however, the depth of the neutral axis so obtained exceeds the thickness of the flange the neutral axis must be in the web; and the whole of the flange and part of the web are in compression. If redistribution does not exceed 10%, the maximum value of the ultimate moment of resistance for a singly reinforced section may then be obtained by considering the concrete stress and assuming that the neutral axis depth ratio $x/d = 0.5$. The forces acting on a singly reinforced section are then as shown in Fig. 6.13.

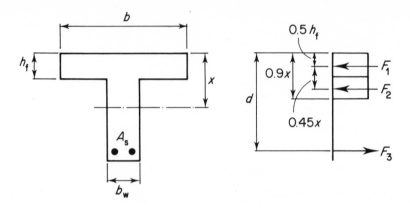

Fig. 6.13   Neutral axis in web.

F_1 and F_2 are the resultant compressive forces acting on the flange and the web respectively. F_3 is the tensile force in the steel. Hence, by taking moments about the centre of the tension reinforcement

$$M(\text{max.}) = F_1(d - 0.5h_f) + F_2(d - 0.5h_f - 0.45x)$$

where

$$F_1 = 0.402f_{cu}bh_f$$
$$F_2 = 0.402f_{cu}b_w(0.45x - h_f)$$

Substituting for F_1 and F_2, putting $x = 0.5d$, and letting $M(\text{max.}) = \beta_f f_{cu}bd^2$

$$\beta_f = 0.45\frac{h_f}{d}\left(1 - \frac{b_w}{b}\right)\left(1 - \frac{h_f}{2d}\right) + 0.15\frac{b_w}{b} \tag{6.31}$$

For ultimate moments of resistance less than $\beta_f f_{cu}bd^2$ an approximate formula for the area of tension reinforcement can be derived by assuming that the depth of the neutral axis has the constant value of $0.5d$ and considering the ultimate moment of resistance in terms of the force F_3 in the tension reinforcement. Taking moments about the centroid of the flange,

$$M = F_3(d - 0.5h_f) - F_2 \times 0.45x$$

If redistribution does not exceed 10% the section is under-reinforced and

$$F_3 = 0.87f_y A_s$$

Substituting for F_2 and F_3, putting $x = 0.5d$, and transposing, the required area of tension reinforcement is given by

$$A_s = \frac{M + 0.1f_{cu}b_w d(0.45d - h_f)}{0.87f_y(d - 0.5h_f)} \tag{6.32}$$

This formula is applicable only when $h_f < 0.45d$, i.e. when the term in brackets in the numerator is positive. This is usually the case in practice.

If the design ultimate moment of resistance exceeds $\beta_f f_{cu} bd^2$, compression reinforcement is required. However compression reinforcement is not usually required in flanged beams when the bending moment is positive, because the compressive stresses are distributed over the relatively large area of the flange.

6.4.3   Flange in tension

When negative bending moments are applied, as for example in continuous construction, the flange is in tension and makes no contribution to the strength of the beam. In this case the beam behaves like a rectangular beam whose width is that of the web. Tension reinforcement is placed in the flange and compression reinforcement – if required – in the web. All the formulae derived for rectangular beams may be applied, substituting b_w for b.

6.4.4   Redistribution in flanged beams

When redistribution is applied, for example in continuous construction, it is usually the negative elastic moments near the supports that are reduced. Since the flange is then in tension all the considerations previously discussed for rectangular beams apply (see Example 6.7). Near mid-span, where the bending moments are positive and the flange is in compression, the elastic moments are correspondingly increased. In these circumstances there is no need to reduce the depth of the neutral axis below the $0.5d$ on which Equations (6.31) and (6.32) are based and the restriction of redistribution to 10% which is applied to these equations can safely be ignored. If the redistributed moment should exceed $\beta_f f_{cu} bd^2$, compression reinforcement would be needed in the flange.

EXAMPLE 6.7   Design of a 'T' beam

A 'T' beam has effective flange width 1370 mm, flange thickness 150 mm, web width 250 mm, and overall depth 500 mm. Characteristic strengths are: concrete 30 N/mm², steel 460 N/mm². Assuming that the centroid of the reinforcement is placed 50 mm from the top or bottom of the beam, design suitable reinforcement for ultimate moments of resistance of:

(a)   400 kN m (positive, with no redistribution)
(b)   300 kN m (negative, with 20% redistribution)

(a)   *Positive moment.*   Assume a rectangular section with width b = effective flange width, i.e. 1370 mm, and effective depth $d = 500 - 50 = 450$ mm.

$$f_{cu} bd^2 = 30 \times 1370 \times 450^2 = 8.323\text{E}9 \text{ N mm}$$
$$0.87 f_y = 0.87 \times 460 = 400.2 \text{ N/mm}^2$$
$$K = M/f_{cu} bd^2 \quad = 400\text{E}6/8.323\text{E}9 = 0.04806$$
$$K' = 0.156, \text{ so } K < K' \text{ and only tension reinforcement is required.}$$
$$z = d\{0.5 + \sqrt{(0.25 - 0.04806/0.9)}\} = 0.9434d = 424.5 \text{ mm}$$
$$x = (d - z)/0.45 = (450 - 424.5)/0.45 = 56 \text{ mm}$$

Since $56 < 150$ the neutral axis is in the flange, as assumed.

$$A_s = M/0.87 f_y z$$
$$= 400E6/(400.2 \times 424.5)$$
$$= 2355 \text{ mm}^2 - \text{say } \underline{3T32 \ (2413 \text{ mm}^2)} - \text{see Fig. } 6.14(a)$$

Note that if z had exceeded 0.95d, it would have been replaced by 0.95d in the above equation.

(b) *Negative moment.* With the negative moment the flange is in tension. Hence the effective section is rectangular, with the tension reinforcement at the top, and the width is the width of the web.

$$b = 250 \text{ mm}; \qquad d = 500 - 50 = 450 \text{ mm}$$
$$f_{cu}bd^2 = 30 \times 250 \times 450^2 = 1.519E9 \text{ N mm}$$
$$K = 300E6/1.519E9 = 0.1975$$

With 20% redistribution $\beta_b = 0.8$

$$K' = 0.402(\beta_b - 0.4) - 0.18(\beta_b - 0.4)^2$$
$$= 0.402 \times 0.4 - 0.18 \times (0.4)^2 = 0.132$$

$K > K'$, so compression reinforcement is required.

$d'/x = 50/(0.4 \times 450) = 0.28 < 0.43$, so the compression reinforcement is at the design strength, and

$$A_s' = (K - K')f_{cu}bd^2/0.87f_y(d - d')$$
$$= (0.1975 - 0.132) \times 1.519E9/(400.2(450 - 50))$$
$$= 622 \text{ mm}^2 - \text{say } \underline{2T20 \ (628 \text{ mm}^2)} - \text{in the bottom of the beam.}$$

$$z = d\{0.5 + \surd(0.25 - K'/0.9)\}$$
$$= 450\{0.5 + \surd(0.25 + 0.132/0.9)\} = 369.7 \text{ mm}$$

$$A_s = K'f_{cu}bd^2/0.87f_y z + A_s'$$
$$= 0.132 \times 1.519E9/(400.2 \times 369.7) + 622$$
$$= 1977 \text{ mm}^2 - \text{say } \underline{2T32 + 2T16 \ (2010 \text{ mm}^2)} - \text{in the top of the beam.}$$

Figure 6.14(b) shows the complete reinforcement.

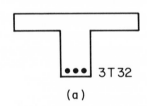

(a)

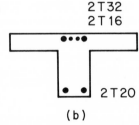

2 T 32
2 T 16

2 T 20

(b)

Fig. 6.14

In practice the arrangement shown would preclude the insertion of a vibrator into the top of the beam. This difficulty could be avoided by putting the top reinforcement in two rows vertically in line – rechecking the design for the smaller effective depth.

6.5   Design procedure for beams

6.5.1   General

The normal design procedure is as follows

1   Choose initial section dimensions. Factors that should be considered are the basic span/depth ratio, the minimum requirements dictated by the 'deemed to satisfy' rules for durability and fire resistance, lateral stability, and whether or not the beam is to be built into brickwork. A rough rule for width is half the depth (see Design Study 13.2).

2   When the initial choice of a section has been made, and the value of the ultimate moment of resistance has been obtained from the bending-moment envelope, the design of the reinforcement to provide the design ultimate moment of resistance is carried out, either by using the design graphs in Appendix B1, or by means of the design formulae shown in a different type in Sections 6.3 and 6.4. The procedure for the use of the design formulae has already been demonstrated in previous examples; however, for ease of reference it is summarised below for rectangular sections.

6.5.2   Use of formulae

(a)   Calculate $K = M/f_{cu}bd^2$
(b)   Calculate $\beta_b = (M$ after redistribution$)/(M$ before redistribution$)$
(c)   Calculate K'

Redistribution $\leqslant 10\%$ . . . . . . $K' = 0.156$
Redistribution $> 10\%$ . . . . . . $K' = 0.402(\beta_b - 0.4) - 0.18(\beta_b - 0.4)^2$

(d) $K \leqslant K'$ design as a singly reinforced section
     $K > K'$ design as a doubly reinforced section

Singly reinforced section

(e)   Calculate $z = d\{0.5 + \sqrt{(0.25 - K/0.9)}\}$
(f)   Calculate $A_s = M/0.87f_yz$

Doubly reinforced section

(g)   Calculate $z = d\{0.5 + \sqrt{(0.25 - K'/0.9)}\}$
(h)   Calculate $x = (d - z)/0.45$
    (or determine x and z from first principles, as in Example 6.4)
(i)   Check d'/x

$\leqslant 0.43$ go to stage (j)
> 0.43 compression reinforcement elastic – see Example 6.4(c)

This check assumes high-yield steel

(j)   Calculate $A_s' = (K - K') f_{cu}bd^2/0.87f_y(d - d')$

(k)   Calculate $A_s = K'f_{cu}bd^2/0.87f_y z + A_s'$

3   Select numbers and diameters of reinforcing bars to provide areas not less than, and as close as practicable to, the calculated values of A_s and A_s'

4   Check that the detailing requirements of Chapter 5 and Appendix A2 are satisfied, including the minimum and maximum allowable areas of reinforcement. If not, increase the depth and/or width of the section and return to stage (a). If the dead weight allowance has been exceeded repeat the structural analysis and return to stage (a).

5   Design shear reinforcement (see Chapter 7) and re-check the detailing requirements with regard to cover. It is advisable to check at stage 4 that the maximum allowable shear stress will not be exceeded.

6.5.3   Use of design graphs

The design graphs for beams in Appendix B1 are derived from the simplified rectangular stress block.

The graph for singly reinforced beams may be used for both high-yield and mild-steel reinforcement. The graphs for doubly reinforced beams, however, may be used only for high-yield reinforcement. This is because the stress in the steel reaches the design strength at different strains for mild and high-yield reinforcement. In a practical design it is unlikely that mild steel would be proposed for a doubly reinforced beam.

Graphs Nos. 1 to 4 have the same form as that adopted by BS 8110. The broken lines represent the limits of x/d for varying amounts of redistribution (reduction). Graphs Nos. 5–7 are alternative design graphs for doubly reinforced beams, from which the area of compression reinforcement can be determined more accurately. They also include lines for $x/d = 0.6$ which may be used when moments are increased by redistribution in amounts exceeding 10%. These graphs have been derived directly from the design formulae (cl 3.4.4.4. Pt 1) and are intended to be used in the same way, i.e. starting with the required ultimate moment of resistance of the section. When the moment of resistance is not known, as for example in the analysis of an existing section, Graph Nos 2–4 should be used. Cases where the stress in the compression reinforcement does not reach the design strength are automatically taken into account in both sets of graphs.

Reading of the graphs is facilitated by scoring two lines at right angles with the point of a compass of a transparent plastic sheet which may then be manoeuvred into position over the graph.

EXAMPLE 6.8   Singly reinforced beam

A rectangular beam has width 400 mm, effective depth 750 mm, 28-day cube strength 35 N/mm^2.

(a)   Design for an ultimate moment of resistance of 1000 kN m with no redistribution:
    (i)   with mild-steel reinforcement
    (ii)   with high-yield reinforcement.

(b) What is the maximum ultimate moment of resistance of the section with 30% redistribution?

(a) $bd^2 f_{cu} = 400 \times 750^2 \times 35 \times 1\text{E}{-}6 = 7875$ kN m

$K = M/bd^2 f_{cu} = 1000/7875 = 0.127$

Since $K < 0.156$ design as singly reinforced.

On the design graph for singly reinforced beams (Graph No. 1) project horizontally to the curve from 0.127 on the vertical axis; then project vertically to obtain the area of reinforcement, i.e.

$A_s f_y/bdf_{cu} = 0.175$

where

$bdf_{cu} = 400 \times 750 \times 35 = 10.5\text{E}6$

(i) *Mild steel*

$A_s = 0.176 \times 10.5\text{E}6/250 = \underline{7392 \text{ mm}^2} - \text{say 6R40 } (7540 \text{ mm}^2)$

(ii) *High-yield steel*

$A_s = 0.176 \times 10.5\text{E}6/460 = \underline{4017 \text{ mm}^2} - \text{say } \underline{5\text{T}32 \ (4021) \text{ mm}^2}$

(b) $M/bd^2 f_{cu}(\text{max}) = 0.104$ (from the design graph—with $x/d = 0.3$)

Hence

$M(\text{max}) = 0.104 \times 7875 = \underline{819 \text{ kN m}}$

EXAMPLE 6.9   Doubly reinforced beam

Design main reinforcement for a rectangular beam of width 350 mm, overall depth 700 mm, and grade C30 concrete, to provide an ultimate moment of resistance of 825 kN m with no redistribution. Cover to the main reinforcement is 40 mm.

Assuming T32 bars in a single line for both sets of reinforcement,

$d = 700 - 40 - 16 = 644$ mm

$d' = 40 + 16 = 56$ mm

Hence

$d'/d = 56/644 = 0.087.$

Conservative results should therefore be obtained from a graph having $d'/d = 0.10$.

$M/bd^2 f_{cu} = 825\text{E}6/(350 \times 644^2 \times 30) = 0.189$

Using Graph No. 2. Projecting horizontally from 0.189 on the vertical axis to intersect the diagonal line representing $x/d = 0.5$ (the limit for no redistribution), the area of compression reinforcement (by interpolation) is given by $A_s' f_y/bdf_{cu} = 0.045$. Projecting vertically gives $A_s f_y/bdf_{cu} = 0.273$.

$$bdf_{cu}/f_y = 350 \times 644 \times 30/460 = 14.7E3$$

Hence

$$A'_s = 0.045 \times 14.7E3 = \underline{662 \text{ mm}^2}$$

and

$$A_s = 0.273 \times 14.7E3 = \underline{4013 \text{ mm}^2}$$

From the tables of bar areas:

tension reinforcement = 5T32 (4021 mm^2)
compression reinforcement = 4T16 (804 mm^2), or 2T25 (982 mm^2)

2T25 is better because it gives more space between the bars for inserting a vibrator, and can be contained by single (two-bar) links (see Appendix A2.6.5).

It is now necessary to check whether the proposed reinforcement can be accommodated in a single row. Allowing for the cover and assuming 32 mm between bars, 5T32 bars require a width of 368 mm. Since this exceeds 350 mm it is necessary to put the tension reinforcement in two rows. This will have the effect of reducing the effective depth, so the design will be repeated with an increased area of tension reinforcement. The area of compression reinforcement should be more than adequate.

Try 4T32 (3217 mm^2) at 644 mm depth, and 2T25 (982 mm^2) at 600 mm depth, making a total of 4199 mm^2.

Taking moments of area about the top of the section,

$$d = (3217 \times 644 + 982 \times 600)/4199 = 634 \text{ mm}$$
$$d' \text{ (assuming } A'_s = 2T25 \text{ (982 mm}^2\text{))} = 52.5 \text{ mm}$$
$$d'/d = 0.083 \text{ (use Graph No. 2)}$$
$$bd^2 f_{cu} = 4.22E9$$
$$bdf_{cu}/f_y = 14.5E3$$
$$M/bd^2 f_{cu} = 0.195$$

Graph No. 2 gives $A'_s = \underline{725 \text{ mm}^2}$, $A_s = \underline{4104 \text{ mm}^2}$, so the proposed reinforcement is satisfactory.

Since the area of compression reinforcement provided is greater than that required, the design could be refined by moving back along the horizontal projection to a point representing the actual area, and then projecting vertically to obtain a smaller area of tension reinforcement. Such a refinement is not usually justified, however, unless the area of tension reinforcement first obtained just exceeds the area of a convenient set of bars.

Using Graph No. 5.   Project horizontally from 0.195 on the vertical axis to intersect the lines for A'_s and A_s corresponding to $x/d = 0.5$. Projecting vertically gives $A'_s f_y/bdf_{cu} = 0.052$ and $A_s f_y/bdf_{cu} = 0.285$, i.e. $A'_s = 754 \text{ mm}^2$ and $A_s = 4133 \text{ mm}^2$.

The design graphs give conservative results because the actual value of d'/d is less than the assumed value. For comparison, the results obtained from the design formulae, using the correct value of α', are:

$$A'_s = 707 \text{ mm}^2$$
$$A_s = 4055 \text{ mm}^2$$

EXAMPLE 6.10   *Design of a beam with incidental compression reinforcement*

A continuous beam of width 350 mm and overall depth 500 mm has 2T25 bars continued into the compression zone. Cover on the main reinforcement is 45 mm and the concrete grade is C30.

(a) Determine the additional reinforcement necessary
    (i)   if the full elastic moment was reduced from 575 kN m to 460 kN m by redistribution
    (ii) for a design moment of 400 kN m without redistribution.
(b) Check the result for (ii) above by means of the design formulae.

    (i)   Assuming initially that tension reinforcement is T32 bars,

$$d = 500 - 45 - 16 = 439 \text{ mm}$$
$$d' = 45 + 12.5 = 47.5 \text{ mm}$$

Hence $d'/d = 0.131$ and the correct results would be obtained by interpolating between the graphs for $d'/d = 0.10$ and 0.15. However, the conservative result obtained by assuming the larger value of d'/d is usually accepted.

$$bd^2 f_{cu} = 350 \times 439^2 \times 30 = 2.024E9$$
$$M/bd^2 f_{cu} = 460E6/2.024E9 = 0.227$$
$$\beta_b = 460/575 = 0.8$$
$$x/d(\text{max.}) = \beta_b - 0.4 = 0.4$$

Using the traditional design graph (Graph No. 3) and projecting horizontally from 0.227 on the vertical scale to the diagonal line representing $x/d = 0.4$, then vertically gives $A_s f_y/bd f_{cu} = 0.314$.
The area of compression reinforcement is obtained by interpolating between the lines for $A_s' f_y/bd f_{cu} = 0.1$ and 0.2. Interpolating linearly gives $A_s' f_y/bd f_{cu} = 0.14$ approximately. The spacing of the lines is not linear, but linear interpolation gives a conservative result.

$$bd f_{cu}/f_y = 350 \times 439 \times 30/460 = 10.02E3$$

Hence, using the above results,

$$A_s = 0.314 \times 10.02E3 = \underline{3146 \text{ mm}^2} - \text{say } \underline{4T32 \ (3217 \text{ mm}^2)}$$
$$A_s' = 0.14 \times 10.02E3 = 1403 \text{ mm}^2$$

But compression reinforcement already present is 2T25, i.e. 982 mm². Hence additional reinforcement required $= 1403 - 982 = \underline{421 \text{ mm}^2} - \text{say } \underline{1T25 \ (491 \text{ mm}^2)}$.

The alternative graph (Graph No. 6) gives a more accurate result for the area of compression reinforcement, as follows:

$$A_s' = 1283 - 982 = \underline{301 \text{ mm}^2 \ (1T10)}$$
$$A_s = \underline{3146 \text{ mm}^2}$$

(ii) $A'_s f_y/bdf_{cu} = 982/10.02E3 = 0.098$ (say 0.10)

$M/bd^2f_{cu} = 400/2.024E9 = 0.198$

Using Graph No. 3 and projecting horizontally, $A'_s f_y/bdf_{cu} = 0.10$ lies to the left of the diagonal representing $x/d = 0.5$, the limit for no redistribution. The compression reinforcement already present is therefore more than adequate. Projecting vertically gives $A_s f_y/bdf_{cu} = 0.273$.

Hence

$$A_s = 0.273 \times 10.02E3 = \underline{2735 \text{ mm}^2}$$

Using Graph No. 6 a horizontal line from $M/bd^2f_{cu} = 0.198$ and a vertical line from $A'_s f_y/bdf_{cu} = 0.098$ intersect at a point between the A'_s lines for $x/d = 0.3$ and 0.4, i.e. at an estimated value of $x/d = 0.38$. Projecting horizontally to the corresponding point between the A_s lines and then projecting vertically gives $A_s f_y/bdf_{cu} \approx 0.273$, i.e. $A_s = \underline{2735 \text{ mm}^2}$.

6T25 bars (2945 mm^2) would be adequate, but they cannot be accommodated in a single row, so 4T32 (3217 mm^2) would probably be used. The reader is invited to try other alternatives, noting that if 40 mm bars or double rows are used the effective depth must be reduced.

(b) *Design formulae*

$$A'_s = (K - K') f_{cu}bd^2/0.87f_y(d - d')$$

Hence

$$(K - K') = 0.87f_y A'_s(d - d')/f_{cu}bd^2$$
$$= 400.2 \times 982 \times 439(1 - 0.131)/2.024E9 = 0.074$$

and

$$K = M/bd^2f_{cu} = 0.198$$

Hence

$$K' = 0.198 - 0.074 = 0.124$$

$$z = d\{0.5 + \surd(0.25 - K'/0.9)\}$$
$$= 439\{0.5 + \surd(0.25 - 0.124/0.9)\} = 366 \text{ mm}$$

$$A_s = K'f_{cu}bd^2/0.87f_y z + A'_s$$
$$= 0.124 \times 2.024E9/400.2 \times 366 + 982 = \underline{2695 \text{ mm}^2}$$

6.6 Tutorial problems

It is suggested that in order to gain experience with alternative methods of design, the following problems should be solved by means of the design graphs and the design formulae where appropriate.

6.6.1 Singly reinforced beam

A beam has a section 250 mm wide with an effective depth of 400 mm. Characteristic strengths are: concrete 40 N/mm², steel 460 N/mm². Given that the ultimate moment of resistance is to be 225 kN m, show that the beam can be singly reinforced and determine:

(a) the lever arm
(b) the depth of the neutral axis
(c) the area of reinforcement
(d) the maximum acceptable percentage reduction of the elastic moment by redistribution.

Answers
$K = 0.141 < 0.156$; (a) 322 mm; (b) 173 mm; (c) 1746 mm²; (d) 16.7%

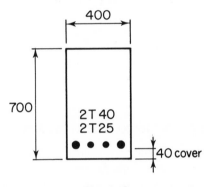

Fig. 6.15

6.6.2 Analysis of a given singly reinforced section

A singly reinforced beam has the section in Fig. 6.15. Given that the concrete grade is C35 determine:

(a) the effective depth
(b) the depth of the neutral axis
(c) the ultimate moment of resistance.

Answers
(a) 642.1 mm; (b) 248.5 mm; (c) 741.7 kN m

6.6.3 Singly reinforced beam with redistribution

A beam has width 300 mm, effective depth 500 mm, and concrete grade C40.

(a) Determine the maximum recommended ultimate moment of resistance from the under-reinforced section if the full elastic moment has been reduced by 25% by redistribution.

(b) Determine the area of reinforcement required using (i) mild steel, (ii) high-yield steel.

Answers
(a) 356 kN m; (b) 3886 mm^2, 2112 mm^2.

6.6.4   Doubly reinforced beam

A beam has width 400 mm, effective depth 700 mm, is made from C25 concrete, and uses high-yield reinforcement. Determine:

(a) the maximum moment of resistance and the corresponding area of tension reinforcement for the singly reinforced section assuming no redistribution,
(b) suitable reinforcement (assuming $d'/d = 0.10$) to provide a moment of resistance of 1000 kN m (i) with no redistribution, (ii) when redistribution results in a reduction of 30% in the elastic bending moment.

Answers
(a) 764.4 kN m, 3521 mm^2; (b) (i) $A_s' = 935$ mm^2, $A_s = 4510$ mm^2; (b) (ii) $A_s' = 1945$ mm^2, $A_s = 4048$ mm^2.

6.6.5   Doubly reinforced beam (compression reinforcement elastic)

Given that, in part (b) (ii) of the previous problem d'/d is increased to 0.15, show that the stress in the compression reinforcement does not reach the design strength in the ultimate limit state. Calculate the steel stress and the new areas of reinforcement required.

Answers
350 N/mm^2, 2224 mm^2, 4048 mm^2.

6.6.6   Maximum and minimum reinforcement

A section has width 375 mm and overall depth 600 mm. Cover on the main reinforcement is 40 mm and the maximum aggregate size is 20 mm. The characteristic strengths are: concrete 30 N/mm^2, steel 460 N/mm^2.

(a) Determine the maximum practical area of tension reinforcement that can be placed in not more than two rows.
(b) Sketch the arrangement in the section and calculate the effective depth.
(c) Determine the corresponding area of effective compression reinforcement and show the complete detail of the section including links.
(d) Calculate the ultimate moment of resistance from first principles.
(e) Determine the minimum recommended area of reinforcement if the section were singly reinforced; and calculate the corresponding ultimate moment of resistance. (*Hint*: z must not exceed $0.95d$ – see Equation (B2.10)).

Answers

(a) 4T40 + 4T32 (8243 mm^2) – theoretical 9000 mm^2

(b) see Fig. 6.16(a), d = 510.3 mm

(c) effective 5360 mm^2 – actual 5428 mm^2; identical R10 links in pairs – see Fig. 6.16(b)

(d) 1413 kN m.

Note: With the above arrangement of reinforcement there would be insufficient space between the top bars for the insertion of a vibrator (75 mm min.). A more practical arrangement, providing a slightly lower moment of resistance, would be to replace the 16 mm bars with 40 mm bars and dispense with the middle bars in the top row. This would also enable single links to be used at an increased spacing.

(e) 273 mm^2 – say 4T10 (314 mm^2), M = 66.9 kN m.

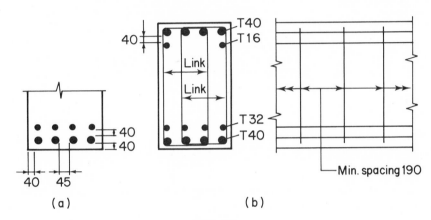

Fig. 6.16

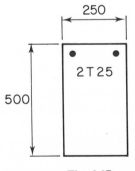

Fig. 6.17

6.6.7 Design of a section with incidental reinforcement

The middle portion of a continuous beam has the section shown in Fig. 6.17. Concrete is C30 and the reinforcement is high-yield steel. What additional reinforcement is needed to provide a moment of resistance of (a) 470 kN m, (b) 200 kN m? The top of the beam is in compression. Cover on the longitudinal reinforcement is 35 mm. Redistribution is less than 10%.

Answers
(a)   475 mm^2 (1T25) compression, 3151 mm^2 (4T32) tension
(b)   ignoring the compression reinforcement, 1339 mm^2 (2T25 + 2T16) tension; allowing for the compression reinforcement, 1194 mm^2 (2T25 + 2T12) tension.

Note: The solution of part (b) from first principles, allowing for the compression reinforcement, involves the solution of a cubic equation because the compression reinforcement is elastic. Either the traditional or the alternative form of the design graphs may be used to solve part (a) (see Example 6.10) but for part (b) the traditional form must be used. If the compression reinforcement is ignored in part (b) and the beam designed as singly reinforced the loss in economy is not very great.

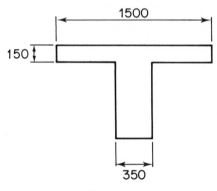

Fig. 6.18

6.6.8   Maximum moment of resistance of a flanged beam

A flanged beam has the effective section shown in Fig. 6.18. Characteristic strengths are: concrete 30 N/mm^2, reinforcement 460 N/mm^2.

(a)   Determine the maximum positive moment of resistance of the singly reinforced section and the corresponding area of tension reinforcement. Assume an effective depth of 800 mm.
(b)   Determine the overall depth of the beam assuming cover on the main reinforcement to be 35 mm and the space between rows of bars to be 20 mm.
(c)   Using the results obtained in (b) above, determine the maximum negative moment that can be resisted by the singly reinforced section and the area of tension reinforcement required in the flange.

Answers
(a)   2696 kN m; 9901 mm^2 – say 8T40 (10 050 mm^2) in two rows;
(b)   885 mm^2;
(c)   1128 kN m (assuming d = 830 mm and 40 mm bars), A_s = 4383 mm^2.

6.6.9 Flanged beam with positive and negative moments

Determine the areas of reinforcement required in the beam of the previous problem to provide ultimate moments of resistance of (a) 1500 kN m positive and (b) 1300 kN m negative. Assume that the effective depths are the same as in the previous problem and that there has been no redistribution.

Answers
(a) 4993 mm^2 (tension only – in web)
(b) 4929 mm^2 (tension – in flange), 546 mm^2 (compression – in web).

7

Shear and Torsion in Reinforced Concrete

7.1 Shear resistance of reinforced concrete

7.1.1 Introduction

The dimensions of the cross-section of a reinforced concrete beam and the area of longitudinal steel are usually determined from calculations which consider resistance to bending moment at the ultimate limit state. In many situations these dimensions will be satisfactory to resist the shear forces at the ultimate limit state, but this must be checked

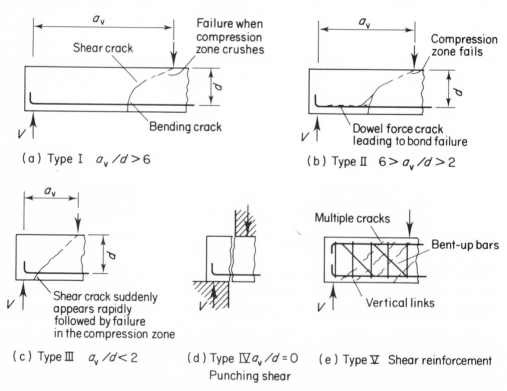

(a) Type I $a_v/d > 6$

(b) Type II $6 > a_v/d > 2$

(c) Type III $a_v/d < 2$

(d) Type IV $a_v/d = 0$ Punching shear

(e) Type V Shear reinforcement

Fig. 7.1 Types of shear failure in reinforced concrete beams.

and shear reinforcement added if necessary. Shear forces exist in members where this is a change in bending moment along the length of the member. The shear force is equal to the rate of change of bending moment.

7.1.2   Types of shear failure

The mechanism of shear failure in reinforced concrete is complicated and despite extensive experimental and theoretical research work it is not completely understood. The appearance of beams failing in shear is shown in Fig. 7.1, and may be collectively described as cracked concrete interacting with, and held together by, the reinforcement. Initially vertical cracks are produced by the bending moment and later these are linked to diagonal cracks produced by the shear forces. There are broadly five types of failure for reinforced concrete beams, as shown in Fig. 7.1. The diagrams show the left-hand support for a simply supported beam carrying a central point load and the first four types of failure are related to the shear span ratio a_v/d. As this ratio increases the shear resistance decreases, but for values of $a_v/d > 2$ the decrease is small.

Type I ($a_v/d > 6$)   The bending moment is large in comparison to the shear force and the mode of failure is similar to that in pure bending. The initial vertical bending cracks become inclined due to the action of the shear stresses and failure occurs in the compression zone (see Fig. 7.1(a)). The stresses in the tensile steel are approximately at yield and only minimum shear reinforcement is required in design situations.

Type II ($6 > a_v/d > 2$)   The initial bending cracks become inclined early in the loading sequence and at collapse horizontal cracks form running along the line of the tensile reinforcement (see Fig. 7.1(b)). The horizontal cracks reduce the shear resistance of the section by destroying the dowel force and reducing the bond stresses between the steel and the concrete. The steel in the tension zone does not reach yield.

Type III ($a_v/d < 2$)   Bending cracks do not develop but shear cracks (at approximately 45°) suddenly appear and often run through to the compression zone and produce collapse (see Fig. 7.1(c)). The steel in the tension zone does not reach yield.

Type IV ($a_v/d = 0$)   Punching shear failure occurs when the plane of failure is forced to run parallel to the shear forces, as shown in Fig. 7.1(d). This can occur when the opposing shear forces are close together or, if shear links have been added, when a failure plane forms which does not intercept the shear links. When this type of failure occurs the shear resistance of the section is at a maximum. The addition of shear reinforcement in the form of vertical links does not increase the shear resistance above the punching shear value and if a section is unable to resist this force it must be increased in size.

Type V   The addition of shear reinforcement increases the shear resistance for types of failure I, II, and III. Numerous diagonal cracks develop as shown in Fig. 7.1(e) and at failure the shear reinforcement and the longitudinal steel yield, provided that the steel is anchored and the member is not over-reinforced.

7.1.3 Components of shear resistance

The shear resistance of a section may be broken down into component strength parts as shown in Fig. 7.2. The approximate percentage of the total shear load resisted by each component, obtained experimentally (Taylor 1974) for a singly reinforced concrete beam without shear reinforcement is also indicated.

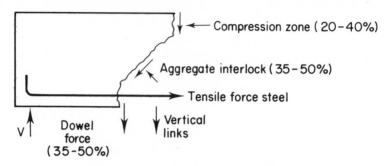

Fig. 7.2   Components of shear resistance.

The shear resistance of a beam can be expressed as the sum of the resistance of the parts:

$$V = \text{(shear span ratio factor)} \times \text{(concrete strength factor)}$$
$$\times \text{(compression zone + aggregate interlock + dowel force)}$$
$$\times \text{(depth of beam factor)}$$
$$+ \text{shear reinforcement} \tag{7.1}$$

The exact interaction of these shear components is not fully understood and theories which are reasonably accurate tend to be too complicated for use in practical situations. The design recommendations given in BS 8110 are therefore a lower-bound fit to experimental results and incorporate a combined steel and concrete materials factor of 1.25.

7.1.4   Average shear stress (cl 3.4.5.2, Pt 1)

The actual shear stress distribution over the depth of a section at the ultimate limit state is not known and therefore in design the average shear stress is calculated, i.e. $v = V/(b_v d)$, where b_v is the width of the web. This value is then used as a guide to determine whether the section is of the correct size and whether shear reinforcement is required.

The average shear stress must have an upper limit to prevent the punching shear type of failure shown in Fig. 7.1(d). The limit given in BS 8110 is $0.8\sqrt{f_{cu}}$ but not greater than $5\,\text{N/mm}^2$. These are empirical values obtained from experiments (ASCE–ACI Committee 426, 1973). In design situations the punching shear stress controls the size of section and if the average shear stress for a section exceeds the punching stress the cross-sectional area must be increased.

7.1.5   Shear resistance of a singly reinforced concrete beam (cl 3.4.5.4, Pt 1)

In BS 8110, for a singly reinforced concrete beam, the design shear stress at the ultimate limit state is expressed as a lower-bound fit to experimental results (Shear Study Group 1969). The first three shear-resistance components are added together and expressed as a design shear stress v_c modified by the (depth/shear span) ratio and strength of concrete.

$$v_c = k_1 k_2 0.79[100A_s/(b_v d)]^{1/3}(400/d)^{1/4}/\gamma_m \qquad (7.2)$$

where

A_s is the area of tension steel
b_v is the thickness of the web
$\gamma_m = 1.25$ is a combined materials factor for steel and concrete
$k_1 = 2d/a_v$ is an enhancement factor for depth/shear span ratios greater than $\frac{1}{2}$, where d is the effective depth and a_v is the distance from the face of the support to a point load, or as defined in cl 3.4.5.8, Pt 1
$k_2 = (f_{cu}/25)^{1/3}$ is a factor which enhances the shear strength for characteristic concrete strengths greater than 25 N/mm^2 but not greater than 40 N/mm^2.
$100A_s/(b_v d)$ should not exceed 3.
$400/d$ should not be less than 1.

When Equation (7.2) is applied to 'T' and 'L' sections the value of b_v is the width of the web, *not* the width of the flange. The term $400/d$ allows for increased shear resistance for shallow depth beams (Chana 1981).

EXAMPLE 7.1   Shear resistance of a singly reinforced concrete beam

A simply supported lintel beam spans 5 m and carries a total uniformly distributed load of 30 kN. The beam section has been designed to resist the bending moment and is shown in Fig. 7.3. Design the beam for shear.

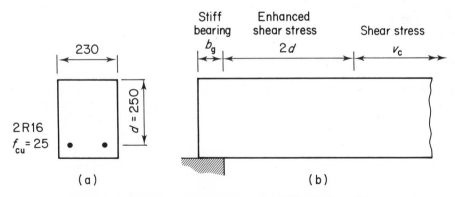

Fig. 7.3   Example: shear resistance of a singly reinforced beam.

Average shear stress at the support

$$v_{support} = V/(b_v d) = 15E3/(230 \times 250) = 0.261 \text{ N/mm}^2$$

Maximum design punching shear stress (cl 3.4.5.2, Pt 1)

$$v_u = 0.8\sqrt{f_{cu}} = 0.8\sqrt{25} = 4 \text{ N/mm}^2 < 5 \text{ N/mm}^2$$

$v_{support}(0.261) < v_u(4) \text{ N/mm}^2$, therefore section is not too small.

Design shear stress for a singly reinforced concrete beam (cl 3.4.5.4, Pt 1)

$$v_c = k_1 k_2 0.79 [100 A_s/(b_v d)]^{1/3} (400/d)^{1/4}/\gamma_m$$
$$= 1 \times 1 \times 0.79 \times [100 \times 402/(230 \times 250)]^{1/3} (400/250)^{1/4}/1.25$$
$$= 0.631 \text{ N/mm}^2$$
$$100 A_s/(b_v d) = 100 \times 402/(230 \times 250) = 0.699\% < 3\%$$

Maximum design shear stress for a singly reinforced concrete beam without shear reinforcement (cl 3.4.5.3, Table 3.8, Pt 1)

$$0.5 v_0 = 0.5 \times 0.631 = 0.315 \text{ N/mm}^2$$

Compare the value of $0.5 v_c$ with the shear stress at a distance $2d$ from the face of the support (see Fig. 7.3(b)) where there is no shear enhancement.

$$v_{2d} = (L/2 - b_g/2 - 2d)/L \times V/(b_v d)$$
$$= (2.5 - 0.2/2 - 2 \times 0.25)/2.5 \times 15\text{E}3/(230 \times 250) = 0.198 < 0.5 v_c$$

$(0.315) \text{ N/mm}^2$, therefore section does not require shear reinforcement.

The calculation of the shear stress at a distance $2d$ from the face of the support can be avoided by comparing $0.5 v_c$ with the shear stress at the support, i.e.

$$v_{support}(0.261) < 0.5 v_c (0.315) \text{ N/mm}^2$$

and therefore section does not require shear reinforcement.

Calculating the shear stress at the support overestimates the value of the shear stress and is therefore a safe method of design.

7.1.6   Shear resistance of a beam with vertical links (cl 3.4.5.3, Pt 1)

At the ultimate limit state in situations where the average shear stress v exceeds the design shear stress $v_c + 0.4 \text{ N/mm}^2$ shear reinforcement is added. The most common type of shear reinforcement is in the form of vertical links spaced at intervals along the length of a member. The shape of the link shown in Fig. 7.4(b) is preferred because it is closed, but the other shapes shown in Figs. 7.4(c) and (d) are also used where there are practical difficulties in fixing the reinforcement. Vertical links strengthen the web of a beam and prevent dowel failure.

The shear resistance of vertical links is based on the following approximate theory which results in the expression given in BS 8110. A more comprehensive derivation is given by Evans and Kong (1967). Vertical links in a beam intercept the cracks in the concrete which are at approximately 45° as shown in Fig. 7.4(a).

Resolve forces vertically:

$$V = V\text{(singly reinforced beam)} + V\text{(links)} \tag{7.3}$$

The shear resistance of a singly reinforced beam can be calculated from Equation (7.2).

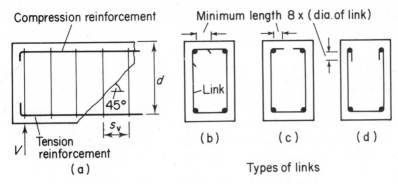

Fig. 7.4 Shear resistance of a beam with links.

The number of links crossing a 45° crack is d/s_v and therefore the total design shear resistance is

$$V = V(\text{singly reinforced beam}) + A_{sv}0.87f_{yv}d/s_v$$

This equation can be expressed in terms of shear stresses by dividing throughout by $b_v d$ and rearranging to determine the spacing of the links:

$$s_v = A_{sv}0.87f_{yv}/[b_v(v-v_c)] \tag{7.4}$$

To ensure that bond failure does not occur in a link the characteristic strength of the links f_{yv} should not exceed 460 N/mm². For most beams single links, for which A_{sv} equals the cross-sectional area of two legs, is sufficient. Where compression bars are numerous, or where shear forces are large, double links (A_{sv} based on four legs), or triple links (A_{sv} based on six legs) are used.

In most building construction work the smallest-diameter link used is 6 mm and the largest diameter is 10 mm. Larger diameter links are not often used because of the difficulties involved in bending and because of the displacement of the longitudinal bars at the corners of links when large corner radii are used. However, for beams with large cross-sections larger diameter links may have to be used.

If shear reinforcement is required close to supports, then the total area (Equation (5), cl 3.4.5.9, Pt 1) is

$$\Sigma A_{sv} = a_v b_v(v-2dv_c/a_v)/(0.87f_{yv}) \geqslant 0.4b_v a_v/(0.87f_{yv}) \tag{7.5}$$

The reinforcement should be provided in the middle three-quarters of the distance a_v, where $a_v < d$. Horizontal reinforcement is more effective than vertical.

7.1.7 Minimum, or nominal, vertical links (cl 3.4.5.3, Pt 1)

If too little shear reinforcement is provided it is not effective (Kreyfeld and Thurston 1966). Where shear stresses exceed $0.5v_c$ and are less than $v_c + 0.4$ N/mm², then minimum shear reinforcement should be added. Therefore the links should have a strength at least equivalent to the shear stress of 0.4 N/mm², which is in excess of v_c. BS 8110 therefore recommends that

$$A_{sv}0.87f_{yv}d/s_v > 0.4b_v d$$

Rearranging to determine the spacing of the links:

$$s_v = A_{sv}0.87f_{yv}/(0.4b_v) \qquad\qquad (7.6)$$

7.1.8   Spacing of links (cl 3.4.5.5, Pt 1)

Practical spacings of links are generally in intervals of 20 mm. If the longitudinal spacing of the links is greater than the lever arm, approximately $0.75d$, then, as can be seen in Fig. 7.4(a), the links do not intercept the 45° crack and therefore will not resist the applied shear force. The maximum longitudinal spacing allowed in BS 8110 is therefore $0.75d$.

The spacing at right angles to the span should be such that no longitudinal tension bar is more than 150 mm from a vertical leg of a link, nor should it exceed d.   This recommendation in BS 8110 is to ensure that a link is adequately anchored. The ideal anchorage is where a longitudinal bar is at the inside corner of the link.

Recommendations for minimum longitudinal spacing for links are not given in BS 8110. However, the minimum longitudinal spacing is controlled by the need for the concrete to flow round the reinforcement during casting, which means that a space of at least the diameter of the maximum size of aggregate plus 5 mm (or bar diameter if greater) is required. For deformed bars the longitudinal spacing should be twice the cover to the outside of the beam in order to ensure the necessary bond strength between steel and concrete.

7.1.9   Anchorage of links (cl 3.12.8.6, Pt 1)

Generally it is not possible to anchor a link by bond alone because of the limited bond length available, and therefore it is necessary to provide longitudinal bars in the bottom and top of a beam which are enclosed by the link and used as an anchorage. This arrangement produces a cage of reinforcement which is easier for the steel fixer to construct as a separate unit and add to the mould when casting the beam. The longitudinal bars should be at least equal in diameter to the link and generally are not less than 12 mm, although some designers prefer larger sizes.

A link may be considered to be fully anchored if it satisfies the following:

(a)   it passes round another bar of at least its own size, through an angle of 90°, and continues beyond for a minimum length of at least eight times its own size; or
(b)   It passes round another bar of at least its own size, and through an angle of 180°, and continues beyond for a minimum length of eight times its own size.

The shape shown in Fig. 7.4(b) is the most common form in use in practice.

If a beam is doubly reinforced, then the compression steel is used for the anchorage of the links. If a beam is singly reinforced and links are required, then compression steel is added to anchor the links. The compression steel increases the strength of the beam in bending which may be redesigned as a doubly reinforced concrete beam, but in practice since it is safe, it is often considered as not worth the effort involved (see the solution to Tutorial Problem 6.6.7(b), which confirms this statement).

7.1.10 Summary of shear requirements for beams (cl 3.4.5.3, Pt 1)

The form and area of shear reinforcement in beams is summarised in Appendix A.2.

EXAMPLE 7.2 Beam with vertical links

A simply supported beam carries a uniformly distributed load of 475 kN, which includes self-weight. The beam cross-section is shown in Fig. 7.5 and shows the tension reinforcement required to resist the bending moment at mid-span at the ultimate limit state. Design the cross-section for shear.

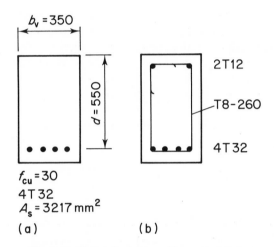

Fig. 7.5 Example: beam with vertical links.

Maximum shear force at the supports $V = 475/2 = 237.5$ kN
Average shear stress from the applied load (cl 3.4.5.2, Pt 1)

$$v = V/(b_v d) = 237.5E3/(350 \times 550) = 1.23 \text{ N/mm}^2$$

Maximum design shear stress (cl 3.4.5.2, Pt 1)

$$v_u = 0.8\sqrt{f_{cu}} = 0.8\sqrt{30} = 4.38 < 5 \text{ N/mm}^2$$

$v_u(4.38) > v(1.23)$ N/mm^2, therefore section is not too small.

Design shear stress for a singly reinforced concrete beam (cl 3.4.5.4, Pt 1)

$$v_c = k_1 k_2 0.79[100A_s/(b_v d)]^{1/3}(400/d)^{1/4}/\gamma_m$$
$$= 1 \times (30/25)^{1/3} \times 0.79 \times [100 \times 3217/(350 \times 550)]^{1/3} \times 1/1.25$$
$$= 0.797 \text{ N/mm}^2$$

$400/d < 1$ therefore use 1, $100A_s/(b_v d) = 1.67\% < 3\%$ (max.)

Shear reinforcement is required because $v(1.23) > (v_o + 0.4)(1.20)$ N/mm^2 (cl 3.4.5.3, Pt 1).

From Equation (7.4), assuming single T8 vertical links

$$s_v = A_{sv}0.87f_{yv}/[b_v(v - v_c)]$$
$$= 2 \times 50 \times 0.87 \times 460/[350 \times (1.23 - 0.797)]$$
$$= 264.1 < 0.75d(412.5) \text{ mm therefore satisfactory.}$$

Use T8-260 mm centres, with 2T12 (or 2R12) as compression reinforcement as shown in Fig. 7.5(b). These links can be used for the full length of the beam, or the spacing can be increased as the shear force reduces.

EXAMPLE 7.3   Bottom-loaded floor beam

Reinforce for shear the section of a simply supported floor beam shown in Fig. 7.6. The beam which spans 3 m is loaded through the bottom flange with a uniformly distributed load of 8 kN/m (which includes self-weight) at the ultimate limit state.

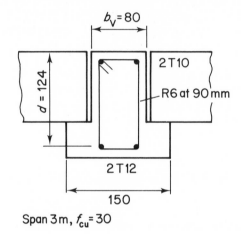

Fig. 7.6   Example: bottom-loaded floor beam.

Maximum applied shear force at the supports $V = wL/2 = 8 \times 3/2 = 12$ kN

Average shear stress from the applied shear force (cl 3.4.5.2, Pt 1)

$$v = V/(b_v d) = 12\text{E}3/(80 \times 124) = 1.210 \text{ N/mm}^2$$

Maximum design shear stress (cl 3.4.5.2, Pt 1)

$$v_u = 0.8\sqrt{f_{cu}} = 0.8\sqrt{30} = 4.38 < 5 \text{ N/mm}^2$$

$v_u(4.38) > v(1.21)$ N/mm^2, therefore section is not too small.

Design shear stress for a singly reinforced concrete beam (cl 3.4.5.4, Pt 1)

$$v_c = k_1 k_2 0.79[100A_s/(b_v d)]^{1/3}(400/d)^{1/4}/\gamma_m$$
$$= 1 \times (30/25)^{1/3} \times 0.79 \times [100 \times 226/(80 \times 124)]^{1/3} \times (400/124)^{1/4} \times 1/1.25$$
$$= 1.184 \text{ N/mm}^2$$

$400/d < 1$ therefore use 1, $100A_s/(b_v d) = 2.28 < 3\%$ (max.)

Nominal shear reinforcement is required because (cl 3.4.5.3, Pt 1)

$$0.5v_c(0.592) < v(1.21) < (v_c + 0.4)(1.584) \text{ N/mm}^2$$

From Equation (7.6) assuming single R6 vertical links

$$s_v = A_{sv}0.87f_{yv}/(0.4b_v)$$
$$= 2 \times 28 \times 0.87 \times 250/(0.4 \times 80)$$
$$= 380.6 > 0.75d \ (93) \text{ mm, therefore use 90 mm.}$$

If 90 mm spacing is used, then the area of links required from rearranging Equation (7.6) is

$$A_{sv} = 0.4b_v s_v/0.87f_{yv} = 0.4 \times 80 \times 90/(0.87 \times 250)$$
$$= 13.24 \text{ mm}^2$$

Additional area of links in tension required to support bottom load for $s_v = 90$ mm

$$A_{sv(extra)} = (Ws_v/L)/(0.87f_{yv}) = (24E3 \times 90/3E3)/(0.87 \times 250)$$
$$= 3.31 \text{ mm}^2$$

Total area of stirrup required $= A_{sv} + A_{sv(extra)} = 13.24 + 3.31 = 16.55 \text{ mm}^2$. Single R6 stirrups, $A_s = 2 \times 28 = 56 > 16.55 \text{ mm}^2$, therefore satisfactory.

Use single R6-90 mm centres with 2T10 as compression reinforcement as shown in Fig. 7.6.

7.1.11 Shear resistance of bent-up bars (cl 3.4.5.6, Pt 1)

In situations where all the tensile reinforcement is not required to resist the bending moment at the ultimate limit state, some of the bars may be bent up to form shear reinforcement, as shown in Fig. 7.7. The tensile bars are shown at different levels in Fig. 7.7 for ease in identification, but in practice they are all at the same level as shown in the cross-section. If the tensile reinforcement is used in this way it must be adequately anchored at the top of the beam to prevent bond failure.

Generally there are insufficient bent-up bars available to resist the total shear force and a maximum of 50% of the total shear force is allowed, the other 50% is to be

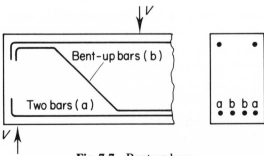

Fig. 7.7 Bent-up bars.

provided by vertical links. When bent-up bars and vertical links are used together their effect is added (Evans and Kong 1967). It should be appreciated that if tensile bars are bent-up then there is a reduction in tensile steel, and in consequence a reduction in resistance to bending and shear resistance of the beam as a singly reinforced concrete beam.

The shear resistance of bent-up bars may be calculated using the truss analogy, which assumes that the bent-up bars act as tension members and the concrete forms the compression members as shown in Fig. 7.8. Experiments (ASCE–ACI Committee 426, 1973) justify these assumptions.

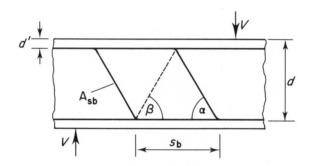

Fig. 7.8   Truss theory for bent-up bars.

The expression given in BS 8110 to determine the shear resistance of bent-up bars is

$$V_b = A_{sb}0.87f_{yb}[\cos \alpha + \sin \alpha \cot \beta](d - d')/s_b$$

rearranging

$$V_b = A_{sb}0.87f_{yb} \sin \alpha (\cot \alpha + \cot \beta)(d - d')/s_b$$

and simplifying

$$V_b = A_{sb}0.87f_{yb} \sin \alpha$$

Alternatively dividing through by $b_v d$, the shear stress resistance:

$$v_b = A_{sb}0.87f_{yb} \sin \alpha/(b_v d) \tag{7.7}$$

This form of the equation shows that the shear resistance is calculated from the vertical resistance of bent-up bars at a section, and is independent of the spacing s_b. However, α and β should be $>45°$, giving a maximum value of $s_b = 1.5d$. This restriction is introduced to ensure that the diagonal cracks in the concrete are intercepted by the bent-up bars.

EXAMPLE 7.4   Beam containing bent-up bars

Determine the shear resistance of the bent-up bars in the beam shown in Fig. 7.9 and add vertical stirrups to resist a total shear force of 500 kN.

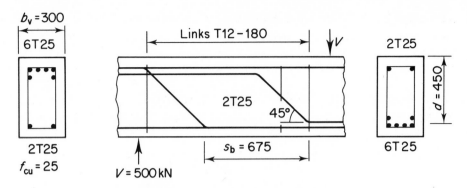

Fig. 7.9 Example with bent-up bars.

Average shear stress from the shear force of 500 kN (cl 3.4.5.2, Pt 1)

$$v = V/(b_v d) = 500E3/(300 \times 450) = 3.704 \text{ N/mm}^2$$

Maximum design shear stress (cl 3.4.5.2, Pt 1)

$$v_u = 0.8\sqrt{f_{cu}} = 0.8\sqrt{25} = 4 \text{ N/mm}^2 < 5 \text{ N/mm}^2$$

$v_u(4) > v(3.704)$ N/mm^2, therefore the section is not too small.

Design shear stress for a singly reinforced concrete beam (cl 3.4.5.4, Pt 1)

$$v_c = k_1 k_2 0.79[100A_s/(b_v d)]^{1/3}(400/d)^{1/4}/\gamma_m$$
$$= 1 \times 1 \times 0.79 \times [100 \times 982/(300 \times 450)]^{1/3} \times 1/1.25$$
$$= 0.568 \text{ N/mm}^2$$

$400/d < 1$, therefore use 1, and $100A_s/(b_v d) = 0.727 < 3\%$(max.)

Shear reinforcement is required because $v(3.704) > (v_c + 0.4)(0.968)$ N/mm^2 (cl 3.4.5.3, Pt 1).

From Equation (7.7) the shear stress resistance of 2T25 bent-up bars

$$v_b = A_{sb}0.87f_{yb} \sin \alpha/(b_v d)$$
$$= 982 \times 0.87 \times 460 \times 0.707/(300 \times 450) = 2.058 \text{ N/mm}^2$$

Check the % of the shear force taken by the bent-up bars.
   $100 \times 2.058/(3.704 - 0.568) = 65.5 > 50\%$, therefore design links to resist 50% of shear force.

From Equation (7.4) and assume single T12 vertical links:

$$s_v = A_{sv}0.87f_{yv}/[b_v \times 0.5 \times (v - v_c)]$$
$$= 2 \times 113 \times 0.87 \times 460/[300 \times 0.5 \times (3.704 - 0.568)]$$
$$= 192.3 < 0.75d \ (337.5) \text{ mm, therefore satisfactory.}$$

Anchor length required for a T20 type 2 deformed bar at the top of the beam (cl 3.12.8.3, Pt 1).

$$l = f_s \phi_e / (4f_b) = 0.87 \times 460 \times 20 / (4 \times 0.5\sqrt{25}) = 800.4 \text{ mm}.$$

Use 2T25 as bent-up bars and T12-180 mm centre links with T25 as compression reinforcement as shown in Fig. 7.9.

7.1.12   Shear resistance of solid slabs (cl 3.5.5, Pt 1)

The design requirements for the shear resistance of slabs are similar to those for beams and are summarised in Appendix A2.2.4.

One difference between beams and slabs is that provided the applied shear stress v is less than v_c (resistance as a singly reinforced slab), then no shear reinforcement is required. One practical consideration is that it is difficult to bend and fix shear reinforcement in slabs with a depth of less than or equal to 200 mm and therefore shear reinforcement is not recommended. If additional shear capacity is needed it can be obtained by increasing the percentage of tensile reinforcement, or increasing the concrete strength, or increasing the depth of the slab. For slabs of thickness greater than 200 mm shear links are bent in the castellated form shown in Fig. 7.10. Shear reinforcement may also be in the form of bent-up bars.

Fig. 7.10   Castellated link (5 legs).

One special shear situation is the application of a point load to a solid slab, which is considered in the next section.

7.1.13   Shear resistance of flat slabs under concentrated loads (cl 3.7.7, Pt 1)

Concentrated loads applied to flat slabs in the form of wheel loads, or more often in the form of columns, tend to punch through the slab. Failure takes the form of a truncated cone as shown in Fig. 7.11. This type of failure is prevented by placing castellated links to intercept the 30° cracks.

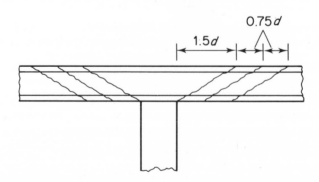

Fig. 7.11   Shear failure of a slab subjected to a concentrated column load.

The design process consists of making checks for shear stress at the column face, then at a perimeter $1.5d$ from the column face, and then successive perimeters at increments of $0.75d$, until shear reinforcement is no longer required, i.e. $v < v_c$. The design formulae, used previously for beams and slabs, are applied, except that the shear enhancement expression is changed to $1.5d/a_v$.

Where a concentrated load is from an axially loaded column, the distribution of shear force round the shear perimeter in the slab is uniform. In practice the axial load may be eccentric because of inaccuracies in construction, or idealisations in design, and the shear stress will be greater locally than that produced by a purely axial force. The axial force is therefore multiplied by a factor (c_1) greater than one to allow for this.

Similarly if a bending moment is applied to a column, then the shear force applied to the shear perimeter of the slab is greatest furthest from the axis of bending and zero at the axis of bending, as shown in Fig. 7.12.

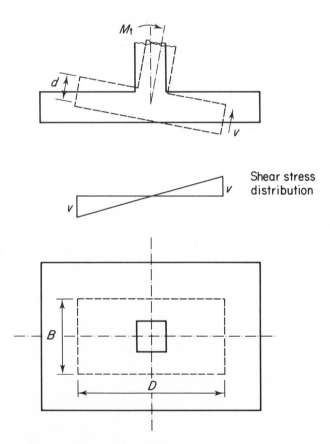

Fig. 7.12 Effective vertical force from a bending moment.

If v is the maximum shear stress in the slab, then by equating moments and assuming a linear variation of shear stress,

$$M_t = vd(BD + D^2/3)$$

rearranging

$$v = M_t/[(BD + D^2/3)d]$$

Effective vertical force from the bending moment is the force that would produce an average shear stress v around the perimeter:

$$V_{eff} = 2(B + D)vd = 2(1 + B/D)/[1 + D/(3B)]M_t/B = c_2 M_t/B$$

Total effective force from the axial load and bending moment

$$V_{eff} = V_t[c_1 + c_2 M_t/(V_t B)]$$

This form of equation is given in cl 3.7.6, Pt 1, Equations (25) and (26), where empirical values of c_1 and c_2 are given for various situations.

EXAMPLE 7.5   *Flat slab subject to a concentrated column load*

Check the flat slab shown in Fig. 7.13 for shear failure. The column load is 1000 kN and the uniformly distributed design load $n = 16$ kN/m². The concrete slab is 300 mm deep, with $d = 250$ mm, and reinforced with T16-200 mm centres in both directions at the top and bottom of the slab.

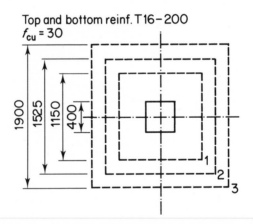

Top and bottom reinf. T 16−200
$f_{cu} = 30$

Fig. 7.13   Example of slab with a concentrated load.

Check punching shear round column perimeter.
   Assume that the column is for a braced structure with approximately equal spans (cl 3.7.6.2, Pt 1) and include an allowance for moment transfer. Average design shear stress on the perimeter (cl 3.7.7.2, Pt 1)

$$v = V_e/(u_0 d) = 1.15 \times 1150E3/(4 \times 400 \times 250) = 2.875 \text{ N/mm}^2$$

Maximum design shear stress

$$v_u = 0.8\sqrt{f_{cu}} = 0.8\sqrt{30} = 4.38 \text{ N/mm}^2 < 5 \text{ N/mm}^2$$

$v_u(4.38) > v(2.875)$ N/mm², therefore the depth of slab is not too small. Check the shear stresses at perimeter 1 at $1.5d$ from the column face.

Length of side of shear perimeter ($u/4$)

$$= 400 + 2 \times 1.5d$$
$$= 400 + 2 \times 1.5 \times 250 = 1150 \text{ mm}$$

Shear force transferred to the column

$$V_t = V_{max} - (\text{area enclosed by perimeter})n$$
$$= 1000 - 1.15^2 \times 16 = 978.8 \text{ kN}$$

Design force for an internal column including an allowance for moment transfer (cl 3.7.6.2, Pt 1)

$$V_e = 1.15 \times 978.8 = 1125.6 \text{ kN}$$

Average design shear stress around perimeter 1 (cl 3.7.7.3, Pt 1)

$$v = V_e/(ud) = 1125.6E3/(4 \times 1150 \times 250) = 0.979 \text{ N/mm}^2$$

Design shear stress for a singly reinforced concrete slab (cl 3.4.5.4, Pt 1)

$$v_c = k_1 k_2 0.79[100A_s/(b_v d)]^{1/3}(400/d)^{1/4}/\gamma_m$$
$$= 1 \times (30/25)^{1/3} \times 0.79 \times [100 \times 1005/(1000 \times 250)]^{1/3}$$
$$\times (400/250)^{1/4}/1.25$$
$$= 0.557 \text{ N/mm}^2$$

$$v - v_c = 0.979 - 0.557 = 0.422 \text{ N/mm}^2 > 0.4 \text{ N/mm}^2$$

Shear reinforcement is required because $v(0.979) > v_c(0.557)$ N mm^2 (cl 3.7.7.5, pt 1)
Rearrange Equation (7.4) and assume $s_v = 180 < 0.75d(187.5)$ mm

$$A_{sv} = (v - v_c)b_v s_v/(0.87f_{yv})$$
$$= 0.422 \times 1150 \times 180/(0.87 \times 460)$$
$$= 218.3 \text{ mm}^2$$
6T8 legs $= 302 \text{ mm}^2$

Use castellated links T8-180 mm centres.

Check the shear stresses at perimeter 2.

Length of side of shear perimeter ($u/4$)
$$= 400 + 2 \times 1.5d$$
$$= 400 + 2 \times 1.5 \times 250 = 1525 \text{ mm}$$

Shear force transferred to the column

$$V_t = V_{max} - (\text{area enclosed by perimeter})n$$
$$= 1000 - 1.525^2 \times 16 = 962.8 \text{ kN}$$

Design force for an internal column including an allowance for moment transfer (cl 3.7.6.2, Pt 1)

$$V_e = 1.15 \times 962.8 = 1107.2 \text{ kN}$$

Average shear stress around perimeter 2 (cl 3.7.7.3, Pt 1)

$$v = V_e/(ud) = 1107.2E3/(4 \times 1525 \times 250) = 0.726 \text{ N/mm}^2$$

Design shear stress for a singly reinforced concrete slab (cl 3.4.5.4, Pt 1)

$v_c = 0.557$ N/mm^2 as perimeter 1

$v - v_c = 0.726 - 0.557 = 0.169$ N/mm$^2 < 0.4$ N/mm^2, therefore use $v - v_c = 0.4$ N/mm^2 in calculations for shear reinforcement.

Shear reinforcement is required because $v(0.726) > v_c(0.557)$ N/mm^2 (cl 3.7.7.5, Pt 1)

Rearrange Equation (7.4) and assume $s_v = 180$ mm as perimeter 1

$$A_{sv} = (v - v_c)b_v s_v/(0.87 f_{yv})$$
$$= 0.4 \times 1525 \times 180/(0.87 \times 460)$$
$$= 274.4 \text{ mm}^2$$

8T8 legs $= 402$ mm^2

Use castellated links T8-180 mm centres as for perimeter 1.

Check the shear stresses at perimeter 3.

Length of side of shear perimeter ($u/4$)

$$= 400 + 2 \times 1.5d + 4 \times 0.75d$$
$$= 400 + 2 \times 1.5 \times 250 + 4 \times 0.75 \times 250 = 1900 \text{ mm}$$

Shear force transferred to the column

$$V_t = V_{max} - (\text{area enclosed by perimeter})n$$
$$= 1000 - 1.9^2 \times 16 = 942.2 \text{ kN}$$

Design force for an internal column including an allowance for moment transfer (cl 3.7.6.2, Pt 1)

$$V_e = 1.15 \times 942.2 = 1083.5 \text{ kN}$$

Average shear stress around perimeter 3 (cl 3.7.7.3, Pt 1)

$$v = V_e/(ud) = 1083.5E3/(4 \times 1900 \times 250) = 0.57 \text{ N/mm}^2$$

Design shear stress for a singly reinforced concrete slab (cl 3.4.5.4, Pt 1)

$v_c = 0.557$ N/mm^2 as for perimeter 1

$v - v_c = 0.57 - 0.557 = 0.013$ N/mm$^2 < 0.4$ N/mm^2

Shear stresses $v(0.57) = v_c(0.557)$ (approximately), therefore shear reinforcement can be omitted, but use castellated links T8-180 mm centres as for perimeter 1.

The next perimeter will not require shear reinforcement (cl 3.7.7.5, Pt 1).

7.1.14   Shear resistance of pad foundations (cl 3.11.3, Pt 1)

The design of a pad foundation for shear is similar to that for concentrated loads on slabs. Checks for shear stresses are made at the column perimeter for punching shear, then at a perimeter, or width, $1.5d$ from the column face, then at successive perimeters and widths of increasing values of $0.75d$. The same criteria are used to decide whether shear reinforcement is necessary. Generally in pad foundations the depth of the foundation is increased rather than introducing shear reinforcement. Further information on foundations is contained in Chapter 11.

EXAMPLE 7.6 Shear resistance of a pad foundation

Design for shear the pad foundation shown in Fig. 7.14. The axial load and bending moment applied to the base at the ultimate limit state produce a pressure distribution beneath the base as shown.

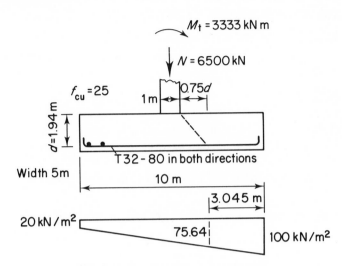

Fig. 7.14 Example of a pad foundation.

Punching shear round the column perimeter.

Average shear stress around column perimeter (cl 3.7.7.2, Pt 1)

$$v = N/(ud) = 6.5\text{E}6/(4 \times 1\text{E}3 \times 1940) = 1.676 \text{ N/mm}^2$$

Shear force (from pressure diagram beneath base) across the width at the face of the column

$$= (100 + 64)/2 \times 4.5 \times 5 = 922.5 \text{ kN}$$

Shear stress across the width at the face of the column

$$= 922.5\text{E}3/(5\text{E}3 \times 1940) = 0.0951 < 1.676 \text{ N/mm}^2$$

Maximum design shear stress (cl 3.7.7.2, Pt 1)

$$v_u = 0.8\sqrt{f_{cu}} = 0.8\sqrt{25} = 4 \text{ N/mm}^2 < 5 \text{ N/mm}^2$$

v_u (4) $> v$ (1.676) N/mm^2, therefore the depth of the foundation is not too small.

If shear stresses are checked at 1.5d from the column face, then the sections are outside the base on the width, and close to the edge for the length. Further checks are not mandatory according to BS 8110, but for interest check at 0.75d (cl 3.7.7.4, Pt 1).

Check the shear stresses at 0.75d from the column face.

Length of shear perimeter (u)

$$= 4 \times (1000 + 2 \times 0.75d)$$
$$= 4 \times (1000 + 2 \times 0.75 \times 1940) = 15\,640 \text{ mm}$$

Average shear stress around perimeter 1 (cl 3.7.7.3, Pt 1)

$$N = (10 \times 5 - 3.91^2) \times 120/2 = 2083 \text{ kN}$$
$$v = N/(ud) = 2.083\text{E}6/(15\,640 \times 1940) = 0.0687 \text{ N/mm}^2$$

Design shear stress as for a singly reinforced concrete slab per metre width (cl 3.4.5.4, Pt 1) using an enhancement factor $k_1 = 1.5d/a_v$.

$$
\begin{aligned}
v_c &= k_1 k_2 0.79 [100A_s/(b_v d)]^{1/3} (400/d)^{1/4}/\gamma_m \\
&= 1.5 \times 1940/(0.75 \times 1940) \times 1 \times 0.79 \times [100 \times 10\,500/(1000 \times 1940)]^{1/3} \\
&\quad \times 1/1.25 \\
&= 1.030 \text{ N/mm}^2
\end{aligned}
$$

$400/d < 1$ therefore use 1, and $100A_s/(b_v d) = 0.541\% < 3\% \text{(max.)}$
$v(0.0687) < v_c(1.03)$ N/mm^2, therefore no shear reinforcement necessary.

Check across the full width of the base of $5m$ at $0.75d$ from the column face (cl 3.11.3.4, Pt 1).

Shear force across a section $0.75d$ from the column face from the pressure diagram shown in Fig. 7.14 is

$$N = (100 + 75.64)/2 \times 3.045 \times 5 = 1337 \text{ kN}$$

Average design shear stress across the full width (cl 3.4.5.2, Pt 1)

$$v = N/(Bd) = 1337\text{E}3/(5000 \times 1940) = 0.138 \text{ N/mm}^2$$

$v(0.138) < v_c(1.03)$ N/mm^2 therefore no shear reinforcement necessary.

7.1.15   Shear resistance of pile caps (cl 3.11.4, Pt 1)

Pile caps are required to transfer a column load to a pile group as shown in Fig. 7.15. Toe-bearing piles are used in situations where the load-bearing stratum is some depth from ground level. Friction piles are used where the bearing capacity of the ground is low and the load is transferred by friction along the length of the pile. Piles are generally in groups of three or more but two can be used if stabilised by tying to another foundation. Further information is given in Chapter 11.

The method of design is similar to that for beams and slabs except for the following, where ϕ is the diameter of the pile.   When the spacing of the piles is less than or equal to 3ϕ the enhancement of the shear stress, based on the shear span/depth ratio, may be applied over the full width of the critical section. When the spacing is greater than 3ϕ the enhancement may only be applied to strips of width equal to 3ϕ, centred on each pile. Minimum strips are not required in pile caps where $v < v_c$.

A check should also be made for punching shear stress around the perimeter of the column. The shear stress should not exceed $0.8\sqrt{f_{cu}}$ or 5 N/mm^2 whichever is the lesser. In addition if the spacing of the piles is greater than 3ϕ, then the punching shear stress should be checked, as for slabs, on the perimeter as shown in Fig. 7.15.

EXAMPLE 7.7   Shear resistance of a pile cap

Check the pile cap shown in Fig. 7.15 for shear resistance and reinforce if necessary.

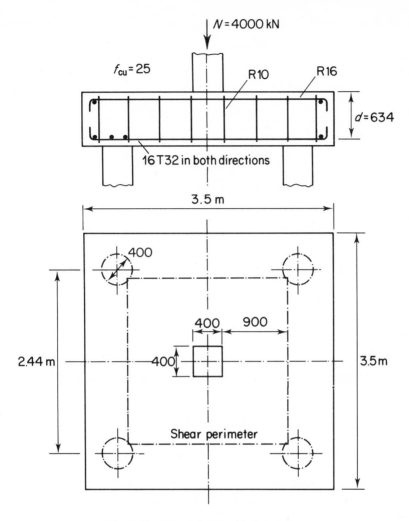

Fig. 7.15   Example of a pile foundation.

Check punching shear stress around the perimeter of the column

$$v = N/(ud) = 4E6/(4 \times 400 \times 634) = 3.94 \text{ N/mm}^2$$

Maximum design shear stress

$$v_u = 0.8\sqrt{f_{cu}} = 0.8\sqrt{25} = 4 \text{ N/mm}^2 < 5 \text{ N/mm}^2$$

$v_u(4) > v(3.94)$ N/mm^2, therefore the section is not too small.

   Spacing of piles $>3\phi$, therefore check shear stress on the shear perimeter (cl 3.11.4.3, Pt 1) shown in Fig. 7.15.

Total perimeter = 4(pile spacing -0.6ϕ)
$$= 4 \times (2440 - 0.6 \times 400) = 8800 \text{ mm}$$

$$v = N/(ud) = 4E6/(8800 \times 634) = 0.717 \text{ N/mm}^2.$$

Average shear stress across the width of the cap from shear force ($N/2$) (cl 3.11.4.3, Pt 1)

$$v = (N/2)/(b_v d) = 2E6/(3500 \times 634) = 0.901 \text{ N/mm}^2$$

Design shear stress for a singly reinforced concrete beam (cl 3.4.5.4, Pt 1)

$$\begin{aligned}
v_c &= k_1 k_2 0.79[100A_s/(b_v d)]^{1/3}(400/d)^{1/4}/\gamma_m \\
&= 1 \times 1 \times 0.79 \times [100 \times 12\,868/(3500 \times 634)]^{1/3} \times 1/1.25 \\
&= 0.527 \text{ N/mm}^2
\end{aligned}$$

Piles spaced at a distance $>3\phi$, therefore $k_1 = 1$ (cl 3.11.4.4, Pt 1), $400/d < 1$, therefore use 1, $100A_s/(b_v d) = 0.580 < 3\%$ (max.).

Shear reinforcement is required because $v(0.901) > v_c(0.527)$ N/mm^2 (cl 3.11.3.4, Pt 1).

$$v - v_c = 0.901 - 0.527 = 0.374 < 0.4, \text{ therefore use } 0.4 \text{ N/mm}^2$$

From Equation (7.4) assuming R10 (8 legs) vertical links

$$\begin{aligned}
s_v &= A_{sv} 0.87 f_{yv}/[b_v(v - v_c)] \\
&= 8 \times 79 \times 0.87 \times 250/[3500 \times 0.4] \\
&= 98.2 < 0.75d \ (475.5) \text{ mm, therefore satisfactory.}
\end{aligned}$$

Use R10-100 mm centres with R16 as compression reinforcement as shown in Fig. 7.15.

7.1.16   Shear resistance of columns (cls 3.8.4.6 and 3.4.5.12, Pt 1)

The design shear strength for columns is related to that for a singly reinforced beam, except that the axial force increases the shear resistance. For a column section without reinforcement

$$v_c' = v_c + 0.75(N/A_c)(Vd/M) < 0.8\sqrt{f_{cu}} < 5 \text{ N/mm}^2. \tag{7.8}$$

The value of Vd/M should not be taken as greater than 1.   The value v_c is the design shear strength for a singly reinforced concrete beam (cl 3.4.5.4, Pt 1) which may be enhanced for short shear spans.

For a section entirely in compression the distance d is from the most highly compressed face to the centroid of the reinforcement on the opposite face.

If $v > v_c'$ shear reinforcement should be provided as for beams (Table 3.8, cl 3.4.5.3, Pt 1)   (see Appendix A2.2).

For rectangular sections, no check is required where the ratio of bending moment to axial load (M/N) is less than $0.75 \times$ (greater dimension of the column section) provided the punching shear stress criterion is not exceeded, i.e. $v_u < 0.8\sqrt{f_{cu}}$ but not greater than 5 N/mm^2.

Generally shear stresses in columns are low except for special situations, e.g. columns subject to earthquake forces.

EXAMPLE 7.8   Shear resistance of a reinforced concrete column

Design the reinforced concrete column to resist the forces shown in Fig. 7.16.

$$M/N = 140E3/1500 = 93.3 \text{ mm}, \ 0.75h = 0.75 \times 500 = 375 \text{ mm}.$$

$M/N < 0.75h$, therefore no shear check is necessary (cl 3.8.4.6, Pt 1), nevertheless a check is carried out for demonstration purposes.

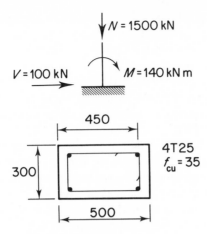

Fig. 7.16 Example of a column.

Average shear stress

$$v = V/(bd) = 100E3/(300 \times 450) = 0.741 \text{ N/mm}^2$$

Maximum design shear stress (cl 3.4.5.12, Pt 1)

$$v_u = 0.8\sqrt{f_{cu}} = 0.8 \times \sqrt{35} = 4.733 < 5 \text{ N/mm}^2$$

$v_u(4.733) > v(0.741)$ N/mm^2 therefore section not too small.

Design shear stress for a singly reinforced concrete beam (cl 3.4.5.4, Pt 1)

$$v_c = k_1 k_2 0.79[100A_s/(b_v d)]^{1/3}(400/d)^{1/4}/\gamma_m$$
$$= 1 \times (35/25)^{1/3} \times 0.79 \times [100 \times 982/(300 \times 450)]^{1/3} \times 1/1.25$$
$$= 0.636 \text{ N/mm}^2$$

$400/d < 1$, therefore use 1, $100A_v/(b_s d) = 0.737\% < 3\%$ (max.)

From Equation (7.8) the design shear stress for a column (cl 3.4.5.12, Pt 1)
$Vd/M = (100E3 \times 450/140E6) = 0.321 < 1$, therefore satisfactory.

$$v_c' = v_c + 0.75(N/A_c)(Vd/M)$$
$$= 0.636 + 0.75 \times [1500E3/(300 \times 500)] \times (100E3 \times 450/140E6)$$
$$= 3.047 < v_u(4.733) \text{ N/mm}^2, \text{ therefore satisfactory.}$$

$v < v_c'$, therefore no shear reinforcement necessary.

7.2 Torsional resistance of reinforced and prestressed concrete members

7.2.1 Introduction

Small torsional moments occur in many structures, e.g. corners of simply supported slabs, but these are of minor importance and a slab can be strengthened by adding additional longitudinal steel (cl 3.5.3.5, Pt 1). In a few situations, however, torsion is of major importance, e.g. edge beams supporting built-in floor slabs and helical staircases, and in these situations calculations are required to determine the reinforcement required to resist the torsional moments (cl 2.4.1, Pt 2).

In general torsional moments occur in conjunction with bending moments and shear forces. The section size is determined from consideration of resistance to the bending moment, and separate, apparently independent calculations are made in order to add reinforcement to resist the shear force and torsional moment. In reality the moments and forces interact but it is convenient in design to consider them separately.

Despite recent research the interaction of torsion, bending and shear is not fully understood and design recommendations are therefore empirical. The torsional strength of prestressed members is greater than that of ordinary reinforced concrete members, but BS 8110 recommends that the methods of design used for ordinary reinforced concrete should be applied to prestressed concrete (cl 4.3.9, Pt 1).

7.2.2   Modes of failure in torsion

The type of failure in torsion depends on the arrangement of reinforcement and the relative magnitudes of the torsional moment, bending moment and shear force.

The action of a pure torsional moment on a plain concrete member is to produce diagonal cracks at approximately 45° which result in failure on a skewed failure plane as shown in Fig. 7.17. Failure occurs as soon as major cracks form and plain concrete is of little use for structural members.

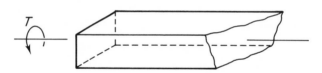

Fig. 7.17   Failure of a plain concrete in torsion.

The addition of longitudinal reinforcement strengthens the member when the ratio of bending moment to torsional moment is high ($M/T>4$), but has little strengthening effect when the ratio is low.

The addition of closed links to the longitudinal reinforcement, however, strengthens the member for the full range of M/T ratios, and it is this fact which forms the basis for design recommendations in BS 8110. There are three main modes of bending failure for members reinforced with longitudinal steel and links (Lessig 1959; Walsh *et al.* 1966) as follows.

Mode 1 type failure   This mode occurs when the M/T ratio is greater than 4 approximately. The mode of failure is comparable to that for pure bending, but the failure plane is skewed to the main longitudinal axis as shown in Fig. 7.18(a).

Mode 2 type failure   This mode occurs when the M/T ratio is less than 4 approximately. This also is a type of bending failure but with the compression zone at the side of the member as shown in Fig. 7.18(b).

Mode 3 type failure This mode occurs when the M/T ratio is less than 2 approximately. This also is a type of bending failure but with the compression zone at the bottom of the member as shown in Fig. 7.18(c). A requirement for this form of failure to occur is that the strength of the top longitudinal reinforcement is less than that for the bottom longitudinal reinforcement.

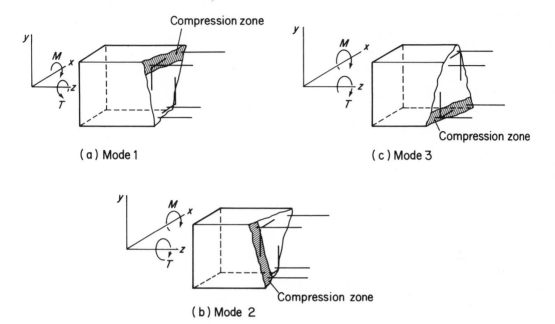

(a) Mode 1

(c) Mode 3

(b) Mode 2

Fig. 7.18 Modes of failure in torsion.

7.2.3 Torsional stiffness of a member (cl 2.4.3, Pt 2)

The elastic analysis of a hyperstatic structure involves the stiffness of the members. The bending stiffness is EI/L and the torsional stiffness is GC/L, where

> G = elastic shear modulus and is equal to 0.42E
>
> L = length of a member between joint centres
>
> C = torsional constant equal to half the St Venant value calculated for plain concrete.

The torsional constant C for a rectangular reinforced concrete section

> $C = 0.5\beta h_{min}^3 h_{max}$

The factor of 0.5 incorporated in the value of C makes allowance for warping by halving the polar second moment of area of the section. The value of the St Venant factor β is obtained from Table 7.1

Table 7.1 Values of the St Venant factor β (Table 2.2, cl 2.4.3, Pt 2)

h_{min}/h_{max}	1	1.5	2	3	5	>5
β	0.14	0.20	0.23	0.26	0.29	0.33

The St Venant torsional stiffness of a non-rectangular section may be obtained by dividing the section into a series of rectangles and summing the torsional stiffness of these rectangles. The division of the rectangles is arranged to maximise the calculated stiffness. This will generally be achieved if the widest rectangle is made as long as possible.

EXAMPLE 7.9   *Torsional stiffness of a member*

Determine the torsional stiffness of a member with a rectangular cross-section 150×300 mm, length between joint centres 4 m, and made of normal weight concrete with a cube strength at 28 days of 35 N/mm^2.

Static modulus of elasticity (cl 7.2, Pt 2)

$$E_{c,28} = K_0 + 0.2f_{cu,28}$$
$$= 20 + 0.2 \times 35 = 27 \text{ kN/mm}^2$$

Shear modulus (cl 2.4.3, Pt 2)

$$G = 0.42E = 0.42 \times 27 = 11.34 \text{ kN/mm}^2$$

Torsional constant (cl 2.4.3, Pt 2), $\beta = 0.23$ from Table 7.1

$$C = 0.5\beta h_{min}^3 h_{max}$$
$$= 0.5 \times 0.23 \times 150^3 \times 300 = 116.4\text{E}6 \text{ mm}^4$$

Torsional stiffness of the member

$$GC/L = 11.34 \times 116.4\text{E}6/4\text{E}3 \times 1\text{E}-3 = 330 \text{ kN m}$$

7.2.4   Torsional shear stress (cl 2.4.4, Pt 2)

To assess the torsional strength of a member it is convenient to calculate the torsional shear stress v_t. This quantity is comparable with the average shear stress v calculated when considering the shear strength of a member.

The torsional shear stress v_t at a section is calculated assuming a plastic stress distribution.

$$v_t = 2T/[h_{min}^2(h_{max} - h_{min}/3)] \tag{7.9}$$

The application of this formula to rectangular sections is straightforward, but it may also be applied to 'T', 'L', 'I' and box sections by dividing them into component rectangles (cl 2.4.4.2, Pt 2) as shown in the following example.   Box and other hollow sections in which the wall thicknesses exceed one-quarter of the overall thickness of the member in the direction of measurement may be treated as solid rectangular sections   (cl 2.4.4.3, Pt 2).

To avoid overstressing a cross-section in torsion there is a maximum design shear stress v_{tu} which is comparable with the punching shear stress limit of v_u for members subject to shear forces. When shear and torsion occur together then

$$v + v_t < v_{tu}$$

where the maximum design shear stress (cl 2.4.5, Pt 2) is

$$v_{tu} = 0.8\sqrt{f_{cu}} \text{ but not more than 5 N/mm}^2$$

For small sections where the larger link dimension $y_1 < 550$ mm

$$v_t < v_{tu} y_1 / 550$$

EXAMPLE 7.10   *Torsional shear stress in an 'L' section*

The 'L' shaped section shown in Fig. 7.19 is subject to a torsional moment of 100 kN m. Determine the maximum torsional shear stress v_t and compare with the maximum design shear stress v_{tu}.

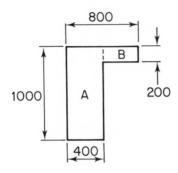

Fig. 7.19   Examples on torsional stress.

The area is subdivided into rectangles in order to maximise the function $\Sigma(h_{min}^3 h_{max})$. This is generally achieved by making the widest rectangle as long as possible (cl 2.4.4.2, Pt 2).

Proportion of the torsional moment ($T = 100$ kN m) resisted by area A

$$\begin{aligned} T_A &= T(h_{min}^3 h_{max})/\Sigma(h_{min}^3 h_{max}) \\ &= 100 \times (400^3 \times 1000)/(400^3 \times 1000 + 200^3 \times 400) \\ &= 95.24 \text{ kN m} \end{aligned}$$

Maximum torsional shear stress v_{tA} in rectangle A from Equation (7.9)

$$\begin{aligned} v_{tA} &= 2T_A/[h_{min}^2(h_{max} - h_{min}/3)] \\ &= 2 \times 95.24\text{E}6/[400^2 \times (1000 - 400/3)] \\ &= 1.37 \text{ N/mm}^2 \end{aligned}$$

This value is less than the maximum design shear stress (cl 2.4.5, Pt 2)

$$v_{tu} = 0.8\sqrt{f_{cu}} = 0.8 \times \sqrt{30} = 4.38 \text{ N/mm}^2 < 5 \text{ N/mm}^2$$

7.2.5   Torsion reinforcement (cls 2.4.6 and 2.4.7, Pt 2)

Plain concrete is able to resist a small torsional moment but for safety   where the torsional shear stress v_t exceeds $v_{tmin} = 0.067\sqrt{f_{cu}}$, shear reinforcement should be provided.   Recommendations in BS 8110 for reinforcement for combinations of shear and torsion are summarised in Appendix A2.2.5. The torsional reinforcement is in the form of closed links identical in shape and additional to those required for shear reinforcement.

BS 8110 considers the design for bending shear and tension as separate methods but in reality they are interactive. Until full understanding is achieved it is convenient, but not strictly accurate, to consider torsion as a separate event as follows.

If a member, reinforced with longitudinal steel and single links, is subject to a torsional moment, then cracks appear in the concrete at an angle of approximately 45° on each face and spiralling along the length of the member as shown in Fig. 7.20.

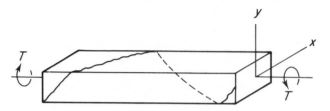

Fig. 7.20   Torsion cracks.

If a section (see Fig. 7.18) is taken through the member, then from equilibrium about the longitudinal axis assuming 45° cracks in the concrete in all faces

$$T = T_o + A_{sv} f_{sv} x_1 y_1 / s_v$$

where A_{sv} is the cross-sectional area of two legs of a link.

Experiments (Hsu 1968) recorded values for T_o which are less than half the torsional strength of plain concrete. T_o is related to the shape of the cross-section and the tensile strength of the concrete but this quantity is ignored in BS 8110. The recorded tensile strains in the links were not always at yield in the experiments by Hsu, but varied with the ratio of h_{max}/h_{min}. To form a lower bound to the experimental results and to be able to use the yield strength of the links the equation given in (cl 2.4.7, Pt 2) is

$$T = 0.8 A_{sv} 0.87 f_{yv} x_1 y_1 / s_v$$

This can be rearranged for design purposes to determine the ratio

$$A_{sv}/s_v = T/(0.8 x_1 y_1 0.87 f_{yv}) \tag{7.10}$$

Equilibrium must also be satisfied about an axis transverse to the length of the member. If moments are taken about the xx axis shown in Fig. 7.18,

$$(A_s/2) f_y y_1 = (A_{sv}/2) f_{sv} (x_1 + y_1) y_1 / s_v$$

where A_s is the cross-sectional area of total the longitudinal steel.

Rearranging produces the equation given in cl 2.4.7, Pt 2

$$A_s = A_{sv} f_{yv} (x_1 + y_1)/(s_v f_y) \tag{7.11}$$

The values of f_y and f_{yv} should not be greater than 460 N/mm².

Note that in Equation (7.11) the material factors for the longitudinal steel and link steel cancel and therefore do not appear in the equation. The same equation can be obtained if moments are taken about the yy axis. The equation states that there must be longitudinal steel to balance any links that are added. The longitudinal steel required to resist torsion must be in addition to the longitudinal steel required to resist the bending moment.

7.2.6 Arrangement of torsion reinforcement (cls 2.4.8–2.4.10, Pt 2)

Careful detailing of the reinforcement is required if it is to be effective. To intercept the diagonal cracks in the concrete the spacing of the links s_v should not exceed the least of x_1, $y_1/2$ or 200 mm. The links should be of the closed type with the shape, i.e. those shown in Fig. 7.4(b).

The links in 'T', 'L' or 'I' sections should be arranged into component rectangles detailed so that they interlock and tie together. Where the torsional shear stress in a minor component rectangle does not exceed $v_{t\,min}$, no torsion reinforcement need be provided in that rectangle.

The longitudinal torsional reinforcement must be distributed evenly round the inside perimeter of the links to prevent a mode 3 type failure as shown in Fig. 7.18(c). The clear distance between bars should not exceed 300 mm and at least four bars, one in each corner of the links, should be used. Additional longitudinal reinforcement required at the level of the tension or compression reinforcement may be provided by using larger bars than those required to resist bending alone.

The torsion reinforcement should extend a distance equal to the largest dimension of the section beyond where it theoretically ceases to be required. This requirement is because torsion cracks spiral for considerable lengths along a member and in addition abrupt changes of reinforcement should be avoided.

EXAMPLE 7.11   Torsion reinforcement

A rectangular section of a beam is subject to a torsional moment $T = 50$ kN m. The cross-section is 600 mm deep and 300 mm wide, $f_{cu} = 30$ N/mm^2 and $f_{yv} = 250$ N/mm^2. Determine the torsion reinforcement required.

The area of tensile reinforcement required from bending calculations not included here is $A_s = 1200$ mm^2, assuming $f_y = 250$ N/mm^2

Check if section is too small to resist the torsional moment.

Maximum torsional shear stress (cl 2.4.4.1, Pt 2) from Equation (7.9)

$$v_t = 2T/[h_{min}^2(h_{max} - h_{min}/3)]$$
$$= 2 \times 50\text{E}6/[300^2 \times (600 - 300/3)] = 2.222 \text{ N/mm}^2$$

Maximum design shear stress (cl 2.4.5, Pt 2)

$$v_{tu} = 0.8\sqrt{f_{cu}} = 0.8\sqrt{30} = 4.382 \text{ N/mm}^2 \leqslant 5 \text{ N/mm}^2$$

$v_{tu}(4.382) > v_t(2.222)$ N/mm^2, therefore section is not too small.

Calculations for torsion reinforcement.

From Equation (7.10)

$$A_{sv}/s_v = T/(0.8x_1\,y_1 0.87 f_{yv})$$
$$= 50\text{E}6/(0.8 \times 230 \times 500 \times 0.87 \times 250) = 2.499 \text{ mm}$$

Try R10 single links

$$s_v = A_{sv}/2.499 = 2 \times 79/2.499 = 63 \text{ mm}$$

The spacing of the links s_v does not exceed the least of $x_1(230)$, $y_1/2(250)$, or 200 mm (cl 2.4.8, Pt 2).
Use single R10-60 mm centres.

Extra area of longitudinal steel required to resist torsion (cl 2.4.7, Pt 2).

$$A_s = A_{sv} f_{yv}(x_1 + y_1)/(s_v f_y)$$
$$= 2.499 \times (230 + 500) = 1824 \text{ mm}^2$$

It is not possible to use 4 bars, i.e. one in each corner of the link, because the vertical spacing would exceed 300 mm (cl 2.4.9, Pt 2). Therefore use 6R20 = 1885 mm². Two of these bars can be combined with the tension reinforcement.

Total area of tension steel

$$A_s = 1200 + 1885/3 = 1828 \text{ mm}^2$$

Use as tension reinforcement 6R20 (1885 mm²)
The arrangement of the reinforcement in the section is shown in Fig. 7.21.

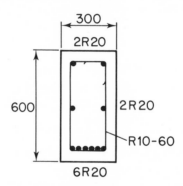

Fig. 7.21 Example of torsion reinforcement.

7.3 Tutorial problems

7.3.1 Shear resistance of a singly reinforced beam

Determine the design ultimate shear resistance of the singly reinforced concrete section shown in Fig. 7.22, without shear enhancement.

Answer
$v_c = 0.806 \text{ N/mm}^2$, $V = 36.27 \text{ kN}$

7.3.2 Average shear stress for sections

Determine the average shear stress for the sections shown in Fig. 7.23, and state whether shear reinforcement is required.

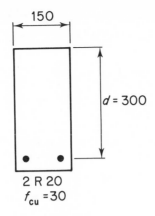

150

d = 300

2 R 20
f_{cu} = 30

Fig. 7.22

Answers
(a) $v(4.444) > v_u(4)$ N/mm^2, therefore increase size of section.
(b) $d = 383.3$ mm, $v(2.935) < v_u(4.382)$ N/mm^2, $v_c = 0.916$ N/mm^2, $v > v_c + 0.4$ N/mm^2, therefore shear reinforcement required.

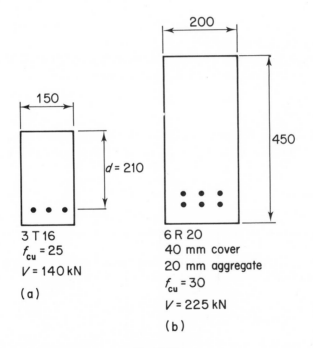

200

150

450

d = 210

3 T 16
f_{cu} = 25
V = 140 kN

(a)

6 R 20
40 mm cover
20 mm aggregate
f_{cu} = 30
V = 225 kN

(b)

Fig. 7.23

7.3.3   Vertical shear links

The sections shown in Fig. 7.24 are subject to shear forces at the ultimate limit state as shown. Determine the spacing of T8 single links.

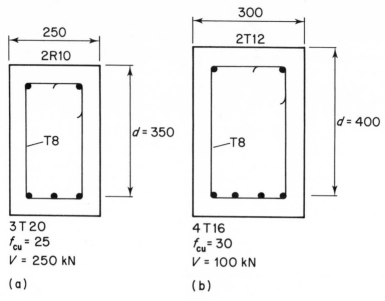

Fig. 7.24

Answers

(a) $v(2.857) < v_u(4)$ N/mm^2, $v_c = 0.670$ N/mm^2, $s_v = 73.2$ mm, use single T8-60 mm centres shear reinforcement.

(b) $v(0.833) < v_u(4.382)$ N/mm^2, $v_c = 0.588$ N/mm^2, $s_v = 333.5 > 0.75d$ (300) mm, use T8-300 mm centres, minimum shear reinforcement.

7.3.4   Bent-up bars

Determine the spacing of T8 double links for the beam section shown in Fig. 7.25. Two of the bottom bars are bent up at 45°, and a further two at a distance of $s_b = 250$ mm.

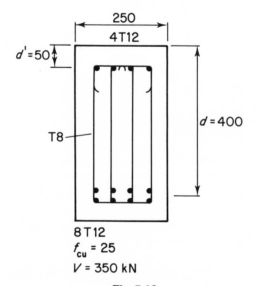

Fig. 7.25

Answer
$v(3.5) < v_u(4)$ N/mm^2, $v_c = 0.485$ N/mm^2, $v + v_c + 0.4$ N/mm^2, therefore shear reinforcement required; $V_b = 63.95$ kN $< V/2$, $s_v = 134.8$ mm, use double T8-120 mm centres.

7.3.5   Pad foundation

Design for shear at the ultimate limit state the pad foundation shown in Fig. 7.26, which is subject to an axial load which produces uniform pressure beneath the base.

Answer
Column perimeter $v(1.379) < v_u(3.578)$ N/mm^2; 1.5d perimeter $v(0.0818) < v_c(0.324)$ N/mm^2, width $v(0.105) < v_c(0.324)$; 0.75d perimeter $v(0.250) < v_c(0.649)$ N/mm^2, width $v(0.180) < v_c(0.649)$ N/mm^2. No shear reinforcement required.

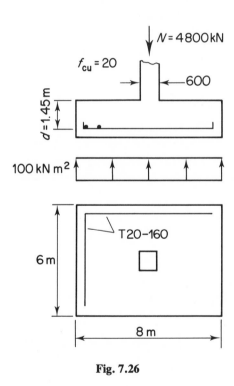

Fig. 7.26

7.3.6   Column in shear

Design for shear at the ultimate limit state the column shown in Fig. 7.27 and determine the spacing of T8 single links.

Answer
$M/N > 0.75h$, $v(1.212) < v_u(4.382)$ N/mm^2, $v_c = 0.557$ N/mm^2, $v'_c = 1.092$ N/mm^2, $s_v = 336.8$ mm, max. $s_v = 12\phi = 240$ mm, use T8-240.

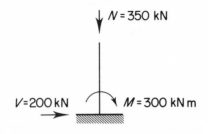

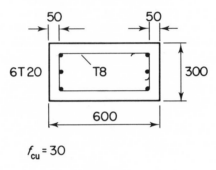

$f_{cu} = 30$

Fig. 7.27

7.3.7 Torsional stiffness

Determine the torsional stiffness of the member of length 5 m which has a cross-section as shown in Fig. 7.28. The member is made from normal-weight concrete with a strength of $f_{cu} = 30$ N/mm^2 at 28 days.

Answer
$E = 26$ kN/mm^2, $G = 10.92$ kN/mm^2, $\Sigma GC/L = 4202$ kN m

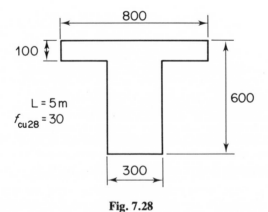

Fig. 7.28

7.3.8 Torsion reinforcement

The beam section shown in Fig. 7.29 is subject to a torsional moment of $T = 20$ kN m at the ultimate limit state. Determine the reinforcement required if $f_{cu} = 30$ N/mm² and $f_y = 460$ N/mm².

Answer
$v_t(3.840) < v_{tu}(4.382)$ N/mm², for T10 links $s_v = 117$ mm, use T10-100 mm centres, $A_s = 580.9$ mm², $y/2 = 107.5$ mm, use 4T16.

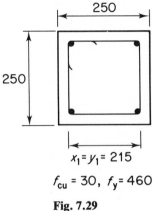

$x_1 = y_1 = 215$

$f_{cu} = 30$, $f_y = 460$

Fig. 7.29

References

ASCE–ACI Committee 426 (1973). The shear strength of reinforced concrete structures. *Proc. ASCE*, **99** (ST6), 1091–187.

Chana P. S. (July 1981). *Some aspects of modelling the behaviour of reinforced concrete under shear loading*, Technical Report 543, Cement and Concrete Association, p. 22.

Evans R. H. and Kong F. K. (1967). Shear design and British Code CP 114, *Structural Engineer*, **45** (4), 153–87.

Hsu T. T. C. (1968). *Torsion of structural concrete – behaviour of reinforced rectangular members*, Special Publication, No 18–10, ACI, Detroit, pp. 261–306.

Kong F. K. (1978). *Bending, shear and torsion* (Chapter 1, Developments in prestressed concrete) Applied Science, London, Vol. 1, pp. 1–68.

Kreyfield W. J. and Thurston C. W. (1966). *Studies of the shear and diagonal tension strength of simply supported reinforced concrete beams*, ACIJ.

Lessig N. N. (1959). *The determination of the load bearing capacity of rectangular reinforced concrete sections subject to combined torsion and bending*. Study No 5, Concrete and Reinforced Concrete Institute, Moscow, pp. 5–28.

Shear Study Group (1969). *The shear strength of reinforced concrete beams*, ISE, London, p. 170.

Taylor H. P. J. (1974). The fundamental behaviour of reinforced concrete beams in bending and shear, *Proc. ACI–ASCE Shear Symposium, Ottawa*, ACI Publication SP 42, ACIJ, Detroit, pp. 43–77.

Walsh P. E., Collins M. P., Archer F. E., and Hall A. S. (1966). The ultimate strength design of rectangular reinforced concrete beams subjected to combined torsion, bending and shear, *Trans. ICE* (Australia), 143–57.

8

Anchorage, Bar Connections, Curtailment and Member Connections

8.1 Anchorage

8.1.1 Introduction

Reinforcing bars are produced in stock lengths, e.g. approximately 6 m for 8 mm diameter, and 12 m for 32 mm diameter. These stock lengths may be cut or terminated for the following reasons:

(a) to fit the member,
(b) to economise in steel, e.g. curtailment of bars in order to use fewer bars where the bending moment decreases along the length of a member,
(c) to make construction easier.

A bar may be terminated as a straight, or 90° bend, or a 180° bend as shown in Fig. 8.1.

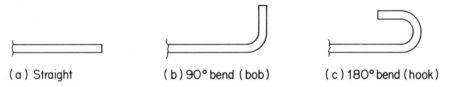

(a) Straight   (b) 90° bend (bob)   (c) 180° bend (hook)

Fig. 8.1 Termination of bars.

A reinforcing bar must be adequately anchored, otherwise it will withdraw from the concrete before it has reached its full tensile strength. The greater the angle change at the end of the bar the more effective the anchorage, but this is offset by the greater cost for shaping. Anchorage is also affected by the surface of the bar. The rougher the surface of the bar the better the bond between the concrete and the steel.

8.1.2 Anchorage of straight bars (cl 3.12.8.3, Pt 1)

The withdrawal of a straight bar, with adequate cover and embedded in concrete, is prevented by the bond shear stresses between the surface of the bar and the concrete.

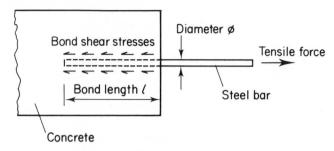

Fig. 8.2   Anchorage of a straight bar.

If for a bar the bond shear stresses are assumed to be uniformly distributed as shown in Fig. 8.2, then from the equilibrium of forces at ultimate load

tensile force in bar = bond shear force

$$F_s = \pi\phi_e l f_b \quad \text{(Equation 48, Pt 1)} \tag{8.1}$$

where

f_b is the bond stress between the steel and the concrete, which varies with the surface condition of the bar, strength of the concrete and whether the bar is in tension of compression;

F_s is the force in the bar or group of bars;

l is the anchorage length;

ϕ_e is the effective bar size which, for a single bar, is equal to the bar size and, for a group of bars in contact, is equal to the diameter of a bar of equal total area.

Values for the design ultimate anchorage bond stress may be obtained from the equation

$$f_{bu} = \beta\sqrt{f_{cu}} \quad \text{(Equation 49, Pt 1)} \tag{8.2}$$

where

f_{bu} is the design ultimate bond stress;

β is a coefficient dependent on the bar type.

For bars in tension in slabs or beams where minimum links have been provided in accordance with Table 3.8, the following values may be taken for β. These values include a partial safety factor (γ_m) of 1.4   (cl 3.12.8.4, Pt 1).

Table 8.1   (Table 3.28, Pt 1)   Values of the bond coefficient β

Bar type	β Bars in tension	Bars in compression
Plain bars	0.28	0.35
Type 1: deformed bars	0.40	0.50
Type 2: deformed bars	0.50	0.63
Fabric (see cl 3.12.8.5, Pt 1)	0.65	0.81

In beams where where minimum links in accordance with Table 3.8 (see **Appendix**

A2.2) have not been provided, the design anchorage bond stresses used should be appropriate to plain bars irrespective of the type used. This does not apply to slabs.

As perhaps would be expected the lowest value in Table 8.1 is for a plain bar in tension, and the value of $0.28\sqrt{f_{cu}}$ is slightly greater than the design tensile strength of surrounding concrete. A plain bar, in tension, withdraws from concrete without cracking or splitting the concrete. Bars in compression are allotted higher bond strengths because the bar diameter increases in compression due to Poisson's ratio effect, and also because of end-bearing.

Deformed bars are more difficult to withdraw from concrete because their surfaces are rougher. A Type 2 deformed (ribbed) bar is shown in Fig. 8.3. At bond failure a deformed bar splits and cracks the surrounding concrete, producing a volume change in the concrete (Reynolds 1982). Despite the different failure mechanism the ultimate bond strength is also related to the tensile strength of the concrete, although as expected, the values are greater than for plain bars.

Fig. 8.3 Type 2 deformed (ribbed) bar.

Welded mesh reinforcement is more difficult to withdraw from concrete because of the transverse reinforcement, and therefore the design bond stresses are increased, provided the fabric is manufactured to BS 4461 and 4482.

For design purposes the anchorage length for a straight bar can be expressed in terms of the bar diameter. Rearranging Equation (8.1) the anchorage length

$$l = F_s/(\pi\phi_e f_b)$$

Substituting $F_s = (\pi\phi_e^2/4)0.87f_y$ and combining with Equation (8.2)

$$l = \phi_e 0.87f_y/(4\beta\sqrt{f_{cu}}) \tag{8.3}$$

8.1.3   Anchorage using bends or hooks (cl 3.12.8.22, Pt 1)

Where there is insufficient length available for anchorage of a straight bar then a 90°, or 180° bend, is used. Standard types of bend for low- and high-strength steels are shown in Fig. 8.4 and it should be noted that the standard extension, beyond the last bend, is 4ϕ.

To prevent overstraining and cracking of the bar the radii of the bends should not be too small. The minimum internal radius for the mild-steel bar is 2ϕ and for the high-yield bar it is 3ϕ for less than 20 mm diameter and 4ϕ for greater than 20 mm diameter. Generally these radii are adopted in practice.

The equivalent anchorage for each bend and hook (cl 3.12.8.23, Pt 1) is also given in Fig. 8.4 in terms of bar diameters. This is useful information for design purposes to be used in conjunction with Equation (8.3).

In practice the use of bends and hooks is kept to a minimum because of the cost involved in their formation. Although improved bond characteristics of bars has reduced the use of bends and hooks they are still required, e.g. the ends of simply supported

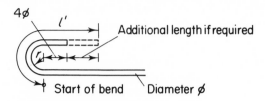

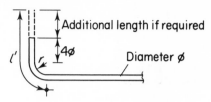

(a) Effective anchorage length, for a hook
$l = 8r \le 24\phi$ or $l = l'$,
whichever is the greater.
Minimum for:
mild steel, $r = 2\phi$, $l = 8r = 16\phi$
high strength, $r = 3\phi$, $l = 8r = 24\phi$
high strength $r = 4\phi$, $l = 8r = 32\phi$

(b) Effective anchorage length for a bend
$l = 4r \le 12\phi$ or $l = l'$,
whichever is the greater
Minimum for:
mild steel, $r = 2\phi$, $l = 4r = 8\phi$
high strength, $r = 3\phi$, $l = 4r = 12\phi$
high strength, $r = 4\phi$, $l = 4r = 16\phi$

Fig. 8.4   Effective anchorage lengths (cl 3.12.8.23, Pt 1).

beams, starter bars in bases, links, bent-up shear reinforcement, member connections, etc., as shown in Section 8.4.

8.1.4   Bearing stresses inside bends (cl 3.12.8.25, Pt 1)

Where bars are bent or hooked to provide the required bond length then bearing stresses are introduced on the inside of the bend as shown in Fig. 8.5.

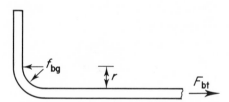

Fig. 8.5   Bearing stresses inside bends.

Bearing stresses need not be checked:

(a)   where the bar does not extend beyond a point four bar diameters past the end of the bend;
(b)   where the bar is assumed not to be stressed beyond a point four bar diameters past the end of the bend at the ultimate limit state.

An increase in the extension of the bar greater than 4ϕ past the end of the bend increases the bearing stresses f_{bg} inside the bend (see Fig. 8.5) and the design bearing stress is calculated from the following relation:

bearing stress = $F_{bt}/(r\phi) \le 2f_{cu}/[1 + 2(\phi/a_b)]$ (Equation 50, Pt 1)   (8.4)

where

F_{bt} is the tensile force due to the ultimate loads in a bar or group of bars in contact at the start of a bend;

r is the internal radius of the bend;

ϕ is the size of the bar (or, for a group, the size of a bar of equivalent area);

a_b for a given bar (or group of bars in contact) is the centre-to-centre distance between bars (or groups of bars) perpendicular to the plane of the bend; for a bar or group of bars adjacent to the face of the member, a_b should be taken as the cover plus ϕ.

Equation (8.4) incorporates a materials factor γ_m and the basis of the equation is as follows:

A 90° bend is shown in Fig. 8.5 and to maintain equilibrium

force in steel = projected area of bar at bend × concrete bearing stress
$$F_{bt} = r\phi f_{bg}$$

rearranging and presenting in the form shown in BS 8110,

$$F_{bt}/(r\phi) = f_{bg}$$

The bearing strength, f_{bg}, is approximately twice the cube-crushing strength of the concrete f_{cu} for small ratios of bearing area/total area (Williams 1979). However, if a bar is near the surface, or close to another bar, the bearing strength has been found experimentally to be reduced by a factor related to the ratio ϕ/a_b. This ratio is incorporated in Equation (8.4).

EXAMPLE 8.1   Anchorage of a bar

A bar is anchored by a hook as shown in Fig. 8.4(a). If the bar is stressed to the design tensile strength, determine (a) the minimum radius r (b) the additional straight length required at the end of the curve. Assume $f_{cu} = 30$ N/mm^2 and the spacing of the bars $a_b = \phi$.

(a)   *Minimum radius*
Rearranging Equation (8.4)

$$r\phi = F_{bt}[1 + 2(\phi/a_b)]/(2f_{cu})$$

Design tensile force in a bar

$$F_{bt} = (\pi\phi^2/4)0.87f_y$$

Combining these two equations and rearranging

$$r/\phi = (\pi/4)0.87f_y[1 + 2(\phi/a_b)]/(2f_{cu})$$

Inserting numerical values:
Mild steel: $r/\phi = (\pi/4) \times 0.87 \times 250 \times 3/(2 \times 30) = 8.54$
High-yield steel: $r/\phi = (\pi/4) \times 0.87 \times 460 \times 3/(2 \times 30) = 15.72$

(b)   *Additional straight length*
From Equation (8.3)

$$l_s = l - \pi r = \phi_e 0.87f_y/(4\beta\sqrt{f_{cu}}) - \pi r$$

Using the values of r/ϕ obtained from part (a) the extra bond lengths are as follows:

Plain mild steel:

$$l_s = \phi \times 0.87 \times 250/(4 \times 0.28 \times \sqrt{30}) - \pi \times 8.54 \times \phi = 8.63\phi$$

Plain high-yield steel:

$$l_s = \phi \times 0.87 \times 460/(4 \times 0.28 \times \sqrt{30}) - \pi \times 15.72 \times \phi = 15.85\phi$$

Type 1 high-yield steel:

$$l_s = \phi \times 0.87 \times 460/(4 \times 0.40 \times \sqrt{30}) - \pi \times 15.72 \times \phi = -3.71\phi,$$

i.e. not required theoretically but use minimum of 4ϕ.

Type 2 high-yield steel:

$$l_s = \phi \times 0.87 \times 460/(4 \times 0.50 \times \sqrt{30}) - \pi \times 15.72 \times \phi = -12.85\phi,$$

i.e. not required theoretically but use minimum of 4ϕ.

8.2 Bar connections

8.2.1 Introduction (cls 3.12.8.9–3.12.8.21, Pt 1)

In reinforced concrete construction connections between the ends of bars are required to extend their length or to facilitate construction.

Connections transferring stress may be lapped, welded or joined with mechanical devices (Ciria Report 92). They should be placed, if possible, away from points of high stress and should preferably be staggered. Laps in fabric may be layered or nested to maintain the lapped bars in one plane   (cl 3.12.8.9 Pt 1).

The various types of bar connection are shown in Fig. 8.6.

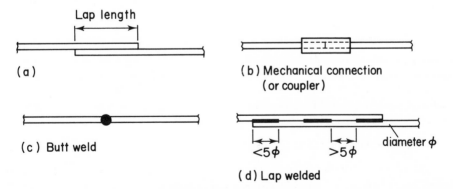

Fig. 8.6 Bar connections.

8.2.2 Tension lap connections (cl 3.12.8.13, Pt 1)

The simplest, cheapest and most common type of connection is the lapped joint shown in Fig. 8.6(a). The force in one bar is transferred to the other by bond between the steel and the concrete. Therefore the lap length should be at least equal to the design tension anchorage length obtained from Equation (8.3).   If bars of different diameter are lapped then the lap length is based on the smaller diameter bar.   At first sight this may seem illogical, but if at a lap the smaller bar diameter (ϕ_{min}) is stressed to its design strength, the larger bar (ϕ_{max}) will be at a lower stress and consequently the bond length will be reduced to

$$l = \phi_{max}0.87(\phi_{min}/\phi_{max})^2 f_y/(4\beta\sqrt{f_{cu}})$$

This is less than the bond length required for the smaller bar.

In practice some bars are not highly stressed and the lap length therefore could be reduced according to Equation (8.3). This could lead to very small lap lengths and therefore a minimum is specified.   The minimum lap length for bar reinforcement should not be less than 15 times the bar size or 300 mm, whichever is the greater, and for fabric reinforcement should not be less than 250 mm   (cl 3.12.8.11, Pt 1).

The bond values for laps depend on the existence of adequate cover, especially for deformed bars. Where cover is inadequate the situation can be improved by links which envelop the longitudinal reinforcement and increase the tensile bursting strength of the concrete.   Where both bars at a lap exceed size 20 and the cover is less than 1.5 times the size of the smaller bar, transverse links should be provided throughout the lap length. At the lap the links should be at least one quarter the size of the smaller bar and the spacing should not exceed 200 mm   (cl 3.12.8.12, Pt 1).

In addition to satisfying the above where there is inadequate cover the following clauses apply (cl 3.12.8.13, Pt 1)

(a)   where a lap occurs at the top of a section as cast and the minimum cover is less than twice the size of the lapped reinforcement, the lap length should be increased by a factor of 1.4;
(b)   where a lap occurs at the corner of a section and the minimum cover to either face is less than twice the size of the lapped reinforcement, or where the clear distance between adjacent laps is less than 75 mm or six times the size of the lapped reinforcement, whichever is the greater, the lap length should be increased by a factor of 1.4;
(c)   in cases where both conditions (a) and (b) apply, the lap length should be increased by a factor of 2.0.

Where a lap occurs in the length of a member, the percentage reinforcement relative to the cross-section is increased. In particular at the level of the reinforcement, the width occupied by the reinforcement may be excessive and reduce the bond. Consequently   at laps, the sum of the reinforcement sizes in a particular layer should not exceed 40% of the breadth of the section at that level   (cl 3.12.8.14, Pt 1).

8.2.3 Compression lap connections

When bars are in compression the design lap length required is greater than that given by Equation (8.3) because of local buckling of the bars.   The length should be at least 25% greater   (cl 3.12.8.15, Pt 1). The increase has the effect of making the actual lap length equal for both tension and compression because in Equation (8.3), β for compression bars is 20% less than for tension bars.

8.2.4 Mechanical connections

The type of coupling sleeve shown in Fig. 8.6(b) is not in common use but is allowed for bars in compression provided the sawn square cut ends are held in concentric contact (cl 3.12.8.16.1, Pt 1). The coupler saves on length of steel and reduces congestion of the bars, but these advantages are offset by the disadvantages of cost and the reduced concrete cover of the coupling. This type of coupler is also allowed for use for bars in tension provided it meets the requirements stated in cl 3.12.8.16.2, Pt 1.

8.2.5 Welded connections (cls 3.12.8.17–3.12.8.21, Pt 1)

Welded connections are not often used on site because of the disadvantages of cost and supervision required. However, if carried out correctly, welding is capable of producing a full strength connection. The following recommendations are made (cl 3.12.8.17, Pt 1):

(a) welded joints should not occur at bends;
(b) where possible, joints in parallel bars of the principal tensile reinforcement should be staggered in the longitudinal direction.

(a) Butt-welded connections (cl 3.12.8.18, Pt 1)
Where cover to bars and congestion of reinforcement is a problem then butt-welding bars, end to end, is a solution, as shown in Fig. 8.6(c).

The following values may be used where the strength of the weld has been proved by tests to be at least as great as that of the parent bar.

(a) *Joints in compression.* 100% of the design strength of the joined bars.
(b) *Joints in tension.* 80% of the design strength of the joined bars (100% if the welding is strictly supervised and if at any cross-section of the member not more than 20% of the tensile reinforcement is welded).

(b) Lap-welded connections (cls 3.12.8.20 and 3.12.8.21, Pt 1)
Lap connections connected by fillet welds are permitted as shown in Fig. 8.6(d). They are intended for use where prefabricated cages of reinforcement, or mesh, are placed in a shutter and welded together in place. Alternatively they may be used for the steel connections for precast reinforced concrete elements.

The length of the weld should be sufficient to transmit the design load in the bar. The length of the weld run should not normally exceed five times the size of the bar. If a longer weld is required, it should be divided into sections and the space between runs made not less than five times the size of the bar.

8.3 Curtailment of reinforcing bars

8.3.1 Introduction

Curtailment of reinforcing bars is the stopping of some of the reinforcing bars in tension, or compression, where they are no longer needed for strength purposes. Curtailment can be applied to simply supported beams but it is generally not economic and the real advantages occur with repetitive multispan beams and slabs. It can also be used to facilitate construction by curtailing bars to practical lengths which are easier to handle.

However, the saving in steel is off-set by increased design calculations, detailing, and site supervision.

8.3.2 Theoretical curtailment (cl 3.12.9.2, Pt 1)

A part of a beam subject to a bending moment which varies along its length is shown in Fig. 8.7.

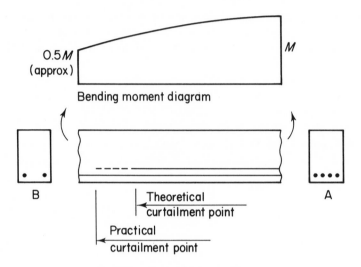

Fig. 8.7 Theoretical curtailment.

At section A the bending moment is a maximum and (say) four bars are required in tension. Further along the beam at section B the bending moment has reduced to approximately half and only two bars are required in the tension zone to resist the bending moment. The bars are shown in Fig. 8.7 at different levels in the elevation for purposes of illustration. Theoretically two bars can be stopped, or curtailed, at this section.   The point at which a bar is no longer required is the point where the design resistance moment of the section, considering only the continuing bars, is equal to the design moment.

8.3.3 Practical curtailment (cl 3.12.9.1–3.12.9.3, Pt 1)

A bar must extend beyond the point at which it is theoretically no longer required for the following reasons:

(a) Curtailed bars, if not extended, would be at the design strength.
(b) Large cracks may appear at the curtailment section because of the abrupt change in section properties. This may reduce the shear strength of the member and therefore it is advisable to stagger the curtailment points in heavily reinforced members.
(c) To allow for inaccuracies in loading and theoretical analysis.
(d) To allow for inaccuracies in placing bars.

The general requirements for practical curtailment are given in Fig. 8.8. Three special requirements for bars in tension are given, but only one requirement needs to be satisfied, and in practice the bond condition is selected because this involves less calculation as can be seen in the following example.

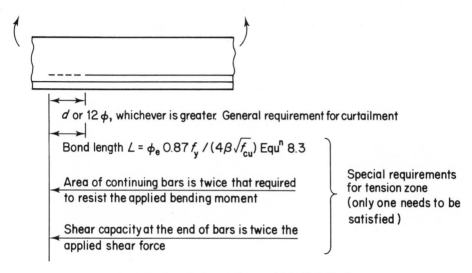

Fig. 8.8   Practical curtailment (cl 3, 12.9, Pt 1).

EXAMPLE 8.2   Curtailment of bars

Determine (a) the theoretical and (b) practical curtailment point for 2-T20 (type 2) bars for the cantilever beam shown in Fig. 8.9. Breadth of the beam $b = 300$ mm, $d = 700$ mm, and $f_{cu} = 25$ N/mm^2.

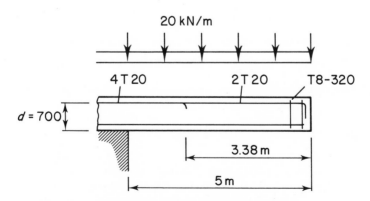

Fig. 8.9   Example: curtailment of bars.

(a) The theoretical curtailment point (cl 3.12.9.2, Pt 1) occurs where the bending moment can be resisted by two 2-T20 (type 2) reinforcing bars.

Depth of compression zone (cl 3.4.4.4, Pt 1)

$$x = A_s 0.87 f_y / [0.9b(0.67/1.5)f_{cu}]$$
$$= 628 \times 0.87 \times 460 / [0.9 \times 300 \times (0.67/1.5) \times 25]$$
$$= 83.4 \text{ mm}$$

Lever arm

$$z = d - 0.45x = 700 - 0.45 \times 83.4 = 662.5 \text{ mm}$$

Moment of resistance of the section

$$M_r = A_s 0.87 f_y z$$
$$= 628 \times 0.87 \times 460 \times 662.5 \times 1\text{E-}6 = 166.5 \text{ kN m}$$

At a distance s from the end of the cantilever the bending moment

$$M_s = ws^2/2 = 20s^2/2$$

If the moment of resistance M_r equals the bending moment M_s

$$M_r = M_s$$
$$166.5 = 10s^2; \text{ hence } s = 4.08 \text{ m}$$

The theoretical curtailment point for the 2-T20 bars is 4.08 m from the end of the cantilever.

(b) The practical curtailment point is obtained from the requirements shown in Fig. 8.8.

From the general conditions the extension is the greater value of

$$12\phi = 12 \times 20 = 240 \text{ mm}$$
$$d = 700 \text{ mm}$$

Distance of the practical curtailment point from the end of the cantilever

$$s' = s - d = 4.08 - 0.7 = 3.38 \text{ m.}$$

From the special conditions for the curtailment of bars in the tension zone:

Bond length from Equation (8.3)

$$l = \phi_e 0.87 f_y / (4\beta \sqrt{f_{cu}})$$
$$= 20 \times 0.87 \times 460 / (4 \times 0.65 \times \sqrt{25}) = 615.7 \text{ mm}$$

Distance of the practical curtailment point from the end of the cantilever

$$s' = s - l = 4.08 - 0.62 = 3.46 \text{ m.}$$

Moment of resistance at the end of the continuing bars is twice the design bending moment

$$M_r = 2M_s$$
$$M_r = 2w(s')^2/2$$
$$166.5 = 2 \times 20(s')^2/2; \text{ hence } s' = 2.89 \text{ m}$$

Shear resistance at the end of the continuing bars. Shear stress from the loading at a distance s' from the end of the cantilever

$$v = V/(bd) = ws'/(bd)$$
$$= 20\text{E}3 \times s'/(300 \times 700)$$

Design shear stress for a singly reinforced concrete beam (cl 3.4.5.4, Pt 1)

$$v_c = k_1 k_2 0.79[100A_s/(b_v d)]^{1/3}(400/d)^{1/4}/\gamma_m$$
$$= 1 \times 1 \times 0.79[100 \times 628/(300 \times 700)]^{1/3} \times 1/1.25$$
$$= 0.423 \text{ N/mm}^2$$

$100A_s/(b_v d) = 0.30 < 3\%$

Design shear stress for single vertical links

$$v \text{ (links)} = A_s 0.87 f_y/(b_v s_v)$$
$$= 101 \times 0.87 \times 460/(300 \times 320)$$
$$= 0.421 \text{ N/mm}^2$$

If the shear resistance at the ends of the continuing bars is twice the applied shear force

$$v_c + v \text{ (links)} = 2v$$
$$0.423 + 0.421 = 2 \times 20\text{E}3 \times s'/(300 \times 700); \text{ hence } s' = 4.43 \text{ m}$$

From the general conditions for curtailment, which must be satisfied, the smallest value of $s' = s - d = 3.38$ mm. This value covers two of the special conditions, i.e. $s' = 3.46$ m (bond requirement), and $s' = 4.43$ m (shear resistance requirement). Only one of these special requirements needs to be satisfied. Use $s' = 3.38$ m.

8.3.4 Simplified rules for curtailment for beams (cl 3.12.10.2, Pt 1)

The rules are presented in diagrammatic form in Fig. 8.10. The rules are conservative and simple to use. They reduce the time spent on design calculations but they are not as economic in the use of steel reinforcement as the detailed rules given in Fig. 8.8.

The simplified rules may be used in the following circumstances.

(a)   The beams are designed for predominantly uniformly distributed loads.
(b)   In the case of continuous beams, the spans are approximately equal.

EXAMPLE 8.3   Simplified curtailment of bars

Determine the practical curtailment point for 2-T20 (type 2) bars for the cantilever beam shown in Fig. 8.9.

From Fig. 8.10 the effective span for a cantilever

$$l = 5 + d/2 = 5 + 0.7/2 = 5.35 \text{ m}$$

Distance of curtailment point from the end of the cantilever

$$s' = 5 - l/2 = 5 - 5.35/2 = 2.33 \text{ m}$$

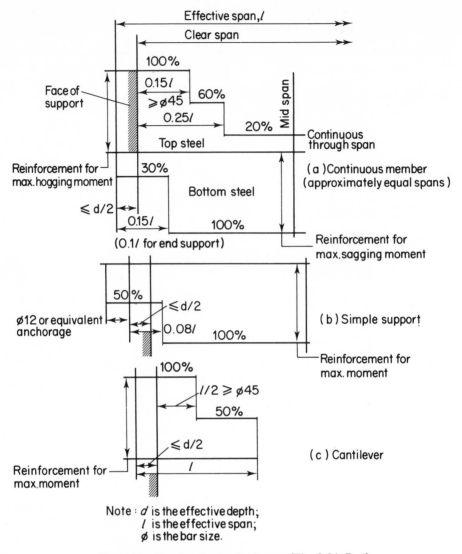

Fig. 8.10 Simplified rules for beams (Fig. 3.24, Pt 1).

Check $l/2 > 45\phi$

$5.35/2 > 45 \times 20 \times 1E-3$

2.675 m > 0.9 m, therefore satisfactory.

The value of $s' = 2.33$ m is less than 3.38 m obtained in Example 8.2 and therefore less economical in the use of steel.

8.3.5   Simplified rules for curtailment for slabs (cl 3.12.10.3, Pt 1)

The corresponding simplified rules for slabs are presented in diagrammatic form in Fig. 8.11.

The rules may be used in the following circumstances.

(a)   The slabs are designed for predominantly uniformly distributed loads.
(b)   In the case of continuous slabs, the design has been carried out for the single load case of maximum design load on all spans and the spans are approximately equal.

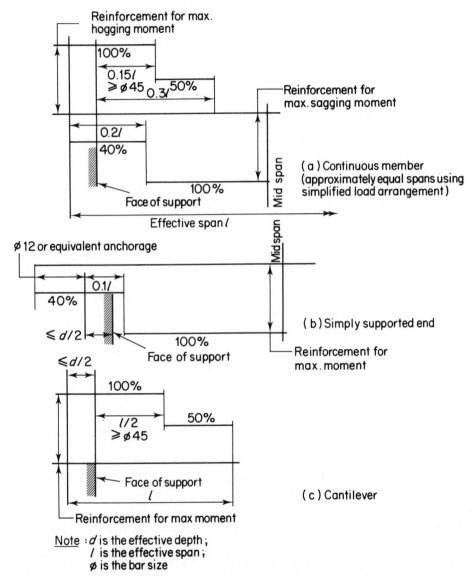

Fig. 8.11   Simplified detailing rules for slabs (Fig. 3.25, Pt 1).

8.3.6   Curtailment of bars at end supports of slabs (cl 3.12.10.3.2, Pt 1)

This clause is applied where a simple support has been assumed in the assessment of moments, and implies that there are no negative end moments.   Despite this assumption, negative moments may arise which could lead to cracking. To control this, an amount of reinforcement equal to half the area of the bottom steel at mid-span but not less than the minimum given in 3.12.5.3, should be provided in the top of the slab at the support. It should have a full effective anchorage into the support and extend not less than 0.15l or 45 times the bar size in the span. Bottom reinforcement may be detailed:

(a)   as indicated in Fig. 3.25 for a simply supported end, in which case the shear strength at the support may be based on the area of the bottom steel continuing into the support; or

(b)   as indicated in Fig. 3.25 for a simply supported end except that the bottom steel is stopped at the line of the effective support; in this case the shear strength at the support should be based on the area of the top steel.

8.4   Member connections

8.4.1   Introduction

Connections and joints in a structure may be classified as follows:

1   Construction joints introduced between concrete pours, sections, or levels to facilitate construction. These are particularly useful for *in-situ* concrete work, e.g. foundations can be concreted first and the columns later. In many cases these joints transmit forces but in other cases the requirements are that they should resist fire, corrosion, and be durable and soundproof (cl 8.2, Pt 2).

2   Movement joints are required to allow free expansion and contraction to occur in the structure due to temperature, shrinkage, creep, settlement, etc., and prevent a build-up of stresses (Section 8, Pt 2). Details of movement joints are given by Alexander and Lawson (1981).

3   Structural connections are required to transmit forces from one member to another, or one part of a structure to another. It is these connections that require detailed structural design.

It is possible for a structural connection to be subject to any combination of axial force, shear force and bending moment in relation to three perpendicular axes. Generally in design the situation is simplified to forces in one plane.

The distribution of forces within the connection is generally complex and complete knowledge and understanding is not available. In practice simple conservative assumptions are made in the design calculations as shown in the following examples.

The forces acting on a structural connection must be consistent with the structural analysis of the whole structure. Connections are assumed to be either 'rigid', or 'pinned', or 'on rollers'. In reality such connections do not exist but some assumptions must be made when analysing the complete structure. The analysis produces moments and forces and the members and connections can then be designed.

8.4.2   Simple beam supports

Beams which are described as simply supported are assumed in structural analysis to have theoretical connections at the ends such as those shown in Fig. 8.12(a). For real

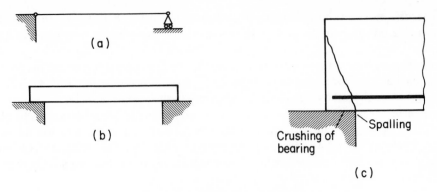

Fig. 8.12 Simple beam supports.

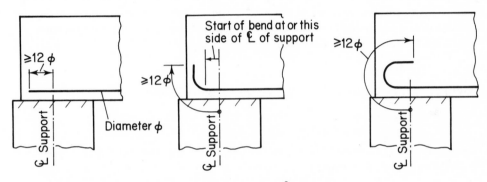

(a) anchorage for bars in members – relative to ₵ support

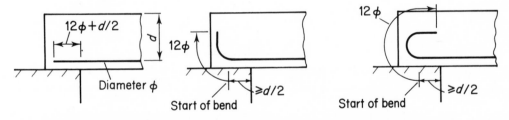

(b) anchorage for bars in members – relative to the face of the support

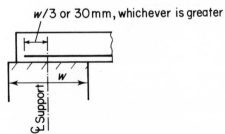

(c) anchorage for bars in slabs – relative to ₵ support

Fig. 8.13 Requirements for simple bearings (cl 3.12.9.4, Pt 1).

structures the most common connection is that shown in Fig. 8.12(b) where the reaction is distributed on the bearing and there is a frictional force acting between the bearing surfaces.

At the supports of simply supported beams there are special requirements to ensure that the bars are anchored and to prevent the type of failure shown in Fig. 8.12(c). Each bar should be anchored by one of the arrangements shown in Fig. 8.13.

The bearing area and bearing stresses also require detailed consideration. In general the length of bearing in line with the span should not be less than 100 mm and the bearing stress not greater than $0.4f_{cu}$ for a dry bearing on concrete. The bearing stress may be increased to $0.6f_{cu}$ for a bedded bearing on concrete. Further detailed advice is given in cl 5.2.3, Pt 1.

EXAMPLE 8.4   *Simple beam support*

Determine the width w for the bearing for a simply supported beam shown in Fig. 8.14. The reaction on the support $R = 250$ kN, the concrete cube strength 25 N/mm², the breadth of the beam 300 mm, the effective depth 550 mm and the cover 40 mm.
Minimum practical width of bearing

$$w = 100 \text{ mm}$$

Width of bearing based on bearing stresses for a dry bearing

$$w = R/(b0.4f_{cu})$$
$$= 250E3/(300 \times 0.4 \times 25) = 83.3 \text{ mm}$$

Minimum width of bearing relative to the face of the support (see Fig. 8.13) if bend starts at $d/2$ from face of the support

$$w = d/2 + r + \phi + \text{cover}$$
$$= 550/2 + 3 \times 25 + 25 + 40 = 415 \text{ mm}$$

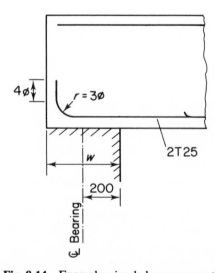

Fig. 8.14   Example: simple beam support.

Minimum width of bearing relative to the centre line of the support (see Fig. 8.13) if bend starts at centre line of the support

$$w = 200 + r + \phi + \text{cover}$$
$$= 200 + 3 \times 25 + 25 + 40 = 340 \text{ mm}$$

Only one of the last two requirements needs to be satisfied. Use $w = 340$ mm.
   Check the shear resistance of the beam.

Shear force at the support

$$V = 250 \text{ kN}$$

Average shear stress at the support (cl 3.4.5.2, Pt 1)

$$v = V/(b_v d) = 250\text{E3}/(300 \times 550) = 1.515 \text{ N/mm}^2$$

Maximum design shear stress (cl 3.4.5.2, Pt 1)

$$v_u = 0.8\sqrt{f_{cu}} = 0.8\sqrt{25} = 4 \text{ N/mm}^2 < 5 \text{ N/mm}^2$$

$v_u(4) > v\,(1.515)$ N/mm^2 therefore section is not too small.

   Design shear stress for a singly reinforced concrete beam (cl 3.4.5.4, Pt 1)

$$v_c = k_1 k_2 0.79[100A_s/(b_v d)]^{1/3}(400/d)^{1/4}/\gamma_m$$
$$= 1 \times 1 \times 0.79 \times [100 \times 982/(300 \times 550)]^{1/3} \times 1/1.25$$
$$= 0.532 \text{ N/mm}^2$$

$100A_s/(bd) = 100 \times 982/(300 \times 550) = 0.595\% < 3\%$

   Shear reinforcement is required because $v\,(1.515) > (v_c + 0.4)(0.932)$ N/mm^2 (cl 3.4.5.3, Pt 1)
   From Equation (7.4), assuming T10 (single) high-strength vertical links

$$s_v = A_s 0.87 f_{yv}/[b_v(v - v_c)]$$
$$= 2 \times 79 \times 0.87 \times 460/[300 \times (1.515 - 0.532)]$$
$$= 214.4 \text{ mm} < 0.75d(412.5) \text{ mm, therefore use } s_v = 200 \text{ mm.}$$

Use T10-200 single links.

8.4.3   Beam-to-beam connections

Secondary beams of the same or different depths intersect main beams at right angles as shown in Fig. 8.15. This connection is assumed to be a 'rigid' connection in the structural analysis and therefore is designed to resist a bending moment, a shear force and sometimes an axial force.
   For the case in which secondary beams intersect the main beam from both sides the practical arrangement of steel is shown in Fig. 8.15. The lap lengths are the full design lengths. Where only one secondary beam intersects the main beam the steel arrangement and design is more complicated, as shown in the design example and in Fig. 8.16.
   Similar arrangements can be used for the intersection of slabs and beams, except that the 'U' bars in the design example are arranged horizontally because of the reduced depth of slab.

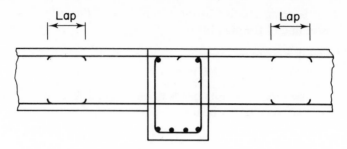

Fig. 8.15 Beam-to-beam connection.

EXAMPLE 8.5 *Beam-to-beam connection*

Design the connection between the secondary beam A and the main beam B shown in Fig. 8.16. The loading and bending moment diagram are shown above the diagram.

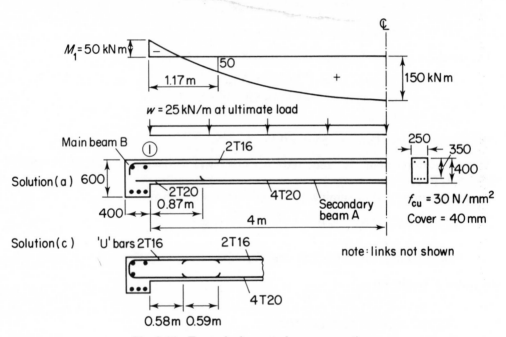

Fig. 8.16 Example: beam-to-beam connection.

Solution (a)

The size of the bars required to resist the hogging bending moment of 50 kN m at point 1 is obtained as follows:

K factor (cl 3.4.4.4, Pt 1)

$$K = M/(bd^2f_{cu}) = 50E6/(250 \times 350^2 \times 30) = 0.0544 < K' = 0.156$$

therefore compression reinforcement is not required.

Lever arm

$$z = d[0.5 + \sqrt{(0.25 - K/0.9)}] = 0.935d < 0.95d,$$

therefore satisfactory.

Area of high yield steel

$$A_s = M/(0.87f_y z)$$
$$= 50E6/(0.87 \times 460 \times 0.935 \times 350) = 381.8 \text{ mm}^2$$

Use 2T16 = 402 mm^2, and continue as top reinforcement in the beam.

Percentage steel $= 100 \times 402/(250 \times 400) = 0.402\% > 0.13\%$ (cl 3.12.5.3, Table 3.27, Pt 1, see Appendix A2.1), therefore satisfactory.

Bond length required to anchor the 16 mm bars (type 2) into beam B

$$l = 0.87f_y \phi_e/(4\beta\sqrt{f_{cu}})$$
$$= 0.87 \times 460 \times 16/(4 \times 0.5 \times \sqrt{30}) = 584.5 \text{ mm, say 590 mm}$$

Standard bend (see Fig. 8.4) equivalent anchor length $= 12\phi = 12 \times 16 = 192$ mm, which is too short and requires an extension.

There is space to extend the 16 mm bar vertically in beam B (see Fig. 8.16).

Length of the vertical leg

$$= l - 0.9b - \pi r/2$$
$$= 590 - 0.9 \times 400 - \pi \times 3 \times 20/2 = 135.8 \text{ mm, say 140 mm.}$$

Two of the T20 bars in the bottom of beam A can be curtailed. The moment of resistance of 2T20 is obtained as follows:

Depth of compression zone (cl 3.4.4.4, Pt 1) assuming that the steel is at design strength

$$x = A_s 0.87f_y/[0.9b(0.67/1.5)f_{cu}]$$
$$= 628 \times 0.87 \times 460/[0.9 \times 250 \times (0.67/1.5) \times 30] = 83.36 \text{ mm}$$

Check if the steel is at design strength.
Steel strain from linear variation over the depth of the section

$$\varepsilon_s = 0.0035(d/x - 1) = 0.0035 \times (350/83.36 - 1) = 0.0112$$

Steel strain at design strength from the stress–strain relationship

$$\varepsilon_y = f_y/(\gamma_s E_s) = 460/(1.15 \times 200E3) = 0.002 < 0.0112, \text{ therefore the steel is at the}$$
design strength.

Lever arm

$$z = d - 0.45x = 350 - 0.45 \times 83.36 = 312.5 \text{ mm}$$

Moment of resistance

$$M_r = A_s 0.87f_y z = 628 \times 0.87 \times 460 \times 312.5 \times 1E\text{-}6 = 78.54 \text{ kN m.}$$

Theoretical curtailment point of 2T20 bars at a distance s from the inside face of beam B

$$M_r = R_1s - M_1 - ws^2/2$$
$$78.54 = 100s - 50 - 25s^2/2$$
$$s^2 - 8s + 10.283 = 0; \text{ hence } s = 1.61 \text{ m}$$

General conditions for curtailment (see Fig. 8.8)

$$12\phi = 12 \times 20 = 240 \text{ mm}, d = 350 \text{ mm}.$$

Bond length required to extend the 20 mm bars (type 2) from Equation (8.3)

$$l = 0.87f_y\phi_e/(4\beta\sqrt{f_{cu}})$$
$$= 0.87 \times 460 \times 20/(4 \times 0.5 \times \sqrt{30}) = 730.7 \text{ mm, say 740 mm}$$

Practical curtailment point

$$= 1.61 - 0.74 = 0.87 \text{ m from the inside face of beam B.}$$

Reduction of steel in the bottom of the beam reduces the shear resistance. Shear force at the support

$$V = wL/2 = 25 \times 8/2 = 100 \text{ kN}.$$

Average shear stress at the support (cl 3.4.5.2, Pt 1)

$$v = V/b_vd) = 100E3/(250 \times 350) = 1.143 \text{ N/mm}^2$$

Maximum design shear stress (cl 3.4.5.2, Pt 1)

$$v_u = 0.8\sqrt{f_{cu}} = 0.8\sqrt{30} = 4.38 \text{ N/mm}^2 \leqslant 5 \text{ N/mm}^2$$

$v_u(4.38) > v(1.143) \text{ N/mm}^2$, therefore section is not too small.

Design shear stress for a singly reinforced concrete beam (cl 3.4.5.4, Pt 1)

$$v_c = k_1k_20.79[100A_s/(b_vd)]^{1/3}(400/d)^{1/4}/\gamma_m$$
$$= 1 \times (30/25)^{1/3} \times 0.79 \times [100 \times 628/(250 \times 350)]^{1/3} \times (400/350)^{1/4}/1.25$$
$$= 0.622 \text{ N/mm}^2$$

$100A_s/(bd) = 100 \times 628/(250 \times 350) = 0.718\% < 3\% \text{(max.)}$

Shear reinforcement is required because v (1.143) $> (v_c + 0.4)(1.022) \text{ N/mm}^2$ (cl 3.4.5.3, Pt 1, see Appendix A2.2)

From Equation (7.4), assuming single T8 high-strength vertical links

$$s_v = A_s0.87f_y/[b_v(v - v_c)]$$
$$= 2 \times 50 \times 0.87 \times 460/[250 \times (1.143 - 0.622)]$$
$$= 307.3 \text{ mm} > 0.75d(262.5) \text{ mm, therefore use } s_v = 260 \text{ mm}.$$

Use T8-260 single links.

Solution (b)
There may be practical difficulties in arranging the reinforcement in solution (a). This

situation can be improved by lapping the 16 mm and 20 mm bars and incorporating starter bars from beam B.

Lap length required for the 20 mm bars (type 2) from Equation (8.3)

$$l = 0.87 f_y \phi_e / (4\beta \sqrt{f_{cu}})$$
$$= 0.87 \times 460 \times 20/(4 \times 0.5 \times \sqrt{30}) = 730.7 \text{ mm, say } 740 \text{ mm}$$

Lap length required for the 16 mm bars (type 2) from Equation (8.3)

$$l = 0.87 f_y \phi_e / (4\beta \sqrt{f_{cu}})$$
$$= 0.87 \times 460 \times 16/(4 \times 0.5 \times \sqrt{30}) = 584.5 \text{ mm say } 590 \text{ mm}$$

This would enable a cage of longitudinal and link reinforcement to be wired together, and when completed, inserted into the shuttering.

Solution (c)

The essence of this variation is the insertion of two 16 mm 'U' bars at the end of beam A as shown in Fig. 8.16. This is sufficient to resist the hogging moment of 50 kN m as shown in solution (a).

Percentage of steel at the support relative to that at mid-span in the bottom of the beam

$$= 402 \times 100/1257 = 31.98\% > 30\% \text{ (Fig. 8.10), therefore satisfactory.}$$

This is recommended in the simplified curtailing rules.

Theoretical curtailment point of the 16 mm bars in the bottom of the beam at a distance s from the face of beam B

$$M_r = R_1 s - M_1 - ws^2/2$$
$$50 = 100s - 50 - 25s^2/2$$
$$s^2 - 8s + 8 = 0; \text{ hence } s = 1.172 \text{ m}$$

General conditions for curtailment (Fig. 8.8)

$$12\phi = 12 \times 16 = 192 \text{ mm}, d = 350 \text{ mm}$$

Lap the 20 mm and 16 mm bars. Use smaller lap length of 0.59 m (see calculations in solution (b)).

The practical curtailment point for the 20 mm bars

$$= 1.17 - 0.59 = 0.58 \text{ m from the inside face of beam B.}$$

Check the bearing stresses on the concrete on the inside of the bend of the 16 mm 'U' bars.

Radius of bend

$$r = (h - 2 \times \text{cover} - 2\phi)/2 = (400 - 2 \times 40 - 2 \times 16)/2 = 144 \text{ mm}$$

Bearing stress

$$= F_{bt}/(r\phi) = 0.87 \times 460 \times 201/(144 \times 16) = 34.92 \text{ N/mm}^2$$
$$a_b = \phi + \text{cover} = 16 + 40 = 56 \text{ mm}$$

Design bearing stress

$$= 2f_{cu}/[1 + 2(\phi/a_b)]$$
$$= 2 \times 30/[1 + 2 \times 16/56] = 38.18 \text{ N/mm}^2 > 34.92 \text{ N/mm}^2, \text{ therefore satisfactory.}$$

The reduction of the steel in the bottom of the beam reduces the shear resistance.

Shear force at the support

$$V = wL/2 = 25 \times 8/2 = 100 \text{ kN.}$$

Average shear stress at the support (cl 3.4.5.2, Pt 1)

$$v = V/(b_v d) = 100\text{E}3/(250 \times 350) = 1.143 \text{ N/mm}^2$$

Maximum design shear stress (cl 3.4.5.2, Pt 1)

$$v_u = 0.8\sqrt{f_{cu}} = 0.8\sqrt{30} = 4.38 \text{ N/mm}^2 \leqslant 5 \text{ N/mm}^2$$

v_u (4.38) $> v$ (1.143) N/mm^2, therefore section is not too small.

Design shear stress for a singly reinforced concrete beam (cl 3.4.5.4, Pt 1)

$$v_c = k_1 k_2 0.79[100A_s/(b_v d)]^{1/3}(400/d)^{1/4}/\gamma_m$$
$$= 1 \times (30/25)^{1/3} \times 0.79 \times [100 \times 402/(250 \times 350)]^{1/3} \times (400/350)^{1/4}/1.25$$
$$= 0.536 \text{ N/mm}^2$$

$100A_s/(bd) = 100 \times 402/(250 \times 350) = 0.459\% < 3\%$.
Shear reinforcement is required because $v(1.143) > (v_c + 0.4)(0.936)$ N/mm^2 (cl 3.4.5.3, Pt 1, see Appendix A2.2)

From Equation (7.4), assuming single T8 high-strength vertical links

$$s_v = A_s 0.87 f_y/[b_v(v - v_c)]$$
$$= 2 \times 50 \times 0.87 \times 460/[250 \times (1.143 - 0.536)]$$
$$= 263.7 \text{ mm} > 0.75d = 262.5 \text{ mm}, \text{ therefore use } s_v = 260 \text{ mm.}$$

Use T8-260 single links.

The arrangement of reinforcement is shown in Fig. 8.16 (solution (c)). The one disadvantage of the use of a 'U' bar in this problem is the abrupt change in reinforcement at the bottom of the beam from 4T20 to 2T16.

8.4.4 Beam-to-column connections

Beams and columns of the same, or different widths, intersect at right angles as shown in Fig. 8.17. These connections are assumed to be 'rigid' in the theoretical structural analysis and therefore are designed to resist a bending moment, a shear force and sometimes an axial force. The connections are most efficient when the intersecting members contain approximately 1% reinforcement.

The two-member connection shown in Fig. 8.17(a) occurs at the top of frames and may be subject to moments which open or close the connection. The 'U' bars are an adequate form of reinforcement when the moments are closing the joint, but additional splay reinforcement is required for opening moments. An example of the design of this connection is shown in Fig. 8.19.

The three-member connection may be reinforced with an 'L' bar as shown in Fig. 8.17(b), or with a 'U' bar as shown in Fig. 8.17(c). Experiments (Taylor 1974) have shown that the closing corner (Fig. 8.17(b)) is stronger than an opening corner.

The four-member connection is straightforward and reinforced with straight bars lapped at construction joints as shown in Fig. 8.17(d).

The three- and four-member connections require checking for possible diagonal cracking in the joint block (see Fig. 8.18) as follows:

Shear stress

$$\tau = T/(bh)$$

Axial stress

$$\sigma = N/(bh)$$

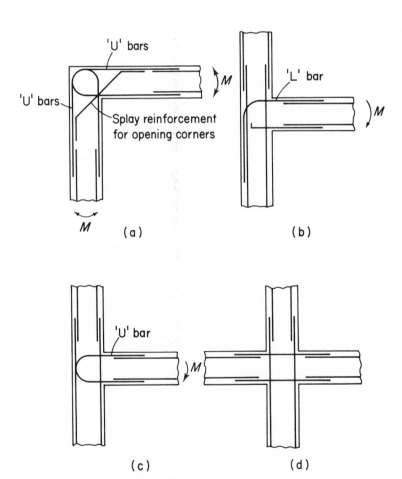

Note : Links have been omitted

Fig. 8.17 Beam-to-column connections.

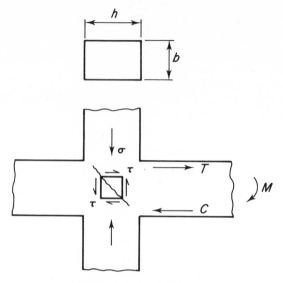

Fig. 8.18   Joint block.

These stresses are combined using a principal tensile stress criterion for concrete:

$$\sqrt{[(\sigma/2)^2 + \tau^2]} - \sigma/2 < f_t$$

where the design tensile strength $f_t = 0.24\sqrt{f_{cu}}$

Where this requirement is not satisfied diagonal links are placed to resist the tensile force, or alternatively the size of the joint block is increased.

EXAMPLE 8.6   Beam-to-column connection

Design the two-member connection shown in Fig. 8.19, which is subject to a moment of 70 kN m which may open or close the connection.

The beam and column are reinforced with 2T16 on both faces, therefore use 2T16 'U' bars.

Lap length required for the 16 mm bars (type 2) from Equation (8.3)

$$l = 0.87f_y\phi_e/(4\beta\sqrt{f_{cu}})$$
$$= 0.87 \times 460 \times 16/(4 \times 0.5 \times \sqrt{30}) = 584.5 \text{ mm, say } 590 \text{ mm}$$

Check the bearing stresses on the concrete on the inside of the bend of the 16 mm 'U' bars in the column.

Radius of bend $= (h - 2 \times \text{cover} - 2\phi)/2$

$$= (400 - 2 \times 40 - 2 \times 16)/2 = 144 \text{ mm}$$

Bearing stress

$$= F_{bt}/(r\phi) = 0.87 \times 460 \times 201/(144 \times 16) = 34.92 \text{ N/mm}^2$$

Distance

$$a_b = \phi + \text{cover} = 16 + 40 = 56 \text{ mm}$$

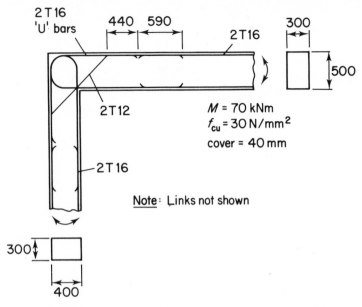

Fig. 8.19 Example: beam-to-column connection.

Design bearing stress

$$= 2f_{cu}/[1+2(\phi/a_b)]$$
$$= 2 \times 30/[1+2 \times 16/56] = 38.18 > 34.92 \text{ N/mm}^2, \text{ therefore satisfactory.}$$

The moment opens the connection, therefore use splay bars. Area approximately 50% of the main steel. Use 2T12.

Length required to anchor the 12 mm bars (type 2) from Equation (8.3)

$$l = 0.87f_y\phi_e/(4\beta\sqrt{f_{cu}})$$
$$= 0.87 \times 460 \times 12/(4 \times 0.5 \times \sqrt{30}) = 438.4 \text{ mm, say 440 mm}$$

The column and beam would be checked for shear forces as shown in Example 8.5. The arrangement of reinforcement to resist the moment is shown in Fig. 8.19 but the necessary links are omitted to avoid confusion.

8.4.5 Column-to-base connection

Columns generally intersect a base at right angles as shown in Fig. 8.20. This connection is assumed to be a 'rigid' connection in the structural analysis and therefore is designed to resist a bending moment, a shear force and an axial force.

The thickness of the base is related to the bond length required for the starter bars, or to the shear resistance of the base. If the base is large and the thickness of the base has to be increased, consideration should be given to a pedestal base (see Fig. 8.20). The lapped bars start approximately 75 mm above the top surface of the base to provide a construction joint and provide a 'kicker' to locate the column shuttering. The shear calculations for a base are shown in Section 7.1.14.

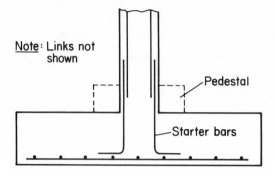

Fig. 8.20 Column-to-base connection.

8.4.6 Column-to-column connections

Columns of the same, or different sizes, are connected in line as shown in Fig. 8.21. This connection is assumed to be a 'rigid' in the structural analysis and therefore is designed to resist a bending moment, shear force and an axial force. Calculations are required for the lap length and for the percentage reinforcement at the lap because at this section the reinforcement is doubled.

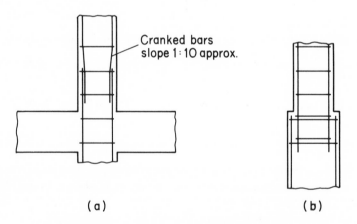

Fig. 8.21 Column-to-column connections.

8.4.7 Corbel connection (cl 5.2.7, Pt 1)

Corbels are designed to support beams as shown in Fig. 8.22(a). The connection between the beam and corbel is assumed to be a 'pinned' in structural analysis and therefore the corbel is designed to resist an eccentric force, shear force and a horizontal force. Corbel dimensions, as defined in BS 8110, are shown in Fig. 8.22(a).

The arrangement of reinforcement recommended in BS 8110 is shown in Figs. 8.22(c) and (d) and is based on tests by investigators such as Somerville and Taylor (1972). The distance of the bearing area of the applied load from the end of the corbel is controlled to prevent the type of failure shown in Fig. 8.22(b). The arrangement with the welded bar gives the smallest horizontal distance from the column to the end of the corbel.

The tensile steel in the top of the corbel should be capable of resisting the bending moment due to the eccentricity of the load plus a minimum horizontal force equal to half the vertical load. The shear resistance is calculated as for a singly reinforced concrete beam with an enhanced shear strength based on the effective depth/shear span ratio. In addition shear reinforcement is provided in the form of horizontal links to ensure satisfactory serviceability performance and to resist the horizontal force (see Figs. 8.22(c) and (d)).

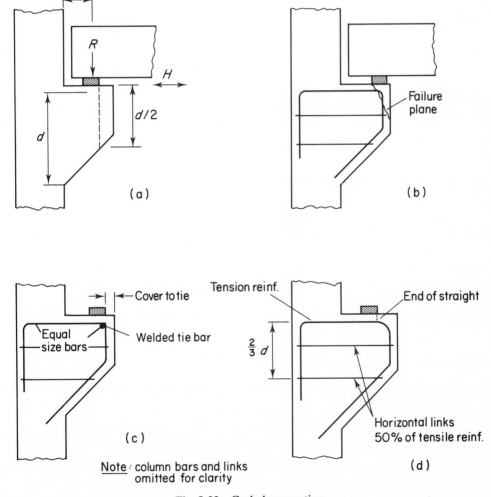

Fig. 8.22 Corbel connection.

EXAMPLE 8.7   Corbel connection

Design the connection shown in Fig. 8.23.

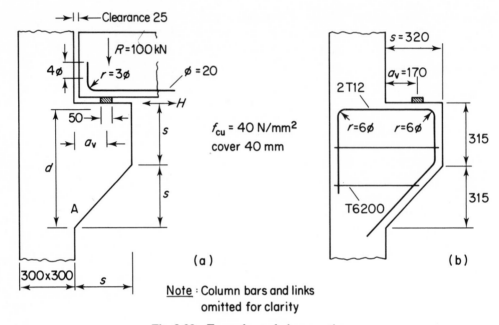

(a)

f_{cu} = 40 N/mm^2
cover 40 mm

(b)

Note : Column bars and links
omitted for clarity

Fig. 8.23   Example: corbel connection.

Check bearing stresses between the concrete and steel bearing.

$$f_{bg} = R/\text{(bearing area)} = 100\text{E3}/(50 \times 300) = 6.67 \text{ N/mm}^2$$

Design bearing stress for concrete (cl 5.2.3.4, Pt 1)

$$= 0.4f_{cu} = 0.4 \times 40 = 16 > 6.67 \text{ N/mm}^2, \text{ therefore satisfactory.}$$

Eccentricity of the load on the corbel based on details at the end of the beam (see Fig. 8.13(a)). Aligning edge of steel bearing with end of straight of bar in beam

$$a_v = 25 + r + \phi + \text{cover} + \text{clearance}$$
$$= 25 + 60 + 20 + 40 + 25 = 170 \text{ mm}$$

Use the larger value $a_v = 170$ mm.

The size of the corbel is related to the horizontal distance s (see Fig. 8.23(a)) assuming $\phi = 20$ mm and a radius of 3ϕ

$$s = a_v + 25 + 3\phi + \phi + \text{cover}$$
$$= 170 + 25 + 4 \times 20 + 40 = 315 \text{ mm.}$$

Effective depth (see Fig. 8.23(a))

$$d = 2s - \text{cover} - \phi/2 = 2 \times 315 - 40 - 20/2 = 580 \text{ mm.}$$

Horizontal force on corbel if $\mu = 0.3$ (cl 5.2.7, Pt 1)

$H = \mu R = 0.3 \times 100 = 30$ kN $<$ minimum of $0.5R$, therefore use 50 kN.

Moments of forces about compression zone A (see Fig. 8.23(a))

$$M_A = Ra_v + H(z + \phi/2 + \text{cover})$$
$$= Ra_v + Hd$$
$$= 100 \times 0.17 + 50 \times 0.58 = 46 \text{ kN m}$$

Area of high-strength steel in top of corbel assuming $z = 0.85d$ (approx.)

$$A_s = M_A/(0.87f_y z)$$
$$= 46E6/(0.87 \times 460 \times 0.85 \times 580) = 233.1 \text{ mm}^2$$

Use 2T12 $= 226$ mm^2

Check shear resistance.

Average design shear stress at inner edge of steel pack

$$v = 100E3/\{[580 - (170 - 25)] \times 300\} = 0.766 \text{ N/mm}^2$$

Average shear stress at column face (cl 3.4.5.2, Pt 1)

$$v = V/(b_v d) = 100E3/(300 \times 580) = 0.575 \text{ N/mm}^2$$

Maximum design shear stress (cl 3.4.5.2, Pt 1)

$$v_u = 0.8\sqrt{f_{cu}} = 0.8\sqrt{40} = 5.06 \text{ N/mm}^2 > 5 \text{ N/mm}^2$$

$v_u(5) > v$ (0.766) N/mm^2, therefore section is not too small.

Enhanced design shear stress for a singly reinforced concrete beam (cl 3.4.5.4, Pt 1)

$$v_c = k_1 k_2 0.79[100A_s/(b_v d)]^{1/3}(400/d)^{1/4}/\gamma_m$$
$$= (2 \times 580/170) \times (40/25)^{1/3} \times 0.79 \times [100 \times 226/(300 \times 580)]^{1/3} \times 1/1.25$$
$$= 2.55 \text{ N/mm}^2$$

$100A_s/(bd) = 100 \times 226/(300 \times 580) = 0.13\%$ equal to minimum allowed (cl 3.12.5.3, Pt 1) and less than maximum of 3%.

Check the bearing stresses on the concrete on the inside of the bend of the 12 mm 'L' bars in the corbel.

Bearing stress ($r = 3\phi$)

$$= F_{bt}/(r\phi) = 0.87 \times 460 \times 113/(3 \times 12 \times 12) = 104.7 \text{ N/mm}^2$$

Distance

$$a_b = \phi + \text{cover} = 12 + 40 = 52 \text{ mm}$$

Design bearing stress

$$= 2f_{cu}/[1 + 2(\phi/a_b)]$$
$$= 2 \times 40/[1 + 2 \times 12/52] = 54.7 < 104.7 \text{ N/mm}^2, \text{ therefore } not \text{ satisfactory.}$$

Increase readius of bend to 6ϕ

Revised bearing stress

$$= F_{bt}/(r\phi) = 0.87 \times 460 \times 113/(6 \times 12 \times 12) = 52.3 < 54.7 \text{ N/mm}^2, \text{ therefore satis-}$$
factory

Check horizontal dimension of corbel

$$s = a_v + 25 + 6\phi + \phi + 40 = 170 + 25 + 6 \times 12 + 12 + 40 = 319 \text{ mm, say } 320 \text{ mm.}$$

Horizontal links, 50% of area of main tension steel (2T12)

$$A_s = 0.5 \times 226 = 113 \text{ mm}^2$$

Use 4T6 = 113 mm² distributed over $2d/3 = 2 \times 580/3 = 386.7$ mm. Use T6-200.

8.4.8 Half joint

This type of connection is useful when the construction depth is to be kept to a minimum, e.g. a beam supported on cantilever beams in line. The general shape and arrangement of reinforcement in a half joint is shown in Fig. 8.24.

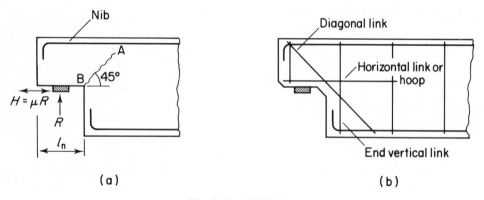

Fig. 8.24 Half-joint.

The reinforcement is required to prevent the type of failure shown in Fig. 8.24(a) (Reynolds 1969). The horizontal link, or loop, resists the moment of forces R and H acting about point A, and must be adequately anchored in the nib and beam from point B. The vertical end link resists the force R. The diagonal link also resists the moment of forces about point A and duplicates the resistance of the horizontal and vertical links. Its prime function is to strengthen an opening joint, as described in beam-to-column connections.

EXAMPLE 8.8   Half joint

Design the connection shown in Fig. 8.25.
There will be a horizontal force present at the bearing because of friction. The value of 50% of the reaction R is adopted as recommended for the design of corbels.

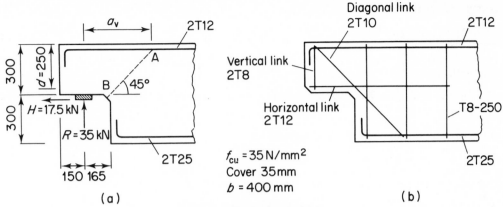

Fig. 8.25 Example: half-joint.

Moment of forces acting about A (approximately)

$$M_A = R(0.165 + d) + Hd$$
$$= 35 \times (0.165 + 0.25) + 0.5 \times 35 \times 0.25 = 18.9 \text{ kN m}$$

Area of high-yield steel required in the horizontal link, assuming that the lever arm $z = 0.85d$

$$A_s = M_A/(0.87f_y z)$$
$$= 18.9E6/(0.87 \times 460 \times 0.85 \times 250) = 222.2 \text{ mm}^2$$

Use single horizontal link 2T12 = 226 mm²

Bond length for T12 type 2 bar

$$1 = 0.87f_y\phi_e/(4\beta\sqrt{f_{cu}})$$
$$= 0.87 \times 460 \times 12/(4 \times 0.5 \times \sqrt{35}) = 405.9 \text{ mm}$$

'L' shaped bond length available in the nib for horizontal link T12 ($r = 3\phi$) from point B

$$= (b/2 + l_n - 2(\text{cover} + \phi + r) + \pi r/2$$
$$= 400/2 + 315 - 2 \times (35 + 12 + 3 \times 12) + \pi \times 3 \times 12/2$$
$$= 405.5 \text{ mm, which is approximately equal to the bond length required, i.e.}$$
405.9 mm

Check the bearing stresses on the concrete on the inside of the bend of the 12 mm horizontal link because it is not a standard hook.

Bearing stress if $r = 3\phi$

$$= F_{bt}/(r\phi) = 0.87 \times 460 \times 113/(3 \times 12 \times 12) = 104.7 \text{ N/mm}^2$$

Distance

$$a_b = \phi + \text{cover} = 12 + 35 = 47 \text{ mm}$$

Design bearing stress

$$= 2f_{cu}/[1 + 2(\phi/a_b)]$$
$$= 2 \times 35/[1 + 2 \times 12/47] = 46.3 \text{ N/mm}^2 < 104.7 \text{ N/mm}^2, \text{ therefore } not \text{ satisfactory.}$$

Increase radius of bend from 3ϕ to 7ϕ

Revised bearing stress

$$= F_{bt}/(r\phi) = 0.87 \times 460 \times 113/(7 \times 12 \times 12) = 44.9 \text{ N/mm}^2 < 46.3 \text{ N/mm}^2, \text{ there-}$$
fore satisfactory.

The change of radius from 3ϕ to 7ϕ slightly reduces the bond length available, but this is negligible.

Area of steel required in the end vertical link

$$A_s = R/(0.87f_y) = 35\text{E}3/(0.87 \times 460) = 87.56 \text{ mm}^2$$

Use single vertical link, 2T8 = 101 mm^2

Area of high-yield steel required in diagonal 45° link, assuming $z = 0.85d\sqrt{2}$ and ignoring the horizontal and vertical links

$$A_s = M_A/(0.87f_y z)$$
$$= 18.9\text{E}6/(0.87 \times 460 \times 0.85 \times 250 \times \sqrt{2}) = 157.1 \text{ mm}^2$$

Use single diagonal link, 2T10 = 157 mm^2

Bond length required for diagonal links from point B

$$l = 0.87f_y\phi_e/(4\beta\sqrt{f_{cu}})$$
$$= 0.87 \times 460 \times 10/(4 \times 0.5 \times \sqrt{35}) = 338.2 \text{ mm}$$

Bond length available in the standard 90° bend with $r = 3\phi$

$$= \sqrt{2}d - r + 12\phi = \sqrt{2}d + 9\phi = \sqrt{2} \times 250 + 9 \times 10 = 443.6 \text{ mm.}$$

There is no need to check bearing stresses for a standard bend.

Check shear resistance of the nib.

Average shear stress on nib (cl 3.4.5.2, Pt 1)

$$v = R/(b_v d) = 35\text{E}3/(400 \times 250) = 0.350 \text{ N/mm}^2$$

Maximum design shear stress (cl 3.4.5.2, Pt 1)

$$v_u = 0.8\sqrt{f_{cu}} = 0.8\sqrt{35} = 4.73 \text{ N/mm}^2 < 5 \text{ N/mm}^2$$

$v_u(4.73) > v (0.35)$ N/mm^2, therefore section is not too small.

Design shear stress for a singly reinforced concrete beam. The shear strength is not enhanced because the effective depth/shear span ratio is conservatively assessed as 1/2 (cl 3.4.5.4, Pt 1)

$$v_c = k_1 k_2 0.79[100A_s/(b_v d)]^{1/3}(400/d)^{1/4}/\gamma_m$$
$$= (40/35)^{1/3} \times 0.79 \times [100 \times 226/(400 \times 250)]^{1/3} \times (400/250)^{1/4}/1.25$$
$$= 0.453 \text{ N/mm}^2$$

$100A_s/(bd) = 100 \times 226/(400 \times 250) = 0.226\% > $ min. allowed (0.13%, cl 3.12.5.3, Pt 1) and maximum allowed (3%).

$0.5v_c (0.226) < v (0.35) < (v_c + 0.4)(0.853)$ N/mm^2, therefore minimum shear reinforcement (see Appendix A2.2).

Minimum single T8 vertical links in the nib from Equation (7.6)

$$s_v = A_{sv}0.87f_{yv}/(b_v0.4)$$
$$= 101 \times 0.87 \times 460/(400 \times 0.4) = 252.6 \text{ mm}$$

Use single T8-250 vertical links.

These examples do not exhaust the subject of connections. Further examples and information on *in-situ* and precast concrete connections is given in Holmes and Martin (1983).

8.5 Tutorial problems

8.5.1 Bond length

A tensile bar is turned up at 45° at the end of a simply supported beam to resist shear forces, as shown in Fig. 8.26. Determine the total bond length required from the start of the bend if the 16 mm diameter high-yield bars (type 2) are stressed in tension to the design strength. Also determine the straight length l_s if $r = 3\phi$.

Answers
$\Sigma l = 36.53\phi_e = 584.5$ mm, $l_s = 409.1$ mm

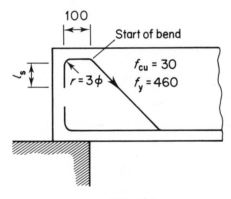

100

Start of bend

$f_{cu} = 30$

$r = 3\phi$

$f_y = 460$

l_s

Fig. 8.26

8.5.2 Curtailment

For the bottom steel reinforcement in the beam shown in Fig. 8.27 determine the distance from A for (a) the theoretical curtailment; (b) all the practical curtailment points (bond, bending, and shear) at X. The details are, bottom reinforcement T16 (type 1), strength of concrete $f_{cu} = 25$ N/mm², shear reinforcement T8-320, $b = 250$ mm and $d = 450$ mm.

Answers
(a) $x = 64$ mm, $z = 421.2$ mm, $M_r = 67.76$ kN m, $M_s = 66.8s - 10s^2$, $V_s = 66.8 - 20s$, $s = 5.43$ m. (b) $s' = 6.23$ m(bond), 6.13 m(bending), 6.02 m(shear)

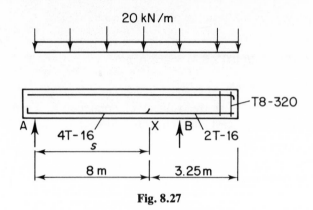

Fig. 8.27

8.5.3 Curtailment

Determine the lengths XX and YY of the curtailed T16 bars in the beam shown in Fig. 8.28 using the simplified detailing rules for beams (see Fig. 8.10).

Answer
XX = 4.5 m, YY = 2.9 m

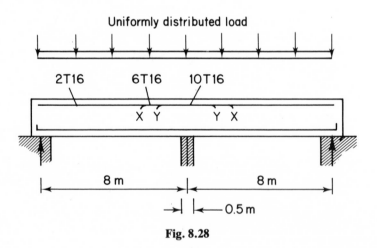

Fig. 8.28

8.5.4 Corbel

Design the corbel shown in Fig. 8.29(a) using grade 30 concrete, high-yield steel type 2, and assuming $H = 0.5R$.

Answer
See Fig. 8.29(b)

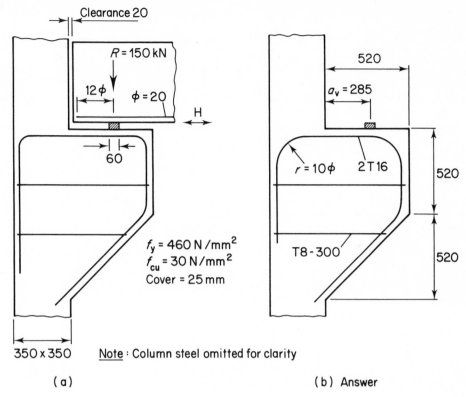

Note : Column steel omitted for clarity

Fig. 8.29

8.5.5 Half joint

Design the half-joint beam connection shown in Fig. 8.30(a). Use high-yield steel (type 2) and grade 30 concrete with 25 mm cover.

Answer
See Fig. 8.30(b)

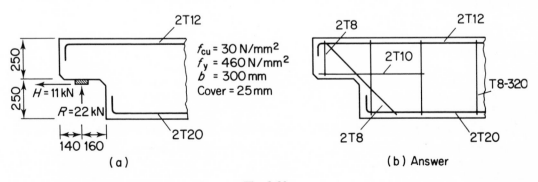

Fig. 8.30

References

Alexander S. J. and Lawson R. M. (1981). *Movement design in buildings*, Technical Note 107, Construction Industry Research and Information.

BS 4461 (1984). *Specification for cold worked steel bars for the reinforcement of concrete*, British Standards Institution, London.

BS 4482 (1985). *Hard drawn mild steel wire for the reinforcement of concrete*, British Standards Institution, London.

Holmes M. and Martin L. H. (1983). *Analysis and design of structural connections in reinforced concrete and steel*, Ellis Horwood, Chichester.

Paterson W. S. and Ravenshill K. R. (1981). *Reinforcement connectors and anchorage*, Report 92, Construction Industry Research and Information Association Publication.

Reynolds G. C. (1969). *The strength of half joints in reinforced concrete beams*, Report 42.415, Cement and Concrete Association.

Reynolds G. C. (1982). *Bond strength of deformed bars in tension*, Technical Report 548, Cement and Concrete Association.

Somerville G. and Taylor H. P. J. (1972). The influence of reinforcement detailing on the strength of concrete structures, *Structural Engineer*, **50**(1), 7–19.

Taylor H. J. P. (1974). The behaviour of in-situ concrete beam to column joints, Report 42.492, Cement and Concrete Association.

Williams A. (1979). The bearing capacity of concrete loaded over a limited area, Technical Report 526, Cement and Concrete Association.

9

Reinforced Concrete Columns

9.1 General principles

9.1.1 Introduction

A column is a vertical member designed primarily to resist axial compression. Most reinforced concrete columns are rectangular in section, but circular sections are not uncommon. This chapter covers the design of rectangular columns and is based on cl 3.8 of BS 8110, Pt 1. The same principles can however be applied to sections with other shapes. When a section is very narrow the question arises whether to treat the member as a column or a wall. BS 8110 defines a wall as a vertical load-bearing member whose length exceeds four times its thickness; if the ratio of length to thickness of the section does not exceed four, the member is designed as a column.

A typical arrangement of reinforcement for a column is shown in Fig. 9.1. The vertical bars are placed near the outside faces to obtain the most effective resistance to bending moments which invariably accompany the axial force in practical columns. The column in Fig. 9.1, for example, is designed to resist bending moments about the x–x axis. Horizontal links are provided at intervals along the length of the column to prevent longitudinal splitting and buckling of the vertical reinforcement. Normally high-yield steel is specified for the vertical reinforcement. For the links, mild steel, which is easier to bend, cheaper, and just as effective as high-yield steel, is normally used.

Columns are usually designed with symmetrical reinforcement. This is necessary in most situations because the bending moments may act in either direction about an axis. In practice, however, symmetrical reinforcement is also used when the bending moments are known to be unidirectional, as for example in corner columns. The cover given to the reinforcement is affected by considerations of durability and fire resistance.

Sections are designed to resist the axial force and bending moments at the ultimate limit state, but in some cases it may also be necessary to check that serviceability limit states of deflection and cracking have not been exceeded.

9.1.2 Bracing

Columns are classified as either *braced* or *unbraced*. A column may be considered braced in a particular plane when other structural elements such as shear walls, cross bracing,

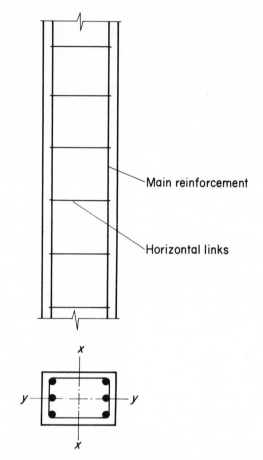

Fig. 9.1 Arrangement of reinforcement in a column.

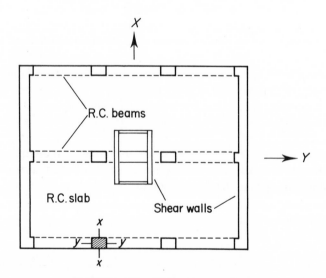

Fig. 9.2 Bracing by shear walls.

buttresses, etc. have been designed to resist all the horizontal forces acting on the structure in that plane.

Consider, for example, the section of a small multistorey structure shown in Fig. 9.2. The end walls and the walls of the lift shaft, combined with the *in-situ* floor slab, constitute a stiff structure capable of resisting all the horizontal forces in the *X*-direction. Significant horizontal forces would not therefore be transmitted to the columns, which would be designed as *braced* in that direction. In the *Y*-direction, however, the stiffness of the walls is much less; and a significant part of the horizontal forces would be resisted by the frame action of the columns and floor beams. The columns would therefore be designed in that direction as *unbraced*.

9.1.3 Effective height

The classical Euler theory of buckling refers to an ideal, pin-ended strut, subjected to a purely axial force. If the ends are not pinned, the critical buckling load can be determined by considering an equivalent pin-ended strut whose length is the distance between points of contraflexure, or imaginary pins, in the buckled strut. This is the *effective length* of the strut.

The *effective height* of a column depends, therefore, upon the rigidity and fixity of the end connections and whether or not the column is braced. In general

$$l_e = \beta l_0 \tag{9.1}$$

where

l_e is the effective height
l_0 is the clear height between end restraints
β is a factor depending on end conditions and bracing.

Ideally, when end conditions are either pinned or rigid, the theoretical values of β are as shown in Fig. 9.3. The dotted lines in the unbraced columns indicate the imaginary extensions required to produce the equivalent pin-ended condition.

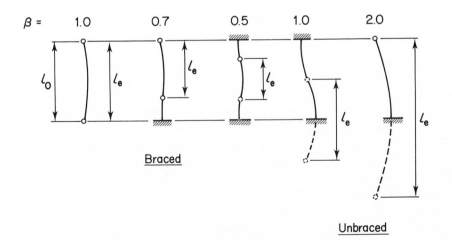

Fig. 9.3 Effective height of an ideal column.

In a real structure the ends of the columns are usually connected either to a system of beams or to a foundation. These effectively prevent lateral movement, but allow varying degrees of rotation (a completely rigid connection cannot be achieved in practice). Practical values of β in Equation (9.1) therefore tend to be greater than the ideal values given in Fig. 9.3. The following practical end conditions are defined in cl 3.8.1.6.2, Pt 1.

Condition 1   The end of the column is connected monolithically to beams on either side which are at least as deep as the overall dimension of the column in the plane considered. Where the column is connected to a foundation structure, this should be of a form specifically designed to carry moment.

Condition 2   The end of the column is connected monolithically to beams or slabs on either side which are shallower than the overall dimension of the column in the plane considered.

Condition 3   The end of the column is connected to members which, while not specifically designed to provide restraint to rotation of the column will, nevertheless, provide some nominal restraint.

Condition 4   The end of the column is unrestrained against both lateral movement and rotation (e.g. the free end of a cantilever column in an unbraced structure).

Monolithic connection implies that there can be no relative translation or rotation between the column and the structure connected to it, as for example where the reinforcement for a beam either passes through the column or is anchored within it. The difference between conditions 1, 2 and 3 lies in the degree of restraint to rotation provided by the connected structure; effective lateral restraint is provided in all three.

The value of β to be used in Equation (9.1) depends upon the combination of conditions at the two ends of the column. It can be obtained by reference to Table 9.1, which is derived from Tables 3.21 and 3.22 of BS 8110, Pt 1.

Table 9.1   Values of β for columns

Braced				Unbraced			
Top condition	Bottom condition			Top condition	Bottom condition		
	1	2	3		1	2	3
1	0.75	0.80	0.90	1	1.2	1.3	1.6
2	0.80	0.85	0.95	2	1.3	1.5	1.8
3	0.90	0.95	1.00	3	1.6	1.8	—
				4	2.2	—	—

Columns are usually connected to beams spanning in two directions at right angles; and since the end conditions are not necessarily the same in each direction, there are usually two values of effective height to be considered.

The above method for determining effective height is the simplified approach recommended in BS 8110, Pt 1 for normal structures. When a more accurate determination is necessary or where a formula is preferable, as in a computer program for example, equations are given in cl 2.5, Pt 2.

EXAMPLE 9.1   Effective height of a column

A column with a 250 mm square section in a two-storey structure is founded on a small mass-concrete base. At first floor level it is monolithically connected in both directions to beams with an overall depth of 300 mm. At roof level a lighter system of beams with a depth of 200 mm is used. Storey heights are: first 3.8 m, second 2.9 m. Determine the effective heights of the column in each storey, assuming that it is (a) braced, (b) unbraced.

First decide on the appropriate end conditions; then obtain the factor β from Table 9.1. In this case the conditions in both directions are the same.

First storey

Bottom the base is not reinforced, so it cannot be assumed to provide restraint against rotation. However, it can be expected to fix the column in position and provide some nominal restraint to rotation – assume condition 3.

Top the depth of the beams exceeds the dimension of the column and they are monolithically connected, so condition 1 applies.
   From Table 9.1 β = 0.90 (braced), 1.6 (unbraced). Hence, from Equation (9.1)

$$l_e \text{ (braced)} = 0.9 \times 3.8 = \underline{3.42 \text{ m}}$$

$$l_e \text{ (unbraced)} = 1.6 \times 3.8 = \underline{6.08 \text{ m}}$$

Second storey

Bottom the condition is the same as the top of the first storey, namely condition 1.

Top since the depth of the beams is less than the dimension of the column, condition 2 applies.
   From Table 9.1 β = 0.80 (braced), 1.3 (unbraced)

Hence

$$l_e \text{ (braced)} = 0.8 \times 2.9 = \underline{2.32 \text{ m}}$$

$$l_e \text{ (unbraced)} = 1.3 \times 2.9 = \underline{3.77 \text{ m}}$$

9.1.4 Applied forces and moments

Columns usually form part of one of the following types of structure.

1 Braced frames, in which the beams may or may not be monolithically connected.
2 Unbraced (sway) frames
3 Flat slab and column construction.

   In the case of braced frames, since the horizontal loads are resisted by other parts of the structure and are not transmitted to the columns, it is generally necessary to take only vertical loads resulting from dead and imposed loads into account. The axial loads on the columns may be determined by considering the beams as simply supported (cl 3.8.2.3, Pt

1). In the case of unbraced frames, however, the effect of wind loads and the sway of the frames must also be considered. Appropriate methods of determining the axial loads and bending moments in the columns have been described in Chapter 4 for both types of frame. The determination of forces and moments in flat-slab construction is described in Chapter 10.

9.1.5   Minimum eccentricity

It is never possible in practice to ensure that a column is perfectly straight or that the load is purely axial. It is necessary therefore to design for a minimum eccentricity of load (cl 3.8.2.4, Pt 1):   At no section in a column should the design moment be taken as less than that produced by considering the design ultimate axial load as acting at a minimum eccentricity e_{min} of 0.05 times the overall dimension of the column in the plane of bending considered, but not more than 20 mm.

9.1.6   Slenderness

The usual methods of structural analysis are based on the assumption of a linear relationship between the applied loads and the resulting deformations. This assumption ignores the non-linear effects of axial loads which, if they are compressive, can produce significant additional deformations and bending moments in slender structures or structures containing slender members. For example, the bending moment at any point in the column shown in Fig. 9.4 is given by

$$M = M_i + Ny$$

where

> M_i is the *initial moment* obtained from an ordinary linear elastic structural analysis. Its minimum value is $e_{min} N$.
> Ny is the *additional moment* due to the axial load.

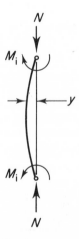

Fig. 9.4   Additional moment due to axial load.

Columns are classified as *short* or *slender*. In a short column the lateral deflection is small and the additional moment may be ignored, but when a column is classed as slender the additional moment is too great to be ignored and must be taken into account in the design. The recommendation of BS 8110 (cl 3.8.1.3, Pt 1) is as follows:

A column may be considered as short when both the ratios l_{ex}/h and l_{ey}/b are less than 15 (braced) and 10 (unbraced). It should otherwise be considered as slender.

In the above definition, referring to Fig. 9.5, l_{ex} and l_{ey} are respectively the effective heights when bending about the *x–x* and *y–y* axes are considered. The ratios l_{ex}/h and l_{ey}/b replace the slenderness ratio *effective length/minimum radius of gyration* in the classical theory.

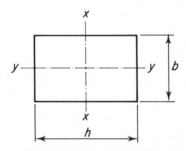

Fig. 9.5 Column axes and dimensions.

EXAMPLE 9.2 *Slenderness of a column*

Referring back to Fig. 9.2, which shows a typical floor plan of a small multistorey building, the reinforced concrete floor slab is 150 mm thick and is supported on beams 450 mm deep running in the *Y* direction. The beams and the slab are monolithically connected to the columns. The bases of the columns are designed to resist bending moments in both directions. The first and second storey heights are 4.5 m and 3.0 m respectively; and the dimensions of the columns are 250 mm by 450 mm. For each storey determine the effective height and slenderness of the columns and state whether they should be designed as short or slender.

Rotation about both *x–x* and *y–y* axes must be considered. The effective heights are obtained by applying Equation (9.1), using values of β from Table 9.1. The results for the column shown hatched are tabulated below.

| | | *x–x* axis (unbraced) | | | | | *y–y* axis (braced) | | | | |
| | | End condition | | | | | End condition | | | | |
Storey	Clear height	Bottom	Top	β	l_{ex}	l_{ex}/h	Bottom	Top	β	l_{ey}	l_{ey}/b
1	4.5	1	1	1.2	5.40	12.0	1	2	0.80	3.60	14.4
2	3.0	1	1	1.2	3.60	8.0	2	2	0.85	2.55	10.2

Comments

1   The column is braced in the *X*-direction (i.e. with respect to rotation about the *y*–*y* axis) by the walls, but no bracing is provided in the *Y*-direction (i.e. with respect to rotation about the *x*–*x* axis). At both levels the lateral movement of the column is constrained by the beams and the slab; so that in the *X*-direction all lateral movement is prevented by the bracing. In the *Y*-direction the lateral movement of all the columns at a particular level and in a particular line is the same and is equal to the lateral deflection of the structure at that point.

2   The limits of slenderness ratio for a short column are 10 for the *x*–*x* axis (unbraced), 15 for the *y*–*y* axis (braced). In storey 2 both slenderness ratios are less than the limit, so the column may be designed as short. In storey 1, however, the slenderness ratio with respect to the *x*–*x* axis exceeds the limit, so the column in this storey must be designed as slender.

3   On examination of the other columns, similar conclusions can be drawn.

9.1.7   Ultimate limit state

In a practical column, since there are always some bending moments or initial curvature, lateral deflections begin to be developed as soon as the axial load is applied and increase progressively as it is increased. A condition of elastic instability, of the type predicted in the classical Euler theory for an ideal strut, is never therefore attained; and the ultimate limit state is reached when the compressive strain in the concrete, due to the combined effect of axial force and bending moment, reaches the limiting value of 0.0035 at a critical section.

9.1.8   Limits-to-slenderness ratio

If a column is very slender it may be possible for the lateral deflection to become excessively large before the ultimate limit state is reached. It is therefore necessary to set an upper limit to the slenderness of a practical column. The following limits are recommended (cls 3.8.1.7–8, Pt 1).

Generally the clear distance, l_0, between end restraints should not exceed sixty times the minimum thickness of a column.

If, in any given plane, one end of an unbraced column is unrestrained (e.g. a cantilever column), its clear height l_0 should not exceed

$$l_0 = 100(b')^2/h' \leqslant 60b'$$

where

h' and b' are respectively the larger and smaller dimensions of the column.

The considerations of deflection may introduce further limitations.   (See Section 9.7 in this book.)

9.1.9   Reinforcement details

The rules for maximum and minimum longitudinal reinforcement in columns and for the diameter and spacing of links are given in Appendix A2.

9.2   Axially loaded short columns

Where axial load dominates, two approximate design formulae are recommended for short columns (cls 3.8.4.3–4, Pt 1).

If the method of construction prevents the column from being subjected to applied moments, the ultimate axial load should not exceed

$$N = 0.4f_{cu}A_c + 0.75A_{sc}\,f_y \tag{9.2}$$

where

A_c is the net cross-sectional area of the concrete
A_{sc} is the total area of vertical reinforcement
f_{cu} and f_y are the characteristic strengths of the concrete and steel.

Situations rarely arise when this formula may be used. A more common case is that of a short braced column supporting an approximately symmetrical arrangement of beams. In this case the ultimate axial load should not exceed

$$N = 0.35f_{cu}A_c + 0.67A_{sc}\,f_y \tag{9.3}$$

where

(a)   the beams are designed for uniformly distributed imposed loads; and
(b)   the beam spans do not differ by more than 15% of the longer.

EXAMPLE 9.3   Short, braced axially loaded column

A beam-and-column system in a three-storey building forms a 6 m grid in plan. The design ultimate dead and imposed roof and floor loadings, including an allowance for the beams, are, from the top down: 4.0, 6.6, 7.0 kN/m². The storey height is 3 m. The building is braced in both directions and the beams have been designed to be 350 mm deep, monolithically connected to the columns. The column bases are designed to resist bending moments. Assuming that the minimum column width necessary for fire resistance is 250 mm, the 28-day cube strength of the concrete is 25 N/mm², and that high-yield reinforcement is to be used, design a suitable section for one of the middle columns in the bottom storey.

End condition 1 applies at both the top and bottom of the column. Hence $\beta = 0.75$ and, assuming the minimum column size as the first trial,

$$l_{ex} = l_{ey} = 0.75 \times 3000/250 = 9.0 < 15$$

Therefore the column is short and, since the arrangement of beams is symmetrical, Equation (9.3) may be used.

The total load on each column is from a 6 m square, so that at ground level, ignoring the self-weight of the columns,

$$W = 36 \times (4.0 + 6.6 + 7.0) = 633.6 \text{ kN}$$

The weight of a 250 mm square column, assuming concrete density 24 kN/m³, will be assumed as an initial estimate of the self-weight.

Characteristic self-weight $= 9 \times (0.25)^2 \times 24 = 13.5$ kN
Design self-weight $= 13.5 \times 1.4 = 18.9$ kN
Total design load $= N = 633.6 + 18.9 = 653$ kN

Dividing Equation (9.3) through by A_c

$$N/A_c = 0.35f_{cu} + 0.67f_y A_{sc}/A_c \tag{1}$$

Putting $f_{cu} = 25$ N/mm^2 and $f_y = 460$ N/mm^2 and rearranging,

$$A_{sc}/A_c = (N/A_c - 8.75)/308.2 \tag{2}$$

It is sufficiently accurate to assume that A_c is the gross area of the section, i.e.

$$A_c = 250^2 = 62\,500 \text{ mm}^2.$$

Hence, from Equation (2),

$$A_{sc}/A_c = (653E3/62\,500 - 8.75)/308.2 = 0.00551$$

This proportional area of reinforcement is greater than the minimum allowable (0.004) and considerably less than the maximum (0.06). Therefore

$$A_{sc} = 0.00551 \times 62\,500 = \underline{344 \text{ mm}^2} - \text{say } \underline{4T12\ (452 \text{ mm}^2)}$$

A 250 mm square column is therefore satisfactory.

9.3   Combined bending and axial load

The basic assumptions made in the design of sections of beams in pure flexure may also be applied to column sections which are subjected to a combination of flexure and axial force. Consider the section in Fig. 9.6, assuming:

(a)   the rectangular stress block
(b)   the neutral axis is within the section
(c)   both sets of reinforcement are in compression
(d)   compressive stress and strain are positive.

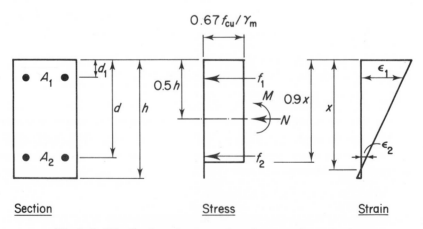

Fig. 9.6   Distribution of stress and strain on a column section.

These assumptions yield expressions that are true generally, except when $h < 0.9x$, i.e. when the whole section is in compression. This case is discussed in Appendix B2.

The section is subjected to an axial force N acting along the centre-line, and a bending moment M, as shown.

From the work on beams, the total compressive force in the concrete is given by $0.402f_{cu}bx$. Resolving horizontal forces, letting f_1 and f_2 be the stresses in the reinforcement,

$$N = 0.402f_{cu}\,bx + f_1A_1 + f_2A_2 \tag{9.4}$$

Taking moments about the centre-line,

$$M = 0.402f_{cu}bx(0.5h - 0.45x) + f_1A_1(0.5h - d_1) + f_2A_2(0.5h - d) \tag{9.5}$$

If the usual case of a symmetrical section is assumed, with a total area of reinforcement A_{sc}, these equations can be simplified by putting $A_1 = A_2 = A_{sc}/2$ and $d_1 = h - d$, as follows:

$$N = 0.402f_{cu}bx + (f_1 + f_2)A_{sc}/2 \tag{9.6}$$
$$M = 0.402f_{cu}bx(0.5h - 0.45x) + (0.5h - d)(f_2 - f_1)A_{sc}/2 \tag{9.7}$$

Normally N and M are known and the problem is to determine the required value of A_{sc} for a particular section. The other unknowns in the equations are the depth x of the neutral axis and the steel stresses f_1 and f_2. These latter can be expressed in terms of x by considering the strain diagram in Fig. 9.6. Thus, from similar triangles,

$$\varepsilon_1/(x - h + d) = 0.0035/x = \varepsilon_2/(x - d)$$

If the stress is below the design strength its value in N/mm² may be obtained by multiplying the above strains by 200E3, the modulus of elasticity of steel in N/mm². Hence

$$f_1 = 700(x - d + h)/x \tag{9.8}$$
$$f_2 = 700(x - d)/x \tag{9.9}$$

When the stress is at the design strength the right-hand sides of the above equations simply become $\pm 0.87f_y$.

Equations (9.6)–(9.9) can be solved to obtain A_{sc} for particular values of N and M, but the solution is difficult and requires a trial-and-error method. It is more convenient to use design graphs derived from the equations. A complete set of these graphs is provided in Appendix B1 and their derivation is explained in Appendix B2.

EXAMPLE 9.4 *Design of reinforcement including links*

A 300 mm square column made from C30 concrete is designed for ultimate loads of 1750 kN axial and 100 kN m bending moment. Design suitable high-yield reinforcement assuming a cover of 20 mm on the links. Draw a part elevation and section showing the detail.

Assume initially 25 mm longitudinal bars.

Diameter of links (see Appendix A2.2.1) = 25/4 = (say) <u>8 mm</u> (7 mm not available.)

Cover on longitudinal bars $= 20 + 8 = 28$ mm
$d/h = (300 - 28 - 12.5)/300 = 0.87$ (Use Graph No. 11 – $d/h = 0.9$)

For the design graph:

$M/bh^2f_{cu} = 100E6/(300^3 \times 30) = 0.1235$
$bhf_{cu} = 300^2 \times 30 = 2.7E6$
$N/bhf_{cu} = 1750E3/2.7E6 = 0.6481$

From the design $\alpha \approx 0.61 = A_{sc}f_y/bhf_{cu}$

Hence $A_{sc} = 0.61 \times 2.7E6/460 = \underline{3580 \text{ mm}^2}$

8T25 bars (3927 mm^2) is a reasonably economical solution.
Spacing of the links (see Appendix A2.6.5) $= 12 \times 25 = \underline{300 \text{ mm}}$.

The links are mild steel arranged in identical pairs, as shown in Fig. 9.7, thus enclosing each of the 8 bars within the corner of a link (see Appendix A2).

Fig. 9.7   Detail of a reinforcement.

The following checks should always be made, although with experience calculation may not be necessary.

1   Is $A_{sc} = 3927$ mm^2 between the maximum and minimum limits (see Appendix A2)?

Max. reinforcement $= 6\%$ of $300^2 = 5400$ mm^2
Min. reinforcement $= 0.4\%$ of $(300^2 - 3927) = 344$ mm^2

Therefore A_{sc} is within allowable limits.

2   Can 4 bars be accommodated in the width?

The minimum space between bars is the greater of $h_{agg} + 5$ mm or the bar diameter, both of which are 25 mm assuming that $h_{agg} = 20$ mm. Hence the space between bars $= (300 - 2 \times 28 - 4 \times 25)/3 = 48$ mm, which is adequate.

EXAMPLE 9.5   Analysis of a given section

The section of a column made from C25 concrete has dimensions 300 mm × 425 mm and has 3T32 bars in each face placed to resist bending moments about the major axis. Cover is 35 mm on the main reinforcement. Determine the ultimate axial load capacity of the column if the design ultimate bending moment is (a) 285 kN m, (b) nominal.

$bhf_{cu} = 300 \times 425 \times 25 = 3.19E6$
$bh^2f_{cu} = 3.19E6 \times 425 = 1.355E9$

$$d/h = (425 - 51)/425 = 0.88$$
$$\alpha = A_{sc}f_y/bhf_{cu} = 2 \times 2413 \times 460/3.19\text{E}6 \approx 0.7$$

(a)   *Bending moment = 285 kN m*

$$M/bh^2f_{cu} = 285\text{E}6/1.355\text{E}9 = 0.210$$
$$N/bhf_{cu} \text{ from Graph No. 10 } (d/h = 0.85) = 0.44$$

Hence

$$N = 0.44 \times 3.19\text{E}6 \times 1\text{E}{-}3 = \underline{1404 \text{ kN}}$$

This is a conservative result. Using the graph for $d/h = 0.9$, $N = 1595$ kN. Interpolating between the two graphs, $N = 1519$ kN. Since α can be read to only approximately two places of decimals it is usually considered to be sufficiently accurate to use the graph with the nearest value of d/h.

(b)   *Nominal bending moment* (assuming $d/h = 0.9$ and using Graph No. 11)

$$e_{min}, \text{ since } h > 400 \text{ mm}, \; = 20 \text{ mm}$$
$$M = e_{min}N = 20 \, N$$
$$M/bh^2f_{cu} = (20/h) \times (N/bhf_{cu}) = 0.047N/bhf_{cu}$$

The solution lies to the left of the chain dotted line on the design graph, on a line joining the origin to a point on the top edge of the graph given by $M/bh^2f_{cu} = 0.047 \times 1.7 = 0.0799$. This line intersects $\alpha = 0.7$ at $N/bhf_{cu} = 0.95$. Hence $N = 0.95 \times 3.19\text{E}6 \times 1\text{E}{-}3 = \underline{3031 \text{ kN}}$

9.4   Biaxial bending

Rigorous analysis of a reinforced concrete section subjected to biaxial bending at the ultimate limit state is beyond the scope of this introductory text. In the absence of a

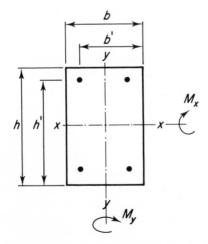

Fig. 9.8   Meaning of symbols for Equations (9.10) and (9.11).

rigorous analysis BS 8110 recommends that the effect of biaxial bending on a symmetrically reinforced section be simulated by designing for an increased equivalent bending moment about a single axis (cl 3.8.4.5, Pt 1). The requirements that the bending moment should not be less than the nominal value (see Section 9.1.5) still applies. However ... Where biaxial bending is considered, it is only necessary to ensure that the eccentricity exceeds the minimum about one axis at a time (cl 3.8.2.4, Pt 1).

The equivalent moment may be determined from one of the following formulae, in which the symbols have the special meaning shown in Fig. 9.8.

(a)   When $M_x/h' \geqslant M_y/b'$ the section is designed for bending about the x–x axis and the increased moment is given by

$$M_x' = M_x + \beta M_y h'/b' \tag{9.10}$$

(b)   When $M_x/h' < M_y/b'$ the section is designed for bending about the y–y axis and the increased moment is given by

$$M_y' = M_y + \beta M_x b'/h' \tag{9.11}$$

(b)   where β is obtained from Table 9.2

Table 9.2   Values of β for biaxially bent columns (from Table 3.24, Pt 1)

N/bhf_{cu}	0.0	0.1	0.2	0.3	0.4	0.5	$\geqslant 0.6$
β	1.00	0.88	0.77	0.65	0.53	0.42	0.30

9.5   Slender columns

9.5.1   General

The sections of both short and slender columns may be designed in the same way, using the design graphs in Appendix B1, except that the design moments for slender columns must be determined by combining the bending moments obtained from an ordinary linear structural analysis with the additional moments produced by the axial load acting through the lateral displacement of the column. When there are significant bending moments about both axes, the additional moment about both axes must be taken into account.

For most slender columns it may be assumed that if the column is bent about a single axis, the additional moment is applied in the same plane as the initial moment; so that it is only necessary to consider uniaxial bending in design. However, very slender columns and columns with narrow sections subject to initial bending moments about the major axis tend to buckle about both axes. For such columns it is recommended (cls 3.8.3.3–5, Pt 1) that if the slenderness ratio l_e/h exceeds 20, or if the ratio of the longer side of the section to the shorter is equal to 3 or more, the columns should be designed as biaxially bent with zero initial moment about the minor axis.

For columns subjected to bending moments about the minor axis there is no restriction to slenderness apart from the limits specified in Section 9.1.8. It is unlikely that columns with sections where the longer side exceeds three times the shorter side would be used in practice to resist bending moments about the minor axis; and BS 8110 makes no recommendations for dealing with such columns.

A further recommendation (cl 3.8.3.9, Pt 1) when the slenderness ratio exceeds 20 is that members monolithically connected to the ends of the column should be designed to resist the additional moments applied to them by the column, or by both columns if there is a column above and below the junction, in addition to the bending moments determined by ordinary methods of structural analysis.

9.5.2 Additional moment (cl 3.8.3.1, Pt 1)

The additional moment is given by the product of the axial force and the lateral deflection of the column at the ultimate limit state, i.e.

$$M_{add} = Na_u \tag{9.12}$$

The lateral deflection a_u may be taken as

$$a_u = Kh(l_e/b')^2/2000 \tag{9.13}$$

where

h and l_e are respectively the overall depth of the section and the effective height of the column, both with respect to the plane under consideration.

b' is normally the smaller section dimension. However, in the case of biaxial bending, b' is taken as h, the dimension in the plane of bending. *Note that b' in this equation must not be confused with the same symbol in Equations* (9.10) *and* (9.11) (see Example 9.9).

K is a reduction factor which corrects for the reduction in curvature as the ratio N/M increases. Lines representing different values of K are shown on the design graphs in Appendix B1.

The factor K depends upon the areas of concrete and reinforcement in the section, so that in order to evaluate Equation (9.13) a trial value of $K = 1$ is first used. This always yields a conservative design which may either be accepted as it stands or refined iteratively, using the design graphs, as shown in Example 9.8. Significant economies can often be achieved by refining the design.

EXAMPLE 9.6   Determination of the additional moment

A braced column with effective heights $l_{ex} = 3800$ mm and $l_{ey} = 3350$ mm has a section 200 mm × 300 mm and is subjected to an axial force of 400 kN. Show that the column is slender and determine a conservative value of the additional moments, assuming

(a) that the column is bent only about its major axis.
(b) that the column is subjected to significant bending moments about both axes.

General

$$l_{ex}/h = 3800/300 = 12.7 < 15$$
$$l_{ey}/b = 3350/200 = 16.8 > 15$$

Since one of the ratios exceeds 15 the column must be designed as slender.

(a)   *Uniaxial bending about the major axis*

In Equation (9.13) $K = 1$, $b' = 200$, $h = 300$. Hence

$$a_u = 300(3800/200)^2/2000 = 54.15 \text{ mm}$$

From Equation (9.12)

$$M_{add} = 400 \times 54.15\text{E}{-}3 = \underline{21.7 \text{ kN m}}$$

(b)   *Biaxial bending*

(i) About the major axis

In Equation (9.13) $K = 1$, $b' = h = 300$, $l_e = 3800$. Hence

$$a_u = 300(3800/300)^2/2000 = 24.1 \text{ mm}$$
$$M_{add} = 400 \times 24.1\text{E}{-}3 = \underline{9.6 \text{ kN m}}$$

(ii) About the minor axis

In Equation (9.13) $K = 1$, $b' = h = 200$, $l_e = 3350$. Hence

$$a_u = 200(3350/200)^2/2000 = 28.1 \text{ mm}$$
$$M_{add} = 400 \times 28.1\text{E}{-}3 = \underline{11.2 \text{ kN m}}$$

9.5.3   Design moments in braced columns (cl 3.8.3.2, Pt 1)

The design moment is the maximum moment obtained by combining the initial and additional moments. Possible combinations for a braced column may be explained by considering the example in Fig. 9.9(a), where the column is bent about a single axis and the initial moments are M_1 and M_2 ($M_1 < M_2$). The initial bending moment diagram is shown in (b). Ignoring the effect of joint rotation the axial load produces additional lateral deflection, with corresponding bending momnents, as in (c).

If combinations of (b) and (c) are considered, and the case of a nominal moment is included, the design moment is the greatest of the following.

(a) M_2
(b) $M_i + M_{add}$
(c) $M_1 + M_{add}/2$
(d) $e_{min}N$ (9.14)

where

> M_{add} is the additional moment obtained from Equations (9.12) and (9.13)
> M_i is the initial moment at the point of maximum lateral deflection a_u
> e_{min} is the minimum eccentricity as defined in Section 9.1.5.

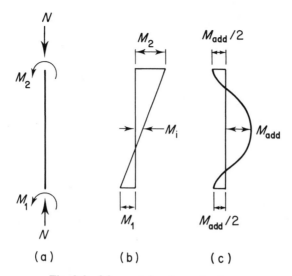

Fig. 9.9 Moments in a braced column.

The maximum deflection occurs near the mid-height position and M_i may be taken as

$$M_i = 0.4M_1 + 0.6M_2 \geqslant 0.4M_2 \tag{9.15}$$

In this equation M_1 is the moment with the smaller numerical value irrespective of direction. The sign of the moments is determined by the curvature they produce. Thus if the column is in single curvature, as in Fig. 9.10(a), both moments are assumed to be positive. If the column is in double curvature, as in Fig. 9.10(b), the bending moments are of opposite sign. In this case the smaller moment M_1 should be assumed negative to obtain a positive result for M_i, which must not be less than $0.4M_2$.

EXAMPLE 9.7   Design moment in a slender column

Using the conservative additional moments already obtained, determine the design moment, for the column in case (a) of Example 9.6 with end moments as shown in Fig. 9.10. The units are kN m.

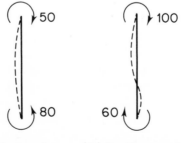

(a) Single curvature   (b) Double curvature

Fig. 9.10 Columns in single and double curvature.

(a)   The column is in single curvature, so both moments are assumed to be positive, i.e.

$M_1 = 50$ kN m, $M_2 = 80$ kN m
$M_i = 0.4 \times 50 + 0.6 \times 80 = 68$ kN m
M_{add} (from Example 9.6) $= 21.7$ kN m
$e_{min} = 0.05h \leqslant 20$ mm $= 0.05 \times 300 = 15$ mm

From Equation (9.14) the design moment is the greater of:

$M_2 = 80$ kN m
$M_i + M_{add} = 68 + 21.7 = 89.7$ kN m
$M_1 + M_{add}/2 = 50 + 21.7/2 = 60.9$ kN m
$e_{min}N = 15\text{E--}3 \times 400 = 6$ kN m

Hence the maximum design moment is 89.7 kN m.

(b)   The column is in double curvature, so M, is assumed to be negative, i.e.

$M_1 = -60$ kN m, $M_2 = 100$ kN m
$M_i = 0.4 \times (-60) + 0.6 \times 100 = 36$ kN m
$0.4M_2 = 0.4 \times 100 = 40$ kN m

Hence

$M_i = 40$ kN m,

Testing the alternatives in Equation (9.14), the maximum design moment is M_2, i.e. 100 kN m.

EXAMPLE 9.8   Refinement of the design moment

A braced slender column 250 mm by 350 mm in section is made from C30 concrete and has an effective length of 4000 mm when considering bending about either axis. The design ultimate loading is as shown in Fig. 9.11, the moments being applied about the major axis. Assuming $d/h = 0.9$, design suitable reinforcement.

1500 kN

75 kN m

75 kN m

Fig. 9.11

$$a_u = Kh(l_e/b')^2/2000$$

Since bending is about the major axis $h = 350$ mm and $b' = 250$ mm. Hence, assuming initially that $K = 1$,

$$a_u = 350(4000/250)^2/2000 = 44.8 \text{ mm}$$
$$M_{add} = Na_u = 1500 \times 44.8\text{E}{-}3 = 67.2 \text{ kN m}$$

As the column is in uniform single curvature $M_i = 75$ kN m and the design moment is

$$M_i + M_{add} = 75 + 67.2 = 142 \text{ kN m}$$

For the design graph:

$$bh^2f_{cu} = 250 \times 350^2 \times 30 = 918.8\text{E}6 = 918 \text{ kN m}$$
$$bhf_{cu} = 2.625\text{E}6 = 2625 \text{ kN}$$

Hence

$$M/bh^2f_{cu} = 142/918.8 = 0.155$$
$$N/bhf_{cu} = 1500/2625 = 0.571$$

From Graph No. 11 ($d/h = 0.9$), $\alpha = 0.58$ and, estimating between the K lines, $K = 0.56$. Using this new value of K to modify the additional moment,

$$M_{add} = 0.56 \times 67.2 = 37.6 \text{ kN m}$$

giving a new design moment of $75 + 37.6 = 112.6$ kN m, and a new value of M/bh^2f_{cu} of 0.123.

Returning to the design graph $\alpha = 0.51$ and $K = 0.48$. A further iteration yields:

$$M_{add} = 32.3$$
$$M_{design} = 107.3$$
$$M/bh^2f_{cu} = 0.117$$

from which $\alpha = 0.48$ and $K = 0.46$.

Since the difference between the last two values of K is small, further iteration is unnecessary, so

$$A_{sc} = 0.48 \times 2.625\text{E}6/460 = \underline{2739 \text{ mm}^2}$$

For comparison, the corresponding design graph in BS 8110, Pt 3, which is based on the parabolic stress block, gives $A_{sc} = 2713 \text{ mm}^2$.

9.5.4 Design moments in unbraced columns

In general the columns in unbraced (sway) frames are in double curvature, with the maximum values of both the initial and additional moments at their ends. It is recommended (cl 3.8.3.7, Pt 1) that the additional moment obtained from Equations (9.12) and (9.13) ... may be assumed to occur at whichever end of the column has the stiffer joint; the additional moment at the other end may be reduced in proportion to the ratio of the joint stiffnesses at either end. The moment will act in a direction such that it increases the absolute magnitude at the critical section.

Thus the design moment for an unbraced column AB is the greater of

$$M_A + M_{add}$$

or

$$M_B + M_{add} \times k_B/k_A \tag{9.16}$$

where k_A and k_B are the joint stiffnesses and $k_A > k_B$.

The stiffness of a joint is the stiffnesses of all the members connected monolithically at the joint in the plane under consideration, including the columns in both storeys if they are continuous; all members not monolithically connected should be assumed to have a stiffness of zero. The stiffness of members may be extracted from the analysis (see Chapter 4) or, since only the ratio is required the stiffness of a member may be defined as the second moment of area divided by its length. The second moments of area may be calculated from the overall dimensions of the sections.

If the columns in a sway frame are constrained by connecting beams or floor slabs so that at a particular level the sidesway deflections are the same, BS 8110 allows an average value of a_u to be applied to all the columns (cl 3.8.3.8, Pt 1). This average deflection may be calculated from

$$a_{uav} = (\Sigma a_u)/n \tag{9.17}$$

where n is the number of columns resisting sidesway at the particular level
    Σa_u is the sum of the lateral deflections, obtained from Equation (9.13).

After calculating a_{uav}, any values of a_u more than twice a_{uav} should be ignored and the average recalculated; in this case n (in Equation (9.17)) should be reduced appropriately.

EXAMPLE 9.9   *Design of a slender column in biaxial bending*

A typical column in the bottom storey of a building has a section 250 mm by 500 mm. In the Y-direction the horizontal forces are resisted by the frame action of the columns and connecting beams. In the X-direction bracing is provided by shear walls. The columns are monolithically connected to an *in-situ* beam and slab floor as shown in Fig. 9.12 and arranged in a $9\,m \times 4\,m$ grid. The column is supported by a reinforced concrete base designed to resist bending moments in both directions. The storey height is 4.5 m. Design suitable reinforcement given the design ultimate bending moments in the figure and an ultimate axial load of 2000 kN. Cover on the main reinforcement may be assumed to be 30 mm.

The solution of the problem divides into five parts.

1   Consideration of bracing, effective height, and slenderness, with respect to both the x–x and y–y axes of the column section.

2   Determination of the additional moments in the slender column.

3   Determination of the design moments.

4   Design of the reinforcement using the design graph.

5   Refinement of the design.

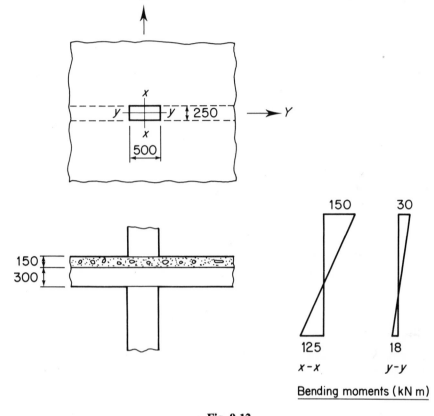

Bending moments (kN m)

Fig. 9.12

1 *Effective height*

Axis	End conditions	β (Table 9.1)	l_e (mm)
x–x (unbraced)	Bottom 1 Top 2	1.3	5850
y–y (braced)	Bottom 1 Top 2	0.8	3600

Hence

$$l_{ex}/h = 5850/500 = 11.7$$
$$l_{ey}/b = 3600/250 = 14.4$$

Since l_{ex}/h exceeds 10, the limit of slenderness for a short unbraced column, the column must be designed as slender.

2 *Additional moments*

$$M_{add} = Na_u$$

where

$$a_u = kh(l_e/b')^2/2000$$

For biaxial bending b' is taken as h, the dimension in the plane of bending (see Section 9.5.2).

Hence, taking $K = 1$ initially.
  x–x axis:

$b' = h = 500$ mm
$a_u = 500 \times 1 \times (5850/500)^2/2000 = 34.2$ mm
$M_{add} = 2000 \times 34.2\text{E}{-}3 = 68.4$ kN m

It is assumed here that all the columns are similar; so that $a_u = a_{uav}$.

  y–y axis:

$b' = h = 250$ mm
$a_u = 250 \times 1 \times (3600/250)^2/2000 = 25.9$ mm
$M_{add} = 2000 \times 25.9 = 51.8$ kN m

3   Design moments

  x–x axis (unbraced):
The stiffness of the base joint is practically indeterminate, so assume that M_{add} occurs at the end of the column with the greater initial moment (i.e. at the top). The design moment is then given by

$$M_x = M_{top} + M_{add} = 150 + 68.4 = \underline{218.4\ \text{kN m}}$$

  y–y axis (braced):

$$M_i = 0.4M_1 + 0.6M_2 \geqslant 0.4M_2, \qquad \text{where } M_2 > M_1$$

The column is in double curvature, so $M_1 = -18.0$ kN m, $M_2 = 30.0$ kN m

$0.4 \times (-18.0) + 0.6 \times 30.0 = 10.8$ kN m
$0.4M_2 = 0.4 \times 30.0 = 12.0$ kN m

Hence

$$M_i = 12.0\ \text{kN m}$$

The alternatives to be considered are:

$M_2 = 30.0$ kN m
$M_i + M_{add} = 12.0 + 51.8 = 63.8$ kN m
$M_1 + M_{add}/2 = 18.0 + 25.9 = 43.9$ kN m
$e_{min}N = 0.05 \times 250\text{E}{-}3 \times 2000 = 25$ kN m

Hence the design moment $M_y = \underline{63.8\ \text{kN m}}$

These moments must be combined using Equation (9.10) or (9.11) to obtain a design moment about a single axis.

Assuming T32 bars and using cover = 30 mm,

$$h' = 500 - 30 - 16 = 454 \text{ mm}$$
$$b' = 250 - 30 - 16 = 204 \text{ mm}$$

Since $M_x/h' > M_y/b'$ use Equation (9.10), i.e.

$$M'_x = M_x + \beta M_y h'/b'$$

β must be extracted from Table 9.2:

$$bhf_{cu} = 250 \times 500 \times 30 = 3.75\text{E}6$$
$$N/bhf_{cu} = 2000\text{E}3/3.75\text{E}6 = 0.533$$

By interpolation $\beta = 0.42 - 0.12 \times 0.033/0.1 = 0.380$

Hence

$$\beta h'/b' = 0.38 \times 454/204 = 0.846$$

and

$$M'_x = 218.4 + 0.846 \times 63.8 = \underline{272.4 \text{ kN m}}$$

4 Design graph

$$bhf_{cu} = 3.75\text{E}6, \quad N/bhf_{cu} = 0.553$$
$$bh^2 f_{cu} = 3.75\text{E}6 \times 500 = 1.875\text{E}9$$
$$M'_x/bh^2 f_{cu} = 272.4\text{E}6/1.875\text{E}9 = 0.145$$
$$d/h = h'/h = 454/500 = 0.908$$

Graph No. 11 ($d/h = 0.9$) gives $\alpha = 0.53$, $K = 0.55$

$$A_{sc} = \alpha bhf_{cu}/f_y = 0.53 \times 3.75\text{E}6/460 = 4321 \text{ mm}^2$$

5 Refining the design

Using $K = 0.55$ the additional moments become 37.6 kN m and 28.5 kN m. Hence the new design moments are $M_x = 187.6$ kN m, $M_y = 40.5$ kN m, and the overall design moment about the major axis is $M'_x = 221.9$ kN m.

For the design graph $M'_x/bh^2 f_{cu} = 0.118$ and $N/bhf_{cu} = 0.553$ as before, giving $\alpha = 0.45$, $A_{sc} = 3669 \text{ mm}^2$, and $K = 0.50$.

A further iteration yields $\alpha = 0.44$ ($A_{sc} = 3587 \text{ mm}^2$). The nearest symmetrical arrangement of bars is 2T32 and 1T16 in each short face ($A_{sc} = 3619 \text{ mm}^2$). As the space between the 32 mm bars and the 16 mm bar does not exceed 150 mm the bars can be enclosed within a single link.

Link diameter = 32/4 = 8 mm.

Link spacing = $12 \times 16 = 192$ mm (say 190 mm).

Note that if 6T32 bars were used instead of the above arrangement the cost of vertical reinforcement would be increased by one third, but the spacing of the links could then be increased, approximately halving their cost.

9.6   Shear strength of columns

Except in special cases, such as earthquake design for example, columns are designed to resist shear forces without the use of shear reinforcement – the horizontal links are provided to contain the longitudinal reinforcement and to resist the effects of axial compression. It is recommended (cl 3.8.4.6, Pt 1) that:

…For rectangular sections no check is required where M/N is less than $0.75h$ provided that the shear stress does not exceed $0.8\sqrt{f_{cu}}$ or 5 N/mm², whichever is the lesser.

If M/N exceeds $0.75h$ the shear stress must not exceed the design shear stress that can be supported by the section. Determination of the shear stress due to ultimate loads and the design shear stress for a column section without shear reinforcement is described in Chapter 7 (see Section 7.1.16).

9.7   Serviceability limit states

For most practical columns the serviceability requirements for deflection and crack control are automatically satisfied when the column is designed for the ultimate limit state.

Deflection (cl 3.8.5, Pt 1) No checks need to be made for deflection of braced columns within the recommended limits of slenderness (see Section 9.1.8). The same limits may be applied to unbraced columns in single-storey construction where no finishes suscepti-ble to damage by deflection are present. For unbraced columns in general no checks need to be made if the average value of l_e/h does not exceed 30 for all the columns at the level and in the direction under consideration.

Crack control (cl 3.8.6, Pt 1) Checks for cracks due to bending are not required if the design ultimate axial load is greater than $0.2f_{cu}A_c$. A more lightly loaded column subject to bending should be considered as a beam for the purposes of crack control. *Note that a column on which the ultimate axial load does not exceed $0.1f_{cu}A_c$ is designed wholly as a beam.*

9.8   Tutorial problems

9.8.1   Effective height and slenderness

Figure 9.13 shows the general arrangement of a column in a frame. Determine the slenderness ratios and state whether the column should be designed as short or slender:

(a)   if the column is braced in both directions
(b)   if it is unbraced in the *Y*-direction (i.e. bending about the *x–x* axis).

All the beams are monolithically connected and the base is designed to resist moments.

Answer

	Braced l_{ey}/b	Braced l_{ex}/h	Unbraced l_{ex}/h
Storey 1	12.0	6.0 (short)	9.6 (short)
Storey 2	12.0	6.4 (short)	10.4 (slender)

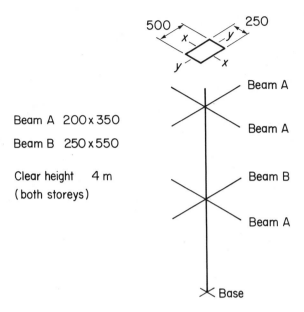

Beam A 200 x 350

Beam B 250 x 550

Clear height 4 m
(both storeys)

Fig. 9.13

9.8.2 Maximum clear height of a cantilever column

A monument has the form of a single column supporting a sculpture at the top. What is the maximum clear height of the column if the section is (a) 1200×600 mm, (b) 1200×800 mm?

Answers
(a) 30 m; (b) 48 m.

9.8.3 Ultimate capacity of a short, axially loaded column

A short braced column reinforced with 6T32 bars has a 300 mm square section and is made from C30 concrete. Calculate its ultimate axial load capacity:

(a) if the form of construction precludes any bending moment,
(b) if the column supports a symmetrical arrangement of beams carrying dead and imposed loads.

Answers
(a) 2687 kN; (b) 2381 kN.

9.8.4 Design of a short column subjected to axial load and bending

A short column made from C25 concrete has a 300×500 mm section. Cover on the links is 25 mm. The design ultimate loads are 2500 kN axial and a bending moment of 365 kN m about the major axis. Design suitable reinforcement and sketch a section showing the detail.

Answer

$A_{sc} = 6359$ mm^2 (8T32), Double 8 mm links as in Example 9.4 (see Fig. 9.7) at 380 mm centres.

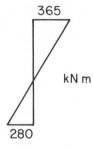

365

kN m

280

Fig. 9.14

9.8.5   Shear resistance of a column

The column in Problem 9.8.4 has a height of 3.5 m and ultimate design moments as shown in Fig. 9.14. Calculate the shear force acting on the column and check that its shear resistance is adequate.

Answer

$V = 184$ kN; $v = 1.29$ N/mm$^2 < 0.8\sqrt{f_{cu}} < 5$ N/mm^2, $M/N < 0.75h$. No further check is necessary.

9.8.6   Capacity of a section in uniaxial and biaxial bending

A 350×450 mm column section has 3T40 bars with a cover of 45 mm in each short face. The characteristic strengths of the concrete and steel are 30 N/mm^2 and 460 N/mm^2. Assuming that the column is short, determine the ultimate axial load capacity:

(a)   if the design ultimate bending moment is 280 kN m about the major axis,
(b)   if there is a further design moment of 180 kN m about the minor axis.

Hint

In part (b), use trial and error to find β from Table 9.2.

Answers

$(d/h = 0.85)$ (a) 3400 kN; (b) 2930 kN.

9.8.7   Braced slender column

A braced column with a 300 mm square section has an effective height of 4.8 m and is made from C35 concrete. The design ultimate loads are as shown in Fig. 9.15. Cover on the links is 25 mm. Show that the column is slender and

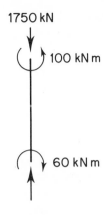

Fig. 9.15

(a) determine the initial moment and conservative values of the additional and design moments,

(b) design suitable reinforcement, refining the design to give an economical result.

Answers

$l_e/h = 16 > 15$;

(a) 84 kN m, 67.2 kN m, 151.2 kN m;

(b) $A_{sc} = 3629$ mm^2 (8T25), links 8 mm at 300 mm centres, as in Example 9.4 (see Fig. 9.7).

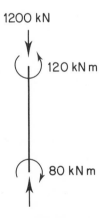

Fig. 9.16

9.8.8 Design moments for an unbraced slender column

For the second storey column in Problem 9.8.1(b) the design loads are 2000 kN axial and bending moments about the major axis of 120 kN m (top) and 80 kN m (bottom). Both moments are in the same direction, i.e. producing double curvature. There is no applied moment about the minor axis. Make a first estimate of the design moments at the top and bottom of the column, taking the stiffness of the joints into account. Assume that all the columns in the first three storeys have similar properties and that the connecting beams are 6 m long.

Answer
Top 255.7 kN m, bottom 296.4 kN m.

9.8.9   Slender column in biaxial bending

A braced column with a 200×600 mm section supports ultimate design loads as shown in Fig. 9.16. The bending moments are applied about the major axis. The column is made from C25 concrete and has an effective height of 5 m with respect to either axis. The longitudinal reinforcement is high-yield steel and has a cover of 35 mm.

(a)   Show that the column is slender and explain why it should be designed as biaxially bent.
(b)   Use a trial-and-error method to determine the design moments and an economical area of main reinforcement.

Answers
(a) $l_{ey}/b > 15$ – slender, $h/b = 3$ – design as biaxially bent.

(b)   Design moments: first estimate 93.9 kN m, final estimate 65.5 kN m, about the minor axis.
Reinforcement: $A_{sc} = 2764$ mm^2, i.e. (3T25) in each long face.

10

Reinforced Concrete Slabs

10.1 Introduction

This chapter will deal with the design process for slabs. A slab, in essence, can be defined as a member which is wider than deep, whereas a beam is generally deeper than wide. This distinction is not necessary when bending is concerned but does need taking into account when considering shear, since for thin members the allowable shear stress is generally enhanced.

This chapter will consider the design of

(i)   one-way spanning slabs;
(ii) two-way spanning slabs;
(iii) flat slabs including waffle slabs;
(iv) staircases;
(v)   retaining walls.

10.2 Methods of construction

The simplest type of slab is uniform thickness solid slab (Fig. 10.1(a)). The main drawback with this type of slab is the very high dead weight compared with the likely live load. Uniform thickness slabs have the simplest requirement for formwork in that the soffit level is constant over the whole slab. This type of slab is little used over spans above 3 m.

For higher spans the dead load is relieved either by placing some sort of void in the slab by adding ribs (as in Fig. 10.1(b)), or by reducing the thickness of the slab at mid-span and retaining an increased thickness near the support (this is known as a drop head). This latter form of construction generally occurs in flat slabs (Section 10.12). If the slab is ribbed in both directions, the slab is then known as a waffle slab. The section around the column is generally solid to the full depth around the column to resist hogging moments. The use of waffle slabs to reduce dead load has come into widespread use owing to the availability of proprietary formwork systems which allow the pan shutters forming the voids to be struck whilst the ribs remain propped off the floor below, so that the slabs may be used to support the formwork for the next floor. The elimination of the need to keep a uniform soffit has led to the virtual obsolescence of slabs with internal voids and hollow clay pots, so these are not covered in this book.

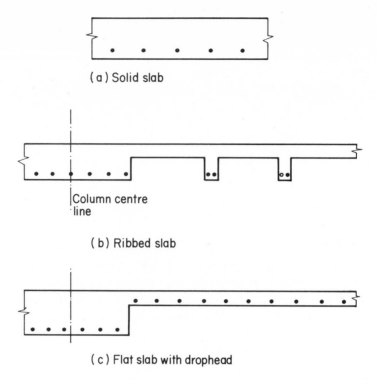

(a) Solid slab

Column centre line

(b) Ribbed slab

(c) Flat slab with drophead

Fig. 10.1   Types of slab.

10.3   Design philosophy

10.3.1   Ultimate limit state

Three possible methods may be used to determine the bending moment:

(a)   elastic analysis;
(b)   Johansen yield-line methods;
(c)   Hillerborg strip method.

If elastic analyses are used, then only part of the slab can be deemed effective in resisting the effect of a point load.

Here a point load refers to the imposition of a point load from the known imposed loading (e.g. a reaction from an item of machinery) and not the point load given in BS 6399 as part of the normal loading.

For solid slabs (or for other slabs where the flexural rigidities in the longitudinal and transverse directions are approximately equal) then the effective width (measured parallel to the supports) may be taken equal to

the load width plus $2.4x(1 - x/L)$

where x is the distance from the nearest support to the load and L the effective span. Where the ratio of the transverse to longitudinal flexural stiffnesses is less than unity a reduced value of the above effective width should be taken subject to a minimum value of the load width plus $4(x/L)(1 - x/L)$ metres.

For a load adjacent to an edge the effective width is to be taken as the load width plus $1.2x(1 - x/L)$ (or if appropriate $4(x/L)(1 - x/L)$) plus the distance from the edge of the slab to the load   (this is illustrated in Fig. 10.2) (cl 3.5.2.2, Pt 1).

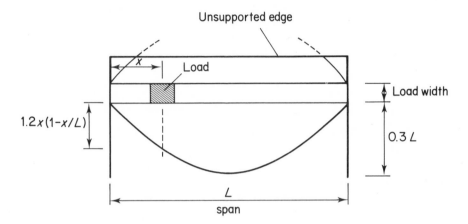

Fig. 10.2   Effective width of a slab at an unsupported edge.

The critical shear condition for slabs is usually punching shear around column heads, or shear due to the effect of imposed point loading. The shear around column heads is generally determined from statics alone, in that one quarter of the load on each slab is transmitted to each corner. In the case of flat slabs this figure is modified to allow for patterned loading (see Section 10.12).

10.3.2   Serviceability limit state

Deflections are, in general, calculated using span/depth ratios (Section 5.6). Explicit calculations for crack widths should be used only for vertically cast slabs forming basement walls or retaining walls, if there is any likelihood whatsoever of exposure to water. These calculations are covered in Section 5.7.

10.3.3   Loading

In general slabs may be designed for all spans loaded with maximum design loading provided the following conditions are satisfied (cl 3.5.2.3, Pt 1):

(i)   for one-way spanning slabs the area of a bay exceeds 30 m^2;
(ii) $q_k/g_k < 1.25$
(iii) $q_k < 5.0$ kN/m^2 excluding partitions.

If an elastic analysis is carried out assuming all spans fully loaded, then a 20% redistribution is allowed in support moments (except at the supports to cantilevers). The redistribution procedure is as demonstrated in Section 4.7. Note, however, that if a panel is adjacent to a cantilever whose span exceeds one third that of the slab, then the load case of maximum load on the cantilever and minimum load on the slab should be considered if an elastic analysis is used.

10.4   Plastic methods of analysis

For a plastic method of analysis to give the true collapse load, by the uniqueness theorem, the following three conditions must be satisfied:

Equilibrium   The moments (and shears or torsions) must be in balance with the applied loading.

Yield   The moments in any part of the structure must be less than or equal to the ultimate moment of resistance (or yield moment) at that point in the structure.

Mechanism formation   In order that total (or in some cases partial) collapse may occur a mechanism must form.

For two-dimensional frame structures it is usually relatively easy to determine a moment field for a given set of applied loading which will satisfy all three of the above conditions. For slabs it is not easy and methods have been formulated which satisfy either the upper or lower bound theorem of plastic collapse.

10.4.1   Upper-bound theorem

Here a set of moments is found which will satisfy equilibrium and the formation of a mechanism but may give moments in the structure which are higher than the yield moments. The collapse load so found will be higher than the true collapse load and thus may be thought of as an 'unsafe' solution. This is essentially the procedure used in the yield-line method first formulated by Johansen (1972).

10.4.2   Lower-bound theorem

Here a set of moments is found which will satisfy equilibrium and the yield criterion but will not necessarily cause collapse. The load so determined will be lower than the true collapse load and thus may be thought of as a 'safe' solution. This will result in the procedure known as the Hillerborg strip method.

10.5   Johansen yield-line method

10.5.1   Introduction

It has been observed in tests that when slabs are loaded to failure large cracks occur normal to the lines of maximum moment. The cracks are observed only on the tension face of the slab and are caused by the reinforced yielding and large ductile rotations occurring similar to those in under-reinforcement beams (Section 4.7). The formation of these yield lines leads to the concept of the occurrence of rigid-body rotation of the areas of the slab between the yield lines and the existence of failure mechanisms. Although in Section 10.4.1 yield-line methods were stated to be upper-bound solutions and thus 'unsafe', it should be noted that yield-line methods tend to underestimate slab strength, because although strain hardening takes place in the reinforcement and membrane action is caused by the existence of in-plane forces in the slab, both of which assist in carrying the load, the yield-line method assumes that bending action alone is responsible for carrying the applied load. It is possible that the actual load capacity of some slabs due to these corrective features may be up to 200% above that predicted by yield-line methods.

10.5.2 Method

The method used is to postulate a possible collapse mechanism, and then to calculate the load that may be carried by that mechanism for a given ultimate moment field (or to determine the ultimate moment for a given load). It is normal to characterize the yield-line positions by unknown dimensions.

There are two methods of carrying out the analysis:

(a) *Virtual work approach*   Here a virtual work equation is set up for the slab and a stationary value is obtained for the virtual work equation (hence, en route, determining any yield-line position parameters.)

(b) *Nodal force approach*   In this method the forces at any points where yield lines (or free edges) meet are evaluated. Equilibrium equations for each rigid body are set up and the unknown yield-line parameters are eliminated and a final equation giving the required load or moment is generated.

It should be noted that the yield criterion implies that only two yield lines may meet at a point, but frequently solutions will be noted whereby more than two meet at one point. In general such solutions are not unsafe, except at point loads or point supports, but there is an implication that an alternative solution may exist often making use of curved yield lines (fans). This point will be dealt with further in Section 10.5.5.

10.5.3 Postulation of yield-line mechanism and yield-line mechanics

There is a series of rules first proposed by Johansen for aiding the prediction of yield-line patterns using straight yield lines.

(i)   Yield lines are straight and form axes of rotation.
(ii)   Yield lines must terminate at the slab boundary.
(iii) Axes of rotation coincide with simply supported edges, cut free edges and pass through column supports.
(iv)   Axes of rotation of adjacent rigid regions intersect at a point (or may be parallel).
(v)   Hogging yield lines often exist along (part of) encastré edges.
(vi)   If the loading comprises point loads then yield lines will be contrained by such loads.

These rules may be seen to apply to a series of examples in Fig. 10.3.

It is usual to fix reinforcement orthogonally and therefore it is likely that reinforcement will be intersected at an angle by the yield line, as in Fig. 10.4.

If the reinforcement has an ultimate moment of resistance of m (per unit width)

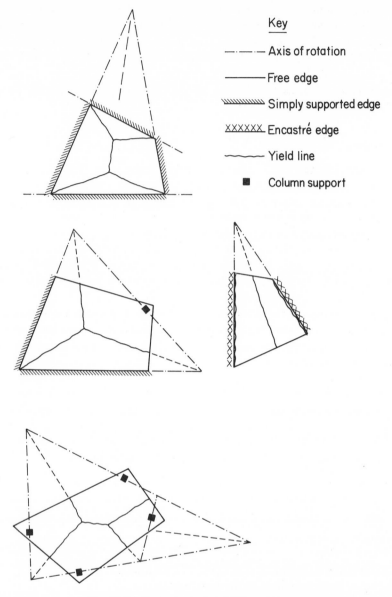

Fig. 10.3   Some typical yield-line patterns.

normal to the reinforcement, then along XY the total moment is $mL \sin \theta$ or, resolving normal to the reinforcement,

$$m_n L = (mL \sin \theta) \sin \theta$$

or

$$m_n = m \sin^2 \theta \qquad\qquad (10.1)$$

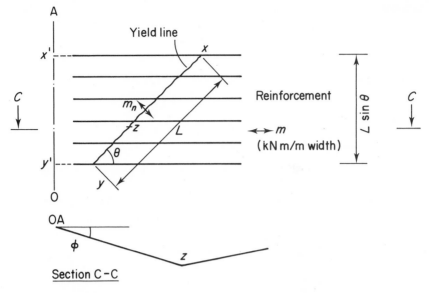

Fig. 10.4 Formation of yield inclined to the reinforcement.

If there is additional reinforcement giving an ultimate moment of μm orthogonal to that shown in Fig. 10.4, then

$$m_n = m \sin^2 \theta + \mu m \sin^2 (90 - \theta)$$
$$= m \sin^2 \theta + \mu m \cos^2 \theta$$

If the reinforcement is isotropic (which will be assumed for all the examples in this text) then $\mu = 1$ and $m_n = m$, i.e. the moment across the yield line is independent of the inclination of the yield line.

Consider again the yield line XY in Fig. 10.4; the work done by the yield line when the rigid body contained by the axis of rotation and the yield line rotates is

(moment) $\times$ (projected length of yield line on the axis of rotation) $\times$ (rotation)

that is

$$m(X'Y')\theta$$

It is conventional in yield-line work to use virtual displacements of unity given to the point of maximum displacement.

The work done by the loading is for a point load, $P\delta$, where P is the load and δ the virtual displacement at the load, and for a UDL is the total load on the rigid region multiplied by the displacement of the centroid of the load.

The formulation of the work equation generally, for one variable, leads to a formulation of the type

$$nf_1(x_1) = mf_2(x_1)$$

or

$$n/m = f_2(x_1)/f_1(x_1) \tag{10.2}$$

For a stationary value $\mathrm{d}(n/m)/\mathrm{d}x = 0$ or

$$(f_2(x_1))/(f_1(x_1)) = (f'_2(x_1))/(f'_1(x_1)) \qquad (10.3)$$

The value of x_1 obtained from Equation (10.3) may be back-substituted into

$$m/n = f'_2(x_1)/f'_1(x_1)$$

to obtain m/n.

EXAMPLE 10.1   *Collapse of a square slab*

Consider an encastré square slab with a load n, sagging moment m and hogging moment im (Fig. 10.5(a)).

The only possible configuration using straight yield lines is that shown in Fig. 10.5(b).

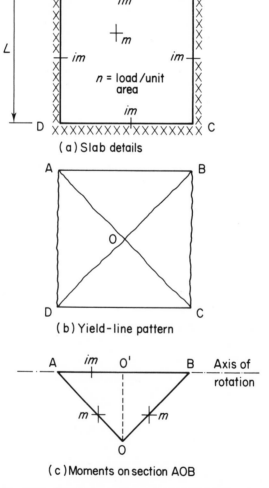

(a) Slab details

(b) Yield-line pattern

(c) Moments on section AOB

Fig. 10.5   Yield-line collapse for an encastré square slab.

Owing to symmetry only one quarter of the slab need be considered (Fig. 10.5(c)).
So, using virtual work and displacing O by unity

For the moments:
(a) *sagging*

Yield line AO

work done is (moment) (projected length) (rotation)
moment = m
projected length of AO = AO' = $L/2$
rotation = $1/(OO)' = 1/(L/2) = 2/L$
so work done = $m(L/2)(2/L) = m$

Yield line OB

as AO, i.e. m

(b) *hogging*

Yield line AB

moment = im
projected length = AB = L
rotation = $1/(OO)' = 2/L$
So total work done by yield lines
$= m(AO) + m(DB) + 2im(AB) = 2m(i + 1)$

Work done by loads:

Total load on AOB = load intensity $\times$ area of AOB

$= n(\tfrac{1}{2}L \cdot L/2) = nL^2/4$

Since O displaces by unity the centroid of the load (i.e. the centroid of AOB) displaces
by $\tfrac{1}{3}$.
So work done by loads is $(nL^2/4)(\tfrac{1}{3}) = nL^2/12$
So, equating work done

$nL^2/12 = 2(1 + i)m$
or $m = nL^2/24(1 + i)$

Note that at each corner there are three yield lines, suggesting that an alternative
pattern may exist (Section 10.5.5).

The case of a rectangular slab with varying edge conditions is given in Examples
10.4–10.6.

10.5.4   Beam-and-slab assemblies

For a single slab supported by beams a two-stage process is used:

(i)   The collapse load of the slab is found assuming the beams are rigid.

(ii)   The collapse load of the beam and slab assembly is found assuming the slab is at least as strong as is found in stage (i).

EXAMPLE 10.2   *Slab and edge beams*

Consider the square slab carrying a UDL of n supported on edge beams and columns at the corners, which is drawn in Fig. 10.6(a). The initial stage is to consider the beams as supplying a rigid support and calculate the collapse load for the slab alone.

From Example 10.1, the collapse load for a square slab with sagging reinforcement

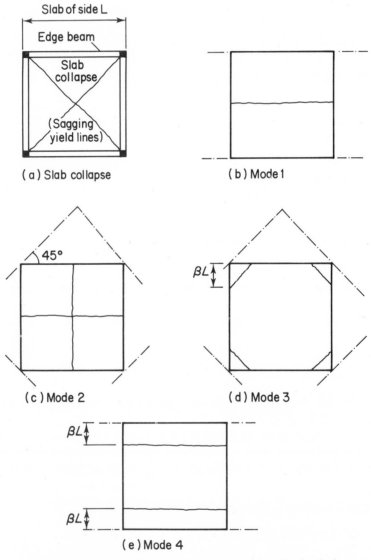

(a) Slab collapse   (b) Mode 1

(c) Mode 2   (d) Mode 3

(e) Mode 4

Fig. 10.6   Collapse mechanisms for a square slab with edge beams.

only is given by

$$m = nL^2/24 \tag{10.4}$$

(The hogging yield lines have zero strength, since any moment would need to be resisted by torsion in the edge beams.)

It is now necessary to consider the possible combined collapse modes.

Mode 1 (Fig. 10.6(b))
The equilibrium equation is

$$(nL^2/2)(L/4) = 2M_b + mL \tag{10.5}$$

Defining $\overline{m} = M_b/mL$, Equation (10.5) may be written as

$$nL^2 = 8m(1 + 2\overline{m}) \tag{10.6}$$

If $m > nL^2/24$, then the mechanism shown in Fig. 10.6(b) cannot occur. The mechanism will occur when $m = nL^2/24$, giving $\overline{m} = 1$ from Equation (10.6), which suggests that the beams should be of uniform strength with $M_b = mL$.

Mode 2 (Fig. 10.6(c))
This will produce the same solution as Mode 1. It can be left as an exercise for the reader to demonstrate this.

Mode 3 (Fig. 10.6(d))
The equilibrium equation for this case is

$$8M_b/\beta L + 4\sqrt{2}\beta Lm(1/(\beta L/\sqrt{2})) = nL^2 - 4n(\beta^2 L^2/2)/3$$

or

$$nL^2/24m = (1 + \overline{m}/\beta)/(3 - 2\beta^2) \tag{10.7}$$

If a collapse load of $m = nL^2/24$ is accepted for the slab at all points, $\overline{m}$ is then to be interpreted as the local non-dimensional beam collapse moment at a distance βL from the supports. This produces the values of m shown in Table 10.1, which indicate that although the collapse moment may be reduced towards the support, the beam will be understrength at mid-span. This is mainly due to the imposition of a uniform slab-collapse moment.

Table 10.1 Beam moments for collapse Mode 3

β	0	0.1	0.2	0.3	0.4	0.5
$\overline{m}$	0	0.20	0.38	0.55	0.67	0.75

Mode 4 (Fig. 10.6(e))
The non-dimensional equilibrium equation for this case is

$$nL^2/m = (2 + 4\overline{m})/(\beta - \beta^2) \tag{10.8}$$

If again a slab-collapse moment of $m = nL^2/24$ is accepted, then Equation (10.8) reduces to

$$\overline{m} = 6\beta(1 - \beta) - 0.5 \tag{10.9}$$

This equation gives the values shown in Table 10.2 where it can be seen that although the same solution as Mode 1 is given at mid-span, it appears that at the supports the beams are required to sustain a hogging moment. This again is due to the assumption of an uniform slab-collapse moment, and the slab then being over-strong at the corners.

Table 10.2   Beam moments for collapse Mode 4

β	0	0.1	0.2	0.3	0.4	0.5
m	−0.50	0.04	0.46	0.76	0.94	1.00

This example indicates that care is needed when considering the design of beam-and-slab assemblies, in that assumptions made on the slab design together with alternative combined collapse mechanisms will affect the final result. In general, in cases of this nature it will be sufficient to consider a beam with uniform collapse moment but in detailing reinforcement (including the provision of top reinforcement) it may well be necessary to bear in mind alternative collapse mechanisms.

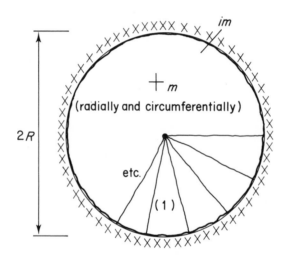

(a) Failure mode of complete slab

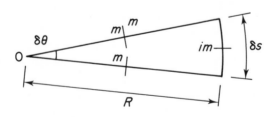

(b) Enlargement of element (1)

Fig. 10.7   Failure of circular slabs.

10.5.5   Point loads and point supports

Consider a circular slab of radius R with sagging ultimate moments of m and hogging of im carrying a point load P at the centre. The failure mechanism is given in Fig. 10.7(a) and with one sector enlarged with all the forces in Fig. 10.7(b).

Considering the load displaced by unity, then the work done by the moments for the sector may be written as

$$\delta E_{\mathrm{m}} = \underset{\text{hogging}}{(im\,\delta s)/R} + \underset{\text{sagging}}{(m\,\delta s)/R} = ((i+1)m\,\delta s)/R \qquad (10.10)$$

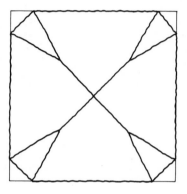

(a) Corner lever failure

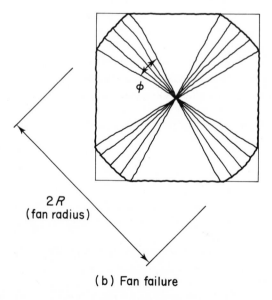

(b) Fan failure

Fig. 10.8   Alternative failure mechanisms for square slabs.

or for the whole slab

$$E_m = \Sigma \delta E_m = \Sigma (i+1)(m\,\delta s)/R = (i+1)m/R \Sigma \delta s$$
$$= ((i+1)m/R).2\pi R = 2\pi (i+1)m \tag{10.11}$$

The work done by the load is $P \times 1$, or

$$P = 2\pi (i+1)m \tag{10.12}$$

indicating that the collapse load is independent of the slab radius. Thus for an irregular slab, the fan (or circular collapse mechanism) will extend until the boundary of the fan reaches the slab edge.

The formation of fan type yield lines may occur in other circumstances. It was pointed out earlier in Example 10.1 that the classical failure mode for a square encastré slab of diagonal and support yield lines violated the yield criterion and that therefore the solution ($m = nL^2/24(i+1)$) must exceed the true value. There are two possible further failure mechanisms that can occur. The first, illustrated in Fig. 10.8(a), makes use of corner levers and gives the solution

$$m = nL^2/24(1.091)$$

The second mechanism, involving fans, is shown in Fig. 10.8(b) and gives the solution

$$m = nL^2/24(1+i) \left[\frac{\{(\phi/2)\sec^2(\pi/4-\phi/2) + \tan(\pi/4-\phi/2)\}}{\{\phi/2 + \tan(\pi/4-\phi/2)\}} \right]$$

The critical value of ϕ is given by $\phi = 30°$, which gives

$$m = nL^2/24(1+i).(1.103)$$

The full solution to the first is given by Jones and Wood (1986) and the second by Moy (1981) and Jones and Wood (1986).

Whilst in this case the error caused by assuming straight yield lines is small (10%), the alternative collapse modes do carry certain implications for detailing in that the hogging reinforcement must be available to allow the mechanisms to form. If the hogging reinforcement does not carry far enough into the slab to allow the hogging yield lines to have a non-zero value of ultimate moment, then the collapse loads will be even lower than that assumed to be calculated, with the result that premature collapse could occur. At best severe local cracking could occur under service loading.

Similar types of mechanism can occur at column supports on flat slabs.

EXAMPLE 10.3   *Slab on column supports*

Consider a square flat slab carrying an UDL supported at its corners by columns, shown in Fig. 10.9(a).

The immediate response to this problem is to adopt the mechanism shown in Fig. 10.9(b), and to arrive at the standard solution $m = nL^2/8$. This solution implies the use of orthogonal sagging reinforcement only.

An alternative solution is given in Fig. 10.10(c), where reinforcement is placed to produce yield lines at 45° to the slab edge.

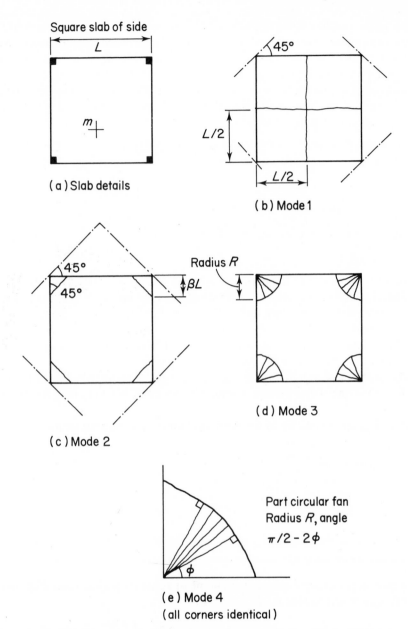

Fig. 10.9 Collapse mechanisms for a square slab on corner columns.

The equilibrium equation for this case may be written as

$$4m(\sqrt{2}\beta L)(\sqrt{2}/\beta L) = n[L^2 - 4(\beta L)^2/2] \times 1 + 4(\beta L)^2 n(\tfrac{2}{3})/2$$

moments   centre section of   four corner
                            slab deflecting   triangles
                            by unity

or

$$m = nL^2(1 - 2\beta^2/3)/8 \tag{10.13}$$

The value of m reaches a maximum as β tends to zero, or, again, $m = nL^2/8$. This solution again implies the use of bottom, or sagging, reinforcement only. An elastic analysis will clearly indicate that hogging moments will arise at the columns. This condition will be satisfied if quarter circle fans are considered as in Fig. 10.9(d).

The centroid of a quarter circle is $4\sqrt{2}R/3\pi$. Thus if the edge of the circle is displaced by unity then the centroid is displaced by $(1/R) \times (4\sqrt{2}R/3\pi) = 4\sqrt{2}\pi/3$. Thus the equilibrium equation can be written as

$$2(m+m)\pi R = n(L^2 - \pi R^2) \times 1 + n\pi R^2(4\sqrt{2}\pi/3) \qquad (10.14)$$

hogging sagging   centre of slab   fans

or

$$m = nL^2[1 - \pi(4\sqrt{2}\pi/3 - 1)(R/L)^2]/4\pi \qquad (10.15)$$

The maximum value of m is achieved as R tends to zero or

$$m = nL^2/12.8$$

Note: should the top reinforcement be omitted then $m = nL^2/6.4$, which is less than that predicted by the simple approach. It should also be apparent that even the solution given by quarter circle fans is not entirely correct since it requires a moment of m to be generated normal to the free edge, which is clearly impossible. The correct formation is given in Fig. 10.9(e), although it is not proposed here to continue with the requisite analysis, which may be left for the reader to investigate.

Should a moment of $m = nL^2/8$ be accepted for the sagging moment of resistance for such a slab, then the value for the hogging moment at the fans may be calculated as follows.

Rewriting Equation (10.15), in the limit as R tends to zero with moments of m and im gives

$$4m(i+1)\pi/2 = nl^2$$

or

$$i+1 = nl^2/2\pi m$$

but $m = nl^2/8$, so

$$i+1 = 1.27 \text{ or } i = 0.27$$

This indicates that top steel giving a moment of resistance of around 25% that of the bottom will suffice to produce a safe solution.

10.6 Hillerborg strip method

10.6.1 Theoretical background

By considering the elastic analysis of plates, it may be shown (Timoshenko) that

$$\partial^2 M_x/\partial x^2 + \partial^2 M_y/\partial y^2 + \partial^2 M_{xy}/\partial x\partial y + \partial^2 M_{yx}/\partial y\partial x = -q \qquad (10.16)$$

where the force system is defined in Fig. 10.10. The use of elastic analysis is justified since collapse has not occurred as the method is a lower bound solution. If it be further assumed that the load is solely resisted by bending moments M_x and M_y and that the contribution from the twisting moments M_{xy} and M_{yx} is zero, then Equation 10.16 may be written as

$$\partial^2 M_x/\partial x^2 + \partial^2 M_y/\partial y^2 = -q \tag{10.17}$$

This solution is safe since the moments M_x and M_y will be overestimated. If it be further assumed that part of the load be carried out by x-axis bending and the remainder by y-axis bending, then Equation (10.17) may be written as

$$\partial^2 M_x/\partial x^2 = -\alpha q$$
$$\partial^2 M_y/\partial y^2 = -(1-\alpha)q \tag{10.18}$$

These two expressions are identical to those for normal beam bending, thus the slab can be split into a series of strips and the loads apportioned between 'x-axis' and 'y-axis' bending. It is convenient, although not essential, to use only two values of α, zero or unity allowing the load to be carried in either the x or y direction. The exact distribution into strips is entirely at the designer's discretion, although it should be recognized that the greater the number of strips, the more detailing problems occur, as each strip may have differing quantities of reinforcement. In general it is acceptable to use load dispersion lines at 45°.

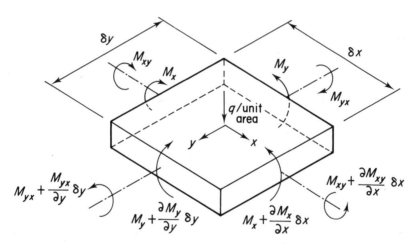

Fig. 10.10 Forces acting on an incremental volume.

10.6.2 Method of applying the Hillerborg strip principle

Consider the simply supported rectangular slab shown in Fig. 10.11(a) and take load distribution lines at 45° from the corner. This is a reasonable distribution since at the slab corners the load must be carried in both directions. Fig. 10.11(b) shows a possible strip formation. (Note this may be too coarse for normal design purposes). Consider each strip in turn:

Strip 1 (Fig. 10.11(c))
Since the whole slab is loaded with a UDL, the maximum sagging moment is

$$m_1 = nL_y^2/8$$

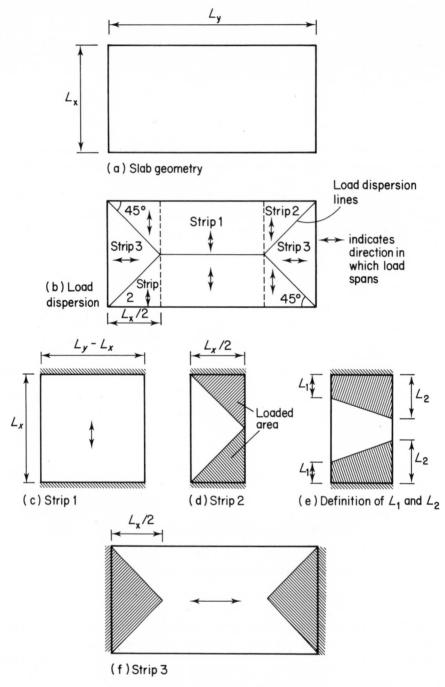

Fig. 10.11   Hillerberg strip method.

Strip 2   (Fig. 10.11(d))
The loading here is complex and it may be shown (Moy 1981) that the maximum bending moment for the case given in Fig. 10.11(c) is given by

$$M = Kn(L_1^2 + L_2)^2/8 \qquad (10.19)$$

where

$$K = \tfrac{4}{3}(1 - 1/(L_1/L_2 + 2 + L_2/L_1)) \qquad (10.20)$$

Strip 3   (Fig. 10.11(f))
This may be treated similarly to Strip 2.

If either of the edges possess continuity with an ultimate moment of im, and the sagging ultimate moment of resistance be m, then plastic collapse theory can be used to relate the loading to the ultimate moments using the principles of virtual work. It will usually be sufficiently accurate to assume the sagging 'hinge' occurs at mid-span (see Example 10.6).

It should be noted that the reactions from the strips directly give the loads applied to support beams, and thus the shears and moments in the support beams can be found directly by statics.

10.7   One-way spanning slabs

10.7.1   Single span

These represent little problem and should be designed in a similar manner to a beam.

10.7.2   Continuous

The analysis may be done either by using an elastic analysis or by considering plastic collapse methods similar to those employed for continuous beams. Provided certain conditions noted in Section 4.9 are met, Table 4.7 may be used to give the moments and shears in an elastic analysis.

Note that any slab with an aspect ratio greater than about 2.5 will effectively become one-way spanning on the short span.

10.8   Two-way spanning slabs

10.8.1   Single-bay simply supported slabs unable to resist corner torsion

In this particular case, for uniformly distributed loading, an approximate analysis given below may be used (cl 3.5.3.3, Pt 1):

The moments M_{sx} and M_{sy} in the x and y directions are given by

$$M_{sx} = [(L_y/L_x)^4/8(1 + (L_y/L_x)^4)]nL_x^2$$
$$M_{sy} = [(L_y/L_x)^2/8(1 + (L_y/L_x)^4)]nL_x^2 \qquad (10.21)$$

where n is the design ultimate load, and L_x and L_y are the spans of the slab with $L_y > L_x$.

10.8.2   Restrained slabs

These may be designed by one of three methods:

(i)   yield line;
(ii)   Hillerborg strip method;
(iii)   BS 8110 moment coefficients.

The bases of the first two methods have already been covered, and their application will be considered in the next examples. The moment coefficients of BS 8110 are dealt with in the next section.

BS 8110 Method (cl 3.5.3.4, Pt 1)   Essentially the method used is a modified yield-line approach. The symbols used are defined in Fig. 10.12.

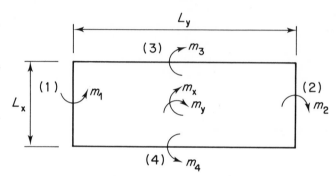

Notes: (1) Edge number thus ( )
(2) The moments m_1 etc. are per unit width

Fig. 10.12   Definition of symbols for BS8110 method.

The moment coefficient β_y is calculated from

$$\beta_y = (24 + 2N_d + 1.5N_d^2)/1000 \tag{10.22}$$

where N_d is the number of *discontinuous* edges ($0 < N_d < 4$). The moment coefficients, β_1 or β_2, are set equal to β_y at mid-span, and at the supports either $\frac{4}{3}\beta_y$ at a continuous edge or zero at a discontinuous edge.

A parameter, γ, is then calculated from the following equation:

$$\gamma = \tfrac{2}{3}[3 - (\sqrt{18})(L_x/L_y)(\sqrt{(\beta_y + \beta_1)} + (\sqrt{(\beta_y + \beta_2)}))] \tag{10.23}$$

The coefficients for the x-direction, β_x, are calculated from

$$\sqrt{(\beta_x + \beta_3)} + \sqrt{(\beta_x + \beta_4)} = \sqrt{\gamma} \tag{10.24}$$

with β_3 or β_4 set equal to $\frac{4}{3}\beta_x$ for a continuous edge or zero for a discontinuous edge.

The moment coefficient β_{sx} is set equal to β_x at mid-span and $\frac{4}{3}\beta_x$ at the support if continuous or zero at the support if discontinuous.

The moments, per unit width, are then given by

$$M_{sx} = \beta_{sx}nL_x^2$$

and

$$M_{sy} = \beta_{sy}nL_x^2 \tag{10.25}$$

10.9 Slab design and detailing

10.9.1 Yield-line methods

The approach used in this text has been to assume a uniform ultimate moment field in both the hogging and sagging regimes within the slab. If it is desired to allow differing sagging moment fields, then alternative yield-line patterns have to be investigated. Since the sagging yield lines extend into the corners, there is the implication that no curtailment of the tension reinforcement is allowed. It is, however, possible to cut off the hogging reinforcement since this is required only at the slab boundary. It can be shown that it is safe to do this at about 0.2 of the span from the support.

10.9.2 Hillerborg strip method

Within each strip (provided the reinforcement is above minimum), the reinforcement can be curtailed using the same approach as for beams. However, it should be noted that since shear links are generally avoided in slabs, all the tension reinforcement may be required to cope with edge shear in the slab.

10.9.3 BS 8110 methods

The slab should be divided up into edge and middle strips (Fig. 10.13).

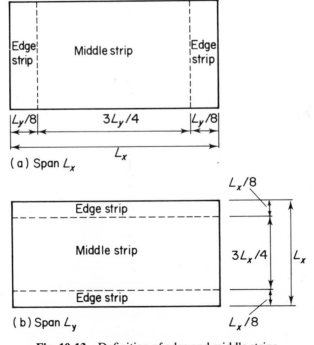

Fig. 10.13 Definition of edge and middle strips.

The moments calculated   (from Equations (10.24))   should only be used to calculate the reinforcement in the middle strip. No redistribution is allowed. Curtailment may be applied in accordance with cl 3.12.10   (see Section 8.3.5).   The edge strips should be reinforced to resist bending with not more than the minimum percentage of reinforcement (cl 3.12.5, Pt 1) plus any reinforcement required for torsion given in the following extract from cl 3.5.3.5, Pt 1.

Torsion reinforcement should be provided at any corner where the slab is simply supported on both edges meeting at that corner. It should consist of top and bottom reinforcement, each with layers of bars placed parallel to the sides of the slab and extending from the edges at a minimum distance of one-fifth of the shorter span. The area of reinforcement in each of these four layers should be three-quarters of the area required for the maximum mid-span design moment in the slab.

Torsion reinforcement equal to half that described in the preceding paragraph should be provided at a corner contained by edges over only one of which the slab is continuous.

Torsion reinforcement need not be provided at any corner contained by edges over both of which the slab is continuous.

The reinforcement for torsion is best provided by 'U' bars, as shown in Fig. 10.14.

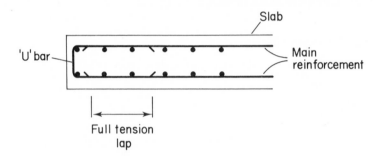

Fig. 10.14   Edge reinforcement for torsion.

10.9.4   Detailing and curtailment

It is becoming clear that the whole question of detailing and curtailment needs very careful thought. It may at ambient conditions be perfectly satisfactory to curtail by either of the two methods shown in Fig. 10.15. However, neither of these methods is satisfactory if it is required, as it almost certainly will be, to develop catenary action to retain the slab during a fire. In the case of the concrete cover spalling, for the detailing approach used in (a) of Fig. 10.15 half the bars will drop onto the slab below giving only half the catenary effect, and in (b) all the bars will hang down alternately from each support, giving no catenary effect. It is therefore recommended that if catenary action is needed during a fire, if only to allow reinstatement afterwards, no curtailment should be undertaken in slabs on the bottom steel. The upper reinforcement if not curtailed should be lapped at mid-span with the usual full-tension lap length and the lower reinforcement lapped on the column grid lines with a full-tension lap length *both* sides of the grid line to ensure full anchorage in the case of a single-compartment fire.

This need for good detailing to ensure adequate performance during a fire was brought out during some recent tests on waffle slabs undertaken by CIRIA (Report No. 107).

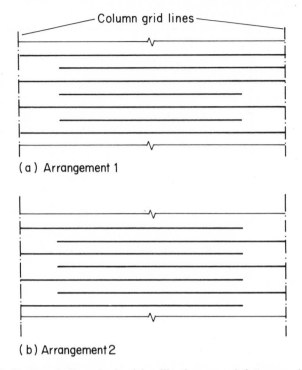

Column grid lines

(a) Arrangement 1

(b) Arrangement 2

Fig. 10.15 Standard methods of detailing bottom reinforcement in slabs.

EXAMPLE 10.4 Comparative design of a simply supported slab

Design a simply supported slab whose corners are restrained against torsion using

(i)   yield-line methods;
(ii) Hillerborg strip method;
(iii) BS 8110 method.

The slab is 6×4.5 m and has an overall depth of 175 mm and carries a UDL of 5 kN/m^2. The concrete is grade 25 (specific weight 25 kN/m^3) and the steel grade 460.

(i)   *Yield-line methods*

Total applied load $1.6 \times 5 + 1.4 \times 25 \times 0.175 = 14.12$ kN/m^2

Since the slab is supported on all four edges the elements of the slab must have axes of rotation on these edges (Rule (iii)) and yield lines must pass through the intersections of these axes (Rule (iv)), the only possible yield pattern is given in Fig. 10.16, where the yield line EF must be displaced by unity and the distance DE' (= CF') is characterised by z.

Only one half the slab need be considered. The yield moment m is uniform throughout the slab.

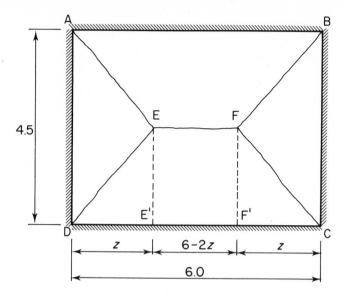

Fig. 10.16   Yield-line solution.

Internal work done:

Portion AED

Projected length of sagging yield line AED is AD, thus work done is

$$AD \times m \times \text{rotation of AED} = 4.5m\,(1/z) = 4.5m/z$$

Portion AFCD

Projected length of sagging yield line DEFC is DC, thus work done is

$$DC \times m \times \text{rotation of EFCD} = 6.0m\,(1/2.25) = 2.67m$$

Thus total internal work done is $m(4.5/z + 2.67)$

External work done:

Portion AED:

(Area of AED) $\times$ (UDL) $\times$ displacement of centroid of load =

$$(\tfrac{1}{2} \times 4.5 \times z) \times (14.12) \times \tfrac{1}{3} = 10.59z$$

Portion EFCD:

This is best done by splitting this area into 3

      Portion EDE': $(\tfrac{1}{2} \times 2.25 \times z) \times 14.12 \times \tfrac{1}{3} = 5.295z$

      Portion FCF': as EDE' $= 5.295z$

      Portion EFF'E': $((6 - 2z) \times 2.25) \times 14.12 \times \tfrac{1}{2} = 95.31 - 31.77z$

Thus total external work done is

$$10.59z + 2(5.295z) + 95.31 - 31.77z = 95.31 - 10.59z$$

So equating internal and external work done

$$m(4.5/z + 2.67) = 95.31 - 10.59z$$

or

$$m = (95.31 - 10.59z)/(4.5/z + 2.67) \qquad (10.26)$$

Differentiating Equation (10.26) for m with respect to z and setting the result to zero gives

$$\frac{95.31 - 10.59z}{4.5/z + 2.67} = \frac{-10.59}{-4.5/z^2} = 2.35z^2$$

or

$$95.31 - 10.59z - 10.59z - 6.27z^2 = 0$$

or

$$6.27z^2 + 21.18z - 95.31 = 0$$

or

$$z = 2.56 \qquad \text{(the other root is negative)}$$

or

$$m = 15.40 \text{ kN m/m}$$

(ii) *Hillerborg strip method*

The distribution into strips is not critical, so draw lines at 45° to the sides from each corner as in Fig. 10.17(a). The short side has been divided into 3 strips and the long side into 5 strips.

Strip 1 (Fig. 10.17(b))

Maximum moment is $Kn(L_1 + L_2)^2/8$
Using Equation (10.20)

$$K = \tfrac{4}{3}(1 - 1/(L_1/L_2 + 2 + L_2/L_1))$$
$$L_2 = 0, L_1 = 1.125, \text{ thus } K = \tfrac{4}{3}$$

so for strip 1, $M_1 = \tfrac{4}{3} \times 14.12 \times 1.125^2/8 = 2.98$ kN m/m

Strip 2 (Fig. 10.17(c))

$$L_1 = 1.125, L_2 = 2.25, \text{ thus } K = \tfrac{4}{3}(1 - 1(2.25/1.125 + 2 + 1.125/2.25))$$
$$= 1.037$$

Maximum moment, $M_2 = 1.037 \times 14.12(2.25 + 1.125)^2/8 = 20.82$ kN m/m

Strip 3 (Fig. 10.17(d))

$$M_3 = 14.12 \times 4.5^2/8 = 35.74 \text{ kN m/m}$$

Strip 4 (Fig. 10.17(e))

$$K = \tfrac{4}{3} \text{ since } L_1 = 0$$

so

$$M_4 = \tfrac{4}{3} \times 14.12 \times (1.5 + 0)^2/8 = 5.30 \text{ kN/mm}$$

272   *Reinforced concrete slabs*

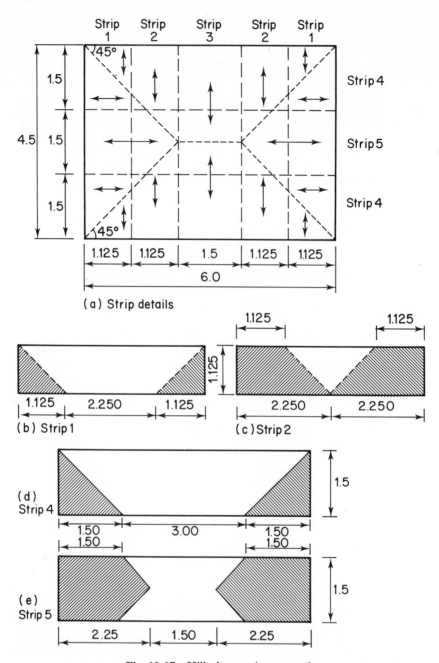

Fig. 10.17 Hillerberg strip approach.

Strip 5   (Fig. 10.17(f))

$L_2 = 2.25$, $L_1 = 1.5$, $K = 1.013$

so

$M_5 = 1.013 \times 14.12 \times (2.25 + 1.5)^2/8 = 25.14$ kN m/m

(iii) *BS 8110 method* (using Equations (10.21)–(10.24))

$$M_{sx} = \beta_{sx}nL_x^2 : M_{sy} = \beta_{sy}nL_x^2$$
$$L_y = 6, \ L_x = 4.5, \ N_d = 4$$

so

$$\beta_y = (24 + 2 \times 4 + 1.5 \times 4^2)/1000 = 0.0560$$

or

$$\beta_{sy} = 0.056$$
$$\gamma = \tfrac{2}{9}[3 - (\sqrt{18})(4.5/6.0)(\sqrt{0.056} + \sqrt{0.056})]$$

since $\beta_1 = \beta_2 = 0$

so

$$\gamma = 0.332$$
$$\beta_3 = \beta_4 = 0 \quad \text{so} \quad \sqrt{\beta_x} + \sqrt{\beta_x} = \sqrt{\gamma}$$

or

$$\beta_x = \gamma/4 = 0.332/4 = 0.083$$

so

$$\beta_{sx} = 0.083$$

Using $M_{sx} = \beta_{sx}nL_x^2$ and $M_{sy}nL^2$

$$M_{sx} = 0.083 \times 14.12 \times 4.5^2 = 23.73 \text{ kN m/m}$$
$$M_{sy} = 0.056 \times 14.12 \times 4.5^2 = 16.01 \text{ kN m/m}$$

Calculation of reinforcement areas for each case:

(i) Yield line

$$m = 15.40 \text{ kN m/m}, \ d = 150, \ b = 1000, \text{ thus}$$
$$M/bd^2f_{cu} = 0.027$$

From the design chart in Fig. B1-1 (Appendix B),

$A_s f_y/bdf_{cu} = 0.033$ or $100A_s/bd = 0.18$ (minimum steel percentage is 0.13%),

thus

$$A_s = 270 \text{ mm}^2/\text{m}$$

so fix T10 250 [314 mm²/m]

Total volume of steel $= 314[4.5 \times 6000 + 6.0 \times 4500]$
$$= 8.5\text{E6 mm}^3 = 0.0085 \text{ m}^3$$

(ii) *Hillerborg strip method*
Strip 1

$$M/bd^2f_{cu} = 2.98\text{E6}/1000 \times 150^2 \times 25 = 5.3\text{E-3}$$

This clearly will give minimum reinforcement of 0.13% (Table 3.27, Pt 1). Note this figure is based on the gross concrete section.

$$100A_s/bh = 0.13$$

so

$$A_s = (0.13 \times 1000 \times 175)/100 = 228 \text{ mm}^2/\text{m}$$

i.e. Fix T10-300 (262 mm^2/m)

Strip 2

$$M/bd^2f_{cu} = 20.82\text{E}6/1000 \times 150^2 \times 25 = 0.037$$

so

$100A_s/bd = 0.25$, which gives also

$$A_s = 390 \text{ mm}^2/\text{m}$$

Fix T10-200 (395 mm^2/m)

Strip 3

$$M/bd^2f_{cu} = 35.74\text{E}6/1000 \times 150^2 \times 25 = 0.064$$

so

$$100A_s/bd = 0.43\%$$

so

$$A_s = 0.43 \times 1000 \times 150/100 = 645 \text{ mm}^2/\text{m}$$

so fix T12-150 (754 mm^2/m)

Strip 4

$$M/bd^2f_{cu} = 5.3\text{E}6/1000 \times 150^2 \times 25 = 0.01$$

This will also give minimum steel

i.e. T10-300 (262 mm^2/m)

Strip 5

$$M/bd^2f_{cu} = 25.14\text{E}6/1000 \times 150^2 \times 25 = 0.045$$

i.e. $100A_s/bd = 0.30\%$

so

$$A_s = 0.30 \times 1000 \times 150/100 = 450 \text{ mm}^2/\text{m}$$

so fix T10-150 (561 mm^2/m)

Thus total volume of reinforcement is

Strip 1 $2 \times 1.125 \times 262 \times 4.500 = 2.65\text{E}6$
     2   $2 \times 1.125 \times 393 \times 4500 = 3.98\text{E}6$
     3   $1.5 \times 754 \times 4500 \qquad = 5.09\text{E}6$
     4   $2 \times 1.5 \times 262 \times 600 \quad \doteq 4.72\text{E}6$
     5   $1.5 \times 561 \times 6000 \qquad = \underline{5.05\text{E}6}$

$$21.49\text{E}6 \ \text{mm}^2$$
$$= 0.021 \ \text{m}^3$$

(iii)   *BS 8110 method*
x-direction

$$M_{sx}/bd^2 f_{cu} = 23.73\text{E}6/1000 \times 150^2 \times 25 = 0.042$$

thus

$$100A_s/bd = 0.27 \times 1000 \times 150/100 = 405 \ \text{mm}^2/\text{m}$$

so fix T12-250 (452 mm²/m)

y-direction

$$M_{sy}/bd^2 f_{cu} = 16.01\text{E}6/1000 \times 150^2 \times 25 = 0.028$$

so

$$A_s = 0.20 \times 1000 \times 150/100 = 300 \ \text{mm}^2/\text{m}$$

so fix T10-250 (314 mm²/m)

This reinforcement applies only to the middle strips (each 0.75 of the width). Over the remaining edge strips minimum reinforcement of

$$0.13bh/100 = 0.13 \times 1000 \times 175/100$$
$$= 227.5 \ \text{mm}^2/\text{m}$$

or T10-250 (314 mm²/m)

So total volume of steel:

$$= (4.5 \times 314) \times 6000 + (4.5 \times 452 + 1.5314) \ 6000 \ \text{mm}^3$$
$$= 2.351\text{E}7 \ \text{mm}^3$$
$$= 0.0235 \ \text{m}^3$$

It is seen that yield-line methods in this case will give the greatest economy in reinforcement and will satisfy deflection criteria. However, the approximate method, which requires greater reinforcement quantities, will in fact not satisfy span/depth ratio requirements (needing a minimum effective depth of 165 mm or an overall depth of about 190 mm).

EXAMPLE 10.5   *Encastré slab*

Design a slab, restrained on all four sides, the details of which are the same as for Example 10.4.

Note that, since the approximate methods of BS 8110 imply a ratio of hogging to sagging moments of resistance of $\frac{4}{3}$, this value will be used throughout the calculations. The designer is at liberty to adjust this value to give any ratio but it must be remembered that the serviceability limit state of deflection must be satisfied.

(i)   Yield-line methods

The failure mechanism is similar to Example 10.4 except that additional yield lines form on the supports, giving additional work done by the moments in the hogging yield lines of 4.5 im/z on AD and 2.67 im on CD, where im is the hogging yield moment.

   If the same procedure is followed through, it will be noticed that m in the previous example is replaced by $m(i+1)$, thus the solution is given by

$$(1+i)m = 15.40 \text{ kN/m}$$

$i = \frac{4}{3}$, thus $m = 6.6$ kN m/m and $im = 8.8$ kN m/m

(ii)   Hillerborg strip method

Here on each of the strips the free moment calculated in the previous example must be resisted by the reactant BM of im and the mid-span BM of m, thus the free BM $= m(1+i)$

Strip 1

$$(i+1)m = 2.98, \text{ so } m = 1.28 \text{ and } im = 1.70 \text{ kN m/m}$$

Strip 2

$$(i+1)m = 20.82: m = 8.92: im = 11.90 \text{ kN m/m}$$

Strip 3

$$(i+1)m = 35.74: m = 15.32: im = 20.42 \text{ kN m/m}$$

Strip 4

$$(i+1)m = 5.30: m = 2.27: im = 3.03 \text{ kN m/m}$$

Strip 5

$$(i+1)m = 25.14: m = 10.77: im = 14.37 \text{ kN m/m}$$

(iii)   BS 8110 method

$$l_x = 4.5, l_y = 6.0, N_d = 0$$

so $\beta_y = (24)/1000 = 0.024$ (from Equation 10.22)

$$\beta_1 = \beta_2 = \tfrac{4}{3}\beta_y = 0.032$$

Using Equation (10.23)

$$\gamma = \tfrac{2}{9}[3 - (\sqrt{18})(l_x/l_y)(\sqrt{\beta_y} + \beta_1) + \sqrt{(\beta_y + \beta_2)})]$$
$$= \tfrac{2}{9}[3 - (\sqrt{18})(4.5/6.0)(\sqrt{(0.024 + 0.032)} + \sqrt{0.056})]$$
$$= 0.332$$

Since in the *x*-direction both edges are fixed $\beta_4 = \beta_3 = \tfrac{4}{3}\beta_x$, Equation (10.24) becomes

$$\sqrt{\gamma} = 2(\sqrt{\beta_x})(\sqrt{(1+\tfrac{4}{3})})$$

or

$$\beta_x = \gamma/(4(1+\tfrac{4}{3})) = 0.332/(4(1+\tfrac{4}{3})) = 0.036$$

$$\beta_3 = \beta_4 = \tfrac{4}{3}\beta_x = 0.048$$

so, in the *y*-direction,

span moment = $0.024 \times 14.12 \times 4.5^3 = 6.86$
support moment = $0.032 \times 14.12 \times 4.5^2 = 9.15$

in the *x*-direction,

span moment = $0.036 \times 14.12 \times 4.5^2 = 10.29$
support moment = $0.043 \times 14.12 \times 4.5^2 = 13.72$ kN m/m

The reinforcement may now be designed in the usual manner. This is left as an exercise for the reader. (Tutorial problem 10.16-1)

EXAMPLE 10.6   Slab with mixed supports

A slab is restrained on one long and one short side, the remainder of the data is as Example 10.4.

Yield line
For the following case a unified solution exists (Johansen), for which the symbols are defined in Fig. 10.18.

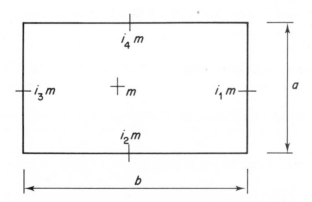

Fig. 10.18   Definition of symbols for Equation (10.27).

$$m = [(na_r^2)/24][\sqrt{(3+(a_r/b_r)^2)} - a_r/b_r]^2 \qquad (10.27)$$

where

$$a_r/2 = a/(\sqrt{(1+i_2)} + \sqrt{(1+i_3)})$$

and

$$b_r/2 = b/(\sqrt{(1+i_2)} + \sqrt{(+i_4)})$$

Note for Equation (10.27) to be valid $b_r > a_r$

thus

$$b_r = (2 \times 6.0)/(\sqrt{(1+\tfrac{4}{3})} + 1)$$

and

$$a_r = (4.5 \times 2)/(\sqrt{(1+\tfrac{4}{3})} + 1)$$

or

$$b_r = 4.75 \text{ and } a_r = 3.56$$

so

$$m = (14.12/24) \times (3.56)^2[\sqrt{(3+(3.56/4.75)^2)} - (3.56/4.75)]^2$$
$$= 9.65 \text{ and}$$

$$im = 12.86 \text{ kN m/m}$$

Hillerborg strip method
The main problem here is that each strip now has to be treated as the equivalent of a beam element with a maximum hogging moment of im at one end only at collapse. This therefore means that plastic collapse methods for beams need to be employed with the usual result that the sagging hinge will not be at mid-span. However, for the purposes of this exercise, the assumption that the sagging hinge will be at mid-span is to be made. This should not cause an error greater than about 5%. All loads will be replaced by equivalent point loads acting at the centroids of the UDLs. Again i is taken as $\tfrac{4}{3}$.

Strip 1   (Fig. 10.19(a))
Equivalent point load $14.12 \times (1.125)^2/2 = 8.94$ kN at a distance of 0.375 from the support.
   Using virtual work,

$$m(2\theta) + im\theta = 2(0.3750 \times 8.94)\theta$$

or

$$m = 2.01 \text{ and } im = 2.68 \text{ kN m/m}$$

or

$$m = 1.79 \text{ kN m/m and } im = 2.38 \text{ kN m/m}$$

Strip 2   (Fig. 10.19(b))
Equivalent point load

rectangle: $1.125^2 \times 14.12 = 17.87$ kN acting at

   $1.125/2 = 0.563$ m from support

triangle: $(1.125)^2 \times 14.12/2 = 8.94$ kN acting at

   $1.125 + 1.125/3 = 1.5$ m from support

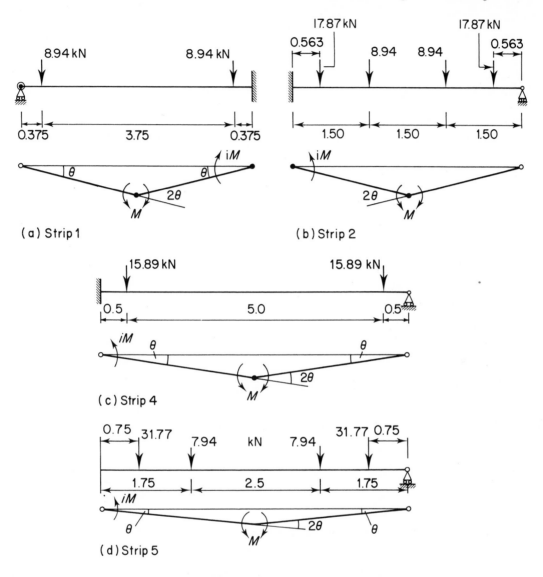

Fig. 10.19 Hillerberg strip mechanisms for Example 10.6.

Working in loads/unit width:

$$m(2\theta) + im(\theta) = 2[0.563\theta \times 17.87 + 1.5\theta \times 8.94]/1.125 = 41.730\theta$$

so

$$m = 12.52 \text{ and } im = 16.69 \text{ kN m/m}$$

Strip 3

$$m(2\theta) + im(\theta) = \tfrac{1}{2}(14.12 \times 4.5 \times (4.5\theta/2))$$
$$= 71.48\theta$$

so

$$m = 21.44 \text{ and } im = 28.59 \text{ kN m}$$

(*Note:*   Exact solution is $m = qL^2(2+i-2\sqrt{(i+1)})/2i^2$ or $m = 22.38$ and $im = 29.84$. This gives errors of 4.2% on both moments.)

Strip 4   (Fig. 10.19(c))
Equivalent point load: $14.12 \times (1.5)^2/2 = 15.89$ at a distance of 0.5 m from support

so

$$m(2\theta) + im(\theta) = 2(0.5 \times 15.89\theta)/1.5$$
$$= 10.59\theta$$

or

$$m = 3.18 \text{ and } im = 4.24 \text{ kN m/m}$$

Strip 5˙   (Fig. 10.19(d))
Equivalent point loads:

rectangle: $1.5^2 \times 14.12 = 31.77$ kN at 0.75 m from support
triangle: $(1.5 \times 0.75)/2 \times 14.12 = 7.94$ kN at $1.5 \times (0.75/3) = 1.75$ from support

or

$$m(2\theta) + im(\theta) = 2[31.77 \times 0.75\theta + 7.94 \times 1.75\theta]/1.5$$
$$= 50.30\theta$$

so

$$m = 15.09, \ im = 20.19 \text{ kN m/m}$$

BS 8110 Methods
$N_d = 2, \ l_x = 4.5, \ l_y = 6.0$
$\quad \beta_y = (24 + 2 \times N_d + 1.5 N_d^2)/1000 = 0.034$
$\quad \beta_1 = 0 \text{ and } \beta_2 = \tfrac{4}{3}\beta_y = 0.045$
$\quad \gamma = \tfrac{2}{9}[3 - (\sqrt{18})(l_x/l_y)(\sqrt{(\beta_y + \beta_1)} + \sqrt{(\beta_y + \beta_2)})]$
$\quad\quad = \tfrac{2}{9}[3 - (\sqrt{18})(4.5/6.0)(\sqrt{0.034} + \sqrt{(0.034 + 0.045)})]$
$\quad\quad = 0.338$

$\beta_3 = 0, \ \beta_4 = \tfrac{4}{3}\beta_x$, so
$$\sqrt{\gamma} = \sqrt{\beta_x} + \sqrt{(\beta_x(1 + \tfrac{4}{3}))}$$

or

$$\beta_x = \gamma/[1 + \sqrt{(1 + \tfrac{4}{3})}]^2 \text{ or } \beta_x = 0.053$$

and

$$\beta_4 = \tfrac{4}{3}(0.053) = 0.071$$

Thus the final moments are,

in the y-direction at the support, $M_{sy} = 0.045 \times 14.12 \times 4.5^2 = 12.87$

in the span, $M_{sy} = 0.034 \times 14.12 \times 4.5^2 = 9.72$

in the x-direction at the support, $M_{sx} = 0.071 \times 14.12 \times 4.5^2 = 20.30$

in the span, $M_{sx} = 0.053 \times 14.12 \times 4.5^2 = 15.15$ kN m/m

10.10 Support beams

10.10.1 Loads on support beams

(a) *Yield-line approach*
The yield-line pattern at collapse will give no indication of the loads carried by the support beams, this means that an analysis must be used which includes the effect of beam collapse.

The method used is to calculate the collapse load on the slab assuming rigid support beams and then to analyse the complete system assuming the slab is as strong as calculated in the slab-only mode.

This has already been dealt with in Example 10.2.

For multibay slabs, the problem becomes complex in that a complete set of beam–slab assemblies may collapse as one (Fig. 10.20). Thus the major drawback of yield-line methods is the difficulty of assessing support beam loads.

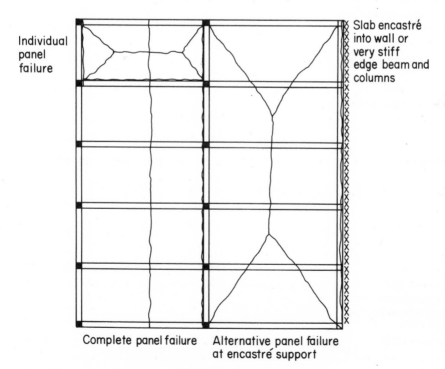

Fig. 10.20 Multibay beam and slab collapse.

(b)   *Hillerborg strip method*
Here the reactions from the strips can be used directly as beam loads and thus give the moments and shears in the beams very quickly. This is one of the advantages of this method.

(c)   *BS 8110 method*
The load on each beam is determined using yield-line methods, in that the area delineated by the yield pattern is deemed to give the reactive load onto the beam. However, for the case with all edges either simply supported or continuous, 45° distribution appears to have been adopted.

The load on each beam is given by   (cl 3.5.3.7)

$$V_{sy} = \beta_{vy} n l_x \qquad \text{(per unit run)}$$

and   (10.28)

$$V_{sx} = \beta_{vx} n l_x \qquad \text{(per unit run)}$$

The values of β_{vy} and β_{vx} are given in Table 10.3 (reproduced from Table 3.16, Pt 1). The

Table 10.3   BS 8110 coefficients for loads on support beams

Type of panel and location	β_{vx} for values of L_y/L_x								β_{vy}
	1.0	1.1	1.2	1.3	1.4	1.5	1.75	2.0	
Four edges continuous									
Continuous edge	0.33	0.36	0.39	0.41	0.43	0.45	0.48	0.50	0.33
One short edge discontinuous									
Continuous edge	0.36	0.39	0.42	0.44	0.45	0.47	0.50	0.52	0.36
Discontinuous edge	—	—	—	—	—	—	—	—	0.24
One long edge discontinuous									
Continuous edge	0.36	0.40	0.44	0.47	0.49	0.51	0.55	0.59	0.36
Discontinuous edge	0.24	0.27	0.29	0.31	0.32	0.34	0.36	0.38	—
Two adjacent edges discontinuous									
Continuous edge	0.40	0.44	0.47	0.50	0.52	0.54	0.57	0.60	0.40
Discontinuous edge	0.26	0.29	0.31	0.33	0.34	0.35	0.38	0.40	0.26
Two short edges discontinuous									
Continuous edge	0.40	0.43	0.45	0.47	0.48	0.49	0.52	0.54	—
Discontinuous edge	—	—	—	—	—	—	—	—	0.26
Two long edges discontinuous									
Continuous edge	—	—	—	—	—	—	—	—	0.40
Discontinuous edge	0.26	0.30	0.33	0.36	0.38	0.40	0.44	0.47	—
Three edges discontinuous (one long edge continuous)									
Continuous edge	0.45	0.48	0.51	0.53	0.55	0.57	0.60	0.63	—
Discontinuous edge	0.30	0.32	0.34	0.35	0.36	0.37	0.39	0.41	0.29
Three edges discontinuous (one short edge continuous)									
Continuous edge	—	—	—	—	—	—	—	—	0.45
Discontinuous edge	0.29	0.33	0.36	0.38	0.40	0.42	0.45	0.48	0.30
Four edges discontinuous									
Discontinuous edge	0.33	0.36	0.39	0.41	0.43	0.45	0.48	0.50	0.33

loading given by Equation (10.28) is deemed to be acting over the centre three-quarters of the span (Fig. 10.21).

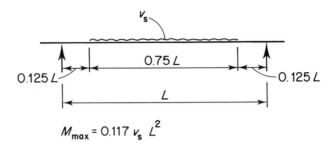

Fig. 10.21   Distribution of loading on support beams.

10.10.2   Support-beam design

A beam on a discontinuous edge should be treated as an 'L' beam with part of the slab taken into account, and at a continuous edge a 'T' beam should have the same pattern of continuity over supports as the slab. The design of 'T' and 'L' beams is covered in Chapter 6.

10.11   Shear in one- and two-way spanning slabs

10.11.1   Shear effects from distributed loads

The shear at any point should be calculated from

$$v = V/bd$$

The allowable shear stress, v_c, is calculated as for beams (Equation 7.2) (Section 7.1.4).

The design of shear reinforcement should be made in accordance with Table 3.17, Pt 1 which is to be found in Appendix A2.

In general, the use of shear reinforcement should be avoided in slabs and the amount of tension reinforcement, or the slab depth, should be increased until $v > v_c$.

The enhancement of shear strength near supports covered by cl 3.4.5.9–10, Pt 1 is covered by Chapter 7 of this book.

10.11.2   Concentrated loads

These are treated in the same manner as column supports in flat-slab construction, which is covered in Example 10.3. The design for concentrated loads applies only when there are concentrated loads in fixed positions in a slab. It is not normally necessary, except for thin slabs, to consider the effect of the point loadings given in BS 6399 unless these are very high. For these loads, shear resistance will be necessary over the whole slab and must be supplied by ensuring a sufficiently high value of v_c.

10.12   Flat slabs

The background to flat-slab design has been covered by CIRIA Report 89, and more recently by CIRIA Report 110, and it is not proposed to cover this material here.

It is, however, proposed to carry out a design study to illustrate some of the points raised in BS 8110, Part 1. This will be found as Design Study No. 13.4.

10.13   Waffle slabs

The design of these in general follows that of flat slabs except that the following observations should be made (also see CIRIA Report 110).

(i)   Owing to the presence of ribs, the deflection is likely to be more critical than that for solid flat slabs, and the span/depth ratio should also be modified for the presence of the rib (as for 'T' and 'L' beams).

(ii)   It is recommended that the section at mid-span should be used for the calculation of the slab stiffness in the equivalent frame analysis unless the solid section at the column is greater than one third the smaller slab dimension, in which case the effect of this solid section should be allowed for.

(iii)   The distribution of moments is similar to that for ordinary flat slabs, except that

   (a)   where the solid portion is greater than one third the smaller dimension, the column strip should be based on the solid area,
   (b)   that the design moments on the middle strip should be increased proportionately, and those in the column strip decreased,

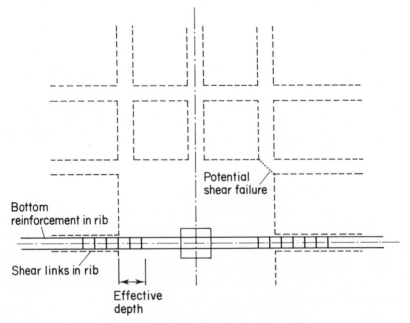

Fig. 10.22   Shear detailing in waffle slabs.

(c)   a rib at a slab edge between solid areas should have nominal shear links, since an external rib will take some degree of torsional moment.

(iv)   It is recommended that the solid area should extend at least $2\frac{1}{2}$ times the slab effective depth from the column face.

(v)   Should shear perimeters lying outside the solid section need considering, then the shear should be divided equally between all ribs. At the corner of a solid section where two ribs frame it, a section at 45° should be considered (Fig. 10.22)

(vi)   Should shear reinforcement be needed it should extend at least a distance equal to the effective depth into the slab to avoid shear cracks (Fig. 10.22).

10.14   Staircases (Section 3.101, BS 110)

These may be designed either

(i)   to cantilever out from a wall, or
(ii)   to span longitudinally between landings, stringer beams or walls.

The loading on a staircase is loading on plan area and should be at least as great as any area giving access to the staircase.

(i)   *Cantilever stairs*
The designer must ensure that the wall, in either masonry or concrete, can resist the fixing moment at the root of the cantilever.

The nominal section of stair used to calculate the moment and shear is as Fig. 10.23.

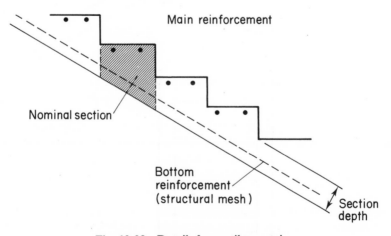

Fig. 10.23   Details for cantilever stairs.

(ii)   *Longitudinally spanning*
Where staircases are nominally built in to walls by at least 110 mm, a strip of 150 mm adjacent to the wall may be neglected in calculating the loading on the staircase   (cl 3.10.1 Pt 1). Where two

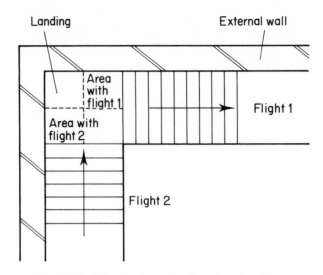

Fig. 10.24   Distribution of loading from landings.

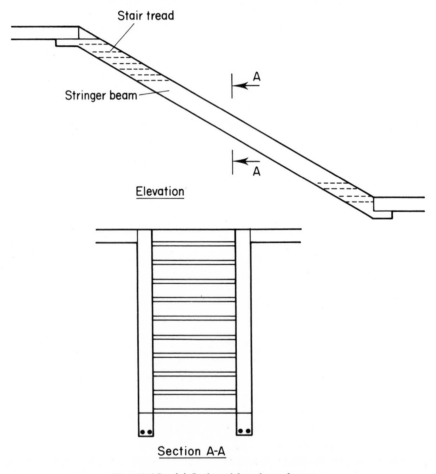

Fig. 10.25   (a) Stairs with stringer beams

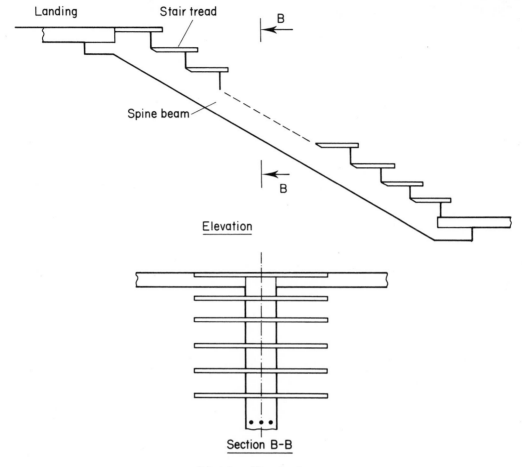

Elevation

Section B-B

(b) stairs with spine beams.

staircases span onto the same landing the load may be distributed equally between the two flights (Fig. 10.24).

For staircases with stringer beams, the stairs should be designed as spanning between the beams and then the stringer beams spanning between landings (Fig. 10.25(a)). Stairs with spine beams are treated similarly (Fig. 10.25(b)).

The effective span of staircases without stringer beams should be taken as follows (cl 10.1.3–4, Pt 1):

(i) For stairs spanning onto landings the effective span shall be taken as $l_a + 0.5(l_{b,1} + l_{b,2})$ (see Fig. 10.26(a)).

(ii) For stairs spanning between discrete supports, the effective length is defined in Fig. 10.26(b).

The effective span is to be taken as shown in Fig. 10.26 (cl 3.10.1.5, Pt 1).

In general staircases without stringer beams are designed as one-way spanning slabs simply supported over the effective length. However, to avoid cracking at the staircase–landing interface, top reinforcement should be provided. It is generally sufficient if the area provided is 25% that at mid-span. For deflection the rules for beams should be used

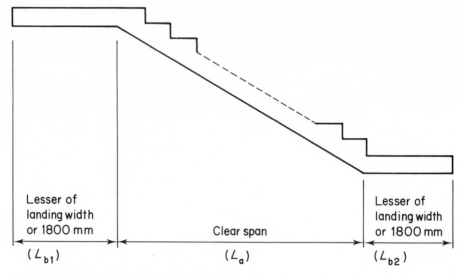

(a) Effective span of monolithic staircases

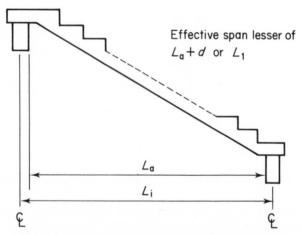

(b) Effective span of discretely supported staircase

Fig. 10.26   Effective spans of staircases.

except that   if the stair flight occupies at least 60% of the effective span, the span/depth ratios calculated normally shall be increased by 15%   (cl 3.10.2.2).

10.15   Retaining walls

10.15.1   Introduction

The three common types of concrete retaining walls – mass concrete, cantilever, and counterfort are illustrated in Fig. 10.27. This text will only be concerned with the design of the wall itself and will not deal with an overall failure of the type illustrated in Fig. 10.28, for which reference should be made to a standard soil mechanics text such as Henry (1986) or Willun and Starzewski (1972/75).

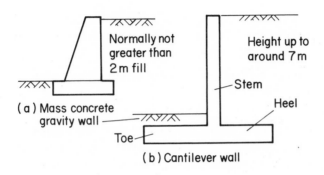

(a) Mass concrete gravity wall

Normally not greater than 2m fill

(b) Cantilever wall

Height up to around 7m

Stem

Heel

Toe

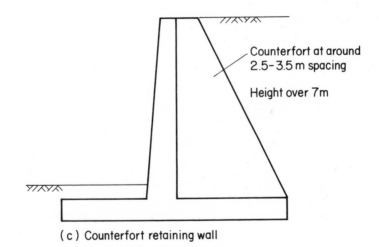

(c) Counterfort retaining wall

Counterfort at around 2.5–3.5 m spacing

Height over 7m

Fig. 10.27   Types of retaining wall.

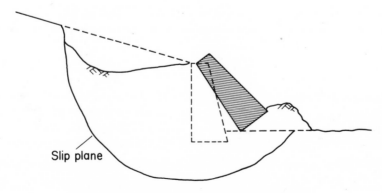

Slip plane

Fig. 10.28   Failure by slip in surrounding soil.

10.15.2   Stability of retaining walls

In general there are five criteria which may need consideration. In all cases the first three must be considered.

(i)   *Sliding*
The factor of safety against sliding is to be taken as 1.5 if only cohesion or base friction is considered or 2.0 if the passive resistance in front of the toe is also considered.

(ii)   *Overturning*
The factor of safety against overturning is to be taken as 3 for gravity walls, 2 for all other walls.

(iii)   *Bearing capacity*
The maximum bearing stress underneath the base should not exceed the allowable bearing capacity. To avoid excessive tilting the ratio of maximum to minimum bearing stresses should not exceed 3. It is preferable if the ratio can be as near unity as possible.

(iv)   *Failure by slip*
This is not covered in this text.

(v)   *Total and differential settlement*
The total and differential settlement should be limited using the following equations:

Settlement:

$$S = (2.12B(1 - v^2))/E_v\sigma_{av} \tag{10.29}$$

Tilt:

$$\tan \beta = 5.1(1 - v^2)M_0/E_vB^2 \tag{10.30}$$

S is the total settlement, B is the width of the base, E_v the deformation modulus of the soil, v the Poisson's ratio of the soil, σ_{av} the average bearing stress, M_0 the moment of the resultant thrust about the centre line, β the angle of tilt. These equations are taken from Henry (19).

The maximum tilt should preferably not exceed 1 in 100. To eliminate the appearance of tilt the front face of a retaining wall is usually battered at 1 in 25.

All stability calculations are performed under service loading.

Values of E_v and v are given in Table 10.4 (after Willun and Starzewski).

Table 10.4   Values of Young's modulus and Poisson's ratio for retaining walls

Soil type	E_v	v
Dense sand	60–100	0.25
Loose sand	15–50	0.30
Clayey sands/silts	15–30	0.30
Firm and stiff sand clays	2–20	0.35
Firm and stiff clays	2–15	0.40
Very stiff clays	30–55	0.20
	MN/m²	

10.15.3 Mass concrete retaining walls

In general rectangular sections are not economic above 2–3 m height, although if stepped walls with or without relieving slabs are used then a greater height may be accommodated. For a discussion of the latter see Henry (1986).

EXAMPLE 10.7 Design of a mass concrete retaining wall

The dimensions and other data are given in Fig. 10.29.

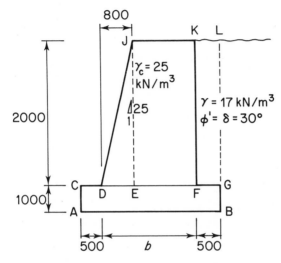

Fig. 10.29 Design data for a mass-concrete retaining wall.

Force due to earth pressure:

$$F_E = \tfrac{1}{2}K_a\gamma h^2$$
$$K_a = (1 - \sin \phi')/(1 + \sin \phi') = \tfrac{1}{3}$$
$$F_E = (\tfrac{1}{2})(\tfrac{1}{3}) \times 17 \times 3^2 = 25.5 \text{ kN/m}$$

Moment about A due to earth pressure

$$= F_E(h/3) = 25.5 \times 3/3 = 25.5 \text{ kN m/m}$$

For each of the design criteria, such as sliding, an explicit solution including the unknown base dimension b is formulated, and an expression obtained for b.

Sliding
Vertical weight:

		kN/m
JDE	$25 \times (2 \times 0.8 \times)/2$	$= 20$
JKEF	$25 \times (2(b) - 0.8)$	$= 50b - 40$
ACGB	$25 \times (b \times 1) \times 1$	$= 25b + 25$
FGLK	$17 \times 0.5 \times 2$	$= 17$
		$22 + 75b$

Factor safety $= 1.5$
Resistance to sliding $= (22 + 75b) \tan \delta$
Available resistance $= (22 + 75b)(\tan \delta)/1.5$
$$= 0.385(22 + 75b)$$
or $25.5 = 0.385(22 + 75b)$
or $b = 0.59$

Overturning
Moments about A due to

		kN m/m
JDE	$25(2 \times 0.8/2) \times (0.5 + 0.8/3)$	$= 15.33$
JKEF	$25 \times 2(b - 0.8)(b + 0.5 - (b/2 - 0.4)) = 50(b - 0.8)(b/2 + 0.9)$	
ACGB	$25 \times (b + 1)(b + 1)/2$	$= 12.5(b + 1)^2$
FGLK	$17 \times 0.5 \times 2 \times (b + 1 - 0.25)$	$= 17(b + 0.75)$

$$37.5b^2 + 67b + 4.58$$

Factor of safety $= 3$
or $(37.5b^2 + 67b + 4.58)/3 = 25.5$
or $37.5b^2 + 67b - 71.92 = 0$
$b = 0.76$

Again any width greater than 0.8 m will suffice.
   So taking moments about the centre line of the base with $b = 1.00$ (positive clockwise)

JDE	$25 \times (0.888 \times 2/2)[0.8/3 - 1.00/2]$	$= -4.67$
JKLFE	$25 \times 0.2 \times 2[0.4]$	$= 4.00$
KLGF	$17 \times 0.5 \times 2[1 - 0.25]$	$= 12.75$
CGBA		$= 0$
Earth pressure		$= -25.5$

$$-13.42 \text{ kN m/m}$$

Total weight $= 22 + 75 \times 1.0 = 97$ kN/m
bearing pressures: $97/2 \pm 13.42/2^2 \times 6$
$$48.5 \pm 20.13 = 68.6 \text{ or } 28.4 \text{ kN/m}^2$$

Although the ratio $\sigma_{max}/\sigma_{min}$ is high (2.4), it will be satisfactory.
   It is advisable to place mesh in the front and the back face of the retaining wall to overcome shrinkage and thermal cracking. The base needs to be designed as a reinforced concrete foundation.

10.15.4   Cantilever retaining wall

The stability calculations follow those for mass concrete retaining walls. Member sizing is such that no shear reinforcement needs to be supplied either in the base or the stem. The base is designed as for a foundation (see Chapter 15) and the stem as a cantilever. The cracking in the cantilever should be controlled by rigorous calculation to mitigate any effect of the ingress of water and resultant corrosion. Longitudinal reinforcement should be supplied to mitigate the effects of shrinkage and early thermal cracking. Base thickness must be sufficient to generate full anchorage bond and the wall thickness to allow steel on front and back face.

EXAMPLE 10.15.2   Cantilever retaining wall (Fig. 10.30)

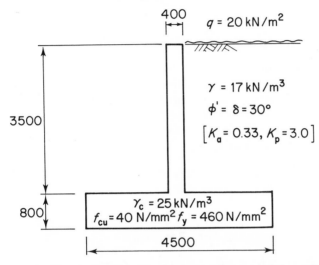

Fig. 10.30   Basic design data for the cantilever retaining wall.

The base length will be taken as 4.5 m, and calculations carried out for bearing capacity and overturning for toe values of 0.5, 1.0, 1.5 and 2.0 m. Any problems with sliding can be overcome using a shear key. The bearing capacity calculations are carried out in Table 10.5, and indicate that a 4.5 m base with a 2 m toe should be adopted.

Table 10.5   Bearing capacity calculations

	0.5 m toe	1 m	1.5 m	2 m
Vertical forces				
Stem $0.4 \times 3.5 \times 25$	35.0	35.0	35.0	35.0
Base $0.8 \times 4.5 \times 25$	90.0	90.0	90.0	90.0
Fill $3.5 \times 17 \times (4.5 - \text{TOE} - 0.4)$	214.2	184.5	154.7	125.0
Total	339.2	309.5	279.7	250.0 kN/m
Net bearing pressure	75.4	68.8	62.2	55.6 kN/m²
Moments about centre line				
Active pressure	−40.1	−40.1	−40.1	−40.1
Surcharge	−122.5	−122.5	−122.5	−122.5
Stem $0.8 \times 25 \times 3.5(2.25 - 0.5 - 0.2)$	−108.5	−73.5	−38.5	−3.5
Fill $(4.1 - \text{TOE}) \times 3.5 \times 17(2.25 - \text{TOE}/2)$	96.39	129.1	147.0	150.0
Net moment	174.71	−107.0	−54.1	−16.1 kN m/m
Pressure due to moment	±51.8	±31.7	±16.0	±4.8 kN/m²
σ_{max}	127.2	100.3	78.2	60.4 kN/m²
σ_{min}	23.6	36.9	46.2	50.8 kN/m²
$\sigma_{max}/\sigma_{min}$	5.39	2.72	1.69	1.19

Overturning:
Taking moments about the toe:

Active pressure	-40.1	
Surcharge	-122.5	
Stem $0.4 \times 25 \times 3.5(2+0.2)$		77.0
Base $0.8 \times 25 \times 4.5^2/2$		202.5
Fill $2.1 \times 3.5 \times 17(4.5 - 2.1/2)$		431.1
Total	-162.6	701.6

Factor of safety = 710.6/162.6 = 4.37, therefore satisfactory.

Sliding
Vertical force = 250 kN/m
Force available to resist sliding = 250 tan δ
$$= 250 \tan 30$$
$$= 144.3 \text{ kN/m}$$
Net horizontal pressure = $20 \times 4.5 + 0.33 \times 17 \times 4.5^2/2$
$$= 146.8 \text{ kN/m}$$

Clearly even without a factor of safety the wall will slide, so a shear key must be provided. So using a factor of safety of 2,

$$(144.3 + P)/2 = 146.8 \qquad \text{or} \qquad P = 149.3 \text{ kN/m}$$

So the depth of key to resist this force P is given by

$$P = \tfrac{1}{2}K_p\gamma h_k^2, \qquad K_p = 1/K_a = 3$$
$$h_k = \sqrt{(2P/3\gamma)} = 2.4 \text{ m}$$

This is high, but if it be placed at the front of the toe the extra depth is

$$2.4 - 0.8 = 1.6 \text{ m}$$

Were a 1.5 m toe to be used, then a 2.3 m deep shear key would be needed. The difference in the two solutions is small and the 2 m toe is preferable from bearing-stress considerations.

The actual maximum bearing stress of 60.4 kN/m^2 will be acceptable. So the final wall is sketched in Fig. 10.31.

Design of the stem
Using an effective span of $3.5 + 0.8/2 = 3.9$ m the moment acting at the base is

$$1.6 \times 20 \times 3.9^2/2 + \tfrac{1}{6} \times 0.33 \times 17 \times 3.9^3 \times 1.4 = 321.0 \text{ kN m/m}$$

Using a concrete of grade 40, then for moderate exposure from Table 5.1 a cover of 30 mm may be used. Assuming a 25 mm diameter bar,

$$d = 400 - 30 - 25/2 = 357.5, \qquad \text{say } 357 \text{ mm}$$
$$M/bd^2f_{cu} = 321.0 \times E6/1000 \times 357^2 \times 40 = 0.063$$

From design charts (Appendix B 1.1)

$$100A_s f_y/bdf_{cu} = 0.079$$

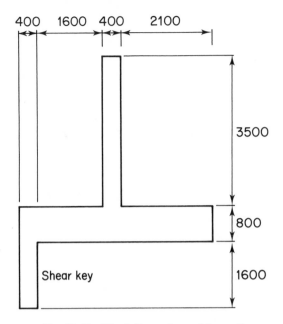

Fig. 10.31 Final dimensions of the wall.

so $A_s = 0.079 \times 1000 \times 357 \times 40/460 = 2452$ mm²/m
Fix T25-200 (2454 mm²/m)
There is no point in curtailing any of this reinforcement.
Calculation of crack widths.
Maximum service moment:

$$20 \times 3.9^2/2 + 0.33 \times 17 \times 3.9^3/6 = 207.6 \text{ kN m/m}$$

$$E_{c,28} = K_0 + 0.2f_{cu,28} \qquad\qquad (2.1)$$

$$K_0 = 20 \quad \text{and} \quad f_{cu,28} = 40, \quad \text{so } E_{c,28} = 28 \text{ kN/mm}^2$$

An effective modulus of $E_{c,28}/2$ or 14 kN/mm² should be used

$$\alpha_e = E_s/E_c = 200/14 = 14.29$$
$$\rho = 2454/1000 \times 357 = 6.9\text{E}{-}3$$
$$x/d = -\alpha_e\rho + \surd(2\alpha_e\rho + \alpha_e^2\rho^2) \qquad\qquad (4.9)$$

so $x/d = 0.36$ and $x = 128$ mm

$$I/bd^3 = (x/d)^3/3\alpha_e + \rho(1-x/d)^2 \qquad \text{(in steel units)}$$

so $I/bd^3 = 3.91\text{E}{-}3$
so $I = 3.91\text{E}{-}3 \times 1000 \times 357^3 = 1.78\text{E}8$ mm⁴

$$f_s = M_s(d-x)/I = (207.6\text{E}6 \times (357 - 126))/1.78\text{E}8$$
$$= 269 \text{ N/mm}^2$$

$$\varepsilon_s = f_s/E_s = (269/200)1\text{E}3 = 1350 \text{ microstrain}$$

Using Equation (5.29),

$$\varepsilon_1 = \varepsilon_s(h-x)/(d-x)$$
$$= 1350(400-128)/(357-128)$$
$$= 1603$$

For tension stiffening

$$\varepsilon_t = -(b_t(h-x)(a'-x))/(3E_sA_s(d-x))$$

since cracks are on the surface, $a' = h$,

so $\varepsilon_t = -b_t(h-x)^2/3E_sA_s(d-x)$
$$= -1000(400-126)^2/3 \times 200 \times E{-}3 \times 2454(357-126)$$
$$= -211 \text{ microstrain}$$

so net strain $\varepsilon_m = \varepsilon_1 + \varepsilon_t = 1603 - 221 = 1382$ microstrain

Calculation of a_{cr} (Fig. 10.32)

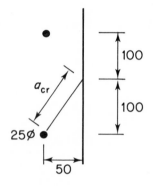

Fig. 10.32   Dimensions for calculating crack widths at root of stem.

$$a_{cr} = \sqrt{(200^2 + 50^2)} - 25/2 = 193.7 \text{ mm}$$
$$w_d = 3a_{cr}\varepsilon_m/[1 + 2(a_{cr}-c_{min})/(h-x)]$$
$$= 3 \times 193.7 \times 1129[-6/[1 + 2(193.7 - 40)/(400 - 126)]$$
$$= 0.38 \text{ mm}$$

This is greater than the allowable of 0.30 mm, so increase the reinforcement to T32-200. This will clearly be adequate for bending, and gives a design crack width of 0.19 mm, which is satisfactory.

d must be reduced to 354 mm
Shear
Maximum shear force:

$$V = 1.6 \times 2.0 \times 3.9 + \tfrac{1}{2} \times 0.33 \times 17 \times 3.9^2 = 167.5 \text{ kN/m}$$

Shear stress, $v = V/bd = 167.5E3/1000 \times 357 = 0.47 \text{ N/mm}^2$

Allowable shear stress, v_c, is given by

$$v_c = 0.79(400/354)^{1/4}(100 \times 4021/1000 \times 354)^{1/3}(40/25)^{1/3}/1.25$$
$$= 0.80 \text{ N/mm}^2$$

Thus, $v_c > v$, therefore no shear reinforcement is required.

Longitudinal reinforcement
Assuming summer concreting, then from Table 5.7, $T_1 = 30$ and $T_2 = 20$, and from Table 5.6 $\alpha_c = 12E-6$ for siliceous aggregate concrete. Since the wall is free at the top and fixed at the bottom take $R = 0.7$ (Table 5.5)

$$\varepsilon_{th} = \alpha \Delta T R$$
$$\varepsilon_{th} = (30 + 20) \times 0.7$$
$$= 420 \text{ microstrain}$$

It is general to supply 0.25% distribution reinforcement, so

$$A_s = 0.25/100 \times 400 \times 1000 = 1000 \text{ mm}^2/\text{m}$$

Fix T12-400 [1130 mm^2/m]
Check crack widths

$\quad a_{cr}$ (Fig. 10.33)

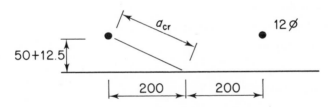

Fig. 10.33   Dimensions for calculating crack widths in distribution.

In tension,

$$w_d = 3a_{cr}\varepsilon_m/[1 + (a_{cr} - c_{min})/h]$$
$$\varepsilon_m = \varepsilon_{th}$$

so $\quad w_d = 3 \times 205.4 \times 4.2E-4/[1 + (205.4 - 62.5)/400]$
$$= 0.19 \text{ mm}$$

This is acceptable.
Ultimate bearing pressures:

Vertical force:		Moment (about centre line)	
Stem	1.4×35	Active	-40.1×1.4
Base	1.4×90	Surcharge	-122.5×1.6
Fill	1.4×125	Stem	-3.8×1.4
		Base	—
		Fill	1.4×150.0
Totals:	350 kN/m		-47.0 kN m/m

so ultimate bearing pressures are (Fig. 10.34)

$$350/4.5 \pm 47/(4.5^2/6) = 77.8 \pm 13.9$$
$$= 63.9 \text{ or } 91.7 \text{ kN/m}^2$$

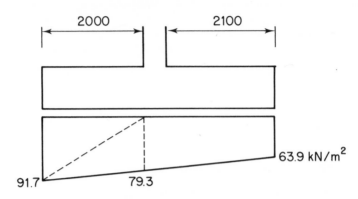

Shear key omitted for clarity

Fig. 10.34   Ultimate bearing pressure distribution.

Clearly the critical section is at **XX**

$$M_x = 91.7 \times 2^3/6 + 79.3 \times 2^3 \times (\tfrac{2}{3})(\tfrac{1}{2}) = 333.7 \text{ kN m/m}$$
$$d = 800 - 50 = 750 \text{ mm}$$
$$M/bd^2f_{cu} = 333.7\text{E6}/1000 \times 750^2 \times 25 = 0.024$$

or $A_s = 0.029 \times 1000 \times 750 \times 40/460 = 1891 \text{ mm}^2/\text{m}$

or T25-200 (2454 mm²/m)

(to preserve same bar spacing as vertical reinforcement). The reinforcement in the shear key will also be found to be T25-200 which will be adequate at all points for shear.

Settlement of the wall

$$S = 2.12B(1 - v^2)\sigma_{av}/E_v$$
$$B = 4.5 \text{ m}$$
$$\sigma_{av} = (60.4 + 50.8)/2 = 55.6 \text{ kN/m}^2$$

assuming dense sand

$$E_v = 80 \text{ N/m}^2 \quad v = 0.3 \quad \text{(from Table 10.1)}$$
$$S = 2.12 \times 4.5(1 - 0.3^2) \times 55.6/8\text{E3}$$
$$= 6 \times \text{E}-3 \text{ m} = 6 \text{ mm}$$

Tilt
This will be small since the bearing pressure is almost uniform

$$\tan \beta = 5.1(1 - v^2)M_0/E_vB^2$$

$M_0 = 16.1$ kN m/m (from Table 10.2)

$\tan \beta = 5.1(1 - 0.3^2) \times 16.1/80 \times 10^3 \times 4.5^2 = 46E - 6$

or movement at top due to tilt $= h \tan \beta = 4300 \times 46E - 5 = 0.2$ mm

In addition deflection will occur due to loading on the wall. This may be calculated according to the methods of Section 5.6.

10.15.5 Counterfort retaining walls

In general these are used when the height of the wall exceeds 7 m. Typical dimensions are given in Fig. 10.35.

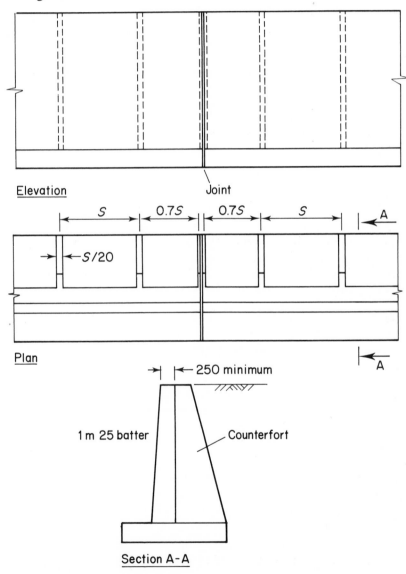

Fig. 10.35 General arrangement of a counterfort retaining wall.

Joints between units should occur about every 20–30 m of wall. To carry out the design the density of the counterforts can initially be assumed to be the same as the soil, since the volume of concrete in the counterforts is small compared with the volume of fill.

A typical design is carried out in Design Study 13.6.

10.16   Tutorial problems

10.16.1   Reinforcement for a slab

Design the reinforcement for the slab analysed in Example 10.5 (grade 30 concrete, grade 460 reinforcement and 25 cover).

Answer
Yield line.   Minimum reinforcement of 228 mm^2/m. T10-300 gives 262 mm^2.

Hillerborg strip.   Strips 1, 2 and 4 minimum (say T10-200). Strip 3 291 mm^2/m sagging and 284 hogging. Fix T12-300 (377 mm^2/m). Strip 5, sagging 207 and hogging 284 mm^2/m. Fix T10-250 (314 mm^2/m).

BS 8110 method.   x-direction middle strip minimum reinforcement, y-direction, middle strip sagging 160 and hogging 234 mm^2/m. All edge strips minimum, so fix T10-300 in all directions.

10.16.2   Slab design

A slab 200 m thick by 7 m by 5 m is encastré on one long side and both short sides and is simply supported on the remaining side. The slab carries an imposed load of 5 kN/m^2. Design the slab using yield-line, Hillerborg strip and the BS 8110 method assuming a ratio of hogging to sagging moments of $\frac{4}{3}$ (i.e. $i = \frac{4}{3}$). The concrete is grade 30 (specific weight 25 kN/m^3), cover 25 mm, and the steel is grade 460.

Answer
Yield line. $m = 10.27$ and $im = 13.7$ kN m/m. (Use Equation (10.27)). Reinforcement requirement is minimum of 260 mm^2. Fix T10-300 (262 mm^2/m).

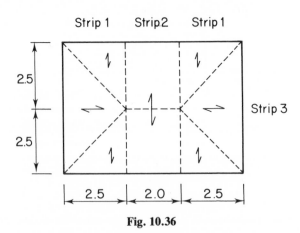

Fig. 10.36

Hillerborg strip. There is more than one possible solution depending on the load distribution chosen. A possible distribution is given in Fig. 10.36, for which a solution will be given.

Strips 1 and 3, minimum. Strip 2, $m = 14.1$ kN m/m, sagging 298, hogging 220 mm², fix T10-250 top (314) and T10-300 bottom (262).

BS 8110. Long side: suppport moment $= 13.24$ kN m/m, mid-span moment 9.94 kN m/m – both require minimum.

Short side: support moment 25.9 and mid-span moment 19.5 kN m/m, requiring 408 (T12-250 (452)) and 209 (T10-300 (262)) mm²/m respectively.

All designs are satisfactory for shear and deflection.

10.16.3   Slab design

A slab 400 m thick by 8 m by 5 m is encastré on both the short sides and one long side and is unsupported on the remaining long side, and carries an imposed load of 5 kN/m². The concrete is grade 30 (specific weight 25 kN/m³), cover 25 mm and the steel is of grade 460. Prepare a suitable design assuming $i = \frac{4}{3}$.

Answer
Yield line.   There are two possible collapse modes illustrated in Fig. 10.37(a) and (b).

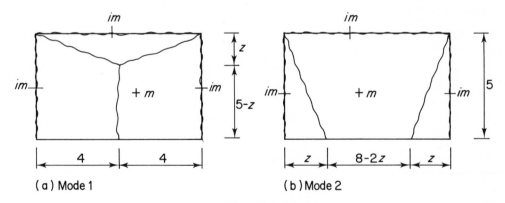

(a) Mode 1   (b) Mode 2

Fig. 10.37

Mode 1 (Fig. 10.37(a)). Work equation:

$$m = 66(20 - 4z/3)/(7(8/z + 5/2))$$
$$z = 4.43, m = 30.9 \text{ kN m/m}$$

Mode 2 (Fig. 10.37(b)). Work equation:

$$m = 22(20 - 5z/3)/(70/(3z) + 2z/5 + 32/15)$$
$$z = 3.83, m = 30.8 \text{ kN m/m}$$

Reinforcement minimum of 520 mm²/m.

Deflection check gives min $d = 357$ (remember basic factor is 7).
Shear is satisfactory.

Hillerborg strip. A possible configuration is given in Fig. 10.38.

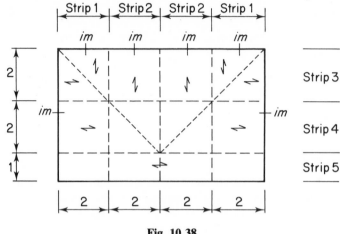

Fig. 10.38

Strips 1, 3 and 4 – minimum reinforcement.
Strip 2 – $im = 102.7$ kN m/m giving $A_s = 742$ mm²/m, T12-150 (754)
Strip 5 – hogging: $im = 100.6$ kN m/m, $A_s = 755$, fix T12-150 (754)
sagging: $m = 75.4$, $A_s = 549$, fix T12-200 (565).

Deflection. $f_s = 283$, $F_1 = 1.53$, giving minimum d of 467, which is not satisfactory.
Increase steel area to T12-100 (1131) which will give a satisfactory solution.

10.16.4 Retaining wall

Determine a suitable toe length for the cantilever retaining wall, for which data are given
in Fig. 10.39.

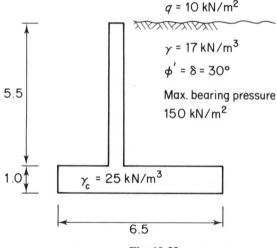

Fig. 10.39

Answer

A toe length of 1.0 m is satisfactory although a 2 m toe gives less tendency to tilt. Important results in the calculations are given in Table 10.6.

Table 10.6

	Toe (m) 0.5	1.0	1.5	2.0	3.0
FoS against overturning	5.56	5.31	5.21	5.05	4.60
FoS against sliding	2.35	2.20	2.05	1.90	1.60
σ_{max}	169.1	143.7	121.7	103.0	75.5
$\sigma_{max}/\sigma_{min}$	2.80	2.00	1.45	1.24	0.98

References

Johansen K. W. (1972). *Yield line formulae for slabs*, Cement and Concrete Association.

Jones L. L., Wood R. H. (1986). *Yield line analysis of slabs*, Chapman and Hall, London.

Lawson R. M. (1985). *Fire resistance of ribbed concrete floors*, Report No. 107, Construction Industry Research and Information Association.

Moy S. S. J. (1981). *Plastic methods for steel and concrete structures*, Macmillan.

Reagan P. E. (1981). *Behaviour of reinforced concrete flat slabs*, Report No. 89, Construction Industry Research and Information Association.

Starzewski K. (1986). Earth retaining structures and culverts. In F. D. C. Henry (ed.), *The design and construction of engineering foundations*, Chapman and Hall (Chapter 6).

Timoshenko S. P. and Woinowsky-Krieger S. (1959) *Theory of plates and shells*, McGraw-Hill.

Whittle R. T. (1985). *Design of reinforced concrete slabs to BS 8110*, Report No. 110, Construction Industry Research and Information Association.

Willun Z. and Starzewski K. (1972 and 1975). *Soil mechanics in foundation engineering* (2 vols), Surrey University Press.

11

Foundations

11.1 Introduction

11.1.1 Types of foundation

The purpose of a foundation is to transmit loads from a structure to the ground in such a way that there is an acceptable factor of safety against the development of any kind of failure mechanism in the foundation or the soil on which it is based. It is also important to ensure that settlement, either immediately after construction or during the intended life of the structure, will be uniform and acceptably small.

The type of foundation selected depends on a number of factors, including the depth to a suitable bearing stratum, the bearing capacity of the stratum, the proximity of existing structures and their foundations, and an assessment of relative costs. Where there is a good uniform bearing stratum at a relatively shallow depth columns may be supported on independent pad foundations. Combined or raft foundations may be used when individual foundations tend to overlap, or where the bearing capacity of the soil is variable, or when differential settlement must be avoided. In order to minimise differential settlement the centre of mass of the structure should be vertically above the centre of area of the foundation or group of foundations.

A good bearing stratum is one whose bearing capacity is adequate to support the foundation safely and economically, and is constant or increases with depth since it must be borne in mind that the soil is stressed at a considerable depth below a foundation, the depth increasing with the area of the foundation or group of foundations. In layered ground, for example, a stratum of soft clay below an apparently good bearing stratum could have a negligible effect on a small test foundation, but could cause excessive settlement of a large group of footings placed close together. Where the cost of excavation to a good bearing stratum would be prohibitive, or where the stratum is not continuous, piled foundations may be used. Piles are vertical pillars which rely on friction along their length or on end support from a good bearing stratum at some depth below ground level.

Some typical examples of foundations are illustrated in Fig. 11.1. In general the design of foundations requires an understanding of the principles of soil mechanics and is covered in specialist literature. This chapter deals mainly with the design of simple pad foundations for an individual column using the recommendations of cl 3.11, Pt 1 of BS 8110 and the simplifying assumptions of CP 2004.

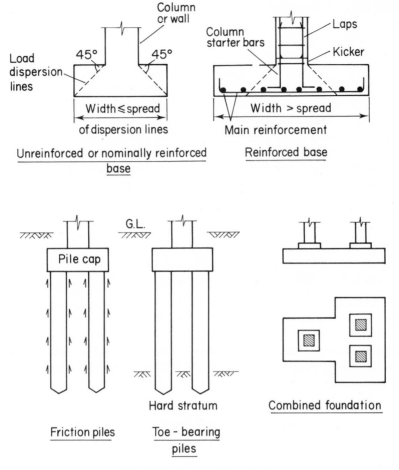

Fig. 11.1 Types of foundation.

11.1.2 Allowable bearing pressure

The actual distribution of earth pressure beneath a foundation depends on its flexibility and the type of soil, but in order to simplify the design it may be assumed that the pressure is linearly distributed across the base. Negative earth pressures (tension) cannot be developed. When determining the bearing pressure that can be safely borne by a particular soil, long-term settlement under working loads as well as failure of the soil at the ultimate limit state should be considered. A thorough site investigation for a large or important structure requires considerable experience and a detailed knowledge of soil mechanics, and may account for a significant part of the overall cost.

For the normal range of buildings and engineering structures the design and construction of foundations is covered by CP 2004, which contains tables of *allowable bearing pressures* for different types of soil. The following are typical examples:

Cohesive soils:
stiff clay	150–300 kN/m^2
firm clay	75–150 kN/m^2

Non-cohesive soils, assuming that the ground water table is at least the width of the foundation below the base:

compact gravel >600 kN/m^2
loose sand <100 kN/m^2

These allowable bearing pressures, which incorporate factors of safety against excessive settlement as well as against failure of the soil, require experience in their application and are intended only to be used in preliminary designs. The size and shape of the foundation should be designed so that the earth pressure beneath it does not exceed the allowable bearing pressure when the structure is subjected to *service loads*. The thickness of the base and its reinforcement, on the other hand, should be designed for the *ultimate limit state* in accordance with BS 8110. Since the partial safety factors of BS 8110 are not compatible with CP 2004, the complete design must be accomplished in two stages.

1   Determine the size and shape of the foundation assuming the axial forces and bending moments obtained from an analysis of the structure under service (characteristic) loads and the allowable bearing pressures.

2   Design the thickness and reinforcement of the foundation using the earth pressures in equilibrium with the axial forces and bending moments obtained by analysing the structure under the design loads for the ultimate limit state. The partial safety factors for earth pressures given in Table 3.2 should not be used in this case because the loads from which the pressures have been derived have already been factored for the ultimate limit state.

11.2   Bearing pressures from pad foundations

11.2.1   Uniaxial bending

Consider a pad base subjected to an axial load N and a bending moment M about a single axis, as shown in Fig. 11.2. Since the bearing pressure acts in the same way as a normal stress and may be assumed to be linearly distributed over the base the simple theory of

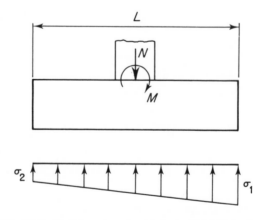

Fig. 11.2   Bearing pressures due to uniaxial bending.

bending can be applied. The section modulus of the base is given by

$$Z = BL^2/6 \tag{11.1}$$

where B is the width of the base and L is the dimension in the plane of bending. The maximum and minimum bearing pressures may then be determined from

$$\sigma_1 = N/BL + M/Z$$
$$\sigma_2 = N/BL - M/Z \tag{11.2}$$

The pressure is uniform across the width of the base.

11.2.2 Partial bearing

As negative pressures cannot be developed beneath a base, Equations (11.2) apply only when $\sigma_2 \geq 0$, i.e. when $L \geq 6M/N$. The effect of the bending moment can be simulated by applying the axial load at an eccentricity e, where

$$e = M/N \tag{11.3}$$

Positive pressures can therefore only be developed over the whole base when $e \leq L/6$. This is the familiar 'middle third' rule. When $e > L/6$, i.e. when the eccentricity lies outside the middle third, the base is only partially in contact with the soil, as in Fig. 11.3. This condition is undesirable, but is sometimes unavoidable in practice.

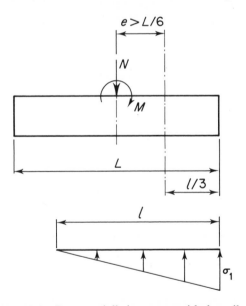

Fig. 11.3 Base partially in contact with the soil.

For equilibrium the load N must be equal to the volume of the bearing pressure diagram; and its line of action must pass through the centroid of the diagram.

Hence

$$\sigma_1 Bl/2 = N$$

and

$$l/3 = L/2 - e = L/2 - M/N$$

Solving these equations gives

$$l = 3(L/2 - M/N) \qquad (11.4)$$
$$\sigma_1 = 2N/[3B(L/2 - M/N)] \qquad (11.5)$$

11.2.3 Biaxial bending

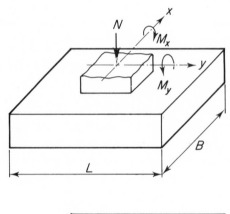

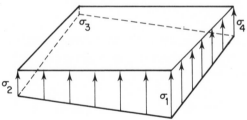

Fig. 11.4 Base subjected to biaxial bending.

If the bending moments are biaxial, as in Fig. 11.4, the bearing pressures vary across both the length and width of the base, as shown. The section moduli are given by

$$Z_x = BL^2/6$$
$$Z_y = LB^2/6 \qquad (11.6)$$

and the bearing pressures by

$$\sigma_1 = N/BL + M_x/Z_x + M_y/Z_y$$
$$\sigma_2 = N/BL - M_x/Z_x + M_y/Z_y$$
$$\sigma_3 = N/BL - M_x/Z_x - M_y/Z_y$$
$$\sigma_4 = N/BL + M_x/Z_x - M_y/Z_y \qquad (11.7)$$

The maximum and minimum bearing pressures are σ_1 and σ_3 respectively. The equations are valid only when $\sigma_3 \geq 0$, i.e. when positive pressure is applied over the whole base area.

11.3   Design of pad foundations

11.3.1   Determination of base dimensions

The aim is to choose values for the length L and width B of a base so that the allowable bearing pressure is not exceeded and the base is proportioned so that an economic design can be achieved. As L and B can be varied independently the solution must be by trial and error. The usual procedure is to select trial values of L and B, calculate the maximum and minimum bearing pressures, and then check that σ_{max} does not exceed the allowable bearing pressure. In order to avoid excessive rotation of the base due to differential settlement it is also necessary to check that the ratio $\sigma_{max}/\sigma_{min}$ is acceptable. For foundations on compressive soils $\sigma_{max}/\sigma_{min}$ is normally limited to 3, or 4 if transient loads are involved.

If the bending is uniaxial, the process can be simplified, as in Examples 11.1 and 11.2, by the use of the design graph (Graph No. 13) in Appendix B1. It can be shown (see Appendix B2) that

$$L = \alpha M/N \tag{11.8}$$
$$B = \beta N^2/M\sigma_{max} \tag{11.9}$$

where α and β are coefficients depending only on the ratio $\sigma_{max}/\sigma_{min}$. In the graph α, β, and α/β are plotted against $\sigma_{max}/\sigma_{min}$.

EXAMPLE 11.1   Determination of base dimensions

The loads on a base from dead and imposed working loads are 600 kN and a bending moment M. The soil is compressive and has an allowable bearing pressure of 150 kN/m^2.

(a)   Given $M = 75$ kN m determine
    (i)   the size of a suitable square base
    (ii)   the width of a base whose length is 3 m.
(b)   Obtain suitable base dimensions if $M = 135$ kN m.

(a) $M/N = 75/600 = 0.125$
       $N^2/M\sigma_{max} = (600)^2/(75 \times 150) = 32.0$

Hence

    $L = 0.125\alpha$ and $B = 32\beta$

(i)   *Square base*
For a square base $L = B$. Hence $\alpha/\beta = 32.0/0.125 = 256.0$.

Now, using the design graph and projecting vertically from 256.0 on the α/β curve on to the $\sigma_{max}/\sigma_{min}$ axis gives $\sigma_{max}/\sigma_{min} = 1.97$, which is acceptable for a compressive soil. Projecting vertically on to the α curve gives $\alpha = 18.6$.

Hence

    $L = 0.125 \times 18.6 = \underline{2.325 \text{ m}}$

(ii) $\underline{L = 3\,m}$

$\alpha = L/0.125 = 3/0.125 = 24.0$

Projecting vertically from 24 on the α curve gives $\beta = 0.0535$

Hence

$B = 32 \times 0.0535 = \underline{1.712\,m}$

(b) $M/N = 135/600 = 0.225$
$N^2/M\sigma_{max} = (600)^2/(135 \times 150) = 17.78$

For a square base $\alpha/\beta = 17.78/0.225 = 79.0$. The corresponding value of $\sigma_{max}/\sigma_{min}$ exceeds 3, the maximum recommended value for a compressive soil. Projecting therefore from $\sigma_{max}/\sigma_{min} = 3$ gives $\alpha = 12$ and $\beta = 0.125$.

Hence
$L = 0.225 \times 12 = \underline{2.700\,m}$
$B = 17.78 \times 0.125 = \underline{2.223\,m}$

The above dimensions are the minimum. In practice they would be rounded up to some convenient values. For example in (a) (i) 2.5 m square, in (a) (ii) 3 m by 1.8 m, and in (b) 2.7 m by 2.3 m.

11.3.2   Alternative method for unidirectional moments

If the bending moments on the base are always in the same direction it is possible to reduce or cancel their effects by offsetting the column from the centre-lines of the base in such a way that opposing moments are created. However, this practice can lead to an unsafe situation unless the effect of variations in the applied bending moments are carefully assessed. For example, if the offset is designed to cancel the *maximum* value of the bending moment, the reverse moment created by the offset axial load may produce bearing pressures in excess of the allowable when the *minimum* bending moment is applied.

EXAMPLE 11.2   Offset column

A base supports a column carrying working loads of 600 kN axial and a bending moment M which varies from 100 kN m to 200 kN m, always in the same direction. Design a suitable arrangement for the column and base if the allowable bearing pressure is 120 kN/m^2.

Designing for the average bending moment the column eccentricity is given by

$e = M_{av}/N = 150/600 = 0.25\,m$

The arrangement is as shown in Fig. 11.5.

The net bending moment on the base is clockwise when the bending moment exceeds 150 kN m and anticlockwise when it is less. The net maximum value is 50 kN m. For the design graph,

$M/N = 50/600 = 0.0833$
$N^2/M\sigma_{max} = (600)^2/(50 \times 120) = 60$

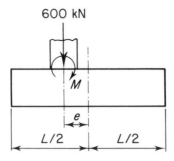

Fig. 11.5   Base with offset column.

For a square base $\alpha/\beta = 60/0.0833 = 720$
From the graph $\alpha = 29.5$ and $\sigma_{max}/\sigma_{min} < 3$

Hence

$L = 0.0833 \times 29.5 = 2.460$ m – say $\underline{2.5\ m}$

Other combinations of L and B could be determined, if required, as in the previous example.

11.3.3   Bending moment and shear force on a critical cross-section

For an isolated pad footing the critical section is defined (cl 3.11.2.2, Pt 1) as . . .   that at the face of the column or wall supported.   For a column base there are thus two critical cross-sections, shown as X and Y in Fig. 11.6.

The bending moment and shear force on a section are determined from the actions produced on the pad by the design ultimate loads, to one side of the section or perimeter (cls 3.11.3.1 and 3.11.3.3, Pt 1). No allowance is made for the two-dimensional behaviour of a base and no redistribution of moments is permitted, although, as will be seen in Section 11.3.5, the distribution of the reinforcement may be modified. Figure 11.6 shows the pressures resulting from the general case of a column subjected to biaxial bending. The earth pressures σ_1 to σ_4 are determined from Equation (11.7) using the design ultimate values of N, M_x, and M_y.

First consider the moment on section X from an element of the pressure diagram to the right of the section. The pressures at each end of the element, by simple proportion, are given by

$\sigma = \sigma_2 + (\sigma_1 - \sigma_2)(L - l + y)/L$
$\sigma' = \sigma_3 + (\sigma_4 - \sigma_3)(L - l + y)/L$

The bending moment from the element is

$dM_x = \tfrac{1}{2}(\sigma + \sigma')By\,dy$

Substituting for σ and σ' and integrating between the limits $y = 0$ and $y = l$ gives the bending moment for section X, thus

$$M_X = \tfrac{1}{4}Bl^2[\sigma_1 + \sigma_4 - l(\sigma_1 + \sigma_4 - \sigma_2 - \sigma_3)/3L] \tag{11.10}$$

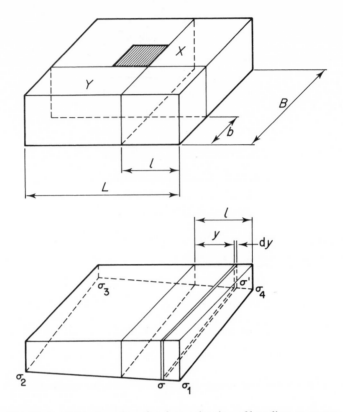

Fig. 11.6   Critical sections for determination of bending moment.

Similarly the bending moment on section Y is given by

$$M_Y = \tfrac{1}{4}Lb^2[\sigma_1 + \sigma_2 - b(\sigma_1 + \sigma_2 - \sigma_3 - \sigma_4)/3B]$$ (11.11)

The shear force contributed by the element is

$$dV_X = \tfrac{1}{2}(\sigma + \sigma')B\,dy$$

Substituting for σ and σ' and integrating as before, the shear force on section X is

$$V_X = \tfrac{1}{2}Bl[\sigma_1 + \sigma_4 - l(\sigma_1 + \sigma_4 - \sigma_2 - \sigma_3)/2L]$$ (11.12)

Similarly the shear force section Y is given by

$$V_Y = \tfrac{1}{2}Lb[\sigma_1 + \sigma_2 - b(\sigma_1 + \sigma_2 - \sigma_3 - \sigma_4)/2B]$$ (11.13)

For uniaxial bending about the x–x axis $\sigma_4 = \sigma_1$ and $\sigma_3 = \sigma_2$. Hence

$$M_X = \tfrac{1}{2}Bl^2[\sigma_1 - l(\sigma_1 - \sigma_2)/3L]$$ (11.14)
$$M_Y = \tfrac{1}{4}Lb^2(\sigma_1 + \sigma_2)$$ (11.15)

$$V_X = Bl[\sigma_1 - l(\sigma_1 - \sigma_2)/2L]$$ (11.16)
$$V_Y = Lb(\sigma_1 + \sigma_2)/2$$ (11.17)

All the above formulae for V_X and V_Y can be used to obtain the shear force on any other cross-sections provided that l and b are measured from the edge of the base.

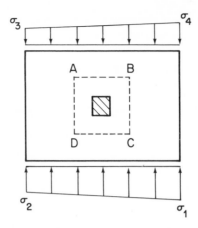

Fig. 11.7 Section around a perimeter.

11.3.4 Shear force on a perimeter

Consider the perimeter ABCD in Fig. 11.7. The shear force on the vertical section is equal to the design ultimate axial load N less the total upward force acting on the part of the base enclosed by the perimeter, i.e.

$$V = N - \sigma_{av} \times \text{area ABCD} \qquad (11.18)$$

If the column is centrally placed on the base σ_{av}, the average pressure on ABCD, is the same as the average pressure on the base as a whole, i.e.

$$\sigma_{av} = N/BL \qquad (11.19)$$

In the case of the perimeter around the column itself the upward force is ignored.

11.3.5 Resistance to bending and shear

In general a base may be considered as an inverted flat slab, for which methods of design have been described in Chapter 10. However, as bases are usually thicker than flat slabs and are generally stiffer than the columns they support, shear forces need not be increased to take account of moment transfer.

For *resistance to bending* the ultimate moment of resistance of the pad at sections X and Y must be at least as great as the bending moments produced by the design loads for the ultimate limit state. Reinforcement must therefore be provided in the bottom of the pad in two directions at right angles to the sections. The total area of reinforcement is calculated by assuming that the pad behaves as a wide singly reinforced beam and using the design formulae of Chapter 6 or the design graph (Graph No. 1) in Appendix B1. The above assumption is not strictly true because the pad actually behaves as a thick plate; and in the case of a wide base it may be necessary to compensate by placing a greater proportion of the reinforcement under the column. The distribution of reinforcement at right angles to a particular section is governed by cl 3.11.3.2, Pt 1, which states that:

... Where l_c exceeds $(3c/4 + 9d/4)$, two thirds of the required reinforcement should be concentrated within a zone from the centre line of the column to a distance 1.5*d* from the face of the column; otherwise the reinforcement should be uniformly distributed over l_c.

This rule is illustrated for both sections in Fig. 11.8.

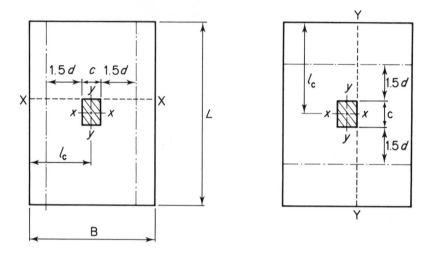

Fig. 11.8   Interpretation of cl 3.11.3.2.

The *shear resistance* of a pad is covered by cl 3.11.3.4, Pt 1, i.e.   the design shear strength near a concentrated load is governed by the more severe of the following conditions.

(a)   Shear along a vertical section extending across the full width of the base . . .   (references to other clauses)
(b)   Punching shear around the loaded area . . .   (references to other clauses)

The references to other clauses relate to the design of solid and flat slabs and have been covered in Chapters 7 and 10. In the design of bases the shear stress on the perimeter around the column itself or on a cross-section at the column face should not exceed the maximum design shear stress of $v_u = 0.8\sqrt{f_{cu}} \leqslant 5\,\text{N/mm}^2$,   otherwise the thickness of the base must be increased. The cross-section may be more critical in some extreme cases, for example in a long narrow combined base with a column at each end.

It is also necessary to check that the shear stress does not exceed the design shear stress v_c on a perimeter 1.5*d* from the column face – unless the entire perimeter falls outside the base. This stress is defined in Chapter 7 – see Equation (7.4) and Example 7.6. If v_c is exceeded, then either shear reinforcement is required or the thickness of the base must be increased. The latter is the more common practice. The principles of cl 3.7.7.8, Pt 1, which recommends that a smaller perimeter should be taken when a concentrated load is near a free edge, may also apply. Some typical examples are given in Fig. 11.9, showing that in most cases the shear stress on one or more cross-sections which include one side of the perimeter should also be checked. The most critical section can usually be inferred from the relative values of the bearing pressure, as shown.

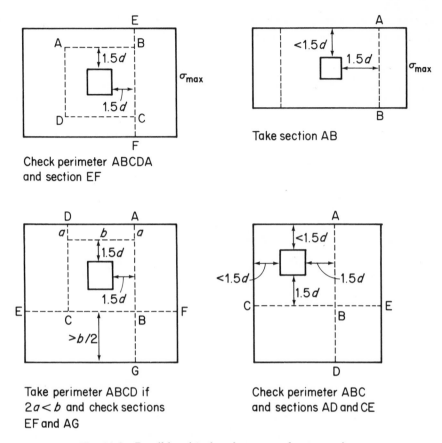

Fig. 11.9 Possible critical perimeters and cross sections.

11.3.6 Column starter bars

Sufficient anchorage must be provided within the thickness of the base for the column starter bars. However (cl 3.12.8.8, Pt 1) ... the compression bond stresses that develop on column starter bars within bases and pile caps do not need to be checked provided:
(a) the starter bars extend down to the bottom layer of reinforcement (see Figs. 11.1 and 11.13).
(b) the base has been designed for moments and shears in accordance with 3.11 (see this chapter and Chapter 7).

11.4 Pile caps

Pile caps distribute the load from a column to a group of supporting piles. The piles are driven about one metre apart in symmetrical groups, usually with the vertical axis of the column passing through the centroid of the group. The smallest number of piles in a group that is inherently stable laterally is three. The lateral stability of pairs of piles and single piles is secured by linking through tie beams to other piles or groups. The design of pile caps is covered in BS 8110 by cl 3.11.4, Pt 1.

Two alternative methods of design are recommended: either as deep beams or slabs reinforced to resist bending and shear, or as a truss with an upper node on the column axis and lower nodes at the intersection of the pile axes with the tension reinforcement. In the first method, since the spans are short and are subjected to heavy concentrated loads, shear is usually predominant. If the cap is designed as a slab punching shear around the column must also be considered (see Chapter 7 – Section 7.1.15 and Example 7.7).

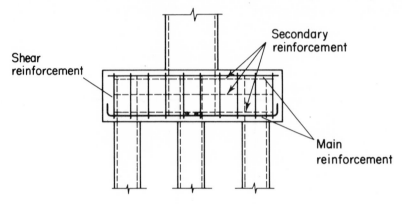

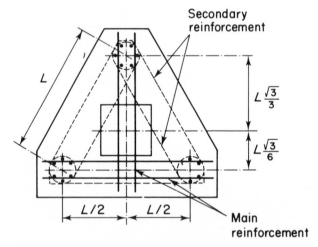

Fig. 11.10   Detail of a pile cap for three piles.

An example of a pile cap for three piles is detailed in Fig. 11.10. In this case the cap is designed as two simply supported beams at right angles. Shear reinforcement in the plan has been omitted for the purposes of clarity. The function of the secondary reinforcement (nominally 12 mm bars) is to tie together laterally the reinforcement in the three piles. If the cap had been designed by the truss analogy reinforcement would have been placed in the bottom of the cap between the piles to act as the tension members of the truss, the concrete between the piles and the axis of the column forming the compression members.

11.5 Tutorial problems

11.5.1 Bearing pressures on a pad with given dimensions

A pad foundation 2.5 m square supports a central column which exerts an axial force of 800 kN and a bending moment of 100 kN m at working load. Determine the maximum and minimum bearing pressures.

Answer
166.4, 89.6 kN/m^2

11.5.2 Determination of pad length

A pad foundation 2.5 m wide supports an axial load and moment of 800 kN and 320 kN m. Working from basic principles, determine

(a) the equivalent eccentricity of the axial load
(b) the minimum length of the base if:
    (i)   the bearing pressure is to be applied over the whole surface of the base
    (ii) the ratio of maximum to minimum pressures is not to exceed 3.
(c) the maximum and minimum bearing pressures in each case.

Answer
(a) 0.4 m; (b) 2.4, 4.8 m; (c) (i) 266.6, 0 kN/m^2; (ii) 100, 33.3 kN/m^2

11.5.3 Pad with partial bearing

A pad foundation carrying characteristic loads of 600 kN and 300 kN m is constrained by an obstruction to a maximum length of 2.4 m.

(a) Prove that only part of the pad bears on the soil.
(b) Calculate from basic principles the minimum width if the allowable bearing pressure is 120 kN/m^2.
(c) Check the result using Equation (11.5).

Answer
(a) $e = 0.5$ m $> L/6$; (b) 4.76 m

11.5.4 Offset column

A pad base is designed with an offset column as shown in Fig. 11.11. The width of the base is 3 m. The loads are characteristic loads. What is the range of the moment M that can be applied if the allowable bearing pressure of 150 kN/m^2 is not to be exceeded?

Answer
Between 200 and 1000 kN m.

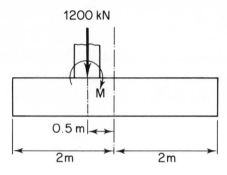

Fig. 11.11

11.5.5   Use of the design graph

The characteristic axial load and moment acting on a pad foundation are 100 kN and 200 kN m. The allowable bearing pressure is 125 kN/m². Use Graph No. 13 to determine:

(a)   the size of a suitable square base
(b)   the ratio of maximum and minimum bearing pressures
(c)   the length of the base if the width is restricted to 3 m.

Check the results using basic principles.

Answer
(a) 3.350 m; (b) 2.15; (c) 3.640 m.

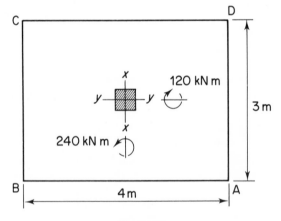

Fig. 11.12

11.5.6   Bearing pressures from biaxial bending

Determine the bearing pressures at the corners of the base in Fig. 11.12. The column is centrally placed and in the ultimate lim state exerts design moments as shown and a design axial load of 1800 kN.

Answer

(kN m) $\sigma_A = 100$, $\sigma_B = 160$, $\sigma_C = 200$, $\sigma_D = 140$.

11.5.7 Reinforcement for bending moments

For the base in Fig. 11.12, the column is 400 mm square, the concrete is C25, and the effective depth is 500 mm.

(a) Using the bearing pressures from the previous problem determine the bending moments on critical sections at the column face.
(b) Design suitable mild-steel reinforcement and make a detailed sketch showing how it is to be placed in the base.

Answer

(a) $M_X = 831$ kN m, $M_Y = 555$ kN m
(b) See Fig. 11.13

Section X (mm²)

	Required	Provided
Inner	5400	5369
Outer	2700	3109
	8100	8478

Section Y (mm²)

Inner	3733	3819
Outer	1867	1808
	5600	5627

Notes

1 *Bar notation* See Section 1.5.
2 *Section* The section shows the upper and lower layers of reinforcement, indicated by their bar marks. The reinforcement for the larger bending moment would normally be placed at the bottom. The size and number of the column starter bars (bar mark 5) would be the same as in the column.
3 *Effective depth* Since the reinforcement for section X is at the bottom, the reinforcement for section Y is at a smaller effective depth. This makes little difference to the area of reinforcement. A common depth of 500 mm has been assumed.
4 *Uniqueness of solution* Design problems do not have a unique solution; other arrangements of the reinforcement giving the required areas and distributions would be equally valid.

11.5.8 Shear resistance

Using the results of the previous two problems draw a diagram showing possible critical perimeters and cross-sections and determine the shear stresses on them. Calculate the design shear stresses and check the shear resistance of the base.

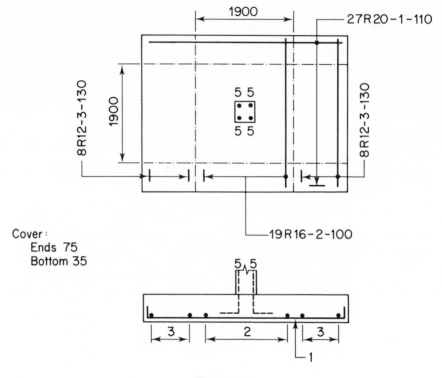

Fig. 11.13

Answer
See Fig. 11.14.

Shear stress (N/mm²) at perimeter 1, section 1; perimeter 2, section 2

$v = 2.25, 0.60; 0.33, 0.36$
$v_c = 4.0, 4.0; 0.48, 0.48$

Shear resistance is adequate without shear reinforcement

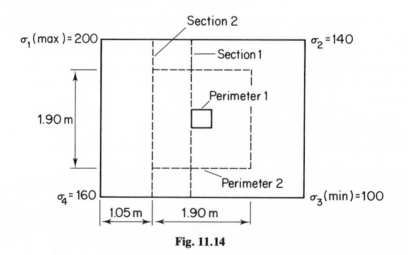

Fig. 11.14

11.5.9 Pile cap

The pile cap in Fig. 11.10 supports a column which exerts a design axial load of 3000 kN and a design moment of 350 kN m. The moment is in the plane of the beam carrying the column and can act in either sense. The axes of the piles are 1.2 m apart. Ignoring the weight of the pile cap, calculate

(a) the maximum axial load on each pile.
(b) the maximum design bending moment and shear force on each beam.

Answer
(a) Pile at apex 1337 kN, piles at base 1169 kN.
(b)

	Max M (kN m)	Max V (kN)
Beam carrying the column	926	2337
Cross beam	701	1169

Reference

CP 2004 (1972) *Code of practice for foundations*, The British Standards Institution, London.

12

Prestressed Concrete

12.1 Bending resistance of prestressed concrete members at ultimate load

12.1.1 Introduction

A member where the concrete is prestressed by the longitudinal reinforcing steel (tendons) before being subject to external loading is called prestressed concrete. There are two methods of manufacturing the specimens: (a) pre-tensioning the tendons before casting the concrete; (b) post-tensioning the tendons after casting the concrete.

A pre-tensioned member is manufactured by first pre-tensioning the steel tendons over the length of the casting bed, as shown in Fig. 12.1(a), and anchoring the steel to rigid anchor blocks at either end. The tendons are generally in the form of straight high-tensile steel wires varying in diameter from 2 to 7 mm. The concrete is then cast around the tendons using shuttering to form the required shape of cross-section of the member. Generally within 3 days, using accelerated curing techniques, the concrete has gained sufficient strength to be able to transfer the prestressing force to the concrete by releasing the anchorages. The shuttering is then removed and the casting bed can be used again. This method favours the re-use of shuttering and the manufacture of identical members, but the members have to be transported from the casting yard to the site.

A post-tensioned member is manufactured by first preparing the shuttering which supports sheaths or ducts. The ducts contain unstressed tendons (see Fig. 12.1(b)) in the form of straight or curved cables, or bars, which are free to move in the direction of their

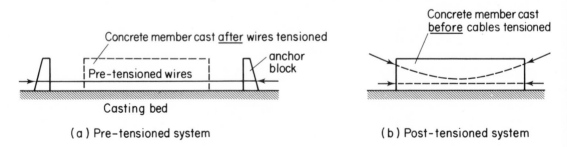

(a) Pre-tensioned system

(b) Post-tensioned system

Fig. 12.1 Prestressing systems.

length but are restrained, as far as possible, from lateral movement. The concrete is then poured into the mould and allowed to gain strength. There is less urgency in this method of manufacture and the shuttering is removed after a few days. Later when the concrete has matured, the steel is stressed by jacking against the ends of the beam and anchored using wedges for cables, or nuts on threaded rods for bars. The method is suitable for members of different cross-section and for members which are cast in place on the construction sites where road access is difficult.

It is important to realise that for prestressed concrete the characteristic strengths of the materials are high. The steel has a value between 1500 and 2000 N/mm^2 and the concrete has a value between 40 and 60 N/mm^2. The corresponding values for ordinary reinforced concrete are steel 250–460 N/mm^2, and concrete 20–40 N/mm^2.

The specified characteristic strengths and preferred sizes of prestressing steel are given in British Standards 4486, 4757, and 5896 and are summarised in Appendix A3. The most commonly used wires for pre-tensioned members are 5 and 7 mm with characteristic strengths between 1570 and 1770 N/mm^2.

The advantages of prestressed concrete as compared with ordinary reinforced concrete are:

(a)   reduced self weight of members;
(b)   no cracks at service load for class 1 members (see Section 12.2.3), and consequently better durability;
(c)   increased shear resistance.

The disadvantages of prestressed concrete as compared with ordinary reinforced concrete are:

(a)   increased cost of materials and shuttering;
(b)   greater supervision required to ensure correct concrete strength and magnitude of prestress forces;
(c)   the design calculations are more extensive.

12.1.2   Analysis of a section in bending at the ultimate limit state (cl 4.3.7.1, Pt 1)

Analysis entails the determination of the moment of resistance of a section given the size

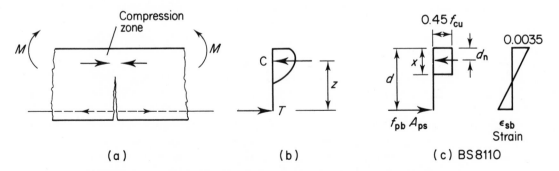

Fig. 12.2   Bending resistance of a prestressed concrete beam at ultimate load.

of the section and reinforcement. The behaviour of a prestressed concrete member in bending at the ultimate limit state is similar to that of an ordinary reinforced concrete member. The appearance of a beam element in bending is shown in Fig. 12.2, where tensile cracks, commencing in the extreme tension fibres, extend to the edge of the compression zone. The compressive force at the top of the section is balanced by the tensile force in the steel at the bottom of the section. In very simple terms the moment of resistance of a section in bending is therefore the magnitude of the couple *Cz* or *Tz*.

The basic concepts are simple and the analysis of a section in bending is based on the following assumptions (cl 4.3.7.1, Pt 1).

(a) The strain distribution in the concrete in compression is derived from the assumption that plane sections remain plane.

(b) The design stresses in the concrete in compression are derived either from the stress–strain curve given in Fig. 2.1 with $\gamma_m = 1.5$, or taken as $0.45f_{cu}$ for a depth (from the compression face) equal to 0.9 times the depth of the compression zone.

Note: In both cases the strain at the outermost compression fibre is taken as 0.0035.

(c) The tensile strength of concrete is ignored.

(d) The strains in bonded prestressing tendons and in any additional reinforcement, whether in tension or compression, are derived from the assumption that plane sections remain plane.

(e) The design stresses in bonded prestressing tendons, whether initially tensioned or untensioned, and in any additional reinforcement are derived from the appropriate stress–strain curves; the stress–strain curves for prestressing tendons are given in Fig. 2.3 and those for reinforcement in Fig. 2.2. (An alternative approach for obtaining the stress in the tendons is given in 4.3.7.3 and Table 4.4.)

(f) The design stress in unbonded prestressing tendons is limited to the values given by Equation 52 unless a higher value can be justified by a more rigorous analysis or on the basis of tests.

The resistance moment of a beam containing bonded or unbonded tendons, all of which are located in the tension zone, may be obtained from the following equation   (cl 4.3.7.3, Pt 1)

$$M_u = f_{pb}A_{ps}(d - d_n) \quad \text{(Equation 51)} \tag{12.1}$$

For a rectangular beam, or flanged beam in which the flange thickness is not less than $0.9x$, d_n may be taken as $0.45x$.

For bonded tendons, values of f_{pb} and x may be obtained from Table 4.4. These values have been derived from the assumptions in 4.3.7.1.

Conditions at the ultimate limit state for rectangular beams with pre-tensioned tendons or post-tensioned tendons having effective bond.

For unbonded tendons, values of f_{pb} and x may be obtained from Equations 52 and 53. The value of f_{pb} should not be taken as greater than $0.7f_{pu}$.

$$f_{pb} = f_{pe} + [7000/(l/d)][1 - 1.7f_{pu}A_{ps}/(f_{cu}bd)] \quad \text{(Equation 52)} \tag{12.2}$$

$$x = 2.47\{[f_{pu}A_{ps}/(f_{cu}bd)][f_{pb}/f_{pu}]d\} \quad \text{(Equation 53)} \tag{12.3}$$

Equation 52 has been derived by taking the length of the zone of inelasticity within the concrete as $10x$. The length l should normally be taken as the length of the tendons between end anchorages. This length may be reduced in the case of continuous multispan members when an analysis is carried out to determine the minimum number of zones of inelasticity associated with each arrangement of design load.

Table 12.1 (Table 4.4, cl 4.3.7.3, Pt 1) Conditions at the ultimate limit state for rectangular beams with pre-tensioned tendons having effective bond

$f_{pu}A_{ps}/f_{cu}bd$	Design stress in tendons as a proportion of the design strength $f_{pb}/0.87f_{pu}$ f_{pe}/f_{pu}			Ratio of depth of neutral axis to that of the centroid of the tendons in the tension zone, x/d f_{pe}/f_{pu}		
	0.6	0.5	0.4	0.6	0.5	0.4
0.05	1.0	1.0	1.0	0.11	0.11	0.11
0.10	1.0	1.0	1.0	0.22	0.22	0.22
0.15	0.99	0.97	0.95	0.32	0.32	0.31
0.20	0.92	0.90	0.88	0.40	0.39	0.38
0.25	0.88	0.86	0.84	0.48	0.47	0.46
0.30	0.85	0.83	0.80	0.55	0.54	0.52
0.35	0.83	0.80	0.76	0.63	0.60	0.58
0.40	0.81	0.77	0.72	0.70	0.67	0.62
0.45	0.79	0.74	0.68	0.77	0.72	0.66
0.50	0.77	0.71	0.64	0.83	0.77	0.69

Equation (12.2) makes allowance for the fact that for unbonded cables, after the beam has cracked, the stress in the steel is approximately uniform between anchorages due to lack of bond.

The derivations of the basic equations for the analysis of a section in bending at the ultimate limit state for bonded tendons, according to the assumptions (a)–(f), are given in Appendix B2.5.

EXAMPLE 12.1   Analysis of a section in bending at ultimate load

Determine the ultimate moment of resistance for the beam section shown in Fig. 12.3 (a) from basic principles, assuming bonded tendons; (b) from Table 12.1 assuming bonded tendons; (c) assuming unbonded tendons and a beam length of 20 m. The characteristic strengths of the steel and concrete are 1700 N/mm² and 60 N/mm² respectively. Other information required: $b = 400$ mm, $d = 600$ mm, $A_{ps} = 846$ mm², $E_s = 205$ kN/mm².

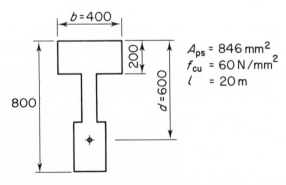

Fig. 12.3   Example of an analysis of a section in bending at ultimate load.

(a)   *From basic principles assuming bonded tendons*
From the equilibrium of horizontal forces, Equation (12.3), assuming the steel is at the maximum design strength, i.e. $f_{pb} = 0.87f_{pu}$:

Depth of compression zone

$$x = 2.47\{[A_{ps}f_{pu}/(bdf_{cu})][f_{pb}/f_{pu}]d\}$$
$$= 2.47 \times \{[846 \times 1700/(400 \times 600 \times 60)] \times 0.87 \times 600\} = 129 \text{ mm}$$

This is less than the thickness of the top flange (200 mm shown in Fig. 12.3), and is therefore satisfactory.

From the linear strain distribution over the depth of the cross-section the bending strain in the steel

$$\varepsilon_{sb} = 0.0035(d/x - 1)$$
$$= 0.0035(600/129 - 1) = 0.0128$$

For an initial stress of $0.7f_{pu}$ in the steel and an estimated loss of prestress at service load of 25%

$$f_{pe}/f_{pu} = 0.70 \times 0.75 = 0.525$$

Total strain in the steel is the sum of the bending and prestress strains

$$= \varepsilon_{sb} + \varepsilon_{sp} = \varepsilon_{sb} + f_{pe}/E_s$$
$$= 0.0128 + 0.525 \times 1700/205E3 = 0.0172$$

If the steel is assumed to be stressed to the maximum design value of $0.87f_{pu}$, then from the stress–strain relationship for steel (see Section 2.5.3) the strain in the steel will be equal to or greater than

$$= 0.005 + 0.87f_{pu}/E_s$$
$$= 0.005 + 0.87 \times 1700/205E3 = 0.0122$$

The actual strain of $0.0172 > 0.0122$, therefore the assumption that the steel is at the maximum design stress of $0.87f_{pu}$ is justified.

From the equilibrium of moments, Equation (12.1), the moment of resistance of the section at the ultimate limit state

$$M_u = A_{ps}0.87f_{pu}(d - 0.45x)$$
$$= 846 \times 0.87 \times 1700 \times (600 - 0.45 \times 129) \times 1E\text{--}6$$
$$= 678.1 \text{ kN m}$$

This particular analysis problem is not difficult using the basic equations because the steel is at the maximum design strength, and consequently the steel strain is greater than the value at the maximum design stress of $0.87f_{pu}$. If the steel strain is less than the strain at the maximum design stress, then the stress corresponding to this steel strain must be determined from the trilinear stress–strain relationship for steel. This is more complicated and tedious and in this situation the use of Table 12.1, or Graphs 14 and 15 (Appendix B1.5), is to be recommended.

(b) *From Table 12.1 assuming bonded tendons*

$$f_{pu}A_{ps}/(f_{cu}bd) = 1700 \times 846/(60 \times 400 \times 600) = 0.10$$

For an initial stress of $0.7f_{pu}$ in the steel and an estimated loss of prestress of 25%

$$f_{pe}/f_{pu} = 0.70 \times 0.75 = 0.525$$

For $f_{pu}A_{ps}/(f_{cu}bd) = 0.1$ and $f_{pe}/f_{pu} = 0.525$ from Table 12.1 (Table 4.4, cl 4.3.7.3, Pt 1), or Graphs 14 and 15 (Appendix B1.5), the design stress in the tendons

$$f_{pb} = \text{factor} \times 0.87 f_{pu} = 1.00 \times 0.87 \times 1700 = 1479 \text{ N/mm}^2$$

and

$$x/d = 0.22$$

Hence depth of compression zone

$$x = 0.22 \times 600 = 132 \text{ mm}$$

which is less than the thickness of the top flange (200 mm, see Fig. 12.3), and is therefore satisfactory.

Moment of resistance at the ultimate limit state from Equation (12.1)

$$\begin{aligned} M_u &= f_{pb}A_{ps}(d - d_n) \\ &= 1479 \times 846 \times (600 - 0.45 \times 132) \times 1\text{E--}6 = 676.4 \text{ kN m.} \end{aligned}$$

This value of 676.4 kN m is to be compared with 678.1 kN m obtained using a method based on first principles.

(c) *From Equations (12.2 and 12.3) for unbonded tendons*
Effective design prestress in the tendons after 25% losses

$$f_{pe} = 0.7 \times 1700 \times 0.75 = 892.5 \text{ N/mm}^2$$

Design stress in the tendons at ultimate load from Equation (12.2)

$$\begin{aligned} f_{pb} &= f_{pe} + [7000/(l/d)][1 - 1.7 f_{pu}A_{ps}/(f_{cu}bd)] \\ &= 892.5 + [7000/(20\text{E}3/600)][1 - 1.7 \times 1700 \times 846/(60 \times 400 \times 600)] \\ &= 1066.8 \text{ N/mm}^2 \end{aligned}$$

This stress is less than $0.7 \times f_{pu} = 0.7 \times 1700 = 1190$ N/mm^2 and therefore is acceptable.
Depth of the compression zone from Equation (12.3)

$$\begin{aligned} x &= 2.47\{[f_{pu}A_{ps}/(f_{cu}bd)][f_{pb}/f_{pu}]d\} \\ &= 2.47 \times \{1700 \times 846/(60 \times 400 \times 600)] \times [1066.8/1700] \times 600\} \\ &= 92.88 \text{ mm,} \end{aligned}$$

which is less than 200 mm, the thickness of the top flange, and is therefore satisfactory.
Moment of resistance at the ultimate limit state from Equation (12.1)

$$\begin{aligned} M_u &= f_{pb}A_{ps}(d - d_n) \\ &= 1066.8 \times 846 \times (600 - 0.45 \times 92.88) \times 1\text{E--}6 = 503.8 \text{ kN m.} \end{aligned}$$

12.1.3   Design of a section in bending at ultimate load

The design of a section in bending at ultimate load entails the determination of the size of the section and reinforcement given the magnitude of the bending moment. The design can be carried out from first principles using the equations given in Section 12.1.2, but this is tedious and can be avoided by using graphs such as those given in Appendix B1.5.

EXAMPLE 12.2   Design of a section in bending at ultimate load

Determine the size of a prestressed concrete section to support a uniformly distributed load of 100 kN at the ultimate limit state over a simply supported span of 15 m.

Use typical characteristic strengths of steel of $f_{pu} = 1570$ N/mm^2 (see Appendix A3), and concrete $f_{cu} = 50$ N/mm^2. Many similar beams are to be made and access to the site is good, therefore use pre-tensioned beams.

Bending moment at ultimate load

$$M_u = WL/8 = 100 \times 15/8 = 187.5 \text{ kN m}$$

The smallest depth of a simply supported beam, where deflection is not likely to be a problem at service load, is approximately span/30. Try $h = 15E3/30 = 500$ mm. To optimise on the weight an I cross-section is generally used in prestressed concrete, but members should not be too slender because of instability (cl 4.3.2, Pt 1). Assume breadth $b = 0.5h = 250$ mm. Web thickness is generally not less than 100 mm to resist shear and should provide room for wires. Assume $d = 425$ mm (see Fig. 12.4). Cover should meet the requirements for durability and fire (see Chapter 5).

The simplest method of design at ultimate load is to use the design graphs in Appendix B1.5. Having decided on values of h, d and b as described previously, calculate

$$M_u/(bd^2f_{cu}) = 187.5E6/(250 \times 425^2 \times 50) = 0.083$$

Assume $f_{pe}/f_{pu} = 0.5$
From Graph 14 in Appendix B1.5

$$A_{ps}f_{pu}/(bdf_{cu}) = 0.105$$

hence

$$A_{ps} = 0.105 \times 250 \times 425 \times 50/1570 = 355.3 \text{ mm}^2$$

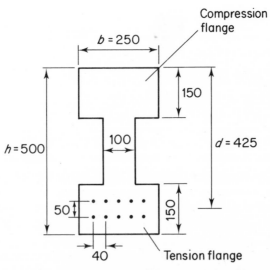

Fig. 12.4   Example of a design of a section in bending at ultimate load.

Use 10–7 mm wires, $A_{ps} = 384.8$ mm^2.

From Graph 15 for $A_{ps}f_{pu}/(bdf_{cu}) = 0.105$, $x/d = 0.22$ hence

$$x = 0.22 \times 425 = 93.5 \text{ mm}.$$

Thickness of top flange should be >100 mm.

The tension flange area must provide room for the wires with adequate spacing and cover (cl 3.12.11, Pt 1). Try all the wires on one row. Width required = cover + 9 spaces + cover = $50 + 9 \times 50 + 50 = 550$ mm. This value is greater than the width of the section, therefore use two layers as shown in Fig. 12.4.

Thickness of tension flange = cover + space + cover = 150 mm. Also make the compression flange the same thickness to produce a symmetrical section which makes calculations easier at the service load conditions.

The reader is invited to check this design using Table 12.1 as shown in Example 12.1.

12.1.4   Redistribution of moments (cl 4.2.3, Pt 1)

Redistribution of moments obtained by elastic analysis may be carried out for the ultimate limit state only, provided certain conditions are satisfied as given in BS 8110. This is beyond the scope of this book.

12.2   Bending resistance of prestressed concrete at service load

12.2.1   Introduction

Prestressed concrete members must satisfy two criteria at the serviceability limit state in bending. The tensile stresses in the concrete must not produce cracks, except in special circumstances, and the compressive stresses must not exceed the design values. These two criteria of tensile stress and compressive stress form the basis for analysis and design at the serviceability limit state in bending.

12.2.2   Analysis of a section in bending at the serviceability limit state

In Section 12.2.3 design formulae are developed with tensile and compressive stress criteria, but because this is complicated it is beneficial first to analyse a section in bending at the serviceability limit state and to identify the critical stresses.

EXAMPLE 12.2   Analysis of a section in bending at the serviceability limit state

Determine the stresses due to prestress and applied service load for the beam of uniform cross-section shown in Fig. 12.5(a). The jacking force of 1600 kN is provided by straight high-tensile steel wires located as shown. The service load bending moment, which includes the self-weight, is 550 kN m.

If the section is not cracked and the compressive stresses are not greater than approximately half the cube crushing strength then elastic behaviour may be assumed. The percentage of steel is generally small in relation to the concrete and therefore composite action is ignored.

The elastic section properties of the concrete are obtained as follows:

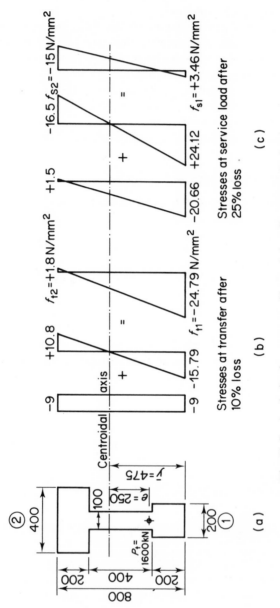

Fig. 12.5   Analysis of a prestressed beam in bending at service load.

Cross-sectional area of the concrete

$$A_c = (80 + 40 + 40)E3 = 160E3 \text{ mm}^2$$

Centroid of the cross-section from moments of areas about the base

$$80E3 \times 700 + 40E3 \times 400 + 40E3 \times 100 = 160E3 \times \bar{y}$$

hence $\bar{y} = 475$ mm from the base.

Second moment of area of the cross-section about the centroidal axis

$$I = \Sigma(bh^3/3)$$
$$= (400 \times 325^3 - 300 \times 125^3 + 200 \times 475^3 - 100 \times 275^3)/3$$
$$= 10.83E9 \text{ mm}^4$$

Elastic section moduli
$$z_1 = I/y_1 = 10.83E9/475 = 22.80E6 \text{ mm}^3$$
$$z_2 = I/y_2 = 10.83E9/325 = 33.32E6 \text{ mm}^3$$

The section properties are now used to determine the stresses in the extreme fibres of the cross-section. Subscript 1 denotes the bottom of the section and subscript 2 the top of the section. Compressive stresses are negative and tensile stresses are positive.

Critical stresses occur at transfer when the jacking force of 1600 kN is applied. Loss of prestress of approximately 10% occurs immediately because of the elasticity of the concrete which reduces the length of the member. A more accurate assessment of the loss is given in Section 12.3.

Prestressing force at transfer after 10% loss

$$P_t = 0.9P_o = 0.9 \times 1600 = 1400 \text{ kN}$$

Stress at the bottom of the section due to the prestressing force at transfer

$$f_{t1} = -P_t/A_c - P_t e/z_1$$
$$= -1400E3/160E3 - 1400E3 \times 250/22.80E6$$
$$= -9 - 15.79 = -24.79 \text{ N/mm}^2$$

Stress at the top of the section due to the prestressing force at transfer

$$f_{t2} = -P_t/A_c + P_t e/z_2$$
$$= -1400E3/160E3 - 1400E3 \times 250/33.32E6$$
$$= -9 + 10.8 = +1.8 \text{ N/mm}^2$$

The axial stresses can be added algebraically to the bending stresses because the principle of superposition is valid for elastic behaviour. Diagrams can now be drawn showing the stresses in the extreme fibres of the beam section at transfer (see Fig. 12.5(b)). The extreme fibre stresses can be joined by straight lines because they vary linearly over the depth.

It is important to note that there is a tensile stress of +1.8 N/mm^2 at the top of the section and a compressive stress of -24.79 N/mm^2 at the bottom of the section. These stresses are critical and if they are too high in relation to the strength of the concrete at that stage of loading, then cracking, or crushing, occurs. These stresses occur at the supports for a straight member with a constant cross-section and straight wires. The stresses at the support for this type of beam are not modified by the self-weight of the beam or the service load.

At mid-span, however, the prestress stresses will be modified by the service load. The critical stresses at the service load occur at mid-span after further loss of prestress due to creep in the steel and concrete. The loss of prestress is determined more accurately in Section 12.3, but at this stage it may be assumed that the loss is 25% of the jacking force.

Prestressing force at service load after 25% losses

$$P_s = 0.75P_o = 0.75 \times 1600 = 1200 \text{ kN}.$$

The service load bending moment M_s, which includes self-weight, is 550 kN m. Stress at the bottom of the section due to the prestressing force at service load and the application of the service load bending moment

$$
\begin{aligned}
f_{s1} &= -P_s/A_c - P_s e/z_1 + M_s/z_1 \\
&= -1200\text{E}3/160\text{E}3 - 1200\text{E}3 \times 250/22.80\text{E}6 + 550\text{E}6/22.80\text{E}6 \\
&= -7.5 - 13.16 + 24.12 = +3.46 \text{ N/mm}^2
\end{aligned}
$$

Stress at the top of the section due to the prestressing force at service load and the application of the service load bending moment

$$
\begin{aligned}
f_{s2} &= -P_s/A_c + P_s e/z_2 - M_s/z_2 \\
&= -1200\text{E}3/160\text{E}3 + 1200\text{E}3 \times 250/33.32\text{E}6 - 550\text{E}6/33.32\text{E}6 \\
&= -7.5 + 9.0 - 16.50 = -15.0 \text{ N/mm}^2
\end{aligned}
$$

These stresses can also be represented on diagrams as shown in Fig. 12.5(c). For the service load condition it is important to notice that there is a tensile stress of $+3.46 \text{ N/mm}^2$ at the bottom of the section and a compressive stress of -15.0 N/mm^2 at the top of the section. These stresses are critical and if they are too high in relation to the strength of the concrete at this stage of loading then cracking, or crushing, occurs.

The analysis of a beam is a good method for checking a section, but in practice it is necessary to be able to determine the required size of a section to satisfy the conditions at transfer and the serviceability limit state.

12.2.3   Design of a section in bending at the serviceability limit state

The critical bending stresses have been identified in the previous section and these may be presented algebraically as follows.

The sign convention for stresses is negative compression and positive tension, with the eccentricity positive below the centroidal axis and negative above. Subscript 1 denotes the bottom of the section and subscript 2 the top of the section.

At transfer of the prestressing force P_t the stresses at the bottom and top of the section

$$f_{t1} = -P_t/A_c - P_t e/z_1 + M_{min}/z_1 \tag{12.4}$$
$$f_{t2} = -P_t/A_c + P_t e/z_2 - M_{min}/z_2 \tag{12.5}$$

where M_{min} is the bending moment that may act immediately the prestress is applied, e.g. the self-weight bending moment.

Equations (12.4) and (12.5) are applicable to a simply supported beam where the critical section is at mid-span, e.g. the prestressing force is not parallel to the centroidal axis at the section as shown in Fig. 12.6(a). However if the critical section is at the support, e.g. the prestressing force is parallel to the centroidal axis as shown in Fig. 12.6(b), then the term containing M_{min} is ignored.

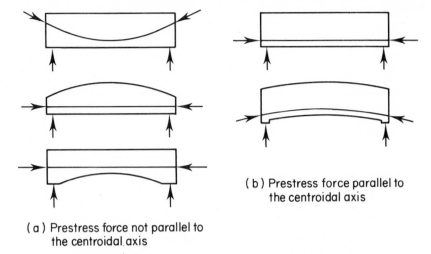

(a) Prestress force not parallel to
the centroidal axis

(b) Prestress force parallel to
the centroidal axis

Fig. 12.6 Cable shapes for prestressed concrete beams.

After losses at the serviceability limit state the stresses at the bottom and top of the section

$$f_{s1} = -P_s/A_c - P_s e/z_1 + M_s/z_1 \tag{12.6}$$
$$f_{s2} = -P_s/A_c + P_s e/z_2 - M_s/z_2 \tag{12.7}$$

where M_s is the service load bending moment and includes the minimum bending moment M_{min}.

If the extreme fibre stresses are now designated as serviceability design stresses such that, $f_{t1} = f_{tc}$, $f_{t2} = f_{tt}$, $f_{s1} = f_{st}$, $f_{s2} = f_{sc}$, then combining Equations (12.4)–(12.7) and eliminating the eccentricity e, the optimum values of the section moduli can be determined.

Combining Equations (12.5) and (12.6)

$$z_1' = (M_s - \eta M_{min})/(f_{st} - \eta f_{tc}) \tag{12.8}$$

where

$$\eta = P_s/P_t = (P_s/P_o)/(P_t/P_o) = \eta_s/\eta_t$$

Combining Equations (12.4) and (12.7)
$$z_2' = (M_s - \eta M_{min})/(\eta f_{tt} - f_{sc}) \tag{12.9}$$

These values of the section moduli are the minimum theoretical values and must not be confused with the actual values which are written without the prime, i.e. as z_1 and z_2. In the design process the actual values of the section moduli are greater than the minimum values, and therefore it is impossible to satisfy all the stress constraints simultaneously.

The minimum initial value of the jacking force $P_{o(min)}$ is obtained by satisfying the tensile stress constraints f_{tt} and f_{st}, i.e. combining Equations (12.5) and (12.6), and dividing by η_t:

$$P_{o(min)} = A_c(f_{st}z_1 + \eta f_{tt}z_2 - M_s + \eta M_{min})/[-\eta_s(z_1 + z_2)] \tag{12.10}$$

The maximum value of the eccentricity e_{max} is obtained by satisfying the tensile stress constraints f_{tt} and f_{st}, i.e. combining Equations (12.5) and (12.6)

$$e_{max} = [z_1z_2(f_{st} - \eta f_{tt}) - \eta M_{min}z_1 - M_sz_2]/[A_c(f_{st}z_1 + \eta f_{tt}z_2 - M_s + \eta M_{min})] \quad (12.11)$$

The maximum initial value of the jacking force $P_{o(max)}$ is obtained by satisfying the compressive stress constraints f_{tc} and f_{sc}, i.e. combining Equations (12.4) and (12.7) and dividing by η_t

$$P_{o(max)} = A_c(f_{sc}z_2 + \eta f_{tc}z_1 + M_s - \eta M_{min})/[-\eta_s(z_1 + z_2)] \quad (12.12)$$

The minimum value of the eccentricity e_{min} is obtained by satisfying the compressive stress constraints f_{tc} and f_{sc}, i.e. combining Equations (12.4) and (12.7)

$$e_{min} = [z_1z_2(-f_{sc} + \eta f_{tc}) - \eta M_{min}z_2 - M_sz_1]/[A_c(f_{sc}z_2 + \eta f_{tc}z_1 + M_s - \eta M_{min})] \quad (12.13)$$

For economy in steel reinforcement it would be ideal to adopt the minimum jacking force and maximum eccentricity. However in design it is often not possible to adopt the minimum value of the jacking force $P_{o(min)}$ because the force is expressed in a discrete number of wires, or cables. Also the associated maximum value of eccentricity e_{max} may not be practical because it lies outside the section. In design calculations therefore a practical magnitude of the practical jacking force, P_{op}, is adopted expressed in number of wires, or cables, fully stressed to the design stress such that

$$P_{o(max)} > P_{op} > P_{o(min)}$$

The eccentricity e which is consistent with the practical jacking force P_{op} is then obtained from Equation (12.14) which is a rearrangement of Equation (12.6) and satisfies the tensile stress constraint f_{st} at service load.

$$e = (M_s - z_1f_{st})/(\eta_sP_{op}) - z_1/A_c \quad (12.14)$$

A practical value of the eccentricity e_p is then calculated by trial and error such that e_p is approximately equal to e, and also

$$e_{max} > e_p > e_{min}$$

If the critical values f_{tt}, f_{to}, f_{st}, f_{so} are related to the characteristic concrete strength, then Equations (12.4)–(12.14) form the basis for a method of design. The design stresses recommended in BS 8110 are simplified and summarised in Table 12.2.

In the assessment of the behaviour of a prestressed concrete structure or element, the amount of flexural tensile stress allowed under service load defines its class as follows (cl 4.1.3, Pt 1):

class 1: no flexural tensile stress;
class 2: flexural tensile stresses but no visible cracking;
class 3: flexural tensile stresses but surface widths of cracks not exceeding 0.1 mm for members in very severe environments (see Table 3.2) and not exceeding 0.2 mm for all other members.

In practical terms class 1 members are used in harsh environments where durability is a problem. Class 2 members are for normal use of prestressed concrete. Class 3 members are used for conditions where corrosion or weathering is not a problem, for long-span beams where the self-weight is large and must be kept to a minimum, where deflections are not critical, or for temporary structures.

Table 12.2 Summary of design stresses at transfer and service load.

	class 1	class 2	class 3	Ref. BS 8110, Pt 1
At transfer				
pre-tensioned	$f_{tt} = 1 \text{ N/mm}^2$	$f_{tt} = 0.45\sqrt{f_{ci}}$	$f_{tt} = 0.45\sqrt{f_{ci}}$	cl 4.3.5.2
post-tensioned	$f_{tt} = 1 \text{ N/mm}^2$	$f_{tt} = 0.36\sqrt{f_{ci}}$	$f_{tt} = 0.36\sqrt{f_{ci}}$	cl 4.3.5.2
	$f_{tc} = 0.5f_{ci}$			cl 4.3.5.1
At service load				
pre-tensioned	$f_{st} = \text{zero}$	$f_{st} = 0.45\sqrt{f_{cu}}$	Tables 4.2	cl 4.3.4.3
post-tensioned	$f_{st} = \text{zero}$	$f_{st} = 0.36\sqrt{f_{cu}}$	and 4.3	cl 4.3.4.3
	$f_{sc} = 0.33f_{cu}$			cl 4.3.4.2

Table 12.3 (Table 4.2, cl 4.3.4.3, Pt 1) Design hypothetical flexural stresses for class 3 members.

Group	Limiting crack width (mm)	Design stress for concrete grade		
		30 (N/mm²)	40 (N/mm²)	50 and over (N/mm²)
(a) Pre-tensioned tendons	0.1	—	4.1	4.8
	0.2	—	5.0	5.8
(b) Grouted post-tensioned tendons	0.1	3.2	4.1	4.8
	0.2	3.8	5.0	5.8
(c) Pre-tensioned tendons distributed in the tensile zone and positioned close to the tension faces of the concrete	0.1	—	5.3	6.3
	0.2	—	6.3	7.3

Table 12.4 (Table 4.3 cl 4.3.4.3, Pt 1)
Depth factors for design tensile stresses for class 3 members.

Depth of member mm	Factor
200 and under	1.1
400	1.0
600	0.9
800	0.8
1000 and over	0.7

Note: Intermediate values are found by interpolation.

EXAMPLE 12.3   *Design of a section in bending at the serviceability limit state*

A beam is simply supported over a span of 15 m and supports an imposed service load of 33 kN. The section shown in Fig. 12.4 is satisfactory at the ultimate limit state in bending; check that it is suitable for service load conditions.

Estimate of self-weight of member

$$W_{sw} = 10L^3 = 10 \times 15^3 \times 1\text{E}{-}3 = 33.75 \text{ kN}$$

Self-weight bending moment

$$M_{sw} = W_{sw}L/8 = 33.75 \times 15/8 = 63.28 \text{ kN m}$$

Imposed load bending moment

$$M_i = WL/8 = 33 \times 15/8 = 61.88 \text{ kN m}$$

Total service load bending moment

$$M_s = M_{sw} + M_i = 63.28 + 61.88 = 125.16 \text{ kN m}$$

The beam has straight wires and a constant cross-section. The site conditions for the beam are class 2. Characteristic strengths for steel and concrete are 1570 and 50 N/mm². Assume a loss of prestress of 10% at transfer and 25% at service load and consequently $\eta_t = 0.9$, $\eta_s = 0.75$ and $\eta = \eta_s/\eta_t = 0.75/0.9 = 0.833$.

Optimum design values of the section moduli from Equations (12.8) and (12.9):

$$z_1' = (M_s - \eta M_{min})/(f_{st} - \eta f_{tc})$$
$$= (125.16\text{E}6 - 0)/[0.45\sqrt{50} - (-0.833 \times 0.5 \times 35)]$$
$$= 7.045\text{E}6 \text{ mm}^3$$

$$z_2' = (M_s - \eta M_{min})/(\eta f_{tt} - f_{sc})$$
$$= (125.16\text{E}6 - 0)/[0.833 \times 0.45\sqrt{35} - (-0.33 \times 50)]$$
$$= 6.687\text{E}6 \text{ mm}^3$$

The value of M_{min} is zero because the prestressing force is parallel to the centroidal axis of the section and consequently the critical section is at the support.

Actual second moment of area for the section shown in Fig. 12.4

$$I = \Sigma bh^3/12 = 250 \times 500^3/12 - 150 \times 200^3/12 = 2.504\text{E}9 \text{ mm}^4$$

Actual section moduli

$$z_1 = z_2 = I/y = 2.504\text{E}9/250 = 10.016\text{E}6 \text{ mm}^3$$

The actual values of $z > z'$, which is satisfactory but conservative. The size of the section could be reduced based on these calculations, but the estimated total loss of prestress may be greater than 25% and this would increase the values of z'. The section must also satisfy deflection and ultimate load conditions.

The values of z' also show that the optimum section is not symmetrical about the horizontal centroidal axis and ideally the centroidal axis should be closer to the bottom of the section. The reason for this is that the strength of the concrete at transfer is not as great as at service load conditions. If self-weight of the member is important, or if a very large number of members are to be made, then an iterative process is carried out to reduce the self-weight of the section. However, the more complicated the cross-section the more costly the shuttering, but this can be justified if there are large numbers to be manufactured.

The values of the prestressing force and its eccentricity at transfer can be obtained from Equations (12.10) to (12.13). Note that in the following calculations the actual values of section moduli are being used, i.e. $z_1 = z_2 = 10.016\text{E}6 \text{ mm}^3$.

Cross-sectional area (see Fig. 12.4)

$$A_c = 250 \times 500 - 150 \times 200 = 95\text{E}3 \text{ mm}^2$$

Maximum value of the eccentricity for minimum jacking force from Equation (12.11)

$$e_{max} = [z_1 z_2 (f_{st} - \eta f_{tt}) - \eta M_{min} z_1 - M_s z_2]/[A_c(f_{st} z_1 + \eta f_{tt} z_2 - M_s + \eta M_{min})]$$
$$= [10.016\text{E}6 \times 10.016\text{E}6 \times (0.45\sqrt{50} - 0.833 \times 0.45\sqrt{35}) - 0$$
$$- 125.16\text{E}6 \times 10.016\text{E}6]/[95\text{E}3 \times (0.45\sqrt{50} \times 10.016\text{E}6 + 0.833 \times 0.45\sqrt{35}$$
$$\times 10.016\text{E}6 - 125.16\text{E}6 + 0)]$$
$$= +171.4 \text{ mm}$$

Minimum value of the eccentricity for maximum jacking force from Equation (12.13)

$$e_{min} = \{z_1 z_2[-f_{sc} + \eta f_{tc}] - \eta M_{min} z_2 - M_s z_1\}/\{A_c[f_{sc} z_2 + \eta f_{tc} z_1 + M_s - \eta M_{min}]\}$$
$$= \{10.016E6 \times 10.016E6 \times [-0.33 \times (-50) + 0.833 \times 0.5 \times (-35)] - 0$$
$$- 125.16E6 \times 10.016E6\}/\{95E3 \times [0.33 \times (-50) \times 10.016E6 + 0.833 \times 0.5$$
$$\times (-35) \times 10.016E6 + 125.16E6 - 0]\}$$
$$= +60.0 \text{ mm.}$$

Maximum value of the prestressing force before losses for minimum eccentricity from Equation (12.12)

$$P_{o(max)} = A_c(f_{sc} z_2 + \eta f_{tc} z_1 + M_s - \eta M_{min})/[-\eta_s(z_1 + z_2)]$$
$$= 95E3 \times [0.33 \times (-50) \times 10.016E6 + 0.833 \times 0.5 \times (-35) \times 10.016E6$$
$$+ 125.16E6 - 0]/[-0.75 \times (10.016E6 + 10.016E6)]$$
$$= 1177.2 \text{ kN.}$$

Minimum value of the jacking force before losses for maximum eccentricity from Equation (12.10)

$$P_{o(min)} = A_c(f_{st} z_1 + \eta f_{tt} z_2 - M_s + \eta M_{min})/[-\eta_s(z_1 + z_2)]$$
$$= 95E3 \times [0.45\sqrt{50} \times 10.016E6 + 0.833 \times 0.45\sqrt{35} \times 10.016E6$$
$$+ 125.16E6 - 0]/[-0.75 \times (10.016E6 + 10.016E6)]$$
$$= 449.4 \text{ kN}$$

The different values of the jacking force and eccentricity show that more than one solution is possible. This is because the actual section moduli, $z_1 = z_2 = 10.016E6 \text{ mm}^3$, are greater than the optimum values $z_1' = 7.048E6 \text{ mm}^3$ and $z_2' = 6.687E6 \text{ mm}^3$.

A practical value of the prestressing force P_{op} must now be chosen such that

$$P_{o(max)}(1177.2) > P_{op} > P_{o(min)}(449.4) \text{ kN.}$$

This relationship may be expressed more practically in the number (n_w) of wires of jacking force P_w.

7 mm diameter wire stressed to a force of

$$P_w = \pi \times 7^2/4 \times 0.7 \times 1570 \times 1E{-}3 = 42.3 \text{ kN.}$$

It should be noted that the values of P_w can be calculated from the characteristic strengths given in Appendix A3.

$$P_{o(max)}/P_w > n_w > P_{o(min)}/P_w$$
$$1177.2/42.3 > n_w > 449.4/42.3$$
$$27.8 > n_w > 10.62$$

10 wires are required at ultimate load (see Fig. 12.4) and two wires are required at the top of the section to prevent bending failure if the beam is inadvertently turned upside down. The two top wires are also useful for fixing shear reinforcement if required. Twelve wires were tried unsuccessfully, and the solution for fourteen is as follows:

$$P_{op} = n_w P_w = 14 \times 42.3 = 592.1 \text{ kN.}$$

If $P_{op} = 592.1$ kN, then the corresponding eccentricity from Equation (12.14)

$$e = (M_s - z_1 f_{st})/(\eta_s P_{op}) - z_1/A_c$$
$$= (125.16E6 - 10.016E6 \times 0.45\sqrt{50})/(0.75 \times 592.1E3) - 10.016E6/95E3$$
$$= 104.6 \text{ mm}$$

This value of the eccentricity is not the practical value, which is obtained as follows.

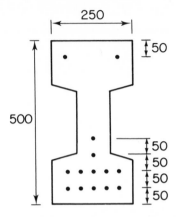

Fig. 12.7   Example of the design of a section in bending at service load.

Cover should meet the requirements for durability and fire (see Chapter 5). Spacing should meet the requirements of cl 3.12.11, Pt 1. The distance from the base of the centroid of the 14 wires (see Fig. 12.7) is obtained by taking moment of areas about the base:

$$5 \times 50 + 5 \times 100 + 1 \times 150 + 1 \times 200 + 2 \times 450 = 14\bar{y}$$

hence $\bar{y} = 142.9$ mm.
   Practical eccentricity

$$e_p = h/2 - y = 250 - 142.9 = 107.1 \text{ mm}$$

$e_p(107.1) \approx e(104.6)$ mm, therefore satisfactory.
   $e_{max}(171.4) > e_p(107.1) > e_{min}(60.0)$ mm and e_p is within the limits.
   $P_{o(max)}(1177.2) > P_{op}(592.1) > P_{o(min)}(449.4)$ kN and P_{op} is therefore within limits.

Using $P_{op} = 592.1$ kN and $e_p = 107.1$ mm, check the design by calculating fibre stresses at transfer (10% loss) and service load (25% loss) as shown in Example 12.3. Compare these stresses with the design stresses.

$$f_{t1} = -11.30 < f_{tc} = 0.5 \times (-35) = -17.50 \text{ N/mm}^2$$
$$f_{t2} = +0.09 < f_{tt} = +0.45\sqrt{35} = +2.66 \text{ N/mm}^2$$
$$f_{s1} = +3.07 < f_{st} = +0.45\sqrt{50} = +3.18 \text{ N/mm}^2$$
$$f_{s2} = -12.42 < f_{sc} = 0.33 \times (-50) = -16.5 \text{ N/mm}^2$$

The stresses are all less than the design stresses and are therefore satisfactory.
   It is necessary to check that the cracking of the concrete in bending precedes the failure of the beam (cl 4.12.2, Pt 1). The moment necessary to overcome the prestress after losses and to produce a tensile stress of $0.6\sqrt{f_{cu}}$ in the extreme fibres

$$M = (\eta_s f_{tc} + 0.6\sqrt{f_{cu}})z_1$$
$$= (0.75 \times 0.5 \times 35 + 0.6\sqrt{50}) \times 10.016\text{E}6 = 174 \text{ kN m}$$

The area of tensile steel of 384.8 mm^2 (10 wires) provided at ultimate load in Example 12.2 and increased to 461.8 mm^2 (12 wires) at the service load conditions is sufficient to provide a moment of resistance greater than the applied ultimate bending moment of 187.5 kN m. The moment of 187.5 kN m > 174 kN m and therefore the area of tensile steel is greater than the minimum required.

The design continues with checks for loss of prestress, shear resistance and deflection as shown later. It should be noted in this example that the design for bending conditions commenced with ultimate load and was modified for service load conditions. The reverse process is also possible and preferred by some designers.

12.2.4 Deflection limits for prestressed concrete members (cls 2.2.3.2, 4.3.6.1, Pt 1)

No numerical limits are set for the deflections for prestressed concrete but as with ordinary reinforced concrete the deformations of the structure, or part of it, should not adversely affect its efficiency or appearance. Deflections should be compatible with the degree of movement, acceptable by other elements including finishes, services, partitions, glazing and cladding.

The span/effective depth ratios for ordinary reinforced concrete are not applicable to prestressed concrete because at service load the concrete is not cracked, except for class 3 members, and also the prestressing force produces an upward camber of the member. The deflections in prestressed concrete members may be described as short-term elastic deflections which occur immediately, and long-term creep deflections which occur after the member has been loaded for a long time.

12.2.5 Short-term elastic deflections

These occur immediately when the prestressing force is applied at transfer, when the self-weight and dead load act, and when the imposed load is applied. The deflection due to the imposed load becomes zero when the imposed load is removed, but the dead load and prestress deflections remain.

The elastic deformation for a beam of uniform section

$$a_e = (L^2/E_{c,t}I)\Sigma kM$$

where
M is the maximum bending-moment in the span
k is a factor which depends on the shape of the bending-moment diagram as shown in Table 12.2
$E_{c,t}$ is the modulus of elasticity at an age t which may be derived from the following equations (cl 7.2, Pt 1)
$E_{c,28} = 20 + 0.2f_{cu,28}$
$E_{c,t} = E_{c,28}(0.4 + 0.6f_{cu,t}/f_{cu,28})$ where $t > 3$ days.

12.2.6 Long-term creep deflections

These are due to creep in the concrete which is dependent on the stress level and the maturity of the concrete. The creep effect due to transient loads is very small and only permanent loads need be considered, i.e. the dead load and permanent imposed load.

Long-term deflections can be calculated using an elastic analysis incorporating an effective modulus of elasticity of the concrete. In determining the effective modulus of

Load	Bending moment diagram	k
w /unit length ←—— *L* ——→	$wL^2/8$	$\dfrac{5}{48}$
W ←— *L*/2 —→←— *L*/2 —→	$wL/4$	$\dfrac{1}{12}$
P→ ↕*e* ←*P*	$-P_e$	$\dfrac{1}{8}$
P ↕*e* *P* Parabolic tendon	$-P_e$	$\dfrac{5}{48}$

Table 12.2

elasticity for the long-term deflections, values for the creep coefficient may be determined from either cl 4.8.5, Pt 1 or from cl 7.3, Pt 2.

Values of the creep coefficient (ϕ) of 1.8 for transfer within 3 days and 1.4 for transfer after 28 days, are generally used for outdoor exposure (cl 4.8.5, Pt 1). $E'_{c,t}$ is the effective creep modulus obtained from the following relationship $E'_{c,t} = E_{c,t}/(1+\phi)$ (cl 7.3, Pt 2).

EXAMPLE 12.4   Deflection of a prestressed beam

Calculate the deflection of the simply supported prestressed beam which spans 15 m designed in Example 12.3. Relevant details are $I = 2.504E9$ mm^4, $f_{cu,3} = 35$, $f_{cu,28} = 50$ N/mm^2, $P_{op} = 592.1$ kN, and $e_p = 107.1$ mm.

The approximate deflections which occur during the manufacture and loading of the beam are as follows. Downwards deflections are positive.

Deflections at transfer
Elastic modulus at 28 days

$$E_{c,28} = 20 + 0.2f_{cu,28}$$
$$= 20 + 0.2 \times 50 = 30 \text{ kN/mm}^2$$

Elastic modulus at 3 days

$$E_{c,3} = E_{c,28}(0.4 + 0.6 f_{cu,3}/f_{cu,28})$$
$$= 30 \times (0.4 + 0.6 \times 35/50) = 24.60 \text{ kN/mm}^2$$

Elastic deflection (upwards) due to prestress at transfer at three days after 10% loss

$$a_e = L^2/(E_{c,3}I)\Sigma kM = L^2/(E_{c,3}I)(1/8)(-\eta_t P_{op} e_p)$$
$$= 15E3^2/(24.6E3 \times 2.504E9) \times (1/8) \times (-0.9 \times 592.1E3 \times 107.1)$$
$$= -26.0 \text{ mm (upwards)}$$

Elastic deflection (downwards) from self-weight (33.75 kN) at transfer when the beam is lifted from the casting bed

$$a_e = L^2/(E_{c,3}I)\Sigma kM = L^2/(E_{c,3}I)(5/48)(WL/8)$$
$$= 15E3^2/(24.6E3 \times 2.504E9) \times (5/48) \times (33.75E3 \times 15E3/8)$$
$$= 24.1 \text{ mm (downwards)}$$

The net deflection at transfer (3 days) $= -26.1 + 24.1 = -2.0$ mm (upwards). This value is of interest but of little practical importance.

Long-term deflections
Effective creep modulus of elasticity related to the three-day concrete strength

$$E'_{c,3} = E_{c,3}/(1 + \phi) = 24.6E3/(1 + 1.8) = 8.79 \text{ kN/mm}^2$$

The general creep coefficient $\phi = 1.8$ is taken from cl 4.8.5.2, Pt 1, or alternatively more accurate values are given in Table 2.2.

Long-term deflection due to eccentricity of prestress after 25% loss

$$a_c = L^2/(E'_{c,3}I)\Sigma kM = (L^2/E'_{c,3}I)(1/8)(-\eta_s P_{op} e_p)$$
$$= 15E3^2/(8.79E3 \times 2.504E9) \times (1/8) \times (-0.75 \times 592.1E3 \times 107.1)$$
$$= -60.8 \text{ mm (upwards)}$$

Long-term deflection due to bending creep from self-weight (33.75 kN)

$$a_c = L^2/(E'_{c,3}I)\Sigma kM = L^2/(E'_{c,3}I)(5/48)(WL/8)$$
$$= 15E3^2/(8.79E3 \times 2.504E9) \times (5/48) \times (33.75E3 \times 15E3/8)$$
$$= 67.4 \text{ mm (downwards)}$$

Short-term deflections
Elastic deflection (downwards) from imposed load (33 kN) related to the 28-day concrete strength

$$a_e = L^2/(E_{c,28}I)\Sigma kM = L^2/(E_{c,28}I)(5/48)(WL/8)$$
$$= 15E3^2/(30E3 \times 2.504E9) \times (5/48) \times (33E3 \times 15E3/8)$$
$$= 19.3 \text{ mm (downwards)}$$

Net long-term creep deflection $= -60.8 + 67.4 = +6.6$ mm (downwards). Short-term elastic deflection from imposed load $= +19.3$ mm (downwards).

No numerical limits are placed on deflections in prestressed concrete in BS 8110. However, if previous elastic limits of span/350 $= 15E3/350 = 42.9$ mm or 20 mm, whichever is the lesser, are used as a guide, then the calculated elastic deflection of 19.3 mm is less. The limit placed previously on the total deflection was span/250 = 60 mm and this is greater than the total calculated deflection.

12.3 Loss of prestress

12.3.1 Introduction

Loss of prestress is the difference between the jacking force in the tendon at the prestressing stage and the force after losses have occurred. Some of the losses occur immediately the force is transferred to the concrete, e.g. elastic shortening of the member. Other losses occur with time, e.g. creep of the concrete. The jacking force should not normally exceed 75% of the characteristic strength of the tendon, but may be increased to 80% under controlled conditions (cl 4.7.1, Pt 1). In practice total losses of the jacking force are within the range 15–40%.

Losses of prestress are related to the jacking stress and expressed as:

% loss of prestress = 100(jacking stress – final stress)/(jacking stress)

In general losses can occur because of shortening of the concrete member, or shortening of the tendon, or because of friction acting along the length of the tendon. The following factors affect the loss of prestress:

(a)   relaxation of the steel (2–8%)
(b)   elastic deformation of the concrete (1–10%)
(c)   shrinkage of the concrete (1–4%)
(d)   creep of the concrete (5–15%)
(e)   draw-in during anchorage (0–5%)
(f)   friction in the ducts and at anchorages (3–7%).

Initially, in design calculations, the loss of prestress is estimated from past experience and later, when the section shape and size has been determined, a more accurate calculation is made. A reasonably accurate estimation of the loss of prestress is required because it affects service load conditions, e.g. the bending moment at which bending cracks occur and also the shear force at which diagonal shear cracks appear.

12.3.2 Relaxation of steel (cl 4.8.2, Pt 1)

If a steel tendon is stressed to 75% of its characteristic strength and anchored over a fixed length, then after 1000 hours the stress will reduce. This phenomenon, which is not fully understood, is called relaxation, and may be defined as a loss of stress at constant strain. In prestressed concrete the fixed length is the concrete member, although in reality this does change slightly.

The long-term loss of force in the tendon allowed for in design is obtained by multiplying the appropriate factor given in Table 4.6 by the 1000 h relaxation test value. The initial force should be taken as the value immediately after stressing in the case of pre-tensioning and immediately after transfer in the case of post-tensioning. The relaxation factors given in Table 4.6 include allowances for the effect of strain reductions due to creep and shrinkage of the concrete and, in the case of pre-tensioning, due to elastic deformation of the concrete at transfer.

Table 12.5 Relaxation factors (Table 4.6, Pt 1)

	Wire and strand		Bar
	Relaxation class as defined in BS 5896: 1980		
	1	2	
Pre-tensioning	1.5	1.2	—
Post-tensioning	2.0	1.5	2.0

The 1000 hour relaxation value should be taken from the manufacturer's UK Certificate of Approval. The information will normally be available for initial loads of 60%, 70% and 80% of the breaking load and values for intermediate loads may be interpolated. For initial loads of less than 60% of the breaking load, the 1000 hour relation value may be assumed to decrease linearly from the stated value at 60% to zero at an initial load of 30% of the breaking load. In the absence of the UK Certificate of Approval the 1000 hour relaxation value should be taken as the maximum value for the appropriate initial load stated in the British Standard for the product, BS 4486 for high tensile (HT) steel bars and BS 5896 for HT wire and strand.

12.3.3   Elastic deformation of the concrete (cl 4.8.3, Pt 1)

If a jacking force from a prestressing tendon is transferred to a concrete member, then, because the concrete behaves elastically, the member immediately decreases in length. If the steel and concrete are bonded together, as in pre-tensioned prestressed concrete, then the decrease in length is the same for the concrete and the steel and is unavoidable. In post-tensioned concrete, because the tendon is not bonded to the concrete during stressing operations, the elastic decrease in length of the concrete can be allowed for when jacking and the loss can be reduced to a very small value.

The simplest method of calculating the loss of prestress due to elastic shortening is as follows. Assuming elastic behaviour for a pre-tensioned member where the steel is bonded to the concrete before the jacking force is transferred to the concrete,

strain in the concrete = strain in the steel

If f'_s is the loss of stress in the steel and f_c is the stress in the concrete adjacent to the steel at transfer,

$$f_c/E_c = f'_s/E_s$$

Percentage loss of prestress, if f_{pi} is the jacking stress in the steel,

$$= 100(f'_s/f_{pi}) = 100(E_s/E_c)f_c/f_{pi} \qquad (12.15)$$

The modulus of elasticity for the tendons may be obtained from BS 4486 for HT bars and BS 5896 for HT wire and strand. The modulus of elasticity for normal weight concrete may be obtained from (cl 7.2, Equation 17, Pt 2)

$$E_c = 20 + 0.2f_{ct} \text{ N/mm}^2$$

where f_{ct} is the strength of the concrete at transfer.

Values of the modulus of elasticity of the tendons are also given in the stress–strain graphs for prestressing steel (see Section 2.5.3).

Equation (12.15) can also be applied to a post-tensioned beam, but if the elastic shortening is allowed for in the jacking process, then the loss will be very small. Losses for elastic shortening can therefore vary between 1% for some post-tensioned beams and 10% for highly prestressed pre-tensioned members.

12.3.4   Shrinkage of concrete (cl 4.8.4, Pt 1)

Shrinkage of concrete is a reduction in dimensions of a concrete member, and when related to loss of prestress it is the shrinkage in length which is important. The mechanism of shrinkage is explained in Section 2.4.3.

The most important factors which influence shrinkage in concrete are:

(a)   aggregate used
(b)   original water content
(c)   effective age at transfer
(d)   effective section thickness
(e)   ambient relative humidity.

In the absence of experimental evidence, BS 8110 recommends values of shrinkage strain ε_c

100E–6 for UK outdoor exposure
300E–6 for indoor exposure.

These values may be incorporated in the following theory.

Assuming elastic behaviour, the loss of prestress in the prestressing steel

$$f_s = E_s \varepsilon_s$$

Assuming equal strains in the steel and concrete

$$\varepsilon_s = \varepsilon_c$$

and the percentage loss of prestress related to the jacking stress

$$= 100(f_s/f_{pi}) = 100 E_s \varepsilon_c/f_{pi} \tag{12.16}$$

12.3.5   Creep of concrete (cl 4.8.5, Pt 1)

Creep is the change in strain which occurs very slowly after the immediate elastic strain has taken place. The mechanism of creep in concrete is described in Section 2.4.2. Creep strain in concrete is stress dependent and the values given in BS 8110 are expressed as the elastic strain multiplied by a creep coefficient $\phi > 1$

$$\varepsilon_c = (f_c/E_t)\phi$$

The creep coefficient depends on the following:

(a)   original water content
(b)   effective age at transfer
(c)   effective section thickness
(d)   ambient relative humidity
(e)   ambient temperature

Values between 1.8 for transfer within 3 days and 1.4 for transfer after 28 days may generally be used for UK outdoor exposure. These values may also be used for the conventional design of class 1 and class 2 members for indoor exposure.

Assuming elastic behaviour, then loss of prestress in the steel

$$f_s = E_s \varepsilon_s$$

Assuming the strain in the steel equals the creep strain in the concrete

$$\varepsilon_s = \varepsilon_c = (f_c / E_t)\phi$$

and the percentage loss of prestress related to the jacking stress

$$= 100(f_s / f_{pi}) = 100(E_s / E_t)\phi f_c / f_{pi} \qquad (12.17)$$

12.3.6 Draw-in during anchorage (cl 4.8.6, Pt 1)

Draw-in is a term used to describe bedding-in of the anchorages, e.g. the slip of the wedges at the anchorage, which leads to a loss of prestress.

When the wires for pre-tensioned prestressed concrete members are being stressed the wires are fixed to a single cross-head and the draw-in can be allowed for and consequently the loss of prestress is small.

In post-tensioning systems allowance should be made for any slip of the tendon at the anchorage when the prestressing force is transferred from the tensioning equipment to the anchorage. This loss may be large for short members. In practice the slip at the anchorage δL is known and the strain $\delta L/L$ can be calculated.

Percentage loss of prestress related to the jacking stress

$$= 100(f_s / f_{pi}) = 100(\delta L/L)E_s / f_{pi} \qquad (12.18)$$

12.3.7 Friction loss (cl 4.9, Pt 1)

If frictional forces act along the length of the tendon, then the force at a point distant from the jack is less than at the jack.

Generally for pre-tensioned members the wires are straight and frictional losses occur only during jacking operations at the anchorage. The magnitude is generally known and allowance can be made.

For post-tensioned members the tendons are contained in straight or curved ducts and during jacking operations the tendons move relative to frictional surfaces.

For a straight duct the force P_x at a distance x from the jack may be calculated from the following equation (cl 4.9.3.2, Pt 1):

$$P_x = P_0 e^{-Kx}$$

where
P_0 is the prestressing force in the tendon at the jacking end
e is the base of the Napierian logarithm

K is the coefficient depending on the type of duct or sheath employed, the nature of its inside surface, the method of forming it and the degree of vibration employed in placing the concrete.

The value of K per metre length generally should be taken as not less than $K = 33E-4$.

When strong rigid sheaths or duct formers are used, closely supported so that they are not displaced during the concreting operation, $K = 17E-4$.

Greased strands running in plastic sleeves $K = 25E-4$.

The percentage loss of prestress force in relation to the jacking force

$$= 100(P_0 - P_x)/P_0 = 100(1 - e^{-Kx}) \tag{12.19}$$

For a curved duct the prestressing force P at any distance x from the tangent point may be calculated from the following equation (cl 4.9.4, Pt 1):

$$P_x = P_0 e^{-\mu x/r_{ps}}$$

where

P_0 is the prestressing force in the tendons at the tangent point near the jacking end

r_{ps} is the radius of curvature

μ is the coefficient of friction and typical values are (cl 4.9.4.3, Pt 1)

0.55 lightly rusted strand running on unlined concrete duct
0.30 lightly rusted strand running on lightly rusted steel duct
0.25 lightly rusted strand running on galvanised duct
0.20 bright strand running on galvanised duct
0.12 greased strand running on plastic sleeves

The percentage loss of prestress force in relation to the jacking force

$$= 100(P_0 - P_x)/P_0 = 100(1 - e^{-\mu x/r_{ps}}) \tag{12.20}$$

Further information on friction losses is contained in CIRIA Report 74. In practice the curved ducts are often parabolic but there is little error if a parabolic curve is treated as a circular curve, and from Fig. 12.8 the relation between a chord and a diameter

$$(L/2)^2 = (2r_{ps} - a_t)a_t$$

rearranging

$$r_{ps} = L^2/(8a_t) + a_t/2 \tag{12.21}$$

A theory to produce the equation for the loss of prestress as expressed in Equations (12.19) and (12.20) is as follows:

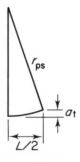

Fig. 12.8   Approximate shape for a parabolic cable.

Figure 12.9(a) represents a tendon with a jacking force P_0 subject to successive small changes in direction $d\theta$. At each change point there is a reaction R, and at the first change in direction, from geometry (see Fig. 12.9(b))

$$R = P_0 d\theta$$

The frictional force at the first reaction is

$$= \mu R = \mu P_0 d\theta$$

After the first change in direction the force in the tendon

$$P_x = P_0 - \mu P_0 d\theta$$

After the second change in direction the force in the tendon

$$P_x = P_0 - \mu(P_0 - P_0 d\theta) d\theta$$

After the third change in direction the force in the tendon

$$P_x = P_0 - \mu[P_0 - \mu (P_0 - P_0 d\theta) d\theta] d\theta$$

The force in a tendon, which changes direction through an angle θ, is

$$P_x = P_0 - \mu P_0 \int_0^\theta d\theta + \mu^2 P_0 \int\int_0^\theta d\theta\, d\theta - \mu^3 P_0 \int\int\int_0^\theta d\theta\, d\theta\, d\theta + \cdots$$
$$= P_0[1 - \mu\theta + (\mu\theta)^2/2 - (\mu\theta)^3/3! + \cdots]$$
$$= P_0[e^{-\mu\theta}]$$

If the radius of curvature is large $\theta = x/r_{ps}$ and

$$= P_0[e^{-\mu x/r_{ps}}]$$

For a straight duct with a wobble $\mu/r_{ps} = K$.

EXAMPLE 12.6   Loss of prestress

Determine the loss of prestress for the post-tensioned beam, shown in Fig. 12.10, which is subject to a total jacking force $P_0 = 1000$ kN. At transfer at 3 days $f_{cu,3} = 40$ N/mm^2, at

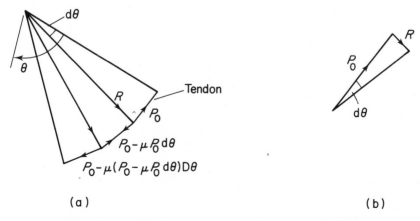

(a)   (b)

Fig. 12.9   Theory for loss of prestress due to duct friction.

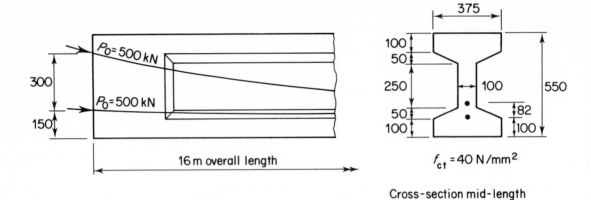

Fig. 12.10   Loss of prestress example.

28 days $f_{cu,28} = 60$ N/mm^2, and $E_s = 195$ kN/mm^2. Assume rigid ducts closely supported, jacking from both ends, and lightly rusted strand running in lightly rusted ducts.
   Steel stress at jacking

$$f_{pi} = 0.7f_{pu} = 0.7 \times 1550 = 1085 \text{ N/mm}^2$$

Percentage loss of prestress from relaxation of the steel (cl 4.8.2, Pt 1) from Table 12.5 and the manufacturer's UK certificate of approval = 4%.
   Cross sectional area of the section

$$A = 550 \times 375 - 275 \times 300 = 123.75\text{E3 mm}^2$$

Second moment of area of the section

$$I = 375 \times 550^3/12 - 275 \times 250^3/12 - 2 \times 275 \times 50^3/36 - 2 \times 0.5 \times 275 \times 50 \times (125 + 50/3)^2$$
$$= 4.563\text{E9 mm}^4$$

Elastic section modulus of the section

$$z = I/y = 4.563\text{E9}/275 = 16.594\text{E6 mm}^3$$

Prestress at the centroid of the prestressing steel

$$f_c = -P_0/A_c - P_0ey/I$$
$$= -1000\text{E3}/123.75\text{E3} - 1000\text{E3} \times 134^2/4.563\text{E9} = -12.0 \text{ N/mm}^2$$

Elastic modulus of the concrete at 28 days (cl 7.2, Pt 2)

$$E_{c,28} = K_0 + 0.2f_{cu,28} = 20 + 0.2 \times 60 = 32 \text{ kN/mm}^2$$

Elastic modulus at transfer at three days

$$E_{c,3} = E_{c,28}(0.4 + 0.6f_{cu,3}/f_{cu,28})$$
$$= 32 \times (0.4 + 0.6 \times 40/60) = 25.6 \text{ kN/mm}^2$$

Percentage loss of prestress from elastic deformation of the concrete (cl 4.8.3, Pt 1) from Equation (12.15)

$$= 100(E_s/E_{c,3})f_c/f_{pi}$$
$$= 100 \times (195\text{E3}/25.6\text{E3}) \times 12/1085 = 8.42\%$$

This value is halved to 4.21% for a post-tensioned beam.

Percentage loss of prestress from shrinkage of the concrete (cl 4.8.4, Pt 1) from Equation (12.16) for outdoor exposure

$$= 100E_s\varepsilon_c/f_{pi}$$
$$= 100 \times 195\text{E}3 \times 100\text{E}{-}6/1085 = 1.80\%$$

Percentage loss of prestress from creep of the concrete transfer at 28 days for outdoor exposure (cl 4.8.5, Pt 1) from Equation (12.17)

$$= 100(E_s/E_{c,3})\phi f_c/f_{pi}$$
$$= 100 \times (195\text{E}3/25.6\text{E}3) \times 1.4 \times 12/1085 = 11.79\%$$

Percentage loss of prestress from draw-in of 1 mm for half the length of beam during anchorage (cl 4.8.6, Pt 1) from Equation (12.18)

$$= 100(\delta L/L)E_s/f_{pi}$$
$$= 100 \times (1/8\text{E}3) \times 195\text{E}3/1085 = 2.24\%$$

Percentage loss of prestress for the bottom approximately straight duct (cl 4.9, Pt 1) jacked from both ends from Equation (12.19)

$$= 100(1 - e^{-Kx})$$
$$= 100 \times (1 - e^{-1.7\text{E}-3 \times 8}) = 1.35\%$$

Radius of curvature for the top curved duct from Equation (12.21) assuming the curve approximates to a circle ($a_t = 450 - 182 = 268$ mm)

$$r_{ps} = L^2/(8a_t) + a_t/2$$
$$= 16^2/(8 \times 0.268) + 0.268/2 = 119.5 \text{ m}$$

Percentage loss of prestress for a curved duct jacked from both ends (cl 4.9, Pt 1) from Equation (12.20)

$$= 100(1 - e^{-\mu x/r_{ps}})$$
$$= 100 \times (1 - e^{-0.3 \times 8/119.5}) = 1.99\%$$

Total loss of prestress

$$= \text{relax} + \text{elastic conc.} + \text{shrink. conc.} + \text{creep conc.} + \text{draw-in} + \text{friction}$$
$$= 4 + 4.21 + 1.80 + 11.79 + 2.24 + (1.35 + 1.99)/2 = 25.71\%$$

The total loss could be reduced further by rejacking to reduce the concrete elastic loss.

12.4   Shear resistance of prestressed concrete members

12.4.1   Introduction

Shear failure in reinforced concrete members is associated with cracks in the concrete which are produced by a combination of bending moment and shear forces. In prestressed concrete the shear failure is similar but the prestressing of the concrete delays the onset of cracking and consequently increases the shear resistance. In addition prestressed concrete members are manufactured from high-strength concrete, which increases the resistance to shear cracking.

12.4.2 Types of shear failure in prestressed concrete

There are three main types of shear failure which may be related to the ratio of bending moment to shear force.

Type I The bending moment is high and the shear force low ($a_v/d > 6$, see Fig. 12.11(a)). The applied bending moment cracks the beam before failure, which reduces the shear resistance to a value comparable with a reinforced concrete beam where $a_v/d > 6$. The shear resistance of the beam is therefore the sum of the shear force associated with the bending moment necessary to crack the section plus the shear resistance of the cracked section.

Type II The bending moment is reduced and the shear force increased ($1 < a/d < 6$, see Fig. 12.11(b)). The applied bending moment is not large enough to crack the beam in flexure and failure is associated with diagonal tensile cracks in the web of the beam produced by shear stresses.

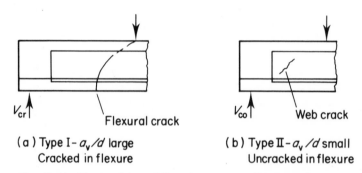

(a) Type I - a_v/d large
Cracked in flexure

(b) Type II - a_v/d small
Uncracked in flexure

Fig. 12.11 Types of shear failure in prestressed concrete beams.

Type III The bending moment is zero and the shear force is high ($a_v/d = 0$). Failure is comparable with the punching shear failure in ordinary reinforced concrete (see Fig. 7.1(d)). This is the maximum shear resistance for a section. Prestressing does increase the resistance to this form of failure but this is ignored in BS 8110.

Type IV Where shear failure of types I and II are likely to occur shear reinforcement is added and subsequent failure is similar to that for a reinforced concrete beam with shear reinforcement (see Fig. 7.1(e)).

12.4.3 Shear resistance of sections cracked in flexure (cl 4.3.8.5, Pt 1)

This type of failure occurs after the section has cracked in bending. If M is the applied bending moment and M_0 is the bending moment necessary to overcome the prestress stress to produce zero stress in the extreme fibres, then equating these moments

$$M = M_0$$

If the applied shear force associated with the bending moment M is V, then multiplying both sides of the equation by the shear force V

$$MV = M_0 V$$

Rearranging

$$V = M_0 V/M$$

V is the shear force associated with the bending moment M necessary to overcome the prestress and produce zero stress in the extreme fibres.

After the section has cracked the shear resistance is comparable with that for a reinforced concrete beam. The total shear resistance V_{cr} (cl 4.3.8.5, Pt 1)

$$V_{cr} = (1 - 0.55 f_{pe}/f_{pu}) v_c b_v d + M_0 V/M$$

The full derivation of this equation is given by Kong. The value of V_{cr} should not be taken as less than $0.1 b_v d \sqrt{f_{cu}}$.

Dividing through by $b_v d$ to express the equation in terms of the design ultimate shear stress,

$$v_{cr} = (1 - 0.55 f_{pe}/f_{pu}) v_c + (M_0/M) v \qquad (12.22)$$

The value of v_c is the same as for a singly reinforced concrete member, given in Equation (7.2), but is reduced by the term in brackets. This term is based on experimental evidence and makes allowance for the effective prestress f_{pe} which increases the force in the compression zone. The magnitude of v_{cr} should not be greater than $v_u = 0.8\sqrt{f_{cu}}$ (cl 4.3.8.2, Pt 1).

Equation (12.22) is difficult to apply because the critical section in the span is not defined. An iterative approach can be adopted but can be avoided by identifying the critical section where $V_{cr} \sim V$ is a minimum.

For the case of a simply supported beam with a central point load, at a section distance x from a support,

$$V_x = W/2, \ M_x = Wx/2$$

and

$$V_{cr} \sim V = (1 - 0.55 f_{pe}/f_{pu}) v_c b_v d + M_0 (W/2)/(Wx/2) - W/2$$

This expression is a minimum when $x = L/2$, i.e. at centre span where the value of $M_0 V/M = (M_0/M_{max}) V_{support}$. In practice values of M_0/M_{max} often lie between 0.4 and 0.6.

For the case of a simply supported beam with a uniformly distributed load, at a section distance x from a support,

$$V_x = (W/2)(1 - 2x/L), \ M_x = (WL/2)(x/L)(1 - x/L)$$

and

$$V_{cr} \sim V = (1 - 0.55 f_{pe}/f_{pu}) v_c b_v d$$
$$+ M_0 (W/2)(1 - 2x/L)/[(WL/2)(x/L)(1 - x/L)] - (W/2)(1 - 2x/L)$$

The value of x/L for which $V_{cr} \sim V$ is a minimum can be found from the differential equation

$$d/dx(V_{cr} \sim V) = 0$$

This gives a quartic equation in x/L, but the relevant solution for x measured from a support is

$$x/L = 0.5\{1 - \sqrt{[1 + 0.5 M_0/M_{max} - \sqrt{(2M_0/M_{max} + 0.25(M_0/M_{max})^2)}]}\} \qquad (12.23)$$

where the maximum bending moment $M_{max} = WL/8$.

For values of M_0/M_{max} between 0.4 and 0.6 the value of x/L lies between 0.23 and 0.3, which agrees with a rule of thumb of span/4 often used in practice. The term M_0V/M is approximately constant at $0.3V$, as compared with $0.4V$ to $0.5V$ for a simply supported beam with a central point load.

12.4.4   Shear resistance of sections uncracked in flexure (cl 4.3.8.4, Pt 1)

This type of failure occurs before the section cracks in bending but where the shear force is large enough to overcome the prestress and produce diagonal tensile cracks in the web of the member.

The theory associated with this type of failure is developed as follows. The stresses acting at the centroidal axis in the web of a prestressed concrete member are the prestress f_{cp} and the shear stress v as shown in Fig. 12.12.

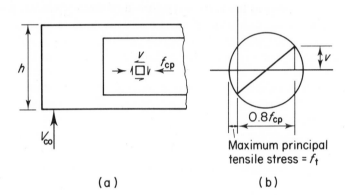

(a)   (b)

Fig. 12.12   Section uncracked in flexure.

The shear stress at a point on a vertical cross-section is

$$v = VA\bar{y}/(Ib)$$

This is a well-known equation derived assuming linear elastic material behaviour, and is acceptable for concrete before cracking occurs.

The maximum shear stress at the centroidal axis for a rectangular cross-section is

$$v = 1.5V_{co}/(b_vh) \tag{12.24}$$

For other shapes of cross-section this expression is approximately correct and errs on the safe side (Reynolds *et al.* 1974).

The prestress stress f_{cp} at the centroidal axis can be determined from the prestress stress diagram at the relevant section along the beam, but for safety, a factored value of $0.8f_{cp}$ is recommended in BS 8110.

If it is assumed that the concrete cracks because the principal tensile stress exceeds the tensile strength of the concrete, then from Mohr's circle of stresses shown in Fig. 12.12(b),

$$f_t = \sqrt{[(0.5 \times 0.8f_{cp})^2 + v^2]} - 0.5 \times 0.8f_{cp}$$

rearranging

$$v = \sqrt{(f_t^2 + 0.8f_{cp}f_t)}$$

Combining with Equation (12.24) the shear force

$$V_{c0} = 0.67b_v h\sqrt{(f_t^2 + 0.8f_{cp}f_t)}$$

or expressed as a shear stress

$$v_{c0} = 0.67\sqrt{(f_t^2 + 0.8f_{cp}f_t)} \tag{12.25}$$

The values of f_t and f_{cp} are considered to be positive, and the tensile strength of concrete $f_t = 0.24\sqrt{f_{cu}}$. The magnitude of v_{c0} should not be greater than $v_u = 0.8\sqrt{f_{cu}}$ (cl 4.3.8.2, Pt 1).

12.4.5   Shear reinforcement in prestressed members (cl 4.3.8.6–4.3.8.10, Pt 1)

The requirements (see summary in Appendix 2.2) are similar to those for ordinary reinforced concrete, except for the spacing of links along the length of the member.

The spacing of the links should not exceed $0.75d_t$ or four times the web thickness for flanged members. When V exceeds $1.8V_c$ the maximum spacing should be reduced to $0.5d_t$. The lateral spacing of the individual legs of links at a cross-section should not exceed d_t.

EXAMPLE 12.7   Shear resistance of a post-tensioned beam

Design for shear at the ultimate limit state the post-tensioned prestressed concrete beam shown in Fig. 12.13. The beam is simply supported over a span of 10 m and supports a uniformly distributed load of 160 kN at the ultimate limit state. The beam has been designed to resist the bending moment. Calculate the shear strength of the beam uncracked in flexure at the ultimate limit state.

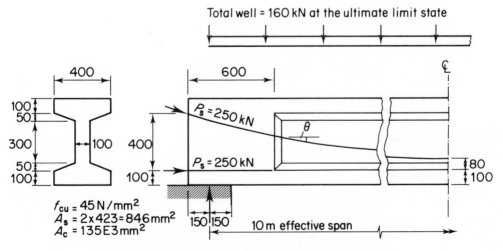

Fig. 12.13   Shear resistance of a post-tensioned beam.

The critical point to consider for the principal tensile stress in the concrete is at the centroid of the I cross-section at a distance of 600 mm from the end of the beam.

Shear force at this section

$$= (5 - 0.45)/5 \times V_{support} = (5 - 0.45)/5 \times 80 = 72.8 \text{ kN}$$

Average shear stress

$$v = V/(b_v h) = 72.8E3/(100 \times 600) = 1.213 \text{ N/mm}^2$$

Design tensile strength of the concrete (cl 4.3.8.4, Pt 1)

$$f_t = 0.24\sqrt{f_{cu}} = 0.24 \times \sqrt{45} = 1.610 \text{ N/mm}^2$$

Area of cross-section

$$A_c = 600 \times 400 - 300 \times 350 = 135E3 \text{ mm}^2$$

Prestress at the centroid of the section after losses

$$f_{cp} = 2P_s/A_c = 2 \times 250E3/135E3 = 3.704 \text{ N/mm}^2$$

From Equation (12.25) the design ultimate shear stress resistance of the uncracked web is

$$v_{c0} = 0.67\sqrt{(f_t^2 + 0.8f_{cp}f_t)}$$
$$= 0.67 \times \sqrt{(1.61^2 + 0.8 \times 3.704 \times 1.61)} = 1.818 \text{ N/mm}^2$$

This value is less than the maximum design shear stress (cl 4.3.8.2, Pt 1)

$$v_u = 0.8\sqrt{f_{cu}} = 0.8\sqrt{45} = 5.367 \text{ N/mm}^2 > 5 \text{ N/mm}^2.$$

$0.5v_{c0}(0.909) < v(1.213) < (v_{c0} + 0.4)(2.218) \text{ N/mm}^2$, therefore only minimum shear reinforcement is required (cl 4.3.8.7, Pt 1), see Appendix A2.2.

In addition there is the shear resistance provided by the curved top cable

$$v' = (P_s/A_w) \sin\theta = (P_s/A_w) \tan\theta$$
$$\tan\theta = dy/dx = 2kx = 2 \times 0.4/5.15^2 \times 4.55 = 0.137$$
$$v' = 250E3/(100 \times 600) \times 0.137 = 0.571 \text{ N/mm}^2$$

This additional shear resistance is not mentioned in BS 8110 and is not taken into account in this problem.

Calculate the shear strength of the beam cracked in flexure at the ultimate limit state.

Elastic second moment of area of the cross-section

$$I = 400 \times 600^3/12 - 300 \times 300^3/12 - 2 \times 300 \times 50^3/36 - 2 \times 0.5 \times 300$$
$$\times 50 \times (150 + 50/3)^2 = 6.106E9 \text{ mm}^4$$

Elastic section modulus

$$z = I/y = 6.106E9/300 = 20.35E6 \text{ mm}^3$$

Prestress at the bottom of the section after losses using an approximate value of the eccentricity, i.e. $e = 160$ mm, the value at mid-span,

$$f_{cp} = -P_s/A - P_s e/z$$
$$= -500E3/135E3 - 500E3 \times 160/20.35E6$$
$$= -7.635 \text{ N/mm}^2$$

Bending moment required to overcome 80% of the prestress stress at the bottom of the section

$$M_0 = 0.8f_{cp}I/y = 0.8 \times 7.635 \times 6.106E9/300 \times 1E{-}6 = 124.3 \text{ kN m}$$

This type of failure is likely to occur when the applied bending moment M_x at a distance x from the support exceeds M_0.

$$M_x = WL(x/L)(1-x/L)/2 = M_0$$

Inserting numerical values

$$160 \times 10 \times (x/L)(1-x/L)/2 = 124.3; \text{ hence } x = 1.924 \text{ m}.$$
$$M_{max} = WL/8 = 160 \times 10/8 = 200 \text{ kN m}$$
$$M_0/M_{max} = 124.3/200 = 0.6215$$

Position of the critical section from Equation (12.23)

$$x/L = 0.5\{1 - \sqrt{[1 + 0.5M_0/M_{max} - \sqrt{(2M_0/M_{max} + 0.25(M_0/M_{max})^2)]}}\}$$
$$= 0.3042; \text{ hence } x = 0.3042 \times 10 = 3.042 \text{ m from a support}$$

At this section

$$V = (W/2)(1 - 2x/L) = (160/2) \times (1 - 2 \times 0.3042) = 31.328 \text{ kN}$$

Design shear stress

$$v = V/(b_v d) = 31.328E3/(100 \times 460) = 0.681 \text{ N/mm}^2$$

Bending moment

$$M = WL(x/L)(1-x/L)/2 = 160 \times 10 \times 0.3042 \times (1 - 0.3042)/2 = 169.3 \text{ kN m}$$

Design shear stress for a singly reinforced concrete beam (cl 3.4.5.4, Pt 1)

$$v_c = k_1 k_2 0.79[100A_s/(b_v d)]^{1/3}(400/d)^{1/4}/\gamma_m$$
$$= 1 \times (40/25)^{1/3} \times 0.79 \times [100 \times 846/100 \times 460)]^{1/3} \times 1/1.25$$
$$= 0.906 \text{ N/mm}^2$$

Note: $400/d < 1$, therefore use 1, $100A_s/(b_v d) = 1.84\% < 3\%$ (max).

From Equation (12.22), assuming $f_{pe}/f_{pu} = 0.6$, the design ultimate shear stress resistance

$$v_{cr} = (1 - 0.55f_{pe}/f_{pu})v_c + (M_0/M)v$$
$$= (1 - 0.55 \times 0.6) \times 0.906 + 124.3/169.3 \times 0.681 = 1.107 \text{ N/mm}^2$$

The value of v_{cr} should not be taken as less than

$0.1\sqrt{f_{cu}} = 0.1 \times \sqrt{45} = 0.671 \text{ N/mm}^2$, therefore this value is not applicable.

Check that the value of $v_{cr} < v_u$ (cl 4.3.8.2, Pt 1)

$v_u = 0.8\sqrt{f_{cu}} = 0.8\sqrt{45} = 5.367 \text{ N/mm}^2 > 5 \text{ N/mm}^2$, satisfactory.

Check if v_{c0} or v_{cr} (cl 4.3.8.3, Pt 1) is critical

$$v_{c0}(1.818) > v_{cr}(1.107) \text{ N/mm}^2$$

therefore v_{cr} is critical since it is the lesser value.

$0.5v_{cr}(0.553) < v(0.681) < (v_{cr} + 0.4)(1.507)$ N/mm^2, therefore minimum reinforcement, see Appendix A2.2.

Spacing for minimum shear reinforcement from Equation (7.6), assuming single R6 links

$$s_v = A_{sv}0.87f_{yv}/(0.4b_v)$$
$$= 2 \times 28 \times 0.87 \times 250/(0.4 \times 100)$$
$$= 304.5 \text{ mm}.$$

Limits placed on the spacing of links (cl 4.3.8.10, Pt 1) are

$$0.75d_t = 0.75 \times 460 = 345 \text{ mm}$$
$$4b_v = 4 \times 100 = 400 \text{ mm}$$

$v(1.213)$ N/mm$^2 < 1.8v_{c0}(1.8 \times 1.818 = 3.272)$ N/mm^2, and therefore the spacing need not be reduced. These limits are not critical therefore use single links R6-300 mm centres.

12.5   End blocks

12.5.1   End blocks for post-tensioned members (cl 4.11, Pt 1)

When a force from a post-tensioned cable is transferred to a small area, or zone, at the end of a beam, high localised stresses are produced. These localised stresses do not extend the full length of the member but are confined to the anchor block. The tensile stresses are of particular concern because they can produce cracks in the concrete which need to be controlled by the use of reinforcing steel. The cross-section of the anchor blocks is generally rectangular in order to reduce the magnitude of the stresses.

The exact distribution of stresses in an anchor block is complex and is not fully understood theoretically, nor has the subject been thoroughly investigated experimentally (CIRIA Guide 1). The distributions of principal compressive and tensile stresses in a simple rectangular anchor block subject to a single force are shown in Fig. 12.14(a). The distribution of stress along the centre-line of the block is shown in Fig. 12.14(b), and this is of particular concern in structural design because reinforcement is required to resist the tensile stresses. These stresses are three dimensional and consequently tensile stresses are also present at right angles to those shown in Fig. 12.14(b).

In addition to the stresses described previously where there is more than one jacking force there are stresses close to the loaded face which may cause cracking and spalling of the surface concrete between the anchor forces. These spalling stresses are greatest with unsymmetrical loading of the end block. Further information is given in CIRIA Guide 1.

When several forces are applied to an end block similar distributions to those described for a single force occur local to each force, and also over the complete end block. It is this fact which is used in design calculations to simplify a complex problem by subdividing the complete end block into simple individual cubic end blocks associated with each anchor force. Examples are shown in Fig. 12.15. The size of each individual cubic end block is based on a controlling dimension y_o which may be a vertical edge distance as in Fig. 12.15(a), or a horizontal edge distance as in Fig. 12.15(b), or distance between anchor forces as in Fig. 12.15(c). The minimum dimension is then used to determine the minimum size of cubic end block, $2y_o$.

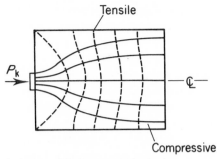

(a) Simplified stress trajectories

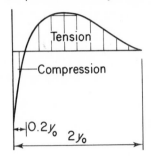

(b) Distribution of stress along ℄ of block

Fig. 12.14 End-block stresses.

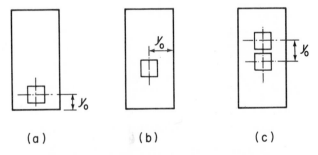

Fig. 12.15 Critical values of y_0 for end blocks.

Each cubic end block is designed individually and the bursting force F_{bst} for each cubic end block is determined from values in Table 12.6.

Table 12.6 Design bursting forces in end blocks   (cl 4.11.2, Table 4.7, Pt 1)

y_{po}/y_o	0.2	0.3	0.4	0.5	0.6	0.7
F_{bst}/P_o	0.23	0.23	0.2	0.17	0.14	0.11

Note: intermediate values may be interpolated.

where
y_o is half the side of the end block
y_{p0} is half the side of the loaded area
P_o is the tendon jacking force

Circular bearing plates should be treated as square plates of equivalent area.

This force, F_{bst}, will be distributed in a region extending from $0.2y_o$ to $2y_o$ from the loaded face, and should be resisted by reinforcement in the form of spirals or closed links, uniformly distributed throughout this region, and acting at a stress of 200 N/mm².

When large blocks contain several anchorages it should be divided into a series of symmetrically loaded prisms and each prism treated in the above manner. However, additional reinforcement will be required around groups of anchorages to ensure overall equilibrium of the end block.

Special attention should also be paid to end blocks having a cross-sectional shape different from that of the general cross-section of the beam.   Information is given in CIRIA Guide 1.

For members with unbonded tendons the design bursting force, F_{bst}, should be assessed from Table 4.7 on the basis of the characteristic tendon force; the reinforcement provided to sustain that force may be assumed to be acting at its design strength $(0.87f_y)$. No check is necessary in the case of members with bonded tendons.

The size and spacing of links to resist the bursting force is obtained from equating the bursting force to the resistance of the links stressed to 200 N/mm²

$$F_{bst} = (A_{sv}200/s_v)(2y_o - 0.2y_o) \qquad (12.26)$$

The same reinforcement should be provided in two directions at right angles.

EXAMPLE 12.8   Post-tensioned end block

Determine the spacing of 8 mm diameter double links to reinforce the end block shown in Fig. 12.16 which is subject to two tendon jacking forces.

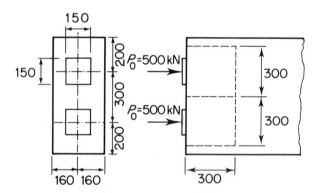

Fig. 12.16 Post-tensioned end-block example.

Width of the bearing plate $2y_{po} = 150$ mm

From the vertical spacing of the tendon forces the minimum width of a cubic block (see Fig. 12.15(c))

$$2y_o = 300 \text{ mm}$$

Ratio

$$2y_{po}/2y_o = 150/300 = 0.5$$

From Table 12.6 (cl 4.11.2, Table 4.7, Pt 1)

$$F_{bst}/P_o = 0.17$$

hence

$$F_{bst} = 0.17P_o = 0.17 \times 500 = 85 \text{ kN}$$

Rearranging Equation (12.26) the spacing of double R8 links

$$\begin{aligned} s_v &= (A_{sv}200/F_{bst})(2y_o - 0.2y_o) \\ &= (2 \times 2 \times 50 \times 200/85\text{E}3)(300 - 0.2 \times 150) \\ &= 127.1 \text{ mm} \end{aligned}$$

Use double R8-120 mm, in two directions at right angles.

12.5.2 End blocks for pre-tensioned members (cl 4.10, Pt 1)

The prestressing force is zero at the end of a pre-tensioned member in contrast to a post-tensioned member where it is a maximum. This means that for a pre-tensioned member the prestressing force is not concentrated at the end of the member and therefore it is not subject to the same localised stresses as a post-tensioned beam.

The distance required for the prestressing force to be transmitted to the concrete for a pre-tensioned member is called the transmission length.

The most important factors affecting the transmission length are (cl 4.10.1, Pt 1)

(a)   the degree of compaction of the concrete;
(b)   the size and type of tendon;
(c)   the strength of the concrete;
(d)   the deformation and surface condition of the steel.

In addition the transmission length is affected by the sudden release of the tension in the wires when the force is transferred to the concrete.

For calculating the transmission length, l_t, in the absence of experimental evidence, the following equation may be used for initial prestressing forces up to 75% of the characteristic strength of the tendon when the ends of the units are fully compacted (cl 4.10.3, Pt 1):

$$l_t = K_t\phi/\sqrt{f_{ci}} \qquad \text{(Equation 60, Pt 1)} \tag{12.27}$$

where
f_{ci} is the concrete strength at transfer
ϕ is the nominal diameter of the tendon

K_t is a coefficient for the type of tendon and is selected from the following:

(a)   plain or indented wire (including crimped wire with a small wave height): $K_t = 600$;
(b)   crimped wire with a total wave height not less than 0.15ϕ: $K_t = 400$;
(c)   7-wire standard or super strand: $K_t = 240$;
(d)   7-wire drawn strand: $K_t = 360$.

The existence of a transmission length in a pre-tensioned member means that the full prestressing force is not developed until the end of the transmission length, and consequently the bending and shear resistance are reduced for a simply supported beam as shown in the following example.

EXAMPLE 12.9 End block for a pre-tensioned beam

Design for shear the pre-tensioned prestressed concrete beam shown in Fig. 12.17. The beam is simply supported over a span of 8 m and carries a uniformly distributed load of 375 kN at the ultimate limit state. The beam has been designed to resist the bending moment.

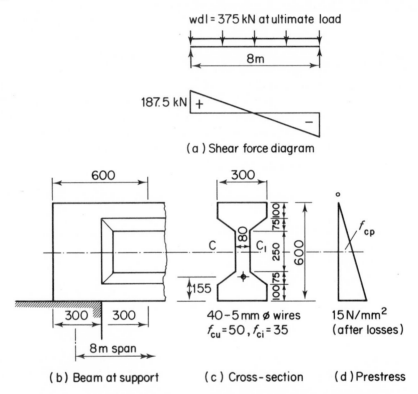

Fig. 12.17 Example of the shear resistance of a pre-tensioned member.

Calculate the shear strength of the beam uncracked in flexure at the ultimate limit state.

The critical point to consider the principal tensile stresses in the concrete is at the centroid of the cross-section, at a distance from the edge of the support equal to the distance of the centroid of the section above the soffit (cl 4.3.8.4, Pt 1).

From Fig. 12.17(b) the distance from the centre-line of the bearing

$$= 300 + 300/2 = 450 \text{ mm}.$$

Shear force at this section

$$= (4 - 0.45)/4 \times V_{\text{support}} = (4 - 0.45)/4 \times 187.5 = 166.4 \text{ kN}$$

Average shear stress

$$v = V/bh = 166.4\text{E3}/(80 \times 600) = 3.467 \text{ N/mm}^2$$

For a 5 mm diameter crimped wire with a total wave height of not less than 0.15ϕ (cl 4.10.3, Pt 1) and a strength of the concrete at transfer $f_{ci} = 35 \text{ N/mm}^2$, the transmission length

$$l_t = K_t\phi/\sqrt{f_{ci}} = 400 \times 5/\sqrt{35} = 338.1 \text{ mm} < h = 600 \text{ mm},$$

therefore use 600 mm (cl 4.3.8.4, Pt 1)

At $x = 600$ mm, i.e. at the end of the transmission length, the prestress stress $f_{cpx} = 1.0f_{cp} = 7.5 \text{ N/mm}^2$ (cl 4.3.8.4, Pt 1)
  Design tensile strength of the concrete (cl 4.3.8.4, Pt 1)

$$f_t = 0.24\sqrt{f_{cu}} = 0.24 \times \sqrt{50} = 1.697 \text{ N/mm}^2$$

From Equation (12.25) the shear stress resistance of the web with $f_{cp} = 7.5 \text{ N/mm}^2$ (see Fig. 12.17(d))

$$v_{c0} = 0.67\sqrt{(f_t^2 + 0.8f_{cp}f_t)}$$
$$= 0.67 \times \sqrt{(1.697^2 + 0.8 \times 1.0 \times 7.5 \times 1.697)} = 2.421 \text{ N/mm}^2$$

This value is less than the ultimate maximum design shear stress (cl 4.3.8.2, Pt 1)

$$v_u = 0.8\sqrt{f_{cu}} = 0.8\sqrt{50} = 5.657 > 5 \text{ N/mm}^2.$$

$v = 3.467 > (v_{c0} + 0.4) = 2.821 \text{ N/mm}^2$, therefore shear reinforcement is required, see Appendix A2.2.
  Calculate the shear strength of the beam cracked in flexure at the ultimate limit state. Elastic second moment of area of the cross-section

$$I = 300 \times 600^3/12 - (300 - 80) \times 250^3/12 - 4 \times 110 \times 75^3/36 - 4 \times 0.5$$
$$\times 110 \times 75 \times (125 + 75/3)^2 = 4737\text{E6 mm}^4$$

Bending moment required to overcome 80% of the prestress stress $f_{cp} = 15 \text{ N/mm}^2$ at the bottom of the section

$$M_0 = 0.8f_{cp}I/y = 0.8 \times 15 \times 4737\text{E6}/300 \times 1\text{E}-6 = 189.48 \text{ kN m}$$

This type of failure is likely to occur when the applied bending moment M_x, at a distance x from the support, exceeds M_0. If

$$M_x = WL(x/L)(1 - x/L)/2 = M_0$$

then inserting numerical values

$$375 \times 8 \times (x/L)(1 - x/L)/2 = 189.48; \text{ hence } x = 1.1864 \text{ m.}$$
$$M_{max} = WL/8 = 375 \times 8/8 = 375 \text{ kN m}$$
$$M_0/M_{max} = 189.48/375 = 0.5053$$

Position of the critical section from Equation (12.23)

$$x/L = 0.5\{1 - \sqrt{[1 + 0.5M_0/M_{max} - \sqrt{(2M_0/M_{max} + 0.25(M_0/M_{max})^2)]}]\}}$$
$$= 0.2676; \text{ hence } x = 0.2767 \times 8 = 2.141 \text{ m from support}$$

At this section

$$V = (W/2)(1-2x/L) = (375/2) \times (1-2 \times 0.2676) = 87.15 \text{ kN}$$
$$v = V/(b_v d) = 87.15\text{E}3/(80 \times 445) = 2.447 \text{ N/mm}^2$$
$$M = WL(x/L)(1-x/L)/2 = 375 \times 8 \times 0.2676 \times (1-0.2676)/2 = 294.0 \text{ kN m}$$

Area of tensile steel $= 40 \times \pi/4 \times 5^2 = 785.4 \text{ mm}^2$

Design shear stress for a singly reinforced concrete beam (cl 3.4.5.4, Pt 1)

$$v_c = k_1 k_2 0.79[100A_s/(b_v d)]^{1/3}(400/d)^{1/4}/\gamma_m$$
$$= 1 \times (40/25)^{1/3} \times 0.79 \times [100 \times 785.4/(80 \times 445)]^{1/3} \times 1/1.25$$
$$= 0.962 \text{ N/mm}^2$$

(*Note:* $400/d < 1$, therefore use 1, $100A_s/(b_v d) = 2.206\% < 3\%$ (max).)

From Equation (12.22), assuming $f_{pe}/f_{pu} = 0.6$, the design ultimate shear stress

$$v_{cr} = (1-0.55f_{pe}/f_{pu})v_c + (M_0/M)v$$
$$= (1-0.55 \times 0.6) \times 0.962 + 189.48/294 \times 2.447 = 2.222 \text{ N/mm}^2$$

The value of v_{cr} should not be taken as less than

$$0.1\sqrt{f_{cu}} = 0.1 \times \sqrt{50} = 0.707 < 2.222 \text{ N/mm}^2$$

therefore this value is not applicable.

The value of 2.222 N/mm^2 is less than the ultimate maximum design shear stress (cl 4.3.8.2, Pt 1)

$$v_u = 0.8\sqrt{f_{cu}} = 0.8\sqrt{50} = 5.657 > 5 \text{ N/mm}^2.$$

Check if $v_{c0} > v_{cr}$ for a section cracked in flexure (cl 4.3.8.3, Pt 1)

$$v_{c0} = 2.421 \text{ N/mm}^2 \text{ (see previous calculation)} > v_{cr} = 2.222 \text{ N/mm}^2$$

therefore v_{cr} is critical.

$(v_{cr}+0.4)(2.622) > v(2.447) < 0.5v_{cr}(1.111)$ N/mm^2, therefore minimum reinforcement required, see Appendix A2.2.

Shear reinforcement is required for the uncracked section at 450 mm from the support. Spacing of single R6 vertical stirrups from Equation (7.4)

$$s_v = A_{sv}0.87f_{yv}/[b_v(v-v_{c0})]$$
$$= 2 \times 28 \times 0.87 \times 250/[80 \times (3.467-2.421)]$$
$$= 145.6 \text{ mm}$$

Limits placed on the spacing of links (cl 4.3.8.10, Pt 1)

$$0.75d_t = 0.75 \times 445 = 333.75 \text{ mm}$$
$$4b_v = 4 \times 80 = 320 \text{ mm}$$
$$v(3.467) < 1.8v_{c0}(4.358) \text{ N/mm}^2, \text{ and therefore spacing need not be reduced.}$$

Spacing limits are not critical, therefore use vertical single links at R6–140 mm centres. This spacing could be gradually increased until $v = v_{c0}$ where only minimum shear reinforcement is required, but in practice the spacing is often maintained for the whole span.

If the calculations are made for changing the spacing as v decreases, then when $v = v_{c0} = 2.421$ N/mm^2,

$$(4 - x)/4 \times 187.5E3/(80 \times 600) = 2.421$$

hence at $x = 1.521$ m from the support only minimum shear reinforcement is required.
Spacing for minimum shear reinforcement from Equation (7.6)

$$s_v = A_{sv}0.87f_{yv}/(0.4b_v)$$
$$= 2 \times 28 \times 0.87 \times 250/(0.4 \times 80)$$
$$= 380.6 \text{ mm}.$$

This value is greater than $4b_v = 320$ mm, therefore use single links R6–320 mm centres.
The simplest safe solution, although not the most economical, is to use single vertical links, R6–140 mm centres, for the full length of the beam.

12.5.3 Uneven distribution of prestress (cl 4.12.4.2, Pt 1)

Cracks sometimes occur in the ends of pre-tensioned members which are not rectangular in cross-section, as shown in Fig. 12.18. This defect is likely to occur if there is an uneven distribution of prestress over the depth and width of a section, and also if there is no rectangular end block. The introduction of horizontal and vertical links ensures that, even if these cracks occur, their development is restricted.

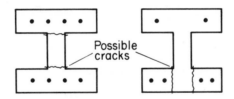

Fig. 12.18 Cracks in the ends of pre-tensioned members.

12.6 Tutorial problems

12.6.1 Analysis of a section in bending at ultimate load

The cross-section of a prestressed concrete beam of overall length 10 m is shown in

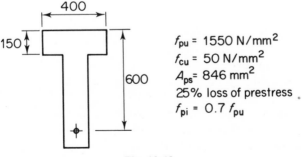

$f_{pu} = 1550$ N/mm^2
$f_{cu} = 50$ N/mm^2
$A_{ps} = 846$ mm^2
25% loss of prestress
$f_{pi} = 0.7 f_{pu}$

Fig. 12.19

Fig. 12.19. Analyse the section in bending at ultimate load assuming (a) bonded tendons (b) unbonded tendons.

Answer
(a) $f_{pb} = 1085$ N/mm^2, $M_u = 496.2$ kN m (b) $f_{pb} = 1085$ N/mm^2, $M_u = 503.9$ kN m.

12.6.2   Analysis of a section in bending at service load

The half elevation and section at mid-span of a post-tensioned prestressed concrete beam is shown in Fig. 12.20. The beam is simply supported over a 10 m span and carries a characteristic imposed load of 50 kN. Given that the initial prestressing force $P_0 = 700$ kN calculate (a) section properties (b) fibre stresses at the support at transfer of the prestressing force with 10% loss (c) fibre stresses at mid-span after 20% loss of prestress force and application of the imposed load and self-weight ($\rho = 2400$ kg/m^3)

Answer
(a) $A_c = 60E3$ mm^2, $I = 1E9$ mm^4, $z_1 = z_2 = 5E6$ mm^3 (b) $e = 10$ mm, $f_{t1} = -11.76$ N/mm^2, $f_{t2} = -9.24$ N/mm^2 (c) $M_s = 80.16$ kN m, $e = 70$ mm, $f_{s1} = -1.14$ N/mm^2, $f_{s2} = -17.52$ N/mm^2.

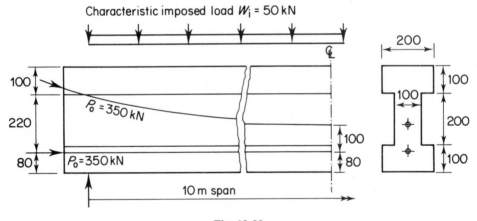

Fig. 12.20

12.6.3   Design of a section in bending at service load

A section at mid-span for a post-tensioned prestressed concrete beam class 2 is shown in Fig. 12.21. The beam is simply supported over a 25 m span and carries a characteristic imposed load of 9 kN/m in addition to the self-weight. The beam is prestressed with four cables, two of which are curved upwards at the support. Calculate (a) section properties (b) optimum section moduli at mid-span if the self-weight ($\rho = 2400$ kg/m^3) acts when the cables are stressed (c) the eccentricity of the prestressing force, to satisfy the tensile stress restraint at service load if $P_{op} = 2304$ kN (d) the fibre stresses at transfer and service load if the practical eccentricity $e_p = 440$ mm (e) limits of eccentricity (f) limits of the prestressing force.

Answer

(a) $A_c = 300E3$ mm^2, $y = 540$ mm from the base, $I_{CG} = 30.12E9$ mm^4, $z_1 = 55.78E6$ mm^3, $z_2 = 65.48E6$ mm^3 (b) $M_{sw} = 551.8$ kN m, $M_i = 703.1$ kN m, $z_1' = 44.75E6$ mm^3, $z_2' = 42.47E6$ mm^3 (c) $e = 437.6$ (d) $f_{t1} = -13.38$, $f_{t2} = -1.41$, $f_{s1} = +3.11$, $f_{s2} = -13.31$ N/mm^2 (e) $e_1(736.1)$ $e_p(440) > e_2(282.4)$ mm (f) $P_{02}(3624.6) > P_{0p}(2304) > P_{01}(1558)$ kN.

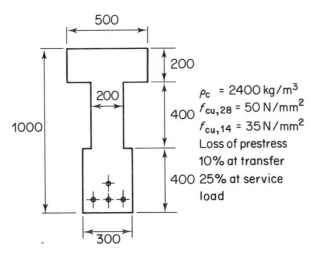

Fig. 12.21

12.6.4 Deflection of a prestressed beam

A section and half elevation of a post-tensioned prestressed concrete beam is shown in Fig. 12.22. Calculate (a) short-term deflection for the imposed load applied at a concrete strength of 50 N/mm^2 at 28 days (b) long-term creep deflection ($\phi = 1.6$) for the bending

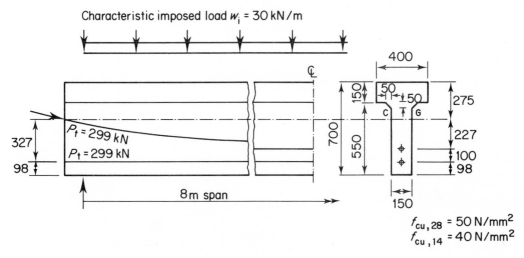

Fig. 12.22

moments from the effective prestress force at transfer ($P_t = 2 \times 299$ kN) and self-weight ($\rho = 350$ kg/m³) for a 14-day concrete cube strength of 40 N/mm² at transfer.

Answer
(a) $I = 6.48E9$ mm⁴, $E_{c,28} = 30$ kN/mm², $a_e = 8.29$ mm (b) $E_{c,14} = 10.15$ kN/mm², a_c (straight) $= -11.9$ mm, a_c (curved) $= -6.9$ mm, a_c (self-weight) $= 2.8$ mm.

12.6.5   Loss of prestress for a pre-tensioned beam

Calculate the vertical distribution of prestress for the pre-tensioned beam shown in Fig. 12.23, and hence the loss of prestress due to elastic shortening and creep of the concrete. The initial prestress force of $P_0 = 900$ kN is transferred within 3 days when $f_{ct} = 35$ N/mm².

Answer
$A_c = 135E3$ mm³, $z = 20.354E6$ mm³, $f_{cp} = 10.44$ N/mm², elastic loss $= 6.44\%$, creep loss $= 11.60\%$.

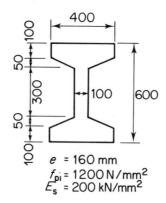

e = 160 mm
f_{pi} = 1200 N/mm²
E_s = 200 kN/mm²

Fig. 12.23

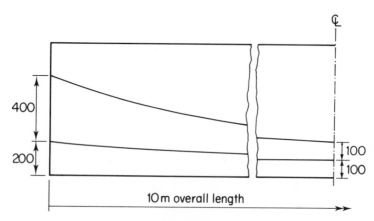

Fig. 12.24

12.6.6   Loss of prestress for a post-tensioned beam

Calculate the loss of prestress due to friction for the post-tensioned beam which is jacked from one end (see Fig. 12.24). The lightly rusted strands run in flexible galvanised ducts which were supported, but not closely supported, during construction.

Answer
Straight 6.39%, curved $r_{ps} = 125.2$ m, 3.91%.

12.6.7   Shear resistance of a prestressed beam

Design for shear, outside the transmission length, the pre-tensioned prestressed concrete beam section shown in Fig. 12.25. The beam is simply supported over a span of 24 m and carries a uniformly distributed load of 165 kN at the ultimate limit state. The beam, which has straight tendons, has been designed to resist the bending moment. The effective prestress at service load $P_s = 850$ kN produces a prestress distribution as shown in Fig. 12.25.

Answer
$v_{c0} = 2.083$ N/mm², $M_0 = 251.3$ kN m at 6.439 m from a support, $v = 0.436$ N/mm², $v_{cr} = 0.771$ N/mm², min. links R6–200.

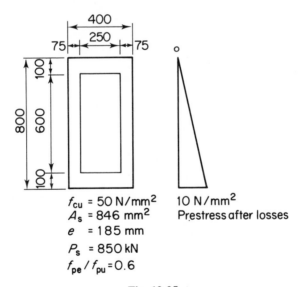

$f_{cu} = 50$ N/mm²
$A_s = 846$ mm²
$e = 185$ mm
$P_s = 850$ kN
$f_{pe}/f_{pu} = 0.6$

10 N/mm²
Prestress after losses

Fig. 12.25

12.6.8   End block of a post-tensioned beam

Determine the spacing of R8 mm diameter single links to reinforce the post-tensioned end block shown in Fig. 12.26 which is subject to a tendon jacking force $P_o = 450$ kN.

Answer

$y_{po}/y_0 = 0.571$, $F_{bst}/P_0 = 0.149$, $s_v = 94.0$ mm, use R8–80.

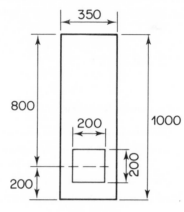

Fig. 12.26

References

BS 4486 (1980). *Specification for hot rolled and hot rolled and processed high tensile alloy steel bars for the prestressing of concrete*, British Standards Institution, London.

BS 4757 (1971). *Nineteen-wire steel strand for prestressed concrete*, British Standards Institution, London.

BS 5896 (1980). *Specification for high tensile steel wire strand for the prestressing of concrete*, British Standards Institution, London.

CIRIA Guide 1 (1976). *A guide to the design of anchor blocks for post-tensioned prestressed concrete members*, Construction Industry Research and Information Association Publication, p. 44.

CIRIA Report 74 (1978). *Prestressed concrete, friction losses during stressing*, Construction Industry Research and Information Association Publication, p. 52.

Kong F. K. (1978). Bending shear and torsion, Chapter 1 in *Developments in Prestressed Concrete*. Applied Science, Vol. 1, pp. 1–68.

Reynolds G. C., Clark J. L. and Taylor H. P. J. (1974). *Shear provisions for prestressed concrete in the unified code CP 110 (1972)*, Technical Report 42.500, Cement and Concrete Association, London, p. 16.

13

Design Studies

13.1 Reinforced concrete lintel beam

Determine the size and reinforcement for a reinforced concrete lintel beam to support a brickwork panel over a series of openings. Each beam is simply supported over an effective span of 3 m and each brickwork panel is 3 m × 2 m × 230 mm thick.

This design is for one of the commonest and simplest types of reinforced concrete beam and often shear reinforcement is not required. The concrete characteristic strength for a lintel is generally the lowest for a structural member, i.e. $f_{cu} = 25$ N/mm^2. The breadth of the beam should fit the width of the brickwork, i.e. $b_v = 230$ mm, and the depth should fit the depth of the brick courses, i.e. 75, 150, 225, 300 etc. mm. The depth of the beam to limit deflection is approximately span/20 = 3E3/20 = 150 mm, which may be too close to the limit, therefore use $h = 225$ mm. Moderate exposure cover = 35 mm, and the density of brickwork $\rho = 1900$ kg/m^3.

Loads

Brickwork

$$W = HLb\rho g = 2 \times 3 \times 0.23 \times 1900 \times 9.81 \times 1E{-}3 = 25.72 \text{ kN}$$

Self-weight of beam

$$W_{sw} = Lbh\rho g = 3 \times 0.23 \times 0.225 \times 2400 \times 9.81 \times 1E{-}3 = 3.66 \text{ kN}$$

Bending moment

$$M_{max} = \Sigma WL/8 = (25.72 + 3.66) \times 3/8 = 11.02 \text{ kN m}$$

At this stage the diameter of the tensile bar is required to determine the dimension d. Assume a bar diameter of 20 mm and if it is incorrect the subsequent modification is small.

$$d = 225 - \text{cover} - 0.5 \text{ (bar dia.)} = 225 - 35 - 20/2 = 180 \text{ mm}.$$

Bending factor (cl 3.4.4.4, Pt 1)

$$K = M/(bd^2 f_{cu}) = 11.02E6/(230 \times 180^2 \times 25) = 0.0592 < 0.156$$

therefore compression reinforcement is not required.
   Lever arm (cl 3.4.4.4, Pt 1)

$$z = d[0.5 + \sqrt{(0.25 - K/0.9)}]$$
$$= 180 \times [0.5 + \sqrt{(0.25 - 0.0592/0.9)}] = 167.3 \text{ mm}$$

but not greater than $0.95d = 0.95 \times 180 = 171 > 167.3$ mm.
Use $z = 167.3$ mm.
   Area of tensile steel (cl 3.4.4.4, Pt 1)

$$A_s = M/(0.87f_y z) = 11.02E6/(0.87 \times 460 \times 167.3) = 164.6 \text{ mm}^2$$

Use 2T 12 (226 mm^2)
   Percentage steel

$$= 100A_s/(bh) = 100 \times 226/(230 \times 225) = 0.437\% > 0.13\% \text{ (min)}$$

therefore satisfactory (cl 3.12.5.3, Table 3.27, Pt 1).
   Try section 230 mm wide $\times$ 225 mm deep with 2T 12.

Shear

Design shear stress at the support (cl 3.4.5.2, Pt 1)

$$v = V/(b_v d) = (25.72 + 3.66)E3/(2 \times 230 \times 180) = 0.355 \text{ N/mm}^2$$

Maximum design shear stress (cl 3.4.5.2, Pt 1)

$$v_u = 0.8\sqrt{f_{cu}} = 0.8\sqrt{25} = 4 \text{ N/mm}^2 < 5 \text{ N/mm}^2,$$

therefore section is not too small.
   Design shear stress for a singly reinforced concrete beam (cl 3.4.5.4, Pt 1)

$$v_c = k_1 k_2 0.79 [100A_s/(b_v d)]^{1/3}(400/d)^{1/4}/\gamma_m$$
$$= 1 \times 1 \times 0.79 \times [100 \times 226/(230 \times 180)]^{1/3}(400/180)^{1/4}/1.25$$
$$= 0.631 \text{ N/mm}^2$$

$$100A_s/(b_v d) = 100 \times 226/(230 \times 180) = 0.546\% < 3\%.$$

   Design shear stress for a singly reinforced concrete beam without shear reinforcement (cl 3.4.5.3, Table 3.8, Pt 1)

$$0.5v_c = 0.5 \times 0.631 = 0.315 \text{ N/mm}^2$$

$v(0.355) > 0.5v_c(0.315)$ N/mm^2, therefore consider redesign.
   There are three alternatives at this stage in design:

(i)   use shear reinforcement
(ii)   increase overall depth h to 300 mm
(iii) increase the percentage of tensile steel.

If the percentage of tensile steel is increased to 2T 16($A_s = 402$ mm^2), then repeating the design shear stress calculation

$$v_c = 1 \times 1 \times 0.79 \times [100 \times 402/(230 \times 180)]^{1/3}(400/180)^{1/4}/1.25$$
$$= 0.764 \text{ N/mm}^2$$

and

$$0.5v_c = 0.5 \times 0.764 = 0.382 \text{ N/mm}^2$$

$0.5v_c(0.382) > v(0.355) \text{ N/mm}^2$, therefore satisfactory.
   Try section 230 mm wide $\times$ 225 mm deep with 2T 16.

Deflection

Tensile stress in the steel (cl 3.4.6.5, Table 3.11, Pt 1) with $\beta = 1$

$$f_s = (5/8)f_y(A_{s,req}/A_{s,prov})/\beta_b$$
$$= 5/8 \times 460 \times 164.6/402 = 117.7 \text{ N/mm}^2$$

Modification factor for tension reinforcement (cl 3.4.6.5, Table 3.11, Pt 1)

$$= 0.55 + (477 - f_s)/[120(0.9 + M/bd^2)]$$
$$= 0.55 + (477 - 117.7)/[120 \times (0.9 + 11.02E6/(230 \times 180^2)]$$
$$= 1.81 < 2.$$

Deflection limits (cl 3.4.6.5, Table 3.11, Pt 1)
Design span/effective depth ratio $= 20 \times 1.81 = 36.2$
Actual ratio $= 3E3/180 = 16.67 < 36.2$, therefore satisfactory.
Use 230×225 mm section with 2T 16.
   A further economy is to use mild-steel reinforcement, i.e. 2R 16 as tension reinforcement.

13.2 Continuous beam

The beam is to be simply supported and continuous over three spans of 6 m, 8 m, and 6 m. The width of the bearing at the supports is 350 mm. The beam is to be designed to carry uniformly distributed characteristic dead and imposed loads of 40 kN/m and 32 kN/m respectively on all three spans. The dead load includes an allowance of 4.5 kN/m for the beam itself. The exposure conditions are severe and the beam must have a fire resistance of 2 h. It is to be built into brickwork and the headroom should be as generous as possible. In no case should the overall depth exceed 8 courses of brickwork. The available aggregates are washed sand and gravel with a maximum size of 20 mm.

Loading

The following three symmetrical load cases must be considered (see Section 4.5.2).

Case 1	$W_1(\text{max})$	$W_2(\text{max})$	$W_1(\text{max})$
Case 2	$W_1(\text{max})$	$W_2(\text{min})$	$W_1(\text{max})$
Case 3	$W_1(\text{min})$	$W_2(\text{max})$	$W_1(\text{min})$

where W_1 and W_2 are the total loads on the spans, as shown in Fig. 13.1.
   The maximum and minimum values of the distributed loads are:

$$w(\text{max}) = 40 \times 1.4 + 32 \times 1.6 = 107.2 \text{ kN/m}$$
$$w(\text{min}) = 40 \text{ kN/m}$$

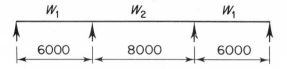

Fig. 13.1   General arrangement and loads.

giving total loads of

$$W_1(\text{max}) = 6 \times 107.2 = 643 \text{ kN}$$
$$W_1(\text{min}) = 6 \times 40 = 240 \text{ kN}$$
$$W_2(\text{max}) = 8 \times 107.2 = 858 \text{ kN}$$
$$W_2(\text{min}) = 8 \times 40 = 320 \text{ kN}$$

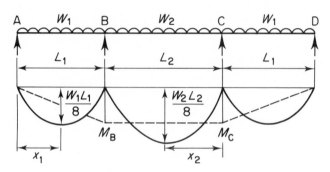

Fig. 13.2   Bending- moment diagram.

Analysis

Since the beam is simply supported, the maximum bending moment in all the spans is the negative moment at the internal supports. A uniform section will therefore be designed. For symmetrical load cases the three-moment theorem can be adapted to give a simple formula for the support moment. All other results can then be obtained from statics, considering each span as a free body. For the two spans AB and BC, referring to Fig. 13.2,

$$M_A L_1 + 2M_B(L_1 + L_2) + M_C L_2 = -6A_1 x_1/L_1 - 6A_2 x_2/L_2 \tag{13.1}$$

where
A_1 and A_2 are the areas of the free bending-moment diagrams for AB and BC
x_1 and x_2 are the distances from the centroids of these areas to the supports A and C.
   In general

$$A = 2L/3 \times WL/8$$
$$x = L/2$$

Furthermore, since the load cases are symmetrical $M_B = M_C$ and $M_A = 0$. Equation (13.1) therefore reduces to

$$M_B = M_C = -(W_1 L_1^2 + W_2 L_2^2)/4(2L_1 + 3L_2) \tag{13.2}$$

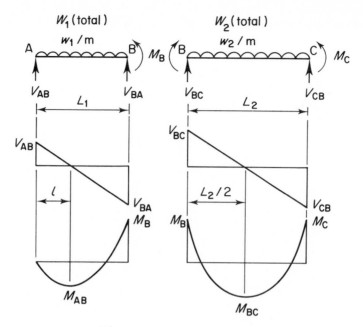

Fig. 13.3   Free body diagrams.

From statics, considering Fig. 13.3,

$$V_{AB} = W_1/2 + M_B/L_1 \tag{13.3}$$
$$V_{BA} = W_1/2 - M_B/L_1 \tag{13.4}$$

and

$$V_{AB} + V_{BA} = W_1 \text{ (check)} \tag{13.5}$$
$$l \text{ (to the point of zero shear)} = V_{AB}/w_1 \tag{13.6}$$

Hence

$$M_{AB} = V_{AB}l - w_1 l^2/2 \tag{13.7}$$
$$V_{BC} = V_{CB} = W_2/2 \tag{13.8}$$
$$M_{BC} = W_2L_2/8 + M_B \tag{13.9}$$

The results for each load case are tabulated below.

Item	Case 1	Case 2	Case 3
w_1	107.2	107.2	40
W_1	643	643	240
w_2	107.2	40	107.2
W_2	858	320	858
M_B	−542	−303	−441
V_{AB}	231	271	46
V_{BA}	412	372	194
l	2.157	2.529	1.160
M_{AB}	249	343	27
V_{BC}	429	160	429
M_{BC}	316	17	417

The elastic envelope for bending moments is given in Fig. 13.4.

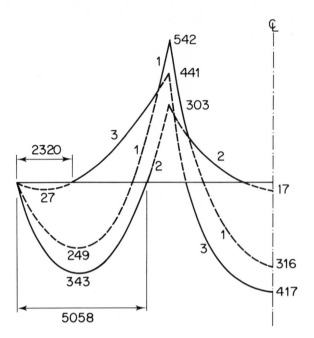

Fig. 13.4   Elastic bending moments.

Redistribution

At this stage the designer has the choice of either designing to the elastic envelope or redistributing the moments in order to achieve a more uniform distribution of the reinforcement. In this problem M_B for all three load cases will be made equal to half the free bending moment on BC, i.e. ignoring signs,

$$M_B = W_2 L_2/16 = 858 \times 8/16 = 429 \text{ kN m}$$

The maximum reduction is from 542 kN m, i.e. 20.8% for case 1.

In order to maintain equilibrium the moments and shears at all other points must comply with Equations (13.3) to (13.9), as in follows.

Item	Case 1	Case 2	Case 3
M_B	−429	−429	−429
V_{AB}	250	250	48.5
V_{BA}	393	393	191.5
l	2.333	2.333	1.213
M_{AB}	292	292	29
V_{BC}	429	160	429
M_{BC}	429	−109	429

The design envelopes after redistribution are given in Fig. 13.5.

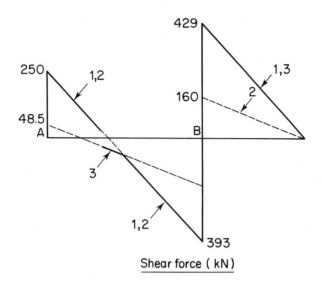

Shear force (kN)

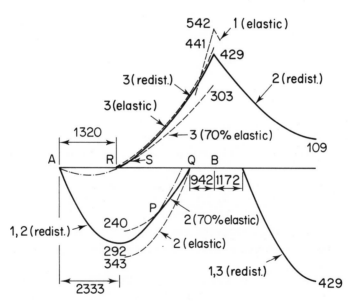

Fig. 13.5 Design envelopes.

On span AB the minimum 70% elastic rule applies, i.e. from P to Q for load case 2 and from R to S for load case 3. Point P is the intersection of the redistributed curve for load case 2 with a curve drawn from Q on the original elastic curve to a maximum of 240 kN m, i.e. 70% of 343 kN m. A similar method is used to determine points R and S for load case 3, although in this case the effect is negligible.

The amount of redistribution must be taken into account in the design of sections, as follows:

M_B	$\beta_b = 429/542 = 0.79$	$x/d \leqslant \beta_b - 0.4 = 0.39$
M_{AB} (bottom)	$\beta_b = 292/343 = 0.85$	$x/d \leqslant 0.45$
M_{AB} (top)	$\beta_b = 429/441 = 0.97$	$x/d \leqslant 0.5$
M_{BC} (bottom)	increase $< 10\%$	$x/d \leqslant 0.5$
M_{BC} (top)	increase $> 10\%$	$x/d \leqslant 0.6$
P to Q	$\beta_b = 0.7$	$x/d \leqslant 0.3$

Cover

Cover is normally specified on drawings as nominal cover to the outermost reinforcement. Factors affecting cover are durability, fire resistance, and the requirements for crack control. Since crack widths are smallest when the cover is minimal the smallest cover consistent with the other requirements will be selected from Table 5.1 and 5.8 (Tables 3.4, Pt 1 and 4.3, Pt 2).

Fire resistance 2 h – Minimum cover to main steel = 50 mm, i.e. 40 mm nominal with 10 mm links.

Severe exposure – three nominal covers: 25, 30, 40 mm.

Since the cover for fire resistance can be increased by an external coating, a nominal cover of 30 mm will be selected with 10 mm of lightweight insulation sprayed on after construction. The concrete specification necessary for durability is therefore:

max. free water/cement ratio – 0.50
min. cement content – 350 kg/m^3
lowest grade – C45

Trial section

The basic span/depth ratio for a continuous beam is 26. Assume 20 to allow for possible modification factors, giving an effective depth of 400 mm for the centre span. Assuming 32 mm main reinforcement and 10 mm links, the overall depth required is 456 mm. Rounding up to the nearest multiple of 75 mm gives 525 mm, i.e. 7 courses of brickwork, which is below the specified maximum. A similar estimate of the width is $h/2 =$ say 300 mm. This width satisfies the requirements for fire resistance (200 mm) and also for lateral stability without lateral supports, i.e. that the span should not exceeed $60b_c$, or $250b_c^2/d$ if less. The first condition is obviously satisfied, and the second also provided $d \leqslant 2800$ mm.

Type 2 deformed bars in high-yield steel will be specified for the main reinforcement, but in order to keep the corner distance to the main bars to a minimum (see *Crack control*) mild steel will be used for the links.

Main reinforcement

Based on the above section:

$d = 525 - 30 - 10 - 16 = 469$ mm
$bd^2f_{cu} = 300 \times (469)^2 \times 45 = 2.97\text{E}9$
$bdf_{cu}/f_y = 13.8\text{E}3$

The maximum moment is at B, i.e. $M_B = 429$ kN m, $x/d \leqslant 0.39$

$M/bd^2f_{cu} = 0.145$

Using Graph No. 6 ($d'/d = 0.15$)

$A_s = 0.205 \times 13.8\text{E3} = 2829$ mm^2

Nominal width available $= 300 - 2 \times 30 - 2 \times 10 = 220$ mm.
Minimum clear distance between bars ($\phi \leqslant 25$ mm) $= h_{agg} + 5 = 25$ mm
$(\phi > 25$ mm) $=$ bar size $= 32$ mm

The maximum number of bars that can be accommodated in a single row is therefore 3T32 or 4T25. For 2829 mm^2 use 4T32 (3217 mm^2), or 6T25 (2945 mm^2). Both require two rows, but 6T25 gives the greater effective depth and is more economical. However, this reinforcement is in the top of the beam and the maximum space available for a vibrator between the middle bars is

$220 - 6 \times 25 = 70$ mm

which is insufficient (75 mm clear minimum). Since the maximum headroom is required the width of the section will be increased to 325 mm and the reinforcement arranged as in Fig. 13.6, giving a clear distance between the middle bars of 95 mm.

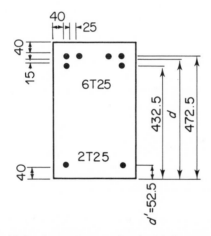

Fig. 13.6 Arrangement of main reinforcement.

Recalculating on this basis:

d (top row) $= 525 - 52.5 = 472.5$ mm
d (second row) $= 472.5 - 15 - 25 = 432.5$ mm
$d = (4 \times 472.5 + 2 \times 432.5)/6 = 459$ mm
d' (assuming 2T25) $= 40 + 12.5 = 52.5$ mm
$d'/d = 0.114$ – use Graph No. 6 ($d'/d = 0.15$)
$bd^2f_{cu} = 3.08\text{E9}$, $bdf_{cu}/f_y = 14.6\text{E3}$, $M/bd^2f_{cu} = 0.14$

From Graph No. 6, using $x/d = 0.39$

$$A_s = 0.194 \times 14.6E3 = 2832 \text{ mm}^2, \quad A_s' = 0.018 \times 14.6E3 = 263 \text{ mm}^2$$

6T25 is therefore adequate tension reinforcement. Compression reinforcement will be provided by continuing tension reinforcement.

Shear reinforcement

Span BC:

$$\text{Max. shear force} = V_{BC} = 429 \text{ kN}$$
$$b_v d = 325 \times 459 = 149.2E3 \text{ mm}^2$$
$$0.8\sqrt{f_{cu}} = 0.8\sqrt{45} = 5.4 \text{ N/mm}^2, \text{ i.e. } > 5 \text{ N/mm}^2$$

Hence

$$v_u = 5 \text{ N/mm}^2$$
$$v_{BC} = 429E3/149.2E3 = 2.88 < 5 \text{ N/mm}^2$$

The section is therefore large enough,

$$v_c = (f_{cu}/25)^{1/3} \times 0.79(100A_s/b_v d)^{1/3} \times (400/d)^{1/4} \times 1/\gamma_m$$
$$f_{cu} > 40 \text{ N/mm}^2, \text{ so } (f_{cu}/25)^{1/3} = (40/25)^{1/3} = 1.170$$
$$(100A_s/b_v d) = (100 \times 2945/149.2E3) = 1.974, \text{ i.e. } < 3$$
$$400/d < 1, \text{ so take as } 1$$

Hence

$$v_c = 1.170 \times 0.79 \times (1.974)^{1/3}/1.25 = 0.928 \text{ N/mm}^2$$

Using the simplified approach shear reinforcement is determined at distance d from the support face, i.e. $459 + 175 = 634$ mm along BC.
Hence

$$V = 429(4000 - 634)/4000 = 361 \text{ kN}$$

and

$$v = 361E3/149.2E3 = 2.420 \text{ N/mm}^2$$
$$A_{sv} \geq b_v s_v (v - v_c)/0.87 f_y$$

For mild steel $f_y = 250$ N/mm^2 and, assuming single 10 mm links (2 bars), $A_{sv} = 157$ mm^2. Hence

$$s_v \leq 157 \times 0.87 \times 250/325(2.420 - 0.928) = 70.4 \text{ mm between centres}$$

which is insufficient for the insertion of a vibrator. Double links will therefore be used at a spacing of 140 mm.

Deflection

Basic span/depth ratio $= 26$
Span/depth ratio provided $= 8000/459 = 17.4$

Even with the worst modification factors the maximum allowable span/depth ratio is not likely to be less than $26 \times 0.75 = 19.5$, so the deflection requirements are satisfied. The reader is invited to confirm that if the modification factors are calculated as described in Chapter 5, they are as follows:

for compression reinforcement 1.19
for tension reinforcement 0.75

i.e. maximum span/depth ratio $= 26 \times 1.19 \times 0.75 = 23.2$

Curtailment of main reinforcement

If all the reinforcement is based on 25 mm bars, useful theoretical curtailment points will be where the moments correspond to 4 and 2 bars respectively at an effective depth of 472.5 mm.

$$bd^2 f_{cu} = 3.27\text{E}9$$
$$bdf_{cu}/f_y = 15.0\text{E}3$$
$$A_s f_y/bdf_{cu}:$$
$$\quad\quad 4 \text{ bars} = 1964/15.0\text{E}3 = 0.13$$
$$\quad\quad 2 \text{ bars} = 0.065$$

Using Graph No. 1 (singly reinforced beams)

$$M/bd^2 f_{cu}:$$
$$\quad\quad 4 \text{ bars} = 0.098, \text{ i.e. } M = 320 \text{ kN m}$$
$$\quad\quad 2 \text{ bars} = 0.052, \text{ i.e. } M = 170 \text{ kN m}$$

The graph shows that since x/d does not exceed 0.3, no compression reinforcement is actually required other than to support the links.

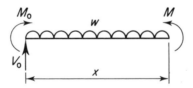

Fig. 13.7 Loading for determination of theoretical curtailment points.

Referring to Fig. 13.7, the moment at curtailment is given by

$$M = V_0 x - wx^2/2 + M_0$$

from which the distance from the left-hand support to the theoretical curtailment point may be obtained, thus

$$x = [V_0 \pm \sqrt{\{V_0^2 - 2w(M - M_0)\}}]/w \quad\quad\quad (13.10)$$

Bars must be extended beyond the theoretical curtailment points by the tension anchorage bond length given by Equation (8.3), thus

$$l = \phi_e \times 0.87 f_y/(4\beta\sqrt{f_{cu}})$$

where β = 0.5 for type 2 deformed bars; hence

$$l = 25 \times 0.87 \times 460/(4 \times 0.5\sqrt{45}) = 746 - \text{say } 750 \text{ mm}$$

Since this exceeds the minimum anchorage length (d or 12ϕ) it is acceptable. The design curtailment points, obtained as described above, are shown in Fig. 13.8. The design dimensions are all given from the same point (support B) to facilitate checking on site, and have been rounded conservatively to multiples of 50 mm.

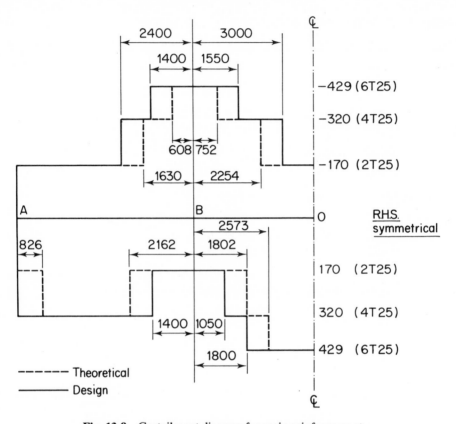

Fig. 13.8   Curtailment diagram for main reinforcement.

Anchorage at laps and simply supported ends

Cover = 40 mm < 2ϕ.
Hence tension lap on corner bars = $2 \times 750 = 1500$ mm
      compression lap = 750 mm
Cover > 1.5ϕ, so no restriction on the spacing of the links is required at the laps.

Since the overall length of the beam is greater than the length of a 25 mm bar laps will be provided where the curtailment diagram indicates two bars, i.e. a tension lap in the top of the beam at mid-span on BC and a compression lap in the bottom of the beam at B.

At simply supported ends A and D:
    anchorage length required from support centre $= 12\phi = 300$ mm
    internal bend radius r for a 25 mm high-yield bar $= 4\phi = 100$ mm
    effective anchorage of 90° bend = lesser of $4r$ (16ϕ) or 12ϕ, i.e. 12ϕ
    space available $= 175$ mm
    space required $= r + \phi + \text{cover} = 100 + 25 + 30 = 155$ mm

A 90° bend will therefore be satisfactory. Bends are needed only on the outer bars because the distance from the end to the theoretical cutailment point of the inner bars exceeds 750 min.

Crack control

Since the cover to the main reinforcement does not exceed 50 mm the maximum clear distance between bars may be obtained from Appendix A2.5

$$s_{max} = 47\,000/f_s \leqslant 300$$

where f_s is the service stress given by

$$f_s = 5f_yA_{s,req}/8A_{s,prov}\beta_b$$

Putting $f_y = 460$ N/mm^2 gives

$$s_{max} = 163\beta_b\alpha \leqslant 300 \tag{13.11}$$

where
$\alpha = A_s(\text{provided})/A_s(\text{required}) \simeq \text{moment of resistance/design moment}$
$\beta_b = \text{moment after redistribution/moment before redistribution}$, β_b is not restricted to a maximum of 1.0 for crack control.

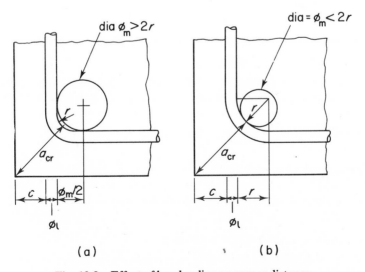

Fig. 13.9 Effect of bend radius on corner distance.

In order to determine the corner distance many designers ignore the effect of the bends in the links, as in Example 5.3, where the conditions are assumed to be as in Fig. 13.9(a) and the corner distance is given by

$$a_{cr} = \sqrt{2} \times (c + \phi_l + \phi_m/2) - \phi_m/2 \tag{13.12}$$

where

> ϕ_l is the diameter of the link
> ϕ_m is the diameter of the main bar

This formula is correct when ϕ_m is greater than or equal to twice the internal radius r of the bend in the link, i.e. (assuming standard bends) when

> $\phi_m \geqslant 4\phi_l$ for mild-steel links
> $\phi_m \geqslant 6\phi_l$ for high-yield steel links <20 mm dia.

Otherwise the result obtained is less than the true corner distance which is at least as great as that shown in Fig. 13.9(b), i.e.

$$a_{cr} = \sqrt{2} \times (c + \phi_l + r) - r \tag{13.13}$$

Since laps will be needed at points B and C in the bottom steel, and at mid-span of BC in the top steel, the bars will not actually be curtailed to less than 4 bars. The most critical points are therefore B and C at the top of the beam, where

> $\beta_b = 0.79$
> $\alpha = 2945/2832 = 1.04$

Hence

> $s_{max} = 163 \times 0.79 \times 1.04 = 134$ mm

and

> Maximum corner distance $= 134/2 = 67$ mm

Actual clear distance $= 95$ mm
Actual corner distance – using Equation (13.13) –

$$a_{cr} = \sqrt{2} \times (30 + 10 + 20) - 20 = 65 \text{ mm}$$

The requirements for crack control are therefore satisfied.

Note that at point P on AB ($\beta_b = 0.7$) the corner distance would have been excessive if the main reinforcement had been curtailed to two bars. In some cases where beams are subjected to heavy shear it is difficult to achieve crack control without increasing the tension reinforcement.

Curtailment of links

Consider first the shear force at distance d from the support face at A.

> $A_s = 4T25$ (1964 mm^2), $d = 472.5$ mm, $b_v d = 153.6E3$ mm^2
> distance from A $= 175 + 472.5 = 648$ mm
> $V = 250 - 643 \times 648/6000 = 181$ kN
> $v = 181E3/153.6E3 = 1.179$ N/mm^2

$100A_s/b_vd = 100 \times 1964/153.6E3 = 1.279$
$v_c = 1.170 \times 0.79 \times (1.279)^{1/3}/1.25 = 0.803 \text{ N/mm}^2$
$A_{sv} \geqslant 325s_v(1.179 - 0.803)/(0.87 \times 250) = 0.562s_v$

Using single 10 mm links (2 bars), $A_{sv} = 157 \text{ mm}^2$.

Hence

$s_v \leqslant 157/0.562 = 279 - \text{say } 275 \text{ mm}$

For simplicity, only double links spaced at 140 mm and single links spaced at 275 mm will be used. More variations in spacing would save steel, but the extra costs of detailing, fixing, and checking could outweigh the saving in the cost of steel. The curtailment points for the double links occur where the shear force drops to 181 kN. The distances from B are as follows:

On AB: $6000(393 - 181)/643 = 1978 - \text{say } 2000 \text{ mm}$
On BC: $4000(429 - 181)/429 = 2312 - \text{say } 2350 \text{ mm}$

Figure 13.8 confirms that there are at least 4T25 tension bars (on which the spacing of 275 mm is based) at the curtailment points. The numbers of links required are as follows:

Near B and C: $4350/140 + 1 = 32$ double links, i.e. 64 single links in pairs
On AB and CD: $(4175 - 75)/275 = 15$ (assuming that the first link is at 75 mm from the end)
At mid-span on BC: $3300/275 - 1 = 11$

The results are summarised in Fig. 13.10.

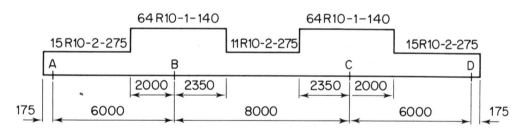

Fig. 13.10 Link curtailment diagram.

Links for containment of compression reinforcement

Maximum spacing $= 12 \times 25 = 300$
Minimum diameter $= 25/4 < 10 \text{ mm}$

The shear reinforcement is therefore adequate for this purpose.

Reinforcement details

Complete details of all the reinforcement are given in Fig. 13.11.

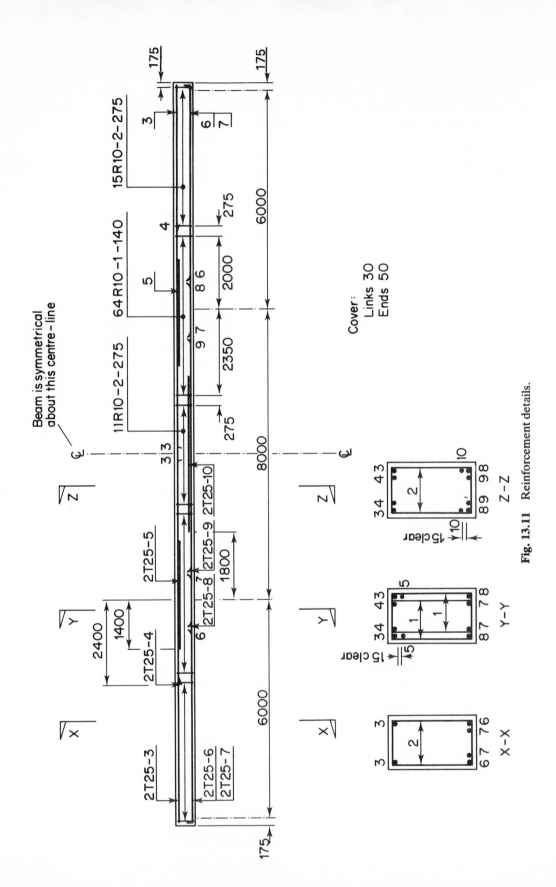

Fig. 13.11 Reinforcement details.

13.3   Pad foundation for a column

A column has a section 600 mm by 300 mm and transmits the following loads to the foundation

	Axial (kN)	M_x (kN m)	M_y (kN m)
Service loads	2000	200	100
Design ultimate loads	3000	300	150

The moments could be applied in either sense.

Design a suitable pad foundation given the following data.

Soil:
   stony clay with allowable bearing pressure 210 kN/m^2
   non-aggressive to concrete

Aggregate:
   washed gravel – max. size 20 mm

Column starter bars:
   5T32, type 2, in each long face of the column.

Size of base

The base is subjected to biaxial bending, but a first approximation can be obtained by adding the two service moments together and using Graph No. 13. That is,

$$N = 2000 \text{ kN}$$
$$M = 200 + 100 = 300 \text{ kN m}$$
$$M/N = 0.150, \ N^2/M\sigma_{max} = 63.5$$

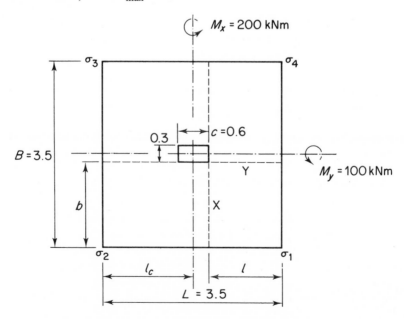

Fig. 13.12   Base dimensions and moments.

For a square base $\alpha/\beta = 63.5/0.150 = 423$

From the graph $r = 1.7$ which is satisfactory, and $\alpha = 23.0$.

Hence $L = B = \alpha M/N = 3.450$ m – say 3.5 m

Since the moments can act in either sense, assume that they act in directions that make σ_1 the maximum, as in Fig. 13.12.

$$BL = (3.5)^2 = 12.25 \text{ m}^2$$
$$Z_x = Z_y = (3.5)^3/6 = 7.146 \text{ m}^3$$
$$N/BL = 2000/12.25 = 163 \text{ kN/m}^2$$
$$M_x/Z_x = 200/7.146 = 28 \text{ kN/m}^2$$
$$M_y/Z_y = 100/7.146 = 14 \text{ kN/m}^2$$
$$\sigma_1 = 163 + 28 + 14 = 205 \text{ kN/m}^2$$

Since $\sigma_1 < 210$ the base size is satisfactory.

Durability

As the soil is not aggressive the exposure is classed as *moderate*, for which the minimum concrete grade is C35 and the nominal cover is 35 mm.

Bending moments on critical sections X and Y

The bearing pressures due to the *design ultimate loads* must now be calculated.

$$N/BL = 3000/12.25 = 245 \text{ kN/m}^2$$
$$M_x/Z_x = 300/7.146 = 42 \text{ kN/m}^2$$
$$M_y/Z_y = 150/7.146 = 21 \text{ kN/m}^2$$
$$\sigma_1 = 245 + 42 + 21 = 308 \text{ kN/m}^2$$
$$\sigma_2 = 245 - 42 + 21 = 224 \text{ kN/m}^2$$
$$\sigma_3 = 245 - 42 - 21 = 182 \text{ kN/m}^2$$
$$\sigma_4 = 245 + 42 - 21 = 266 \text{ kN/m}^2$$

From Equations (11.10) and (11.11) the bending moments on the critical sections are

$$M_X = \tfrac{1}{4}Bl^2[\sigma_1 + \sigma_4 - l(\sigma_1 + \sigma_4 - \sigma_2 - \sigma_3)/3L]$$
$$M_Y = \tfrac{1}{4}Lb^2[\sigma_1 + \sigma_2 - b(\sigma_1 + \sigma_2 - \sigma_3 - \sigma_4)/3B]$$

where

$$l = (3.5 - 0.6)/2 = 1.45 \text{ m}$$
$$b = (3.5 - 0.3)/2 = 1.60 \text{ m}$$

Hence

$$M_X = 1.013\text{E3 kN m}, \quad M_Y = 1.163\text{E3 kN m}.$$

Minimum thickness of base

The minimum thickness is determined by considering punching shear around the column perimeter

$v_u = 0.8\sqrt{f_{cu}} \leqslant 5$ N/mm$^2 = 0.8\sqrt{35} = 4.73$ N/mm^2
Perimeter $= 2(600 + 300) = 1800$ mm
$v \leqslant 3000\text{E}3/1800d_{min} = 4.73$

Hence

$d_{min} = 352$ mm

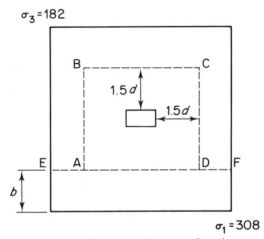

$\sigma_3 = 182$

$\sigma_1 = 308$

Fig. 13.13   Critical perimeter and section.

Shear stress on a critical perimeter or section

The critical perimeter is $1.5d$ from the column face, i.e. ABCDA in Fig. 13.13. Since the bending moment on section Y was greater than on section X the shear stress on Section EF parallel to section Y should also be considered. Neither shear stress should exceed v_c, the design shear stress for the concrete. Since v_c cannot yet be determined, the procedure is to try various effective depths until a satisfactory section is obtained to resist both bending and shear. From experience v_c will probably be between 0.4 and 0.5 N/mm^2.
   Try $d = 400$ mm, $1.5d = 600$ mm, i.e. 0.6 m

Perimeter $= (0.6 + 2 \times 0.6)$ by $(0.3 + 2 \times 0.6) = 1.8$ m by 1.5 m
$V = N - \sigma_{av} \times$ area ABCDA
$\sigma_{av} = 245$ kN/m^2

Hence

$V = 3000 - 245 \times 1.8 \times 1.5 = 2339$ kN
$v = 2339\text{E}3/[2 \times (1800 + 1500) \times 400] = 0.886$ N/mm^2 which is too large.

After other trials it was found that a depth of 550 mm gives a critical perimeter of

1.95 m by 2.25 m and a shear stress v on the perimeter of 0.417 N/mm². From Equation (11.13) the shear force on section EF is given by

$$V = \tfrac{1}{2}Lb[\sigma_1 + \sigma_2 - b(\sigma_1 + \sigma_2 - \sigma_3 - \sigma_4)/2B]$$

where

$$b = (3.5 - 1.95)/2 = 0.775 \text{ m}$$

Hence

$$V = 3.5 \times 0.775/2 \times [308 + 224 - 0.775(308 + 224 - 182 - 266)/(2 \times 3.5)] = 708 \text{ kN}$$
$$v = 708\text{E}3/(3500 \times 550) = 0.368 < 0.417 \text{ N/mm}^2$$

The design shear stress is therefore 0.417 N/mm².

Tension reinforcement – High-yield steel will be specified

Considering section Y

$$bd^2f_{cu} = 3500 \times 550^2 \times 35 = 37.06\text{E}9$$
$$bdf_{cu}/f_y = 3500 \times 550 \times 35/460 = 146.5\text{E}3$$
$$M_y/bd^2f_{cu} = 1.163\text{E}9/37.06\text{E}9 = 0.0314$$

From Graph No. 1

$$A_sf_y/bdf_{cu} = 0.040$$

Similarly, considering section X

$$M_x/bd^2f_{cu} = 1.013\text{E}9/37.06\text{E}9 = 0.027$$
$$A_sf_y/bdf_{cu} = 0.034$$

Design shear stress for the concrete

Taking an average value of the tension reinforcement,

$$100A_s/b_vd = 100 \times 35 \times (0.040 + 0.034)/(2 \times 460) = 0.282$$
$$v_c = (f_{cu}/25)^{1/3} \times 0.79(100A_s/b_vd)^{1/3} \times 1/1.25$$
$$= (35/25)^{1/3} \times 0.79(0.282)^{1/3} \times 1/1.25 = 0.464 \text{ N/mm}^2$$

Therefore $v < v_c$, so no shear reinforcement is required.

Distribution of reinforcement

The requirements of cl 3.11.3.2, Pt 1 must be checked (see Section 11.3.5 and refer to Fig. 13.12 for reinforcement at right angles to section Y).

$$3c/4 + 9d/4 = (3 \times 600 + 9 \times 550)/4 = 1688$$
$$l_c = 1750 > 1688$$

Hence two thirds of the tension reinforcement must be in a band $1.5d$ from the column face, i.e. in a band 2.250 m wide

$$A_s = 0.040 \times 146.5\text{E}3 = 5860 \text{ mm}^2$$

Within the band

$$A_s = 5860 \times 2/3 = 3907 \text{ mm}^2, \text{ i.e. } 3907/2.250 = 1736 \text{ mm}^2/\text{m}$$
$$100A_s/bd = 0.316$$

For crack control (see Chapter 5), since the reinforcement within the band exceeds 0.3%, the clear spacing between tension bars $\leqslant 160/0.316 = 506$ mm. Using the bar tables in Appendix A1, 20 mm bars at 180 mm spacing (1746 mm^2/m) will be satisfactory; and, since the band width is only just less than two thirds of the total width, this spacing will be used across the whole width.

The above reinforcement will be placed in the bottom layer. The same reinforcement will also be used in the upper layer because M_x is only slightly smaller than M_y. The number of bars, assuming end cover = 75 mm, is

$$(3500 - 150 - 20)/180 + 1 = 20$$

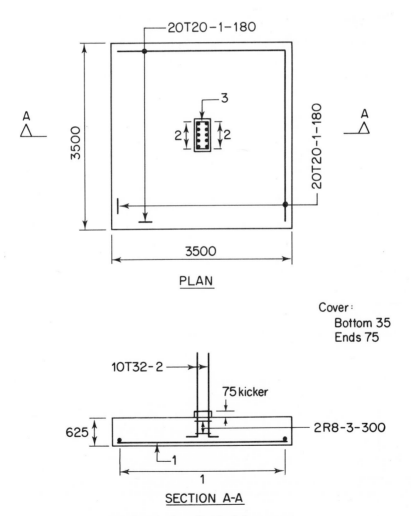

Fig. 13.14 Details of reinforcement.

Note that since the band width corresponds with the edge of the shear perimeter the enhanced values of $100A_s/bd$ may be used in the calculation of v_c if necessary.

The detail of the base is given in Fig. 13.14. The base is constructed to include a small kicker of 75 mm, through which the column starter bars protrude. The column reinforcement starts at the kicker, which is used to locate the formwork for the column. The starter bars are located during construction by attaching them with wire ties to one or more links within the base. The size of the links is the same as those in the column. At the bottom the starter bars conclude in a standard bend, as shown, which enables them to rest conveniently on the tension reinforcement.

The overall depth of the base is

$$h = 550 + 20 + 35 = 605 - \text{say } 625 \text{ mm}.$$

13.4   Flat slab

The layout of a 9-panel flat slab without dropheads is given in Fig. 13.15. The slab is 200 mm thick and carries an imposed load of 5 kN/m^2. The columns are 400 mm square and 3500 mm high. Prepare a design for the bays B1C4 and 2D3A, using grade 30 concrete and grade 460 steel.

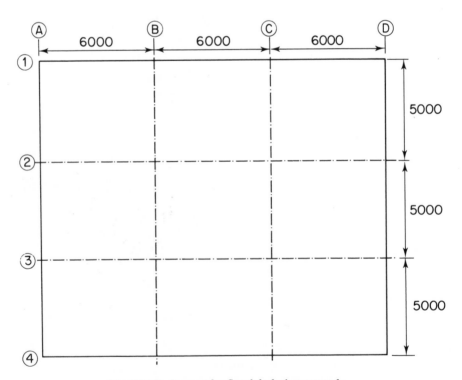

Fig. 13.15   Layout for flat slab design example.

Analysis

Total load, n, $= 1.4G_k + 1.6Q_k$
$= 1.4 \times 0.2 \times 25 + 1.6 \times 5$
$= 15.0 \text{ kN/m}^2.$

(a) Bay B1C4

Line load $= n \times (\text{bay width}) = 15 \times 6 = 90 \text{ kN/m}.$

The bending-moment diagram for the slab which has been obtained by analysing the subframe containing the floor and the remote ends of the columns have been assumed fixed. All spans are under full loading, and the results are given in Fig. 13.16(a).

The maximum redistribution that may be carried out is 20% (cl 3.5.2.3, Pt 1).

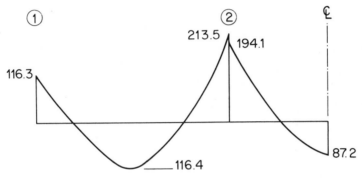

(a) BMD before any redistribution

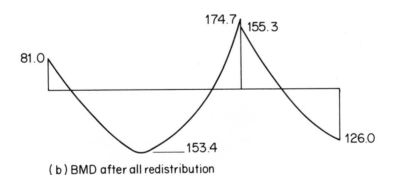

(b) BMD after all redistribution

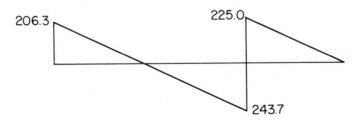

(c) SFD after all redistribution

Fig. 13.16 Analysis of slab B1C4.

The limit at edge columns depends on the moment that may be transferred to the edge columns $(M_{t,max})$

$$M_{t,max} = 0.15 b_e d^2 f_{cu} \tag{13.14}$$

The value of the effective width, b_e, to be taken is defined in Fig. 13.17. A restriction placed on the value of $M_{t,max}$ is that it shall not be less than 50% of the moment obtained from a frame analysis nor 70% of that from a grillage or finite-element analysis (cl 3.7.4.2, Pt 1).

Assuming $d = 150$, then from Case 3 of Fig. 13.17, $b_e = C_x + C_y$, then

$$\begin{aligned}
M_{t,max} &= 0.15(0.4 + 0.4) \times 0.15^2 \times 30 \times 1000 \\
&= 81 \text{ kN m},
\end{aligned}$$

which satisfies the 50% limit.

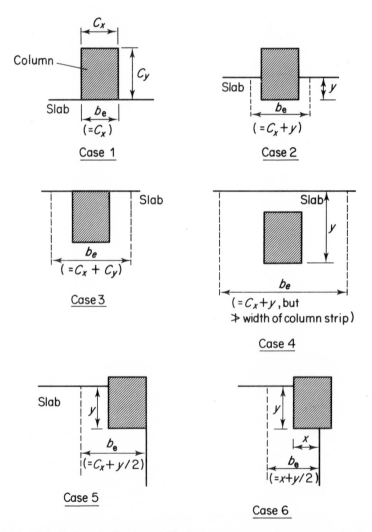

Fig. 13.17   Calculation of effective widths for moment transfer to external columns.

Thus the moment at the column may be reduced to 81 kN m and the mid-span moment increased accordingly. This has been done in Fig. 13.16(b). The resultant shear force diagram is given in Fig. 13.16(c).

(b) Bay 2D3A

Line load $= 15 \times 5 = 75$ kN/m.

A similar procedure is adopted here except that d is taken as 175 with $M_{t,max}$ as 110.3 kN m. The bending-moment and shear-force diagrams are plotted in Fig. 13.18.

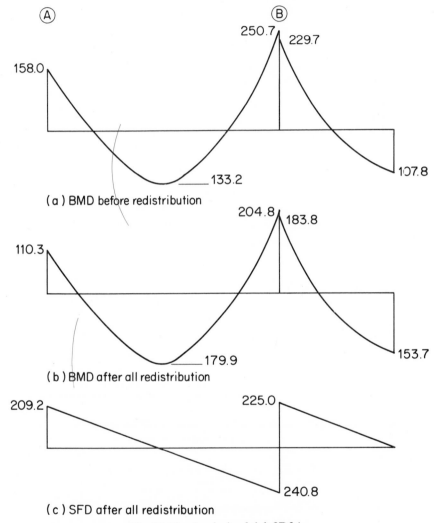

Fig. 13.18 Analysis of slab 2D3A.

Design

(a) Bending The slab must be divided into column and middle strips according to Fig. 13.19 (from Fig. 3.12, Pt 1). This is carried out in Figs. 13.20(a) and (b) for each of the bays.

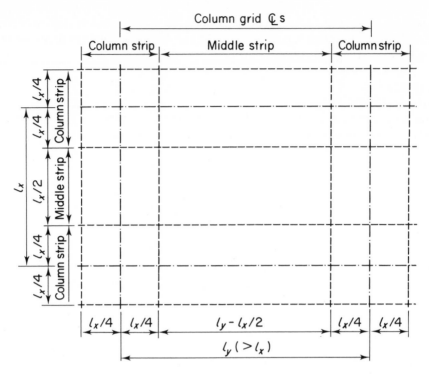

Fig. 13.19 Definition of column and middle strip for a flat slab without drops.

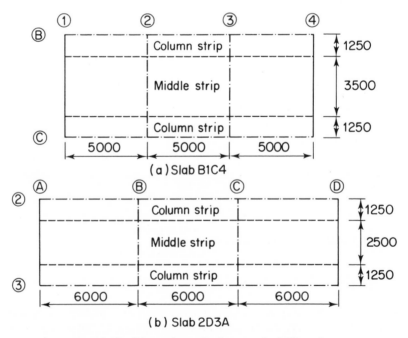

Fig. 13.20 Dimensions of column and middle strips.

The moments from the analysis should be apportioned to the column and middle strips using Table 13.1 (from Table 3.20, Pt 1). This, together with the flexural design, is carried out in Table 13.2.

Table 13.1 Distribution of moments between the column and middle strips

	Column strip	Middle strip
Negative moments	0.75	0.25
Positive moments	0.55	0.45

(b) Shear
Maximum shear stress (cl 3.4.5.2, Pt 1) $= 0.8(f_{cu})^{0.5}$
$$= 0.8(30)^{0.5}$$
$$= 4.38 \text{ N/mm}^2.$$

This is less than 5.0 N/mm^2.
The shear must be checked on successive perimeters $1.5d$ apart commencing $1.5d$ from the column face (Chapter 7).
The actual shear from the shear-force diagrams must be enhanced to allow for the effect of relative rotation between the slab and the column owing to the transfer of moment (M_t) to the column. Cl 3.7.6, Pt 1 deals with this and is summarised below.
For internal columns:

$$V_{eff} = V_t(1 + 1.5M_t/(V_t x)) \tag{13.15}$$

Note: for approximately equal spans in braced structures V_{eff} may be taken as $1.15V_t$.
For external columns:

$$V_{eff} = V_t(1.25 + 1.5M_t/(V_t x)) \tag{13.16}$$

Note: for approximately equal spans in braced structures V_{eff} may be taken as $1.4V_t$,

where

V_{eff} is the design shear force
V_t is the shear transferred to the column

x is the length of the side of the shear perimeter being considered.

Consider the column B2.

(i)   along grid line B.

$V_t = 469 \text{ kN}$, $M_t = 19.4 \text{ kN m}$ and $x = 0.4 + 2 \times 1.5 \times 0.15 = 0.85$ m.
$V_{eff} = 469(1 + 1.5 \times 19.4/(468 \times 0.85))$
$= 503 \text{ kN}.$

(ii)   along grid line 2.

$V_t = 466 \text{ kN}$, $M_t = 21.0 \text{ kN m}$, $x = 0.4 + 2 \times 1.5 \times 0.175 = 0.925$ m
$V_{eff} = 466(1 + 1.5 \times 21/(466 \times 0.925))$
$= 500 \text{ kN}.$

Table 13.2　Slab design for flexure

Bay	Column strip					Middle strip					Calculation
	End span			Interior span		End span			Interior span		
	Ext. col.	Mid-span	Int. col.	Int. col.	Mid-span	Ext. col.	Mid-span	Int. col.	Int. col.	Mid-span	
B1C4	60.8	84.4	131.0	116.5	69.3	20.2	69.0	43.7	38.8	56.7	M (kN m)
	0.036	0.050	0.078	0.069	0.041	0.009	0.029	0.018	0.016	0.024	M/bd^2f_{cu}
	0.044	0.061	0.099	0.087	0.050	0.010	0.035	0.022	0.020	0.029	$A_s f_y/bd f_{cu}$
	0.29	0.40	0.65	0.57	0.33	0.070	0.23	0.14	0.13	0.19	$100A_{s,req}/bd$
	1088	1500	2438	2138	1238	368*	1207	490	455	665	$A_{s,req}$ (mm^2)
	16	16	20	20	16	10	12	10	10	10	Bar diam. (mm)
	0.48	0.48	0.75	0.75	0.48	0.21	0.30	0.21	0.21	0.21	$100A_{s,prov}/bd$
2D3A	82.7	98.9	153.6	137.9	84.5	27.3	81.0	51.2	45.9	69.2	M (kN m)
	0.036	0.043	0.067	0.060	0.037	0.012	0.035	0.022	0.020	0.030	M/bd^2f_{cu}
	0.044	0.052	0.084	0.074	0.045	0.013	0.042	0.027	0.025	0.036	$A_s f_y/bd f_{cu}$
	0.29	0.34	0.55	0.48	0.29	0.09	0.27	0.18	0.16	0.23	$100A_{s,req}/bd$
	1269	1488	2407	2100	1269	394*	1181	788	700	1006	$A_{s,req}$ (mm^2)
	16	16	20	20	16	10	16	10	10	12	Bar diam. (mm)
	0.41	0.41	0.65	0.65	0.41	0.18	0.46	0.18	0.18	0.26	$100A_{s,prov}/bd$

Notes
(1) For bay B1C4 $d = 150$, and bay 2D3A $d = 175$.
(2) All strip widths 2500 mm except middle strips of bay B1C4 which is 3500.
(3) The design chart in Appendix B1.1 has been used.
(4) Minimum reinforcement (0.13bh/100) is indicated by an asterisk.
(5) Since from cl 3.12.2.7(a)(2) slab depth is not greater than 200 and steel grade is 460 no check on bar spacing is required, so a spacing of 250 mm has been used throughout.
(6) A minimum bar diameter has been set at 10 for practical purposes.

Thus the total shear on column B2 is 1003 kN, with a mean effective depth of $(150 + 175)/2 = 162$.

The ultimate shear should be checked at the column face (cl 3.7.6.4, Pt 1).

Taking u as the column perimeter, i.e. $u = 4 \times 400 = 1600$ mm

$$v = V/ud = 1003\text{E}3/(1600 \times 162)$$
$$= 3.87 \text{ N/mm}^2$$

This is less than the allowable of 4.38, and is therefore satisfactory.

At a shear perimeter 1.5d out from the column of $4 \times 400 + 8 \times 1.5 \times 162 = 3544$ mm,

$$v = V/ud$$
$$= 1003\text{E}3/(3544 \times 162)$$
$$= 1.75 \text{ N/mm}^2.$$

This is less than the maximum of 4.38 N/mm^2.

The allowable shear stress, v_c, may be calculated using the mean value of $100A_s/bd$ crossing the shear perimeter, that is

$$(0.65 + 0.75)/2 = 0.7\%$$

so from Equation (7.2),

$$v_c = 0.79(100A_s/bd)^{0.33}(400/d)^{0.25}(f_{cu}/25)^{0.33}/1.25$$
$$= 0.79(0.70)^{0.33}(400/162)^{0.25}(30/25)^{0.33}/1.25$$
$$= 0.75 \text{ N/mm}^2.$$

Thus shear reinforcement is needed and must be designed to resist the greater of $v - v_c$ or 0.4 N/mm^2 (cl 3.5.5.3, Pt 1).

Using vertical links, i.e. $\sin \alpha = 1$, then the shear steel required is given by cl 3.7.7.5, Pt 1,

$$A_{sv} = (v - v_c)ud/(0.87f_{yv})$$

Using high-yield links $f_{yv} = 460$ N/mm^2.

So,

$$A_{sv} = (1.75 - 0.75) \times 3544 \times 162/(0.87 \times 460)$$
$$= 1435 \text{ mm}^2$$

This may be divided into two layers with the legs spaced at not greater than 1.5d (cl 3.7.7.5, Pt 1).

Number of bars = shear perimeter/spacing
$$= 3544/(1.5 \times 162)$$
$$= 14.6, \quad \text{say } 16$$

Cross-sectional area per bar = area of steel per layer/no. of bars
$$= (1435/2)/16$$
$$= 45 \text{ mm}^2$$

Fix T8 bars (50 mm^2).

The next zone that needs checking is between 0.75d and 2.25d. The effective shear force will not be recalculated since the enhancement is low, nor will it be reduced by the effect of the applied load. The effect will give a conservative figure for the shear force.

At 2.25d,

$$u = 4 \times 400 + 8 \times 2.25 \times 162$$
$$= 4516 \text{ mm}$$
$$v = 1003E3/(4516 \times 162)$$
$$= 1.37 \text{ N/mm}^2$$

As before, $v_c = 0.75$, and the links are designed for the greater of $v - v_c$ ($= 1.37 - 0.75 = 0.62$) or 0.4 N/mm^2

$$A_{sv} = 0.62 \times 4516 \times 162/(0.87 \times 460)$$
$$= 1133 \text{ mm}^2$$

Number of bars $= 4516/(1.5 \times 162)$
$$= 18.6, \quad \text{say } 24$$
Area per bar $= (1133/2)/24$
$$= 23.6 \text{ mm}^2$$
Fix T6 (28 mm^2)

At 3.0d out from the column face,

$$u = 4 \times 400 + 8 \times 3 \times 162$$
$$= 5488 \text{ mm}$$
$$v = 1003E3/(5488 \times 162)$$
$$= 1.13 \text{ N/mm}^2.$$

$v_c = 0.75$ as before, and the links are designed for the greater of $v - v_c$ ($= 1.13 - 0.75 = 0.38$) or 0.4 N/mm^2,

$$A_{sv} = 0.4 \times 5488 \times 162/(0.87 \times 460)$$
$$= 889 \text{ mm}^2.$$

Number of bars $= 5488/(1.5 \times 162)$
$$= 22, \quad \text{say } 24$$
Area per bar $= (889/2)/24$
$$= 18.5 \text{ mm}^2$$
Fix T6 (28 mm^2)

At 3.75d, $u = 6460$ mm

$$v = 1003E3/(6460 \times 162)$$
$$= 0.96 \text{ N/mm}^2$$

again $v > v_c$ and links must be designed for 0.4 N/mm^2

$$A_{sv} = 0.4 \times 6460 \times 162/(0.87 \times 460)$$
$$= 1047 \text{ mm}^2$$

Number of bars $= 6460/(1.5 \times 162)$
$$= 26.6, \quad \text{say } 28$$
Area per bar $= (1047/2)/28$
$$= 18.7 \text{ mm}^2$$
Fix T6

Check at 4.5d, $u = 7432$ mm

$$v = 1003E3/(7433 \times 162)$$
$$= 0.83 \text{ N/mm}^2.$$

Again $v > v_c$, so links must be designed for 0.4 N/mm^2.

$$A_{sv} = 0.4 \times 7432 \times 162/(0.87 \times 460)$$
$$= 1203 \text{ mm}^2$$

Number of bars $= 7432/(1.5 \times 162)$
$$= 30.6, \quad \text{say } 32$$
Area per bar $= (1203/2)/32$
$$= 18.8 \text{ mm}^2$$

Fix T6

At $5.25d$, $u = 8404$ mm,

$$v = 1003E3/(8404 \times 162)$$
$$= 0.74 \text{ N/mm}^2$$

$v < v_c$ so no further links are required.

(c) Deflection

It is usually only necessary to check the short span (cl 3.5.7, Pt 1). Basic span depth ratio = 26 (Table 5.3).

(i) *End span* (middle strip)

$$100A_{s,prov}/bd = 0.30$$
$$100A_{s,req}/bd = 0.23$$
$$M/bd^2 = 0.029 \times 30 = 0.87 \text{ (from Table 13.4)}$$
$$1/\beta_b = 116.4/153.4 = 0.76 \text{ (from Fig. 13.16)}$$

Using Equation (5.8) to calculate the service stress,

$$f_s = (5/8)f_y((100A_{s,req}/bd)/(100A_{s,prov}/bd)) \times (1/\beta_b)$$
$$= (5/8) \times 460 \times (0.23/0.30) \times 0.76$$
$$= 168 \text{ N/mm}^2$$
$$F_1 = 0.55 + (477 - f_s)/(120(0.9 + M/bd^2)) \quad \text{(from (5.7))}$$
$$= 0.55 + (477 - 168)/(120(0.9 + 0.87))$$
$$= 2.00$$

So minimum effective depth = span/(basic ratio $\times F_1$)
$$= 5000/(26 \times 2.00)$$
$$= 104 \text{ mm}$$

Actual effective depth is 150 mm.

(ii) *Centre span* (middle strip)

$$100A_{s,prov}/bd = 0.21$$
$$100A_{s,req}/bd = 0.19$$
$$M/bd^2 = 0.024 \times 30 = 0.72 \text{ (from Table 13.4)}$$
$$1/\beta_b = 87.2/126 = 0.69 \text{ (from Fig. 13.16)}$$

$$f_s = (5/8) \times 460(0.19/0.21) \times 0.69$$
$$= 179 \text{ N/mm}^2.$$
$$F_1 = 0.55 + (477 - 179)/(120(0.9 + 0.72))$$
$$= 2.08$$

Maximum value of F_1 that may be taken is 2.0

Minimum effective depth $= 5000/(26 \times 2.0)$
$$= 96 \text{ mm, which is satisfactory.}$$

(d)   Fire Engineering Design

Centre panel (B2C3)

The slab is part of a structure that has a 2 h fire resistance and thus its load-carrying capacity will need checking after a standard fire of two hours.

It will be assumed that the middle strip and the column strip may be considered separately. Any additional strength capacity due to catenary action being developed will be ignored, as will any development of membrane action.

The total loading under the fire condition is $1.05G_k + 1.0Q_k$ (cl 4.5.7, Pt 2), i.e.

$$n = 1.05 \times 0.2 \times 25 + 1.0 \times 5$$
$$= 10.25 \text{ kN/m}^2.$$

6 m span

The udl for the 6 m span $= 10.25 \times 5$
$$= 51.25 \text{ kN/m.}$$

(1)   *Column strip*

(a)   *Mid-span*

The reinforcement at mid-span is T16–250 (Fig. 13.21).

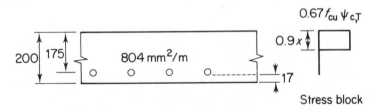

Fig. 13.21   Moment calculations for column strip at midspan.

From Fig. 5.11(b) the reinforcement has a temperature of 680°C, whilst the concrete temperature is below 300°C.

From Fig. 5.12(b) the steel strength is reduced to $0.28f_y$, whilst the concrete suffers no strength loss.

The neutral axis depth, x, is given by

$$0.9xb(0.67f_{cu}/\gamma_m) - \psi_{T,s}f_yA_y/\gamma_m = 0$$

or

$$0.9x \times 1000 \times (0.67 \times 30/1.3) - 0.28 \times 460 \times 804/1.0 = 0$$

or

$$x = 7.4 \text{ mm.}$$

Note that the partial safety factor, γ_m, for concrete is 1.3 and that for steel, γ_m, is 1.0 (cl 4.5.7, Pt 2)

$$M_u = (\psi_{T,s} f_y) \times A_s \times (d - 0.45x)$$

so

$$\begin{aligned} M_u &= (0.28 \times 460) \times 804 \times (175 - 0.45 \times 7.4) \times 1E\text{-}6 \\ &= 17.8 \text{ kN/m.} \end{aligned}$$

Note however that cl 3.4.4.1(e), Pt 1 places a restriction of $0.95d$ on the maximum lever arm. This now needs checking:

$$\begin{aligned} M_u &= (\psi_{T,s} f_y) \times A_y (0.95d) \\ &= (0.28 \times 460) \times 804 \times (0.95 \times 175) \times 1E-6 \\ &= 17.2 \text{ kN m/m.} \end{aligned}$$

It is therefore this latter value that must be used.

(b) *Support* (Fig. 13.22)

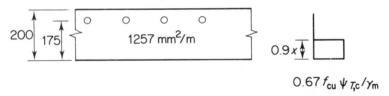

$0.67 f_{cu} \, \psi_{T,c}/\gamma_m$

Fig. 13.22 Moment calculations for column strip at the support.

At the support concrete is being heated, so it is necessary to assume a neutral axis depth and to further assume the temperature at the centre of compression is then uniform over the whole stress block and may be used to determine the strength reduction in the concrete. This latter assumption is not strictly accurate, since no account has been taken of strain compatibility. The assumption is, however, likely to be conservative since the values of strength reduction have been derived from tests on concrete specimens which have been heated in an unloaded state before the determination of strength, whereas the concrete in the structure will have been loaded during the fire by virtue of the applied moments and it has been shown that concrete loaded during heating shows lower strength losses.

Assume $x = 50$ mm.

Depth to centre of compression is $0.45x = 0.45 \times 50 = 22.5$ mm.

From Fig. 5.11(b) the resultant concrete temperature is 630°C, and from Fig. 5.12(a) the strength reduction is 0.5, so

$$(0.9x) \times 1000 \times (0.5 \times 0.67 \times 30/1.3) - 460 \times 1257 = 0$$

or

$x = 83$ mm.

The original guess for the neutral axis depth was too large, so try 70 mm. Concrete temperature is 520°C, and strength reduction 0.7, so

$$(0.9x) \times 1000 \times (0.7 \times 0.67 \times 30/1.3) - 460 \times 1257 = 0$$

or

$x = 60$ mm.

Try $x = 60$, then concrete temperature $= 560$°C, strength reduction is 0.68 giving a neutral axis depth of 61 mm. Thus,

$$M_u = 1257 \times 460(175 - 0.45 \times 60) \times 1E{-}6$$
$$= 85.6 \text{ kN m/m}$$

(2)   Middle strip

(a)   Mid-span (T12–250)
A similar calculation gives $x = 3.6$ mm and $M_u = 11.1$ kN m/m

(b)   Support (T10–250)
The results of the calculations are $x = 32$ mm and $M_u = 23.2$ kN m/m.
   Calculation of load capacity:

$$\text{load capacity} = (M_{sup} + M_{mid}) \times 8/L^2$$

where M_{sup} and M_{mid} are the ultimate moments at the support and mid-span respectively and L is the span.
   So for the column strip,

$$q = (17.2 + 85.6) \times 8/6^2$$
$$= 22.84 \text{ kN/m}^2$$

for the middle strip

$$q = (11.1 + 23.2) \times 8/62$$
$$= 7.62 \text{ kN/m}^2$$

Total load capable of being carried is

$$n = (1/b)\Sigma (\text{load/strip}) \times (\text{width of strip})$$

where b is the total width of the strips, or

$$n = (1/(2.5 + 2.5))(22.84 \times 2.5 + 7.62 \times 2.5)$$
$$= 15.23 \text{ kN/m}^2.$$

The applied fire loading is 10.25 kN/m^2, thus the slab is satisfactory on the 6 m span.

5 m span
A similar check is now carried out on the 5 m span and is summarised in Table 13.3.

Table 13.3   Summary of fire design for the 5 m span

Strip	Position	Reinf.	NA depth (mm)	M_u (kN m/m)	Load (kN/m^2)
Column	Mid-span	T16–250	17.0	33.70	32.71
	Support	T20–250	70.0	68.52	
Middle	Mid-span	T10–250	8.2	16.26	11.32
	Support	T10–250	39.0	19.13	

Thus the total load, n, that can be carried is given by

$$n = (1/(2.5+3.5) \times (2.5 \times 32.71 + 3.5 \times 11.32)$$
$$= 20.23 \text{ kN/m}^2.$$

Thus the slab is adequate in this direction also for 2 h fire resistance.

13.5   Prestressed concrete floor beam

Design a prestressed concrete floor beam to span 5 m. The beam is simply supported and carries floor units as shown in Fig. 13.23. The beam is to be cast upside down.

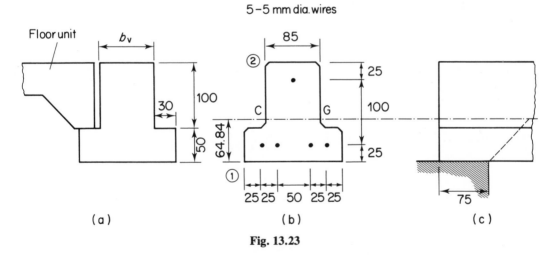

Fig. 13.23

To support the floor units the beam cross-section is an inverted 'T' as shown in Fig. 13.23(a). The depth of the beam should be approximately span/30, say 150 mm, and the thickness of the bottom flange should be 50 mm to support the slabs. The width of the flange which supports the floor slabs should be 30 mm and the only variable dimension is the width b at the top of the section.

Design for service load bending conditions

Characteristic loads per unit length of beam	kN/m
Imposed load (1.5 kN/m^2) = 1.5 × 0.5	= 0.75
Dead load floor slabs (1.0 kN/m^2) = 1.0 × 0.5	= 0.50
Dead load finishes (0.6 kN/m^2) = 0.6 × 0.5	= 0.30
Self-weight of beam (estimated)	= 0.40
Total dead load	= 1.20

Minimum self-weight bending moment at transfer

$$M_{\min} = w_{sw}L^2/8 = 0.4 \times 5^2/8 = 1.25 \text{ kN m}$$

Dead load bending moment

$$M_d = w_d L^2/8 = 1.20 \times 5^2/8 = 3.75 \text{ kN m}$$

Imposed load bending moment

$$M_i = w_i L^2/8 = 0.75 \times 5^2/8 = 2.34 \text{ kN m}$$

Service load bending moment

$$M_s = M_d + M_i = 3.75 + 2.34 = 6.09 \text{ kN m}$$

The site conditions for this beam are class 2, and cover 20 mm. Characteristic strengths for steel $f_{pu} = 1770 \text{ N/mm}^2$, and for concrete $f_{cu,3} = 35 \text{ N/mm}^2$ and $f_{cu,28} = 55 \text{ N/mm}^2$. Many similar beams to be made therefore use the pre-tensioned system.

In this design study the dimensions of the beam section will be obtained from service load bending design stresses, and then checked for ultimate load bending conditions. The reverse process is also acceptable.

The loss of prestress is assumed to be 7.5% at transfer and 25% at service load and therefore prestress ratio factors are

$$\eta_t = 0.925, \ \eta_s = 0.75, \text{ and } \eta = \eta_t/\eta_s = 0.75/0.925 = 0.811$$

The beams are cast upside down and therefore the sign for $M_{\min}$ is negative in the following calculations and has the effect of increasing the size of the section.

The optimum design values of the section moduli from Equations (12.8) and (12.9) are

$$z_1' = (M_s - \eta M_{\min})/(f_{st} - \eta f_{tc})$$
$$= [6.09\text{E}6 - 0.811 \times (-1.25\text{E}6)]/[0.45\sqrt{50} - 0.811 \times 0.5 \times (-35)]$$
$$= 0.4053\text{E}6 \text{ mm}^3$$
$$z_2' = (M_s - \eta M_{\min})/(\eta f_{tt} - f_{sc})$$
$$= [6.09\text{E}6 - 0.811 \times (-1.25\text{E}6)]/[0.811 \times 0.45\sqrt{35} - (-0.33 \times 50)]$$
$$= 0.3498\text{E}6 \text{ mm}^3$$

Actual section properties (Fig. 13.23(b)) assuming $b_v = 85$ mm.
Cross-sectional area

$$A_c = 150 \times 50 + 85 \times 100 = 16\text{E}3 \text{ mm}^2$$

Position of the centroid of the section from the base

$$150 \times 50 \times 25 + 85 \times 100 \times 100 = 16\text{E}3\bar{y}; \text{ hence } \bar{y} = 64.84 \text{ mm}$$

Second moment of area

$$I = \Sigma bd^3/3 = [85 \times (150 - 64.84)^3 + 150 \times 64.84^3 - 65 \times 14.84^3]/3$$
$$= 31.058\text{E}6 \text{ mm}^4$$

Section moduli

$$z' = I/\bar{y} = 31.058\text{E}6/64.84 = 0.4790\text{E}6 \text{ mm}^3 > 0.4053\text{E}6^3 \text{ mm}^3$$
$$z_2 = I/(h - \bar{y}) = 31.058\text{E}6/(150 - 64.84) = 0.3647\text{E}6 \text{ mm}^3 > 0.3498\text{E}6 \text{ mm}^3.$$

The actual value of $z_1 >$ the optimum value of z_1' and $z_2 > z_2'$, which is satisfactory.

Note that in the following calculations the actual values of section moduli are used, i.e. z_1 and z_2. Also M_{min} is negative because the beam is cast upside down.

From Equation (12.11) the maximum value of the eccentricity for the minimum prestressing force

$$e_{max} = \{z_1z_2[f_{st} - \eta f_{tt}] - \eta M_{min}z_1 - M_sz_2\}/\{A_c[f_{st}z_1 + \eta f_{tt}z_2 - M_s + \eta M_{min}]\}$$
$$= \{0.4790E6 \times 0.3647E6 \times [0.45\sqrt{55} - 0.811 \times 0.45\sqrt{35}]$$
$$- 0.811 \times (-1.25E6) \times 0.4790E6 - 6.09E6 \times 0.3647E6\}/$$
$$\{16E3 \times [0.45\sqrt{55} \times 0.4790E6$$
$$+ 0.811 \times 0.45\sqrt{35} \times 0.3647E6 - 6.09E6 + 0.811 \times (-1.25E6)]\}$$
$$= +20.26 \text{ mm}$$

From Equation (12.13) the minimum value of the eccentricity for the minimum jacking force

$$e_{min} = \{z_1z_2[-f_{sc} + \eta f_{tc}] - \eta M_{min}z_2 - M_sz_1\}/\{A_c[f_{sc}z_2 + \eta f_{tc}z_1 + M_s - \eta M_{min}]\}$$
$$= \{0.4790E6 \times 0.3647E6 \times [-0.33 \times (-55) + 0.811 \times 0.5 \times (-35)]$$
$$- 0.811 \times (-1.25E6) \times 0.3647E6 - 6.09E6 \times 0.4790E6\}/$$
$$\{16E3 \times [0.33 \times (-55) \times 0.3647E6$$
$$+ 0.811 \times 0.5 \times (-35) \times 0.4790E6 + 6.09E6 - 0.811 \times (-1.25E6)]\}$$
$$= +18.37 \text{ mm}$$

From Equation (12.12) the maximum value of the jacking force before losses

$$P_{0(max)} = A_c[f_{sc}z_2 + \eta f_{tc}z_1 + M_s - \eta M_{min}]/[-\eta_s(z_1 + z_2)]$$
$$= 16E3 \times [0.33 \times (-55) \times 0.3647E6 + 0.811 \times 0.5 \times (-35) \times 0.4790E6$$
$$+ 6.09E6 - 0.811 \times (-1.25E6)]/[-0.75 \times (0.4790E6 + 0.3647E6)]$$
$$= 159.6 \text{ kN}$$

From Equation (12.10) the minimum value of the jacking force before losses

$$P_{0(min)} = A_c[f_{st}z_1 + \eta f_{tt}z_2 - M_s + \eta M_{min}]/[-\eta_s(z_1 + z_2)]$$
$$. = 16E3 \times [0.45 \times \sqrt{55} \times 0.4790E6 + 0.811 \times 0.45 \times \sqrt{35} \times 0.3647E6$$
$$- 6.09E6 + 0.811 \times (-1.25E6)]/[-0.75 \times (0.4790E6 + 0.3647E6)]$$
$$= 119.3 \text{ kN}$$

The number of wires (n_w), each of jacking force P_w, is such that

$$P_{0(max)}/P_w > n_w > P_{0(min)}/P_w$$

From Appendix A3, for 5 mm wire with $f_{pu} = 1770 \text{ N/mm}^2$

$P_w = 0.7 \times 34.7 = 24.32 \text{ kN and}$
$159.6/24.32 > n_w > 119.3/24.32$
$6.57 > n_w > 4.91$

Try five 5 mm diameter wires ($f_{pu} = 1770 \text{ N/mm}^2$) stressed to $0.7f_{pu}$ (cl 4.7.1, Pt 1). Practical jacking force

$$P_{0p} = 5P_w = 5 \times 24.32 = 121.6 \text{ kN.}$$

This value lies within the prestressing force limits

$$P_{0(max)}(159.6) > P_{0p}(121.6) > P_{0(min)}(119.3) \text{ kN}$$

If $P_{0p} = 121.6$ kN, then the corresponding eccentricity (Equation (12.14))

$$e = (M_s - z_1 f_{st})/(\eta_s P_{0p}) - z_1/A_c$$
$$= (6.09E6 - 0.479E6 \times 0.45 \times \sqrt{55})/(0.75 \times 121.6E3) - 0.479E6/16E3$$
$$= +19.31 \text{ mm}$$

Try various arrangements of five wires with adequate cover for durability and fire (see Chapter 5), and suitable spacing (see Appendix A2). Use positions as shown in Fig. 13.23(b).

$$4 \times 25 + 1 \times 125 = 6\bar{y}; \text{ hence } \bar{y} = 45.0 \text{ mm from the base.}$$

Practical eccentricity

$$e_p = 64.84 - \bar{y} = 64.84 - 45 = 19.84 \text{ mm} > 19.31 \text{ mm but the error is small.}$$
The eccentricity lies with the limits

$$e_{max}(20.26) > e_p(19.84) > e_{min}(18.37) \text{ mm.}$$

Using $P_{0p} = 121.6$ kN and $e_p = 19.84$ mm check the design by calculating the fibre stresses at transfer (7.5% loss) and at service load (25% loss).

$$f_{t1} = -14.30 < -17.5 \text{ N/mm}^2$$
$$f_{t2} = +2.50 < +2.66 \text{ N/mm}^2$$
$$f_{s1} = +3.24 < +3.34 \text{ N/mm}^2$$
$$f_{s2} = 17.44 < -18.15 \text{ N/mm}^2$$

These stresses are acceptable.

Check for ultimate load bending conditions

The moment of resistance of the section at the ultimate limit state for bonded tendons is obtained as follows.

For four wires in the tension zone

$$A_{ps} = 4 \times \pi \times 5^2/4 = 78.54 \text{ mm}^2$$

Ratio

$$f_{pu}A_{ps}/(f_{cu}bd) = 1770 \times 78.54/(55 \times 85 \times 125) = 0.238$$

From Table 12.1 (cl 4.3.7.3, Table 4.4, Pt 1) for an initial stress of $0.7f_{pu}$ and an estimated loss of prestress of 25%

$$f_{pe}/f_{pu} = 0.70 \times 0.75 = 0.525$$

Approximate design stress in the tendons at the ultimate limit state

$$f_{pb} = 0.84 \times 0.87 \times 1770 = 1294 \text{ N/mm}^2$$

Approximate value of

$$x/d = 0.52$$

This is a relatively large value of x/d and consequently there is less warning of failure in bending.

Approximate depth of compression zone

$$x = 0.52 \times 125 = 65 \text{ mm}$$

Moment of resistance at the ultimate limit state (cl 4.3.7.3, Pt 1)

$$
\begin{aligned}
M_u &= f_{pb} A_{ps}(d - d_n) \\
&= 1294 \times 78.54 \times (125 - 0.45 \times 65) \times 1E{-}6 = 9.73 \text{ kN m.}
\end{aligned}
$$

This value is to be compared with the design moment at ultimate load.
Ultimate design load per unit length

$$1.4w_d + 1.6w_i = 1.4 \times 1.2 + 1.6 \times 0.75 = 2.88 \text{ kN/m}$$

Design moment at ultimate load

$$M_u = (1.4w_d + 1.6w_i)L^2/8 = 2.88 \times 5^2/8 = 9.0 \text{ kN m}$$

The moment of resistance of 9.73 kN m is greater than the design moment of 9 kN m, and is therefore satisfactory.

Check that the cracking of the concrete in bending precedes the failure of the beam (cl 4.12.2, Pt 1). The moment necessary to overcome the prestress after losses and to produce a tensile stress of $0.6\sqrt{f_{cu}}$ in the extreme fibres

$$
\begin{aligned}
M &= (\eta_s f_{tc} + 0.6\sqrt{f_{cu}})z_1 \\
&= (0.75 \times 0.5 \times 35 + 0.6\sqrt{55}) \times 0.479E6 \times 1E{-}6 = 8.42 \text{ kN m}
\end{aligned}
$$

The ultimate moment of resistance of 9.73 kN m > 8.42 kN m and therefore the concrete cracks before ultimate load.

Check deflections

Elastic modulus at 28 days (cl 7.2, Pt 2)

$$
\begin{aligned}
E_{c,28} &= 20 + 0.2f_{cu,28} \\
&= 20 + 0.2 \times 55 = 31 \text{ kN/mm}^2
\end{aligned}
$$

Elastic modulus at transfer at 3 days

$$
\begin{aligned}
E_{c,3} &= E_{c,28}(0.4 + 0.6f_{cu,3}/f_{cu,28}) \\
&= 31 \times (0.4 + 0.6 \times 35/55) = 24.24 \text{ kN/mm}^2
\end{aligned}
$$

Effective creep modulus of elasticity related to the 28-day concrete strength using a general creep coefficient $\phi = 1.8$ (cl 4.8.5.2, Pt 2)

$$E'_{c,28} = E_{c,28}/(1 + \phi) = 31/(1 + 1.8) = 11.07 \text{ kN/mm}^2$$

Effective creep modulus of elasticity related to the 3-day concrete strength using a general creep coefficient $\phi = 1.8$ (cl 4.8.5.2, Pt 2)

$$E'_{c,3} = E_{c,3}/(1 + \phi) = 24.24/(1 + 1.8) = 8.66 \text{ kN/mm}^2$$

Long-term deflection due to bending creep from prestress at service load after 25% loss

$$
\begin{aligned}
a_c &= L^2/(E'_{c,3}I)\Sigma kM = (L^2/E'I)(1/8)(-n_s P_{0p}e_p) \\
&= 5E3^2/(8.66E3 \times 31.058E6) \times (1/8) \times (-0.75 \times 121.6E3 \times 19.84) \\
&= -21.02 \text{ mm}
\end{aligned}
$$

Long-term deflection due to bending creep from self-weight (2 kN)

$$a_c = L^2/(E'_{c,3}I)\Sigma kM = L^2/(E'I)(5/48)(WL/8)$$
$$= 5E3^2/(8.66E3 \times 31.058E6) \times (5/48) \times (2E3 \times 5E3/8)$$
$$= 12.10 \text{ mm}$$

Long-term deflection due to bending creep from dead load (4 kN)

$$a_c = L^2/(E'_{c,28}I)\Sigma kM = L^2/(E'I)(5/48)(WL/8)$$
$$= 5E3^2/(11.07E3 \times 31.058E6) \times (5/48) \times (4E3 \times 5E3/8)$$
$$= 18.94 \text{ mm}$$

Short-term elastic deflection (downwards) from imposed load (3.75 kN) related to the 28-day concrete strength

$$a_e = L^2/(E_{c,28}I)\Sigma kM = L^2/(E_{c,28}I)(5/48)(WL/8)$$
$$= 5E3^2/(31E3 \times 31.058E6) \times (5/48) \times (3.75E3 \times 5E3/8)$$
$$= 6.34 \text{ mm}$$

Net long-term creep deflection $= -21.02 + 12.10 + 18.94 = +10.02$ mm downwards.
Short-term elastic deflection from imposed load $= +6.34$ mm downwards.

No numerical limits are now placed on deflections for prestressed concrete beams, but previously short-term elastic limits of span/350 = 5E3/350 = 14.3 mm or 20 mm, whichever is the less, were used as a guide. The actual elastic deflection is less than these limits. The limit placed on the total deflection was span/250 = 5E3/250 = 20 mm, and this is greater than the actual deflection.

Check for losses of prestress (assumed to be 7.25% at transfer and 25% at service load)

Jacking steel stress

$$f_{pi} = 0.7f_{pu} = 0.7 \times 1770 = 1239 \text{ N/mm}^2$$

Percentage loss of prestress from relaxation of the steel (cl 4.8.2, Pt 1). From Table 4.6, Pt 1 and the manufacturer's UK certificate of approval = 2%.
Prestress at the centroid of the wires at transfer

$$f_c = -P_{0p}/A_c - P_{0p}e_p^2/I$$
$$= -121.163E/16E3 - 121.6E3 \times 19.84^2/31.058E6$$
$$= -9.14 \text{ N/mm}^2$$

Percentage loss of prestress from elastic deformation of the concrete at transfer at 3 days (cl 4.8.3, Pt 1) from Equation (12.15)

$$= 100(E_s/E_{c,3})f_c/f_{pi}$$
$$= 100 \times (205E3/24.24E3) \times 9.14/1239 = 6.24\%$$

Percentage loss of prestress from shrinkage of the concrete (cl 4.8.4, Pt 1) from Equation (12.16) for indoor exposure

$$= 100E_s\varepsilon_c/f_{pi}$$
$$= 100 \times 205E3 \times 300E - 6/1239 = 4.96\%$$

Percentage loss of prestress from creep of the concrete (cl 4.8.5, Pt 1) from Equation (12.17)

$$= 100(E_s/E_{c,3})\phi f_c/f_{pi}$$
$$= 100 \times (205E3/24.24E3) \times 1.8 \times 9.14/1239 = 11.23\%$$

Percentage loss of prestress from draw-in during anchorage (cl 4.8.6, Pt 1) is assumed to be 1% for a long casting bed.

Loss of prestress at transfer

$$= \text{elasticity of concrete and anchorage loss} = 6.24 + 1 = 7.24\%$$

This is approximately the value assumed (7.5%) for transfer.

Loss of prestress at service load

$$= \text{relax.} + \text{elastic conc.} + \text{shrink. conc.} + \text{creep conc.} + \text{anchorage}$$
$$= 2 + 6.24 + 4.96 + 11.23 + 1 = 25.43\%$$

This is the total value at service load and is approximately the value assumed (25%).

Check shear strength

The shear strength of the beam uncracked in flexure at the ultimate limit state with the critical section within the transmission length is obtained as follows.

The critical point to consider the principal tensile stresses in the concrete is at the centroid of the cross-section at a distance from the edge of the bearing equal to the distance of the centroid of the section from the soffit of the section (cl 4.3.8.4, Pt 1).

From Figs. 13.23(b) and (c) the distance from the centre-line of bearing

$$= 75/2 + 64.84 = 102.34 \text{ mm.}$$

Shear force at this section

$$= (2.5 - 0.1023)/2.5 \times V_{\text{support}} = (2.5 - 0.1023)/2.5 \times 4.875 = 4.676 \text{ kN}$$

Average shear stress

$$v = V/bh = 4.676E3/(85 \times 150) = 0.367 \text{ N/mm}^2$$

For a 5 mm diameter crimped wire with a total wave height of not less than 0.15ϕ (cl 4.10.3, Pt 1) and a strength of the concrete at transfer $f_{ci} = 35$ N/mm^2, the transmission length

$$l_t = K_t\phi/\sqrt{f_{ci}}$$
$$= 400 \times 5/\sqrt{35} = 338.1 \text{ mm} > h = 150 \text{ mm}$$

therefore use 338.1 mm (cl 4.3.8.4, Pt 1)

Within the transmission length of 338.1 mm, at $x = 102.34 + 75/2 = 139.84$ mm from the end of the beam, the prestress stress (cl 4.3.8.4, Pt 1)

$$f_{cpx} = (x/l_p)(2 - x/l_p)f_{cp}$$
$$= (139.84/338.1) \times (2 - 139.84/338.1)f_{cp} = 0.656 f_{cp}$$

Tensile strength of the concrete (cl 4.3.8.4, Pt 1)

$$f_t = 0.24\sqrt{f_{cu}} = 0.24 \times \sqrt{55} = 1.78 \text{ N/mm}^2$$

Prestress at service load (25% loss) at the centroidal axis of the section

$$f_{cp} = -\eta_s P_{0p}/A_c$$
$$= -0.75 \times 121.6E3/16E3$$
$$= -5.70 \text{ N/mm}^2$$

From Equation (12.25) the design ultimate shear stress resistance of the web (cl 4.3.8.4, Pt 1)

$$v_{co} = 0.67\sqrt{(f_t^2 + 0.8f_{cpx}f_t)}$$
$$= 0.67 \times \sqrt{(1.78^2 + 0.8 \times 0.656 \times 5.7 \times 1.78)} = 1.953 \text{ N/mm}^2$$

This value is less than the maximum design shear stress (cl 4.3.8.2, Pt 1)

$$v_u = 0.8\sqrt{f_{cu}} = 0.8\sqrt{55} = 5.93 \text{ N/mm}^2 > 5 \text{ N/mm}^2.$$

$v(0.367) < (v_{co} + 0.4)(2.353)$ N/mm^2, and less than $v_{co}/2$, therefore no shear reinforcement is required (cl 4.3.8.6, Pt 1).

The shear strength of the beam cracked in flexure at the ultimate limit state is obtained as follows.

Prestress at service load after 25% losses, at the bottom of the section

$$f_{cp} = -n_s P_{0p}/A_c - n_s P_{0p}e_p/z_1$$
$$= -0.75 \times 121.6E3/16E3 - 0.75 \times 121.6E3 \times 19.84/0.4790E6$$
$$= -9.48 \text{ N/mm}^2$$

Bending moment required to overcome 80% of the prestress stress

$$M_0 = 0.8f_{cp}I/y = 0.8 \times 9.48 \times 31.058E6/64.84 \times 1E-6 = 3.633 \text{ kN m}$$

This type of failure is likely to occur when the applied bending moment M_x, at a distance x from the support, exceeds M_0. If

$$M_x = WL(x/L)(1 - x/L)/2 = M_0$$

then inserting numerical values

$$9.75 \times 5 \times (x/L)(1 - x/L)/2 = 3.633; \text{ hence } x/L = 0.1823 \text{ and } x = 0.912 \text{ m}.$$
$$M_{max} = WL/8 = 9.75 \times 5/8 = 6.094 \text{ kN m}$$
$$M_0/M_{max} = 3.633/6.094 = 0.596$$

Position of the critical section, from Equation (12.23),

$$x/L = 0.5\{1 - \sqrt{[1 + 0.5M_0/M_{max} - \sqrt{(2M_0/M_{max} + 0.25(M_0/M_{max})^2)}]}\}$$
$$x/L = 0.296; \text{ hence } x = 0.296 \times 5 = 1.48 \text{ m from support}$$

At this section

$$V = (W/2)(1 - 2x/L) = (9.75/2) \times (1 - 2 \times 0.296) = 1.989 \text{ kN}$$
$$v = V/(b_v d) = 1.989E3/(85 \times 125) = 0.187 \text{ N/mm}^2$$
$$M = WL(x/L)(1 - x/L)/2 = 9.75 \times 5 \times 0.296 \times (1 - 0.296)/2 = 5.079 \text{ kN m}$$

Area of steel in tension $= 4 \times \pi/4 \times 5^2 = 78.54 \text{ mm}^2$, $d = 125$ mm.

Design ultimate shear stress for a singly reinforced concrete beam (cl 3.4.5.4, Pt 1)

$$v_c = k_1 k_2 0.79[100 A_s/(b_v d)]^{1/3}(400/d)^{1/4}/\gamma_m$$
$$= 1 \times (40/25)^{1/3} \times 0.79 \times [100 \times 78.54/(85 \times 125)]^{1/3} \times 1/1.25$$
$$= 0.668 \text{ N/mm}^2$$

Note: $400/d < 1$, therefore use 1, $100 A_s/(b_v d) = 0.739\% < 3\%$ (maximum).

If $f_{pe}/f_{pu} = 0.7 \times 0.75 = 0.525$, from Equation (12.22), the design ultimate shear stress resistance (cl 4.3.8.5, Pt 1)

$$v_{cr} = (1 - 0.55 f_{pe}/f_{pu})v_c + (M_0/M)v$$
$$= (1 - 0.55 \times 0.525) \times 0.668 + 3.633/5.079 \times 0.187 = 0.609 \text{ N/mm}^2$$

The value of v_{cr} should not be taken as less than

$$0.1\sqrt{f_{cu}} = 0.1 \times \sqrt{55} = 0.742 \text{ N/mm}^2.$$

Outside the transmission length check if $v_{co} > v_{cr}$ (cl 4.3.8.3, Pt 1).

$$v_{co} = 0.67\sqrt{(f_t^2 + 0.8 f_{cp} f_t)}$$
$$= 0.67 \times \sqrt{(1.78^2 + 0.8 \times 5.7 \times 1.78)} = 2.251 \text{ N/mm}^2$$
$$= 2.251 \text{ N/mm}^2 > v_{cr} = 0.742 \text{ N/mm}^2, \text{ therefore } v_{cr} \text{ is critical.}$$

Check that the value of v_{cr} is less than the maximum design shear stress (cl 4.3.8.2, Pt 1)

$$v_u = 0.8\sqrt{f_{cu}} = 0.8\sqrt{55} = 5.93 \text{ N/mm}^2 > 5 \text{ N/mm}^2.$$

$(v_{cr} + 0.4)(1.142) > v(0.187) \text{ N/mm}^2 < v_{cr}/2$, therefore no shear reinforcement is required (cl 4.3.8.6, Pt 1).

Cl 5.2.8, Pt 1 states that where a continuous nib is less than 300 mm deep, it should normally be designed as a short cantilever slab. However, the nib on this beam is only 50 mm deep and it is short and continuous. The shear and bending stresses are not high and it is therefore considered not to be necessary, nor economical, to provide reinforcement when numerous members are to be manufactured. This decision could be tested by proving experiments on the beam. If, after tests, reinforcement were considered necessary, it could be in the form of links which extend into the nib and welded to a continuous bar running the length of the beam at the toe of the nib.

13.6   Counterfort retaining wall

For this design study an interior bay has been chosen. An end bay will be essentially the same except for the reduced span and the resultant thickness of the counterfort at the free end where there will be no moment transfer from the stem.

The basic design data are given in Fig. 13.24.

From practical considerations – i.e. that the base should be as long as the wall is high – a base length of 10 m has been used. In order to determine the design length of the toe, calculations for bearing pressure distribution, sliding and overturning have been carried out for toe lengths of 1, 2, 3, 4 and 4.5 m. The results of these calculations are presented in Table 13.4. If passive resistance is needed to be mobilised, i.e. if the factor of safety

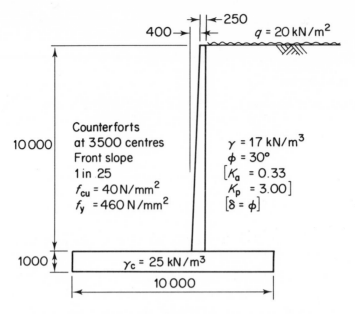

Fig. 13.24   General arrangement drawing and design data for a counterfeit retaining wall.

for sliding is below 1.5, then the overall height of the face needed for passive resistance, h, is given by,

$$h = ((2(2H - N \tan\delta)/K_p\delta) \tag{13.17}$$

It may be seen that for all values of toe length there is an adequate factor of safety against overturning, that for a toe length greater than 2 m a shear key is required and that a toe length of less than 3 m gives an unsatisfactory distribution of bearing stress. If an allowable bearing stress of 150 kN/m² is used, then a 4 m toe will be adequate. If the shear key be located under the toe of the wall, then the additional depth will be 2.88 m for 1 m deep base.

Design of the stem

(a) Bending
The Hillerborg strip method will be used to determine the bending moments in the stem. The distribution of loading given in Fig. 13.25 will be used. The slight deviation from the 45° distribution normally used is to allow a relatively easy calculation of loads using 1 m strips.

(i) Horizontally spanning strips

The wall will be divided up into 1 m wide strips and the load will be assessed assuming it is uniform over the width of the strip with a value calculated for the mid-height of the strip. The effective depth will also be calculated at the mid-height.

For all strips, the total ultimate load is given by

$$q_{av,n} = 1.6 \times 20 + 1.4 \times K_a \times \gamma \times (2n - 1)/2 \tag{13.18}$$

Table 13.4 Sizing of retaining wall

Calculation	Toe length (m)				
	1.0	2.0	3.0	4.0	4.5
Vertical forces					
Fill: $(9.55 - \text{toe}) \times 17 \times 10$	1419.5	1249.5	1079.5	909.5	824.5
Base: $1.0 \times 10 \times 25$	250.0	250.0	250.0	250.0	250.0
Stem: $(0.25 + 0.65) \times 25 \times 10/2$	112.5	112.5	112.5	112.5	112.5
Total (N) (kN/m)	1782.0	1612.0	1442.0	1272.0	1187.0
Net vertical bearing pressure (N/A) (kN/m²)	178.2	161.2	144.2	127.2	118.7
Net horizontal resistance $(N \tan\delta)$ (kN/m)	1028.8	930.7	832.5	734.4	685.3
Moments about base centre line					
Active pressure: $-(1/6)(0.33) \times 17 \times 11^3$	-1244.5	-1244.5	-1244.5	-1244.5	-1244.5
Surcharge: $-(1/2) \times 20 \times 11^2$	-1210.0	-1210.0	-1210.0	-1210.0	-1210.0
Stem: $0.25 \times 10 \times 25(5 - \text{toe} - 0.4 - 0.125)$	-277.2	-154.7	-92.2	-29.7	1.6
$0.2 \times 10 \times 25(5 - \text{toe} - 0.8/3)$	-186.7	-136.7	-86.7	-36.7	-11.7
Base:					
Fill: $(9.35 - \text{toe}) \times 17 \times 10(5 - (9.35 - \text{toe})/2)$	1171.1	1655.6	1970.1	2114.6	2123.1
Total (M) (kN m/m)	-1687.3	-1090.3	-663.3	-406.3	-341.5
Bearing pressure due to moment (M/Z) (kN/m²)	-101.2	-65.4	-39.8	-24.4	-20.5
Maximum bearing pressure (σ_1) $(=N/A - M/Z)$ (kN/m²)	279.4	226.6	184.0	151.6	139.2
Minimum bearing pressure (σ_2) $(=N/A + M/Z)$ (kN/m²)	77.0	95.8	104.4	102.8	98.2
Ratio σ_1/σ	3.63	2.37	1.76	1.47	1.42
Sliding (horizontal forces)					
Fill: $(1/2)(0.33) \times 17 \times 11^2$	339.4	339.4	339.4	339.4	339.4
Surcharge: 20×11	220.0	220.0	220.0	220.0	220.0
Total (H) (kN/m)	559.4	559.4	559.4	559.4	559.4
Factor of safety $= N \tan\delta/H$	1.84	1.66	1.49	1.31	1.23
Depth of shear key (h) (m)	—	—	3.35	3.88	4.12
Overturning (moments about toe)					
Active: Surcharge: } as moments about centre line (M_1) (kN m/m)	2454.5	2454.5	2454.5	2454.5	2454.5
Base: $10^2 \times 1 \times 25/2$	1250.0	1250.0	1250.0	1250.0	1250.0
Stem: $0.25 \times 25 \times 10(\text{toe} + 0.4 + 0.125)$	95.3	157.8	220.3	282.9	314.1
$0.4 \times 25 \times 10(\text{toe} + 0.8/3)/2$	63.3	113.3	163.3	213.3	238.3
Fall: $(9.35 - \text{toe}) \times 17 \times 10(10 - (9.35 - \text{toe})/2)$	8268.6	7903.1	7367.6	6662.1	6183.8
Total (M_2) (kN m/m)	9677.2	9424.2	9001.2	8408.3	7986.2
Factor of safety $= M_2/M_1$	3.94	3.84	3.67	3.43	3.25

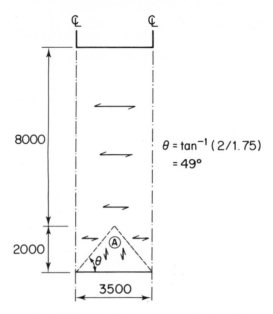

Fig. 13.25 Load dispersion on front wall.

where n is the strip number counting from the top.

For the ninth and tenth strips where the loading is not over the whole strip, the value of $q_{av,n}$ must be modified by using the factor K calculated from Equation (10.20),

$$K = \tfrac{4}{3}(1 - 1/(L_1/L_2 + 2 + L_2/L_1)) \qquad (10.20)$$

For strip 9, $L_1 = 1.75$ and $L_2 = 0.875$, giving $K = 1.04$, and for strip 10, $L_1 = 0.875$ and $L_2 = 0$ giving $K = 1.33$.

Assuming the hogging and sagging moments of resistance are equal, then for strips 1 to 8,

$$M_u = q_{av,n}L^2/16$$

and for strips 9 and 10

$$M_u = K \times q_{av,n}(L_1 + L_2)^2/16.$$

These calculations together with the reinforcement design are given in Table 13.5. Note, for convenience values of $A_s f_y/bd f_{cu}$ have been converted to values of $100A_s/bd$, using $f_{cu} = 40$ and $f_y = 460$ N/mm^2 respectively.

From Table 5.1 a cover of 30 is required and a bar diameter of 32 has been assumed to calculate the value of d. For detailing, the stem has been divided into two portions: 0–5 m and 5–10 m.

0–5 m
Maximum value of h is 450 so fix $0.13 \times 5000 \times 450/100 = 2925$ mm^2 or 585 mm^2/m or T16–250 (804 mm^2/m) on each face.

Table 13.5 Flexural design of stem

Strip No.	Height (m)	$q_{av,n}$ (kN/m²)	M_u (kN m/m)	d (mm)	M/bd^2f_{cu}	$100A_s/bd$ (%)
1	0–1	35.9	27.5	220	0.0142	0.17
2	1–2	43.8	33.5	260	0.0125	0.13
3	2–3	51.6	39.5	300	0.0110	M
4	3–4	59.6	45.6	340	0.0098	I
5	4–5	67.3	51.5	380	0.0090	N
6	5–6	75.2	57.8	420	0.0083	I
7	6–7	83.1	63.6	460	0.0075	M
8	7–8	90.9	69.6	500	0.0070	U
9	8–9	98.9	44.3	540	0.0038	M
10	9–10	106.6	6.8	580	0.001	

5–10 m

Maximum value of h is 650 giving a steel area of 4225 mm² or 845 mm²/m or T16–200 (1005 mm²/m).

(ii) Vertically spanning strips

The loading is given in Fig. 13.26.

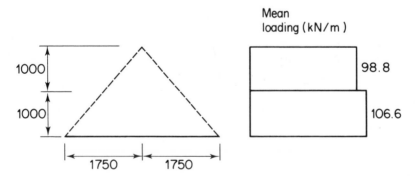

Fig. 13.26 Loading on area A.

Moment at base $= 106.6 \times (1.75 \times 1.0 \times 0.5 + (1.75 \times 1.0/2) \times (1.0/3)) + \cdots$
$+ 98.8 \times ((1.75 \times 1.0/2) \times (1.0 + 1.0/3)) = 239.6$ kN m

$M/bd^2f_{cu} = 239.6E6/(3500 \times 540^2 \times 40) = 0.006$.

This will give minimum reinforcement, so fix

$0.13 \times 3500 \times 650/100 = 2958$ mm²

or   T16–200 (1005 mm²/m).

This reinforcement is for the inner face and should extend to the whole height of the wall. Similar reinforcement will need to be supplied on the outer face to support the main flexural steel in the stem.

(b)   Shear

(i)   Horizontally spanning strips (Table 13.6)

Table 13.6   Shear design of stem

Strip No.	Height (m)	$q_{av,n}$ (kN/m^2)	V (kN/m)	v (N/mm^2)	$100A_{s,prov}/bd$ (%)	v_c (N/mm^2)
1	0–1	35.9	62.8	0.29	0.37	0.62
2	1–2	43.8	76.7	0.30	0.31	0.56
3	2–3	51.6	90.3	0.30	0.27	0.51
4	3–4	59.6	104.3	0.31	0.24	0.48
5	4–5	67.3	117.8	0.31	0.21	0.45
6	5–6	75.2	131.6	0.31	0.24	0.46
7	6–7	83.1	145.4	0.32	0.22	0.45
8	7–8	90.9	159.1	0.32	0.20	0.43
9	8–9	98.9	129.7	0.24	0.19	0.42
10	9–11	106.6	46.6	0.08	0.17	0.41

The shear force has been calculated as half the total load on each strip. The allowable shear stress, v_c, has been calculated from Equation (7.2) and includes the allowance for section depth and cube strength.

In all cases the actual shear stress is less than the allowable, so no provision need be made for shear reinforcement.

(ii)   Vertically spanning strips

From Fig. 13.26, the total shear, V, is given by

$$V = 106.6 \times (3.5 + 1.75)/2 + 98.8 \times 1.75/2$$
$$= 366.3 \text{ kN}$$
$$v = V/bd = 366.3\text{E3}/(3500 \times 540)$$
$$= 0.19 \text{ N/mm}^2.$$

Clearly this figure is low and no shear reinforcement is required.

(c)   Reactions

The direction of the loading is such that the reaction on the counterforts is tensile and the force must be transmitted through shear links. Since the horizontal flexural reinforcement has been treated in two bands, so also will the links be.

0–5 m

The maximum shear force is 117.8 kN, the links will act at a stress of f_y/γ_m, so the area of link steel is given by

$$117.8\text{E3}/(460/1.15) = 295 \text{ mm}^2$$

Using the same spacing as for the flexural steel i.e. 250 mm, then the area per metre is $295/4 = 74 \text{ mm}^2$.

So fix T10–250 (79 mm^2/m).

5–10 m
Maximum shear is 159.1 kN, so area of steel per metre at 200 centres is

$$(159.1E3/(460/1.15)/5) = 80 \text{ mm}^2/\text{m}$$

So fix T10–200 (79 mm²/m).

(d) Counterforts
The loading on each counterfort is twice the shear from Table 13.6, giving the bending-moment and shear-force diagrams plotted in Fig. 13.27.

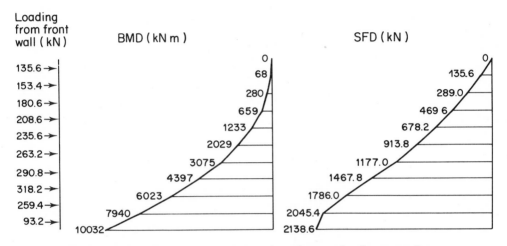

Fig. 13.27 Bending moment and shear face diagrams for the counterforts.

The depth of the counterfort at the top of the wall is 400 mm and extends to the rear of the heel at the bottom, i.e. a depth of 5350 mm. The thickness is $0.15 \times$ span or $0.05 \times 3500 = 175$. Use 200 for convenience. The counterforts can be designed as T beams with the table of the T comprising the front slab and the stem as the counterfort. The effective width of the T beams will be 3500 and since the neutral axis will be within the top flange, the beams can be designed as rectangular sections with $b = 3500$. Assuming an effective depth of 100 less than the overall depth to allow for the possibility of two layers of reinforcement since the stem is thin, then the calculations in Table 13.7 can be carried out.

At all points the requirement for bending is minimum reinforcement of $0.13bh/100$. For the lower 5 m this will be supplied by 4T32 in two layers (3217 mm²) and the inner bars will be curtailed at 5 m, leaving 2T32 in the top.

For the shear, again consider the counterfort in two sections.

0–5 m
Maximum value of $A_{sv}/s_v = 0.38$ mm, so using $s_v = 250$, $A_{sv} = 95$ mm² for two legs, i.e. T10–250.

This means the total link requirement for shear and reaction is T10–125.

5–10 m
With $s_v = 200$, and $A_{sv}/s_v = 0.71$, the total link requirement becomes T10–100.

Table 13.7 Counterfort design

Strip No.	Height (m)	M (kN m)	h (mm)	d (mm)	M/bd^2f_{cu} ($\times10^{-3}$)	$0.13b_t h/100$ (mm²)	$(100A_s/bd)_{prov}$ (%)	V (kN)	v (N/mm²)	v_c (N/mm²)	$b(v-v_c)/(f_{yv}/\gamma_m)$ (mm)
1	0–1	68	1140	1040	0.46	296	1.55	135.6	0.65	0.86	—
2	1–2	280	1680	1580	0.80	437	1.02	289.0	0.91	0.74	0.09
3	2–3	659	2220	2120	1.03	577	0.76	469.6	1.11	0.67	0.22
4	3–4	1233	2760	2660	1.26	718	0.60	678.2	1.27	0.62	0.33
5	4–5	2029	3300	3200	1.43	858	0.50	913.8	1.43	0.59	0.38
6	5–6	3075	3840	3740	1.60	998	0.43	1177.0	1.57	0.56	0.51
7	6–7	4397	4380	4280	1.71	1139	0.38	1467.8	1.71	0.54	0.59
8	7–8	6023	4920	4820	1.83	1279	0.33	1768.0	1.85	0.51	0.67
9	8–9	7940	5460	5360	2.00	1420	0.30	2045.4	1.91	0.49	0.71
10	9–10	10032	6000	5900	2.06	1560	0.27	2138.6	1.81	0.48	0.67

(e) Base

Calculation of ultimate bearing pressure:
Taking moments about the base centre-line,

Active pressure: $1.4 \times (-1244.5) = -1742.3$
Surcharge: $\quad 1.6 \times (-1210.0) = -1936.0$
Stem: $\quad\quad 1.4 \times (\quad -29.7) = \quad -41.6$
$\quad\quad\quad\quad\quad 1.4 \times (\quad -36.7) = \quad -51.4$
Fill: $\quad\quad 1.4 \times 2114.6 \quad = \quad 2960.4$
$\quad\quad\quad\quad\quad\quad$ Total $\quad = -810.9$ kN m/m

Total vertical load $= 1.4 \times 1272.0 = 1780.8$ kN/m
Bearing pressures $= 1780.8/10 \pm 810.9/(10^2/6)$
$$= 178.08 \pm 48.65$$
$$= 226.73 \text{ or } 129.43 \text{ kN/m}^2.$$

Thus giving the bearing pressure distribution plotted in Fig. 13.28.

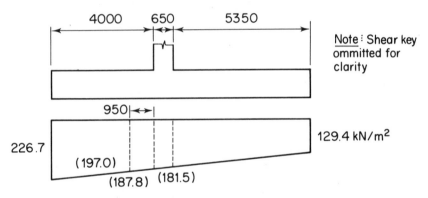

Fig. 13.28 Ultimate bearing pressures on the base.

Design of reinforcement:

(i) Toe

$$M = (4 \times 226.7/2)(2 \times 4/3) + (187.8 \times 4/2)(4/3)$$
$$= 1710 \text{ kN m/m}.$$

Taking $d = 950$.

$$M/bd^2f_{cu} = 1710E6/(1000 \times 950^2 \times 40)$$
$$= 0.047,$$
$$A_s f_y/bdf_{cu} = 0.057$$

or

$$A_s = 0.057 \times 1000 \times 950 \times 40/460$$
$$= 4710 \text{ mm}^2/\text{m}.$$

Using centres of 100 to match the vertical reinforcement in the stem, fix T25–100 (4910 mm²/m).

Shear force at a distance d (950 mm) from the toe,

$$V = 3.05(226.7 + 197.0)/2 = 646 \text{ kN/m}$$
$$v = V/bd = 646E3/(1000 \times 950) = 0.68 \text{ N/mm}^2$$

Using Equation (7.2)

$$v_c = 0.79 \times (40/25)^{0.33} \times (100 \times 4910/(1000 \times 950))^{0.33}/1.25$$
$$= 0.59 \text{ N/mm}^2.$$

v is greater than v_c.

So increase the reinforcement to T32–100 and recalculate v_c:

$$v_c = 0.79 \times (40/25)^{0.33} \times (100 \times 8040/(1000 \times 950))^{0.33}/1.25$$
$$= 0.70 \text{ N/mm}^2 > 0.68, \text{ which is satisfactory.}$$

(ii)   Heel

(f)   Bending

The Hillerborg strip method is used with the load dispersion given in Fig. 13.29.

Assuming equal hogging and sagging design moments, then

Strip 1
$L_1 = 1.75$, $L_2 = 0$, so $K = 4/3$.

Average load on the strip is $(181.5 + 164.5)/2 = 173 \text{ kN/m}^2$.

Free bending moment $= Kq \times (L_1 + L_2)^2/8$
$$= (4/3) \times 173 \times (1.75 + 0)^2/8$$
$$= 88.3 \text{ kN m/m}$$

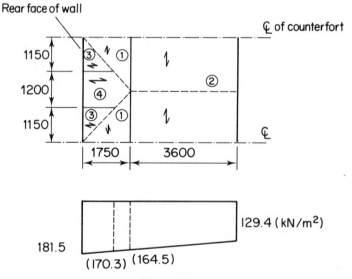

Fig. 13.29

Design moment is half this value, i.e. 44.2 kN m/m

$$M/bd^2f_{cu} = 44.2E6/(1000 \times 950^2 \times 40)$$
$$= 1.25E-3,$$

thus requiring minimum reinforcement of $0.13bh/100$,

$$A_s = 0.13 \times 1000 \times 1000/100$$
$$= 1300 \text{ mm}^2/\text{mm}$$

i.e. fix T20–200 (1575 mm²/mm)

Strip 2

$$M = qL^2/16$$
$$= ((164.5 + 129.4)/2) \times 3.5^2/16$$
$$= 112.6 \text{ kN m/m}$$

$$M/bd^2f_{cu} = 112.6E6/(1000 \times 950^2 \times 40)$$
$$= 3E-3$$

This also gives minimum reinforcement, i.e. T20–200.

Strip 3

Mean loading $= (181.5 + 170.3)/2$
$$= 175.9 \text{ kN/m.}$$

Total load $= 175.9 \times 1.15^2/2$
$$= 116.3 \text{ kN.}$$

Moment $= 116.3 \times 1.15/3$
$$= 44.6 \text{ kN m}$$

$$M/bd^2f_{cu} = 44.6E6/(1000 \times 950^2 \times 40)$$
$$= 1E-3$$

This also clearly gives minimum reinforcement, so fix T32–200 (4021 mm²/m), i.e. extending alternate bars through from the toe.

Strip 4

Mean loading on triangular section $= (170.3 + 164.5)/2$
$$= 167.4 \text{ kN/m}^2$$

Moment $= 1.2(175.9 \times 1.15^2/2 + (167.4 \times 0.6/2)(1.15 + 0.6/3))$
$$= 220.9 \text{ kN m}$$

$$M/bd^2f_{cu} = 220.9E6/(1200 \times 950^2 \times 40)$$
$$= 5E-4$$

Again fix minimum T32–200.

(g)   Shear

Strip 1

$$V = 173 \times 1.75/2$$
$$= 151.4 \text{ kN/m}$$
$$v = V/bd$$
$$= 151.4\text{E}3/(1000 \times 950)$$
$$= 0.16 \text{ N/mm}^2$$

Clearly this is negligible.

Strip 2

$$V = (3.5 \times (164.5 + 129.4)/2)/2$$
$$= 257.2 \text{ kN/m}$$
$$v = 257.2\text{E}3/(1000 \times 950)$$
$$= 0.27 \text{ N/mm}^2, \text{ again negligible.}$$

Strip 3

$$V = 175.9 \times 1.15/2$$
$$= 101.4 \text{ kN/m}$$
$$v = 101.4\text{E}3/(1000 \times 950)$$
$$= 0.11 \text{ N/mm}^2, \text{ again negligible.}$$

Strip 4

$$V = 175.9 \times 1.15 + 0.6 \times 167.4/2$$
$$= 252.5 \text{ kN/m}$$
$$v = 252.5\text{E}3/(1000 \times 950)$$
$$= 0.27 \text{ N/mm}^2, \text{ again negligible.}$$

(h)   Shear key (Fig. 13.30)

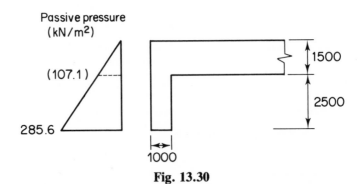

Fig. 13.30

Assuming full passive pressure to be acting, then pressure is given by

$$1.4 \times K_p \times \gamma = 1.4 \times 3.0 \times 17$$
$$= 71.4 \text{ kN/m}^2.$$

Moment at the base of the toe:

$$M = (107.1 \times 2.5/2)(2.5/3) + (285.6 \times 2.5/2)(2 \times 2.5/3)$$
$$= 706.6 \text{ kN m/m}$$

$$M/bd^2f_{cu} = 706.6E6/(1000 \times 950^2 \times 40)$$
$$= 0.02$$

$$A_s f_y / bd f_{cu} = 0.024$$

$$A_s = 0.024 \times 1000 \times 950 \times 40/460$$
$$= 1983 \text{ mm}^2/\text{m}.$$

Since the reinforcement in the toe is T32–100 and to avoid shear problems, fix the same in the shear key.

Maximum shear at the root of the key,

$$V = 2.5 \times (107.1 + 285.6)/2$$
$$= 490.9 \text{ kN/m}$$
$$v = 490.9E3/(1000 \times 950)$$
$$= 0.52 \text{ N/mm}^2.$$

Shear capacity v_c,

$$v_c = 0.79(f_{cu}/25)^{0.33}(100A_s/bd)^{0.33}/1.25$$
$$= 0.79(40/25)^{0.33}(100 \times 8042/(1000 \times 950))^{0.33}/1.25$$
$$= 0.70 \text{ N/mm}^2$$

Thus shear is satisfied.

(i) Serviceability

Base
The base may be treated as a slab.

Calculated clear distance between bars is given by Equation (5.31)

$$s = 75\,000\beta_b/f_y \tag{5.31}$$

in this case $\beta_b = 1$, so

$$s = 163 \text{ mm}.$$

With no modification this is clearly satisfied by the reinforcement in the toe – 100 centres.

For the heel the spacing may be modified.

In strips 3 and 4 the percentage of reinforcement is 0.42%, so spacing may be modified to

$$163/0.42 = 388 \text{ mm}.$$

This clearly is not exceeded since the maximum spacing is 200.

Stem
Checks will be made using the explicit method for crack-width calculation on strips 5 and 8. The critical position will be on the inside of the wall at the junction between the stem and the counterfort.

$$E_{c,28} = K_0 + 0.2f_{c,28} \tag{2.1}$$
$$= 20 + 0.2 \times 40$$
$$= 28 \text{ kN/mm}^2.$$

Value of E_c to be used in calculation is $0.5E_{c,28}$.

$$\alpha_e = E_s/E_c$$
$$= 200/14$$
$$= 14.29$$

Strip 5
Applied service loading is given by Equation (13.18) with the load factors set equal to unity, i.e.

$$q = 20 + 0.33 \times 17 \times (2 \times 5 - 1)/2$$
$$= 45.25 \text{ kN/m}^2$$

Assuming full fixity at the support,

$$M = qL^2/12$$
$$= 45.25 \times 3.5^2/12$$
$$= 46.2 \text{ kN m/m}$$

Using Equation (4.9) (with $\rho' = 0$) to calculate x/d

$$x/d = -\rho\alpha_e + (2\alpha_e\rho + (\alpha_e\rho)^2)^{0.5}$$
$$\alpha_e\rho = 14.29 \times (804/(1000 \times 380))$$
$$= 0.03,$$

hence

$$x/d = -0.03 + (2 \times 0.03 + 0.03^2)^{0.5}$$
$$= 0.217$$

or $x = 0.217d = 0.217 \times 380 = 82.4$ mm.

Using Equation (4.8) (in steel units) to calculate I,

$$I/bd^3 = (x/d)^3/(3\alpha_e) + \rho(1 - x/d)^2$$
$$= 0.217^3/(3 \times 14.29) + (0.03/14.29) \times (1 - 0.217)^2$$
$$= 1.54\text{E}-3$$

$$I = 1.54\text{E}-3 \times 1000 \times 380^3$$
$$= 0.843\text{E}8 \text{ mm}^4.$$

steel stress, $f_s = M(d-x)/I$

$$= 46.2E6 \times (380 - 82.4)/0.843E8$$
$$= 163 \text{ N/mm}^2$$

steel strain, $\varepsilon_s = f_s/E_s$

$$= 163/200E-3$$
$$= 815 \text{ microstrain.}$$

$\varepsilon_1 = \varepsilon_s(h-x)/(d-x)$

$$= 815 \times (430 - 82)/(380 - 82)$$
$$= 952 \text{ microstrain}$$

Tension stiffening,

$$\varepsilon_t = -b_t(h-x)(a'-x)/(3A_sE_s(d-x)) \tag{5.28}$$

At this level $h = 430$ and $a' = h$, so

$$\varepsilon_t = -1000 \times (430 - 82.4)^2/(3 \times 804 \times 200E-3 \times (380 - 82.4))$$
$$= -842 \text{ microstrain.}$$

Thus the mean strain, ε_m, is given by

$\varepsilon_m = \varepsilon_1 + \varepsilon_t$

$$= 952 - 842$$
$$= 110 \text{ microstrain}$$

thus indicating that under flexure alone there is negligible cracking.

Strip 8
Applied loading $= 20 + 0.33 \times 17(2 \times 8 - 1)/2$

$$= 62.1 \text{ kN/m}^2$$

$M = 62.1 \times 3.5^2/12$

$$= 63.4 \text{ kN m/m}$$

$\rho\alpha_e = 14.29 \times 1005/(1000 \times 500)$

$$= 0.029$$

$x/d = 0.214$ or $x = 107$ mm
$I/bd^3 = 1.47E-3$ or $I = 1.84E8$ mm^4
$f_s = 135$ N/mm^2 $\varepsilon_s = 675$ microstrain
$\varepsilon_1 = 675 \times (550 - 107)/(500 - 107) = 761$ microstrain
$h = 590$, so $\varepsilon_t = -984$ microstrain
Net strain, $\varepsilon_m = -223$ microstrain.
This indicates the section is uncracked under flexure alone.

Early thermal cracking.

Assuming summer concreting, then from Table 5.5, $T_1 = 30$ and $T_2 = 20°C$.
It is not proposed to increase T_1 because the wall is thicker than 400 at the base.

Thermal strain for siliceous aggregate is

$$\varepsilon_{th} = \alpha(T_1 + T_2)/2$$
$$= 12 \times (30 + 20)/2$$
$$= 300 \text{ microstrain.}$$

On strip 8 the sum of the thermal strain and the flexural strain is small (77 microstrain), indicating that little cracking will occur. For strip 5 the sum of strains is 410 microstrain and thus the crack width will need checking. Figure 13.31 should be consulted for the relevant dimensions.

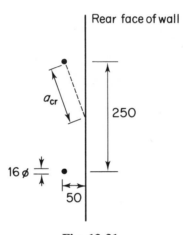

Fig. 13.31

$$a_{cr} = (125^2 + 50^2)^{0.5}$$
$$= 127$$

$$w_d = 3a_{cr}\varepsilon_m/(1 + 2(a_{cr} - c_{min})/(h - x)) \quad\quad (5.27)$$

$a_{cr} = 127$, $c_{min} = 42$, $h = 430$, $x = 82.4$ and $\varepsilon_m = 410$, giving

$$w_d = 3 \times 127 \times 410\text{E}{-}6/(1 + 2(127 - 42)/(430 - 82.4))$$
$$= 0.11 \text{ mm}$$

This is less than the allowable of 0.30 mm.

(j)   Main reinforcement schedule

Wall	0–5 m	T16–250 EF	Horizontal
	5–10 m	T16–200 EF	Horizontal
		T16–200 EF	Vertical (1)
Counterforts		4T32	Vertical
	0–5 m	T10–125	Links
	5–10 m	T10–100	Links (2)

Base slab	Toe	T32–100 B	Longitudinal
		T20–200 B	Transverse
	Heel	T32–200 B	Longitudinal
		T20–200 EF	Transverse
	Shear key	T32–100	Vertical
		T20–200	Longitudinal

Detailing notes
(1) Additional vertical bars will be needed in the front face to anchor the links used to transfer the reaction to the counterforts.
(2) It may be better toward the bottom of the counterfort to detail the links as pairs of lapped 'U' bars. Additional side reinforcement will be needed in accordance with cl 3.12.5.4, Pt 1.
(3) The main vertical bars should be lapped at mid-height to facilitate construction, since owing to its height the wall is unlikely to be poured in one operation.

13.7 Bending, shear and torsion reinforcement

A beam of rectangular cross-section is subject to a bending moment $M = 225$ kN m, a torsional moment $T = 45$ kN m and a shear force $V = 270$ kN. Given that the cross-section is 650 mm deep and 350 mm wide with $f_{cu} = 30$ N/mm^2 and $f_y = 460$ N/mm^2, determine the reinforcement required.

Bending

$$d = h - \text{cover} - \text{link} - 0.5 \times (\text{long. bar dia.})$$
$$d = 650 - 30 - 10 - 10 = 600 \text{ mm}$$

Bending K factor (cl 3.4.4.4, Pt 1)

$$K = M/(bd^2 f_{cu}) = 225\text{E}6/(350 \times 600^2 \times 30) = 0.0595 < 0.156,$$

therefore compression reinforcement is not required.
  Lever arm (cl 3.4.4.4, Pt 1)

$$z = d[0.5 + \sqrt{(0.25 - K/0.9)}]$$
$$= 600 \times [0.5 + \sqrt{(0.25 - 0.0595/0.9)}] = 557.3 \text{ mm}$$

but not greater than $0.95d = 0.95 \times 600 = 570$ mm
  Use $z = 557.3$ mm.
  Area of tensile steel (cl 3.4.4.4, Pt 1)

$$A_s = M/(0.87 f_y z) = 225\text{E}6/(0.87 \times 460 \times 557.3) = 1009 \text{ mm}^2$$

The size of the longitudinal bars is not calculated at this stage because later this area is increased to resist torsion.

Shear stresses

Check if section able to resist combined shear stresses.
  Shear stress from transverse shear force (cl 3.4.5.2, Pt 1)

$$v = V/(b_v d) = 270\text{E}3/(350 \times 600) = 1.286 \text{ N/mm}^2$$

Maximum torsional shear stress (cl 2.4.4.1, Pt 2) from Equation (7.9)

$$v_t = 2T/[h_{min}^2(h_{max} - h_{min}/3)]$$
$$= 2 \times 45E6/[350^2 \times (650 - 350/3)] = 1.378 \text{ N/mm}^2$$

Sum of the shear stress and torsional stress (cl 2.4.5, Pt 2)

$$v + v_t = 1.286 + 1.378 = 2.664 \text{ N/mm}^2$$

Maximum design shear stress

$$v_{tu} = 0.8\sqrt{f_{cu}} = 0.8\sqrt{30} = 4.382 \text{ N/mm}^2 < 5 \text{ N/mm}^2$$

$v + v_t(2.664) < v_{tu}(4.382)$ N/mm^2, therefore section not too small.

Minimum design torsional shear stress

$$v_{t,min} = 0.067\sqrt{f_{cu}} = 0.067\sqrt{30} = 0.367 \text{ N/mm}^2$$

$v_t(1.378) > v_{t,min}(0.367)$ N/mm^2, therefore design torsion reinforcement (cl 2.4.6, Pt 2) (see Appendix A2).

Now determine the torsion reinforcement and find the total area of longitudinal steel, which is used to calculate the shear force resistance.

Torsion reinforcement

From Equation (7.10)

$$A_{sv}/s_v = T/(0.8x_1y_10.87f_{yv})$$
$$= 45E6/(0.8 \times 280 \times 550 \times 0.87 \times 460) = 0.913 \text{ mm}$$

Later this value will be added to the corresponding value for shear reinforcement.
Extra area of longitudinal steel required to resist torsion (cl 2.4.7, Pt 2).

$$A_s = A_{sv}f_{yv}(x_1 + y_1)/(s_vf_y)$$
$$= 0.913 \times (280 + 550) = 758 \text{ mm}^2$$

It is not possible to use 4 bars, i.e. one in each corner of the link, because the vertical spacing exceeds 300 mm (cl 2.4.9, Pt 2). Therefore use 6T16 = 1206 mm^2 (two bars as compression reinforcement, two half-way down the section and two combined with the tension reinforcement).
Total area of tension steel

$$A_s > 1009 + 1206/3 = 1441 \text{ mm}^2.$$

Use as tension reinforcement 6T20 (1885 mm^2).

Shear reinforcement

Design shear stress for a singly reinforced concrete beam (cl 3.4.5.4, Pt 1)

$$v_c = k_1k_20.79[100A_s/(b_vd)]^{1/3}(400/d)^{1/4}/1.25$$
$$= 1 \times (30/25)^{1/3} \times 0.79 \times [100 \times 1885/(350 \times 600)]^{1/3} \times 1/1.25$$
$$= 0.648 \text{ N/mm}^2$$

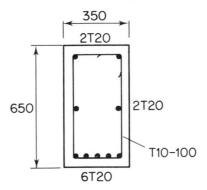

$v(1.286) > v_c(0.684)$ N/mm^2 therefore design for shear reinforcement (cl 2.4.6, Pt 2) (see Appendix A2).

Rearranging Equation (7.4) (cl 3.4.5.4, Pt 1)

$$A_{sv}/s_v = b_v(v - v_c)/(0.87f_{yv})$$
$$= 350 \times (1.286 - 0.648)/(0.87 \times 460) = 0.558 \text{ mm}$$

Total value of A_{sv}/s_v required to resist torsion and shear (cl 2.4.7, Pt 2)

$$\Sigma(A_{sv}/s_v) = 0.913 + 0.558 = 1.471 \text{ mm}$$

Spacing of T10 vertical links

$$s_v = A_{sv}/1.471 = 2 \times 79/1.471 = 107 \text{ mm}$$

The spacing of the links s_v should not exceed the least of x_1, $y_1/2$ or 200 mm (cl 2.4.8, Pt 2).

Use T10–100 mm centres.

13.8 Design in lightweight concrete

Lightweight concrete is made from normal cement, sand and lightweight aggregate. Lightweight aggregate can either come from natural sources normally of volcanic extraction such as pumice or be manufactured from materials such as vermiculite, expanded clay or shale, foamed blast furnace slag or clinker. Owing to the increased porosity of these aggregates a higher water–cement ratio is often required. This increased porosity does give a slightly inferior performance as far as durability is concerned. Typical specific weights of lightweight concrete are of the order of 15–20 kN/m^3. There is no problem in attaining any required design strength.

The major advantages of lightweight concrete are:

(1) The dead load of the structure is reduced, thereby often giving a more economic structure since member sizes are often reduced, which leads to reduced problems with foundations.
(2) It is a better insulator leading to increased fire performance for a given member size or a reduced section size for the same performance.

The major reason why lightweight concrete is not used to a far larger extent considering its advantage is lack of familiarity by both consultants and contractors and a higher degree of site supervision required since lightweight concrete has a greater tendency to segregate than normal-weight concrete.

The design of lightweight concrete does not differ from normal-weight concrete except that some design parameter values are different. The use of lightweight concrete is covered by Section 5, Pt 2 of BS 8110, which is summarised below:

(i)   *Cover*

Durability. All the covers in Table 5.1 should be increased by 10 except for those with mild exposure which are unchanged.

Fire. These have been summarised in Table 5.9.

(ii)   *Shear*

The values for both design and ultimate are reduced to 80% of the values for normal-weight concrete. This also applies for torsion.

(iii)   *Deflection*

The methods of Section 5.6 may be used, except that when the imposed characteristic load exceeds $4 \, kN/m^2$ the basic/span effective depth ratios of Table 5.3 should be reduced by 15%.

(iv)   *Columns*

Columns are to be considered short when the slenderness ratio is less than 10, and the deflection factor, β_a, is given by

$$\beta_a = (l_e/b')/1200$$

A similar set of conditions applies to walls.

(v)   *Anchorage bond and laps*

The bond stresses given for normal-weight concrete are to be reduced to 80% of these values when applied to lightweight concrete.

To illustrate the design of lightweight concrete the flat slab in Design Study 13.4 will be redone using it.

The layout of the 9-panel flat slab without dropheads remains that given in Fig. 13.15. The slab is 200 mm thick and carries an imposed load of $2.5 \, kN/m^2$. The columns are 400 mm square and 3500 mm high. Prepare a design for the bays B1C4 and 2D3A, using grade 30 lightweight concrete of specific weight $20 \, kN/m^3$ and grade 460 steel.

Analysis

Total load, $n = 1.4G_k + 1.6Q_k$
$$= 1.4 \times 0.2 \times 20 + 1.6 \times 2.5$$
$$= 9.6 \, kN/m^2.$$

The minimum cover is 20 mm for both durability and fire. So assuming a maximum bar size of 20 the effective depth for the long span is 170 and for the short span 150.

(a)   Bay B1C4

Line load $= n \times$ (bay width) $= 9.6 \times 6 = 57.6 \, kN/m$.

The bending-moment diagram for the slab which has been obtained by analysing the subframe containing the floor and the remote ends of the columns have been assumed fixed. All spans are under full loading, and the results are given in Fig. 13.33(a).

The maximum redistribution that may be carried out is 20% (cl 3.5.2.3, Pt 1).

The limit at edge columns depends on the moment that may be transferred to the edge columns ($M_{t,max}$)

$$M_{t,max} = 0.15b_e d^2 f_{cu} \tag{13.14}$$

The value of the effective width, b_e, to be taken is defined in Fig. 13.17. A restriction placed on the value of $M_{t,max}$ is that it shall not be less than 50% of the moment obtained from a frame analysis, nor 70% of that from a grillage or finite-element analysis (cl 3.7.4.2, Pt 1).

Assuming $d = 150$, then from Case 3 of Fig. 13.17, $b_e = C_x + C_y$, so

$$M_{t,max} = 0.15(0.4 + 0.4) \times 0.15^2 \times 30 \times 1000$$
$$= 81 \text{ kN m.}$$

The moment at the column is already less than this and thus no further adjustment may be made. The redistribution has been done in Fig. 13.33(b). The resultant shear-force diagram is given in Fig. 13.33(c).

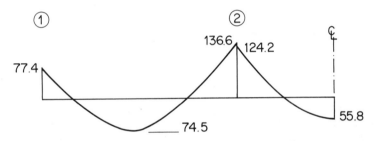

(a) BMD before any redistribution

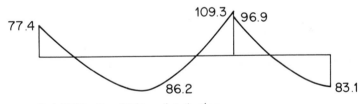

(b) BMD after 20% redistribution

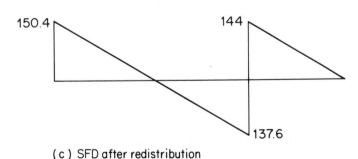

(c) SFD after redistribution

Fig. 13.33

(b)   Bay 2D3A
Line load $= 9.6 \times 5 = 48$ kN/m.

A similar procedure is adopted here except that d is taken as 170 with $M_{t,max}$ as 104.0 kN m. The bending-moment and shear-force diagrams are plotted in Fig. 13.34.

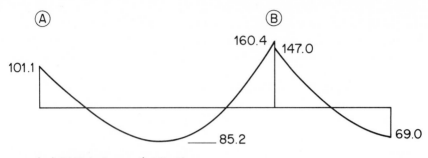

(a) BMD before redistribution

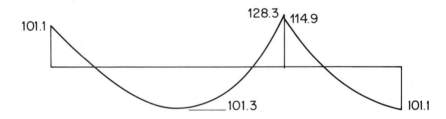

(b) BMD after 20% redistribution

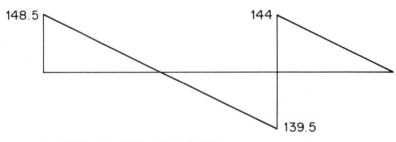

(c) SFD after 20% redistribution

Fig. 13.34

Design

(a)   Bending
The slab must be divided into column and middle strips according to Fig. 13.19.

This is carried out in Fig. 13.20(a) and (b) for each of the bays.

The moments from the analysis should be apportioned to the column and middle strips using Table 13.1.

This is carried out in Table 13.8, together with the flexural design.

Table 13.8 Slab design for flexure

Bay	Calculation	Column strip — End span Ext. col.	Mid-span	Int. col.	Interior span Int. col.	Mid-span	Middle strip — End span Ext. col.	Mid-span	Int. col.	Interior span Int. col.	Mid-span
B1C4	M (kN m)	58.1	47.7	82.0	72.7	45.7	19.3	39.0	27.3	24.2	37.4
	M/bd^2f_{cu}	0.034	0.028	0.049	0.43	0.027	0.008	0.017	0.012	0.010	0.016
	$A_s f_y/bdf_{cu}$	0.042	0.035	0.060	0.052	0.035	0.010	0.020	0.013	0.012	0.020
	$100A_{s,req}/bd$	0.27	0.23	0.39	0.34	0.23	0.07	0.13	0.05	0.08	0.13
	$A_{s,req}$ (mm^2)	1028	856	1467	1272	856	342	685	445	411	685
	Bar diam. (mm)	12	12	16	16	12	10*	10	10*	10*	10
	$100A_{s,prov}/bd$	0.30	0.30	0.54	0.54	0.30	0.21	0.21	0.21	0.21	0.21
2D3A	M (kN m)	75.8	55.7	96.2	86.2	55.6	25.3	45.6	32.1	28.7	45.5
	M/bd^2f_{cu}	0.035	0.026	0.044	0.040	0.026	0.012	0.021	0.015	0.013	0.021
	$A_s f_y/bdf_{cu}$	0.043	0.021	0.054	0.049	0.032	0.013	0.025	0.018	0.16	0.025
	$100A_{s,req}/bd$	0.28	0.14	0.35	0.32	0.21	0.085	0.16	0.12	0.10	0.16
	$A_{s,req}$ (mm^2)	1192	582	1497	1358	887	360	693	499	443	693
	Bar diam. (mm)	16	10*	16	16	12	10*	10	10*	10*	10
	$100A_{s,prov}/bd$	0.47	0.18	0.47	0.47	0.27	0.18	0.18	0.18	0.18	0.18

Notes:
(1) For bay B1C4 $d = 150$ and bay 2D3A $d = 170$
(2) All strip widths are 2500 mm except middle strip of bay B1C4 which is 3500
(3) The design chart in Appendix B1.1 has been used.
(4) Minimum reinforcement has been indicated thus *
(5) As in Design Study 13.6 the spacing has been kept as 250 throughout, and the minimum bar diameter as 10 mm.

(b)   Shear

Maximum shear stress $= 0.8(0.8(f_{cu})^{0.5}$

$$= 0.8 \times 0.8(30)^{0.5}$$

$$= 3.50 \text{ N/mm}^2.$$

This is less than 4.0 N/mm^2, therefore satisfactory.

The ultimate shear must be checked at the column face and then the allowable shear must be checked on successive perimeters $0.75d$ apart commencing $1.5d$ from the column face (Chapter 7).

The actual shear from the shear-force diagrams must be enhanced to allow for the effect of relative rotation between the slab and the column owing to the transfer of moment (M_t) to the column.

Consider the column B2.

(i)   Along grid line B
Using Equation (13.15)

$$V_t = 281.6 \text{ kN}, \ M_t = 12.4 \text{ kN and } x = 0.4 + 2 \times 1.5 \times 0.15 = 0.85 \text{ m}$$
$$V_{eff} = 281.6(1 + 1.5 \times 12.4/(281.6 \times 0.85)$$

$$= 300.3 \text{ kN}.$$

(ii)   Along grid line 2
Using Equation (13.15)

$$V_t = 283.5 \text{ kN}, \ M_t = 13.4 \text{ kN m}, \ x = 0.4 + 2 \times 1.5 \times 0.170 = 0.910 \text{ m}$$
$$V_{eff} = 283.5(1 + 1.5 \times 13.4/(283.5 \times 0.910))$$
$$= 302.3 \text{ kN}.$$

Thus the total shear on column B2 is 602.6 kN, with a mean effective depth of $(150 + 170)/2 = 160$, the ultimate shear at the column face is given by

$$v = V/ud = 602.6\text{E}3/(4 \times 400 \times 160) = 2.35 \text{ N/mm}^2$$

This is less than the allowable shear stress of 3.5 and is therefore satisfactory.

At a shear perimeter $1.5d$ out from the column of $4 \times 400 + 8 \times 1.5 \times 160 = 3520$ mm.

$$v = V/ud$$
$$= 602.6\text{E}3/(3520 \times 160)$$
$$= 1.07 \text{ N/mm}^2.$$

This is less than the maximum of 3.50 N/mm^2.

The allowable shear stress, v_c, may be calculated using the mean value of $100A_s/bd$ crossing the shear perimeter, i.e.

$$(0.54 + 0.47)/2 = 0.51$$

so from Equation (7.2)

$$v_c = 0.8(0.79(100A_s/bd)^{0.33}(400/d)^{0.25}(f_{cu}/25)^{0.33}/1.25)$$
$$= 0.8 \times 0.79(0.70)^{0.33}(400/162)^{0.25}(30/25)^{0.33}/1.25$$
$$= 0.54 \text{ N/mm}^2.$$

Thus shear reinforcement is needed and must be designed to resist the greater of $v - v_c$ or 0.4 N/mm^2 (cl 3.5.5.3, Pt 1).

Using vertical links, i.e. $\sin \alpha = 1$, the shear steel required is given by cl 3.7.7.5, Pt 1,

$$A_{sv} = (v - v_c)ud/(0.87f_{yv})$$

Using high-yield links $f_{yv} = 460$ N/mm^2.

So

$$A_{sv} = (1.07 - 0.54) \times 3520 \times 160/(0.87 \times 460)$$
$$= 746 \text{ mm}^2.$$

This may be divided into two layers with the legs spaced at not greater than 1.5d (cl 3.7.7.5, Pt 1).

Number of bars = shear perimeter/spacing
$$= 3520/(1.5 \times 160)$$
$$= 14.6, \quad \text{say } 16$$

Cross-sectional area per bar = Area of steel bar per layer/no. of bars
$$= (746/2)/16$$
$$= 23 \text{ mm}^2$$

Fix T6 bars (28 mm^2).

The shear must now be checked at 2.25d out from the column face. The effective shear force will not be recalculated since the result is conservative.

$$u = 4 \times 400 + 8 \times 2.25 \times 160 = 4480 \text{ mm}.$$

$$v = 602.6E3/(4480 \times 160)$$
$$= 0.84 \text{ N/mm}^2$$

$v_c = 0.54$ as before, and the links must be designed for the greater of $0.84 - 0.54$ (=0.30) or 0.4 N/mm^2.

$$A_{sv} = 0.4 \times 4480 \times 160/(0.87 \times 460)$$
$$= 716.8 \text{ mm}^2$$

Number of bars = $4480/(1.5 \times 160)$
$$= 18.7, \quad \text{say } 20$$

Area per bar = (716.8/2)/20
$$= 17.9 \text{ mm}^2$$

Fix T6

At 3d,

$$u = 4 \times 400 + 8 \times 3 \times 160$$
$$= 5440 \text{ mm}$$

$$v = 602.6E3/(5440 \times 160)$$
$$= 0.69 \text{ N/mm}^2.$$

$v_c = 0.54$ as before, and the links are designed for the greater of $v - v_c$ ($= 0.69 - 0.54 = 0.15$) or 0.4 N/mm^2,

$$A_{sv} = 0.4 \times 5440 \times 160/(0.87 \times 460)$$
$$= 870 \text{ mm}^2.$$

Number of bars $= 5440/(1.5 \times 160)$
$$= 22.6, \quad \text{say 24}$$

Area per bar $= (870/2)/24$
$$= 18.1 \text{ mm}^2$$

Fix T6 (28 mm^2)
  At $3.75d$, $u = 6400$

$$v = 602.6\text{E}3/(6400 \times 160) = 0.59 \text{ N/mm}^2$$

The links must be designed to take 0.4 N/mm^2, so

$$A_{sv} = 0.4 \times 6400 \times 160/(0.87 \times 160)$$
$$= 1024 \text{ mm}^2$$

Number of bars $= 6400/(1.5 \times 160)$
$$= 26.7, \quad \text{say 28}$$

Area per bar $= (1024/2)/28$
$$= 18.3 \text{ mm}^2$$

Fix T6
  At $4.5d$, $u = 7360$ mm

$$v = 602.6\text{E}3/(7360 \times 160)$$
$$= 0.51 \text{ N/mm}^2.$$

$v < v_c$ so no further links are required.

(c)   Deflection
It is usually only necessary to check the short span (cl 3.5.7, Pt 1).
  Basic span depth ratio $= 26$ (Table 5.3).

(i)   *End span* (middle strip)
$100A_{s,prov}/bd = 0.21$
$100A_{s,req}/bd = 0.13$
$M/bd^2 = 0.017 \times 30 = 0.51$ (from Table 13.10)
$1/\beta_b = 85.2/101.3 = 0.84$ (from Fig. 13.33)
  Using Equation (5.8) to calculate the service stress,

$$f_s = (5/8)f_y((100A_{s,req}/bd)/(100A_{s,prov}/bd)) \times (1/\beta_b)$$
$$= (5/8) \times 460 \times (0.13/0.21) \times 0.84$$
$$= 150 \text{ N/mm}^2$$
$$F_1 = 0.55 + (477 - f_s)/(120(0.9 + M/bd^2)) \tag{5.7}$$
$$= 0.55 + (477 - 150)/(120(0.9 + 0.51))$$
$$= 2.48$$

The maximum value that may be taken is 2.00

So minimum effective depth = span/(basic ratio $\times F_1$)

$$= 5000/(26 \times 2.00)$$

$$= 104 \text{ mm}$$

Actual effective depth is 150 mm.

(ii) *Centre span* (middle strip)

$100A_{s,prov}/bd = 0.21$

$100A_{s,req}/bd = 0.33$

$M/bd^2 = 0.016 \times 30 = 0.48$ (from Table 13.8)

$1/\beta_b = 55.8/83.1 = 0.67$ (from Fig. 13.33)

$$f_s = (5/8) \times 460(0.13/0.21) \times 0.67$$
$$F_1 = 119 \text{ N/mm}^2$$
$$= 0.55 + (477 - 119)/(120(0.9 + 0.48))$$
$$= 2.71$$

Maximum value of F_1 that may be taken is 2.0.

Minimum effective depth = $5000/(26 \times 2.0)$

$$= 96 \text{ mm, which is satisfactory.}$$

(d) Fire engineering design

It is not proposed to carry out the fire engineering calculations again since the principles are exactly the same as for normal-weight concrete except that the strength reduction factors for the concrete at a given temperature are less and the temperatures within the slab are also lower. Both these factors enhance the performance, giving an even higher load capacity than the design with normal-weight concrete, which itself was excellent.

Appendix A1 Bar Area Tables

Cross-sectional areas of groups of bars (mm²)

Bar size (mm)		6	8	10	12	16	20	25	32	40
Number of bars	1	28	50	79	113	201	314	491	804	1256
	2	57	101	157	226	402	628	982	1608	2513
	3	85	151	236	339	603	942	1473	2413	3770
	4	113	201	314	452	804	1257	1964	3217	5026
	5	141	251	393	565	1005	1571	2455	4021	6283
	6	170	302	471	679	1206	1885	2945	4825	7540
	7	198	352	550	792	1407	2199	3436	5630	8796
	8	226	402	628	905	1608	2533	3927	6434	10050
	9	254	452	707	1018	1809	2827	4418	7238	11310
	10	283	503	785	1131	2011	3142	4909	8042	12570
Circumference		18.9	25.1	31.4	37.7	50.3	62.8	78.5	100.5	125.7

Cross-sectional areas of bars per metre width (mm²)

Bar size (mm)		6	8	10	12	16	20	25	32
Pitch of bars	60	471	837	1309	1884	3350	5234	8181	13404
	80	353	628	982	1414	2512	3926	6136	10053
	100	283	503	785	1131	2011	3141	4909	8042
	120	236	419	654	942	1674	2617	4091	6702
	140	202	359	561	808	1435	2244	3506	5745
	150	189	335	524	754	1338	2094	3273	5362
	160	177	314	491	707	1256	1964	3068	5027
	180	157	279	436	627	1115	1746	2727	4468
	200	141	251	393	565	1005	1572	2454	4021
	250	113	201	314	452	804	1257	1964	3217
	300	95	168	262	377	669	1047	1636	2681

Appendix A2 Maximum and Minimum Percentages of Reinforcement

A2.1   General

Sufficient reinforcement must be provided to resist the design forces and to control the width and length of cracks in the concrete. The quantity of reinforcement should not be so small that it is ineffective, but on the other hand it should not be so great that it prevents the placing and compaction of the concrete. Percentages of steel are related to the gross cross-sectional area, and in practice vary between 0.1 and 10%. Recommendations for various situations are as follows.

A2.2   Minimum reinforcement

When considering minimum percentages of reinforcement the diameters of the bars involved are often small. The minimum bar diameter used in practice is generally not less than 6 mm. Beams should not contain less than 2 bars as tension reinforcement, a rectangular column not less than a total of 4 bars, and a circular column not less than a total of 6.

A2.2.1   Beams and columns

The minimum size of bars in the side face of a beam to control cracking should be not less than $\sqrt{(s_b b/f_y)}$, where s_b is the bar spacing and b is the breadth of the beam, but not less than 500 mm (cl 3.12.5.4, Pt 1).

For beam or column compression reinforcement links should be $0.25 \times$ (largest compression bar) or 6 mm, whichever is the greater (cl 3.12.7.1, Pt 1). See also A2.6.5.

Reinforcement may be needed to control cracking due to thermal or/and hydration shrinkage. In walls the following is recommended (cl 3.9.4.19, Pt 1). In each direction at least:

(1) $0.0025A_c$ for grade 460 steel and above
(2) $0.003A_c$ for grade 250 steel.

These recommendations may also be adopted for other situations (cl 3.12.11.2.9, Pt 1).

Minimum percentages of steel for members in flexure and compression (beams and columns).

Table A2.1 Minimum percentages of reinforcement (Cl 3.12.5.3, Pt 1, Table 3.27)

Situation	Definition of percentage	Minimum percentage $f_y = 250$ N/mm²	$f_y = 460$ N/mm²
Tension reinforcement		%	%
Sections subjected mainly to pure tension	$100A_s/A_c$	0.8	0.45
Sections subjected to flexure:			
(a) Flanged beams, web in tension:			
(1) $b_w/b < 0.4$	$100A_s/b_wh$	0.32	0.18
(2) $b_w/b \geqslant 0.4$	$100A_s/b_wh$	0.24	0.13
(b) Flanged beams, flange in tension over a continuous support:			
(1) T-beam	$100A_s/b_wh$	0.48	0.26
(2) L-beam	$100A_s/b_wh$	0.36	0.20
(c) Rectangular section (in solid slabs this minimum should be provided in both directions)	$100A_s/A_c$	0.24	0.13
Compression reinforcement (where such reinforcement is required for the ultimate limit state)			
General rule	$100A_{sc}/A_{cc}$	0.4	0.4
Simplified rules for particular cases:			
(a) rectangular column or wall	$100A_{sc}/A_c$	0.4	0.4
(b) flanged beam:			
(1) flange in compression	$100A_{sc}/bh_f$	0.4	0.4
(2) web in compression	$100A_{sc}/b_wh$	0.2	0.2
(c) rectangular beam	$100A_{sc}/A_c$	0.2	0.2
Transverse reinforcements in flanges of flanged beams (provided over full effective flange width near top surface to resist horizontal shear)	$100A_{st}/h_f l$	0.15	0.15

A2.2.2 Prestressed beams

To ensure that cracking precedes failure of a prestressed beam the tensile steel should exceed the moment necessary to produce a flexural tensile stress at the extreme fibres of $0.6\sqrt{f_{cu}}$. The prestress is the value after all losses have occurred (cl 4.12.2, Pt 1).

A2.2.3   Beams subject to shear forces

Table A2.2   Form and area of shear reinforcement in beams (Cl 3.4.5, Pt 1, Table 3.8)

Value of v (N/mm^2)	Form of shear reinforcement to be provided	Area of shear reinforcement to be provided
Less than $0.5v_c$ throughout the beam	See note 1	
$0.5v_c < v < (v_c + 0.4)$	Minimum links for whole length of beam	$A_{sv} \geqslant 0.4b_v s_v / 0.87f_{yv}$ (see note 2)
$(v_c + 0.4) < v < 0.8\sqrt{f_{cu}}$ or 5 N/mm^2	Links or links combined with bent-up bars. Not more than 50% of the shear resistance provided by the steel may be in the form of bent-up bars (see note 3)	Where links only provided: $A_{sv} \geqslant b_s s_v (v - v_c)/0.87f_{yv}$ *Where links and bent-up bars provided:* (see cl 3.4.5.6)

Note 1:   While minimum links should be provided in all beams of structural importance, it will be satisfactory to omit them in members of minor structural importance such as lintels where the maximum design shear stress is less than half v_c.

Note 2:   Minimum links provide a design shear resistance of 0.4 N/mm^2.

Note 3:   See cl 3.4.5.5 for guidance on spacing of links and bent-up bars.

A2.2.4   Slabs subject to shear forces

Table A2.3   Form and area of shear reinforcement in solid slabs (Cl 3.5.5, Pt 1, Table 3.17)

Value of v (N/mm^2)	Form of shear reinforcement to be provided	Area of shear reinforcement to be provided
$v < v_c$ $v_c < v(v_c + 0.4)$ $(v_c + 0.4) < v < 0.8\sqrt{f_{cu}}$ or 5 N/mm^2	None required Minimum links in area where $v > v_c$ Links and/or bent-up bars in any combination (but the spacing between links or bent-up bars need not be less than d)	None $A_{sv} \geqslant 0.4bs_v/0.87f_{yv}$ *Where links only provided:* $A_{sv} \geqslant bs_v (v - v_c)/0.87f_{yv} \ldots$ *Where bent-up bars only provided:* $A_{sb} \geqslant bs_b (v - v_c)/$ $(0.87f_{yv}(\cos \alpha + \sin \alpha \cot \beta))$ (see 3.4.5.7)

Note 1:   It is difficult to bend and fix shear reinforcement so that its effectiveness can be assured in slabs less than 200 mm deep. It is therefore not advisable to use shear reinforcement in such slabs.

Note 2:   The enhancement in design shear strength close to supports described in cls 3.4.5.9 and 3.4.5.10 may also be applied to solid slabs.

For slabs greater than 200 mm deep and subject to concentrated loads where $v > v_c$ shear reinforcement should be provided such that

$$\Sigma A_{sv} \sin \alpha > (v - v_c)ud/(0.87f_{yv})$$

Where v_c should not be taken as less than 0.4 N/mm^2 (cl 3.7.7.5, Pt 1).

A2.2.5   Members subject to torsion and shear forces

When the torsional shear stress v_t is greater than $v_{t,min} = 0.067\sqrt{f_{cu}}$, shear reinforcement to resist shear and torsion should be provided as shown in Table A2.4.

Table A2.4   Reinforcement for shear and torsion (Table 2.4, cl 2.4.6, Pt 2)

	$v_t \leqslant v_{t,min}$	$v_t > v_{t,min}$
$v \leqslant v_c$	Nominal shear reinforcement; no torsion reinforcement	Designed torsion reinforcement only
$v > v_c$	Designed shear reinforcement; no torsion reinforcement	Designed shear and torsion reinforcement

A2.3   Maximum reinforcement

The maximum diameter bar used in practice is generally not greater than 40 mm. The smaller the bar diameter the better the bond characteristics and crack control, but this is off-set by increased labour in fixing.

A2.3.1   Beams (cl 3.12.6.1, Pt 1)

Neither tension nor compression reinforcement should exceed 4%.

A2.3.2   Columns (cl 3.12.6.2, Pt 1)

Longitudinal reinforcement should not exceed:

  6% for vertically cast
  8% for horizontally cast
10% for laps in vertically or horizontally cast.

Maximum reinforcement in a layer including tension laps should not exceed 40% of the breadth of the section (cl 3.12.8.14, Pt 1).

A2.4   Minimum spacing between bars

The minimum spacing of bars is controlled to ensure that the maximum size of coarse aggregate passes between the bars. Also if bars are placed too close together the bond strength is reduced.

The horizontal distance between bars (cl 3.12.11, Pt 1) should not be less than

$h_{agg} + 5$ mm, where h_{agg} is the maximum size of coarse aggregate.

When there are two or more rows the gaps between the corresponding bars in each row should be in line, and the vertical distance between bars should not be less than $2h_{agg}/3$. When the bar size exceeds $h_{agg} + 5$ mm a spacing less than the bar size or equivalent bar size should be avoided. In addition, for prestressed tendons in ducts the vertical and horizontal spacings should be greater than the internal dimensions of the ducts (cl 4.12.4.2, Pt 1).

A2.4.1 Beams and columns

Bars are generally not in contact except at laps. However in special circumstances groups of bars in contact are acceptable provided the effective bar size is used for bond stress calculations (cl 3.12.8.3, Pt 1).

A2.4.2 Links

To be effectively anchored they are generally at right angles to and in contact with longitudinal bars. Single links are spaced no closer than that recommended for longitudinal reinforcement. Multiple links however are in contact at the laps.

A2.5 Maximum spacing between bars

The maximum spacing is controlled by effectiveness in resisting forces, redistribution, and crack control. In normal circumstances, when the limitation of the crack widths to 0.3 mm is appropriate, the clear horizontal distance between adjacent bars, or groups, near the tension face of a beam should be not greater than the value given in Table A2.5.

Table A2.5 Clear distance between bars according to percentage redistribution (Table 3.30, cl 3.12.11.2.3, Pt 1)

f_y	Redistribution to or from section considered						
	-30	-20	-10	0	$+10$	$+20$	$+30$
	%	%	%	%	%	%	%
250	210	240	270	300	300	300	300
460	115	130	145	160	180	195	210

Note: The values are derived from the expression:

$$\text{clear spacing} \geq \frac{75\,000\beta_b}{f_y} \leq 300$$

where β_b is the ratio:

$$\frac{\text{(moment at the section after redistribution)}}{\text{(moment at the section before redistribution)}}$$

from the respective maximum moments diagram.

Alternatively (cl 3.12.11.2.4, Pt 1)

$$\text{clear spacing} \leq 47\,000/f_s \leq 300$$

where $f_s = 5f_y A_{s,req}/(8A_{s,prov}\beta_b)$.

To control cracking longitudinal bars should be distributed at a spacing not exceeding 250 mm near the side faces of a beam (cl 3.12.11.2.6, Pt 1).

A2.5.1   Slabs

In no case should the clear spacing between bars exceed $3d$ or 750 mm (cl 3.12.11.2.7, Pt 1). In addition no further check on bar spacing is required for:

(1)   grade 250 steel where $h < 250$ mm, or
(2)   grade 460 steel where $h < 200$ mm, or
(3) $100A_s/(bd) < 0.3\%$

Where conditions (1) to (3) do not apply and where $p > 1\%$, bar spacings should be those given in Table A2.5. Where $p < 1\%$ use values from Table A2.5 divided by $p\%$.

A2.6   Maximum spacings of links

Shear links should be spaced so that at least one link intercepts a diagonal shear crack.

A2.6.1   Ordinary reinforced concrete beams

Longitudinal spacing $s_v \leqslant 0.75d$.

A2.6.2   Prestressed concrete beams

Longitudinal spacing $s_v \leqslant 0.75d_t$, or $4 \times$ (web thickness) for flanged members. When $V > 1.8V_c$, $s_v \leqslant 0.5d_t$. Lateral spacing of the individual legs at cross-section $\leqslant d_t$ (cl 4.3.8.10, Pt 1).

A2.6.3   Slabs subject to concentrated loads

Shear reinforcement should be evenly distributed around the zone on at least two sides. The spacing around the perimeter should not exceed $1.5d$ (cl 3.7.7.5, Pt 1).

A2.6.4   Torsion

Links should intercept diagonal cracks and the spacing should not exceed the least of x_1, $y_1/2$ or 200 mm (cl 2.4.8, Pt 2). Longitudinal reinforcement (at least 4 bars) should be distributed evenly round the inside perimeter of the links and the clear distance between bars should not exceed 300 mm. Torsion reinforcement should extend a distance at least equal to the largest dimension of the section beyond where it ceases to be required (cl 2.4.9, Pt 2).

A2.6.5   Containment of Compression reinforcement

Links are placed at a maximum spacing of $12 \times$ (diameter of smallest compression bar) (cl 3.12.7.1, Pt 1). This is to prevent buckling of the longitudinal bars and to enhance the crushing strength of the concrete by controlling the volumetric increase of the concrete at failure.

In an outer layer of compression reinforcement every corner bar and alternate bar should be supported by the corner of a link passing round the bar, with an included angle not less than 135°. No bar in the compression zone should be further than 150 mm from a restrained bar (cl 3.12.7.2, pt 1).

A2.6.6   Bent-up bars

Spacing not to exceed $1.5d$ (cl 3.4.5.6, Pt 1).

Appendix A3 Properties of Prestress Tendons

Type	Nominal diameter (mm)	Nominal area (mm^2)	Nominal tensile stress (N/mm^2)	Specified characteristic strength (kN)
Cold drawn wire	7	38.5	1570	60.4
BS 5896 (1980)	7	38.5	1670	64.3
	6	28.3	1670	47.3
	6	28.3	1770	50.1
	5	19.6	1670	32.7
	5	19.6	1770	34.7
	4.5	15.9	1620	25.8
	4	12.6	1670	21.0
	4	12.6	1770	22.3
Cold drawn wire in mill coil	5	19.6	1570	30.8
BS 5896 (1980)	5	19.6	1670	32.7
	5	19.6	1770	34.7
	4.5	15.9	1620	25.8
	4	12.6	1670	21.0
	4	12.6	1720	21.7
	4	12.6	1770	22.3
	3	7.07	1770	12.5
	3	7.07	1860	13.1
7-wire strand standard	15.2	139	1670	232
	12.5	93	1770	164
	11.0	71	1770	125
	9.3	52	1770	92
7-wire strand super	15.7	150	1770	265
BS 5896 (1980)	12.9	100	1860	186
	11.3	75	1860	139
	9.6	55	1860	102
	8.0	38	1860	70
7-wire strand drawn	18.0	224	1700	380
	15.2	165	1820	300
	12.7	112	1860	209
19-wire strand	31.8	660	1480	979
BS 4757 (1971)	28.6	535	1540	823
	25.4	423	1560	659
	18	210	1760	370
Hot-rolled alloy steel	40	1257	1030	1300
BS 4486 (1980)	32	804	1030	830
	25	491	1030	505
	20	314	1035	325
Hot-rolled and processed alloy steel	32	804	1230	990
	25	491	1220	600
	20	314	1225	385

Appendix B1 Design Graphs

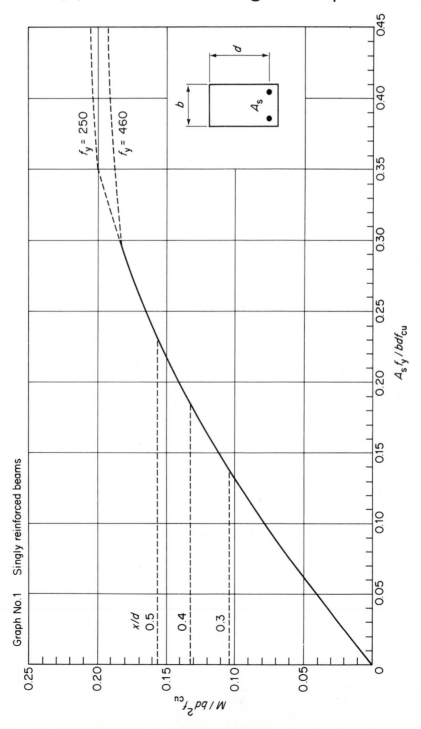

Graph No.1   Singly reinforced beams

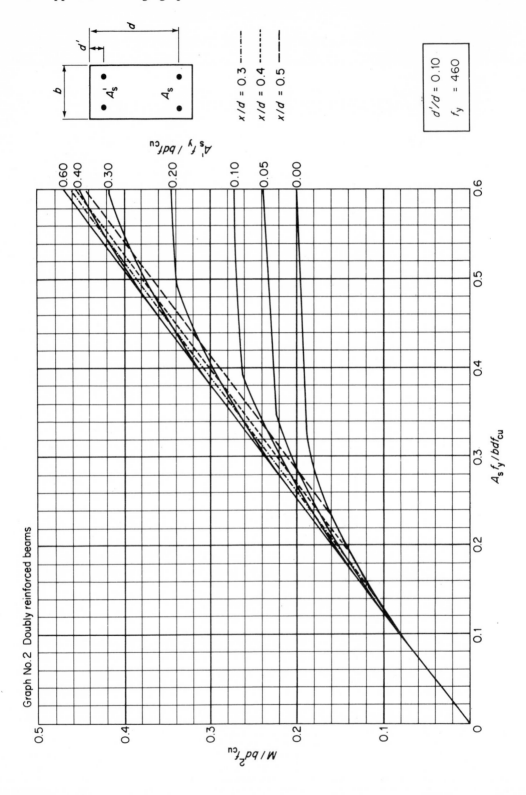

Graph No. 2 Doubly reinforced beams

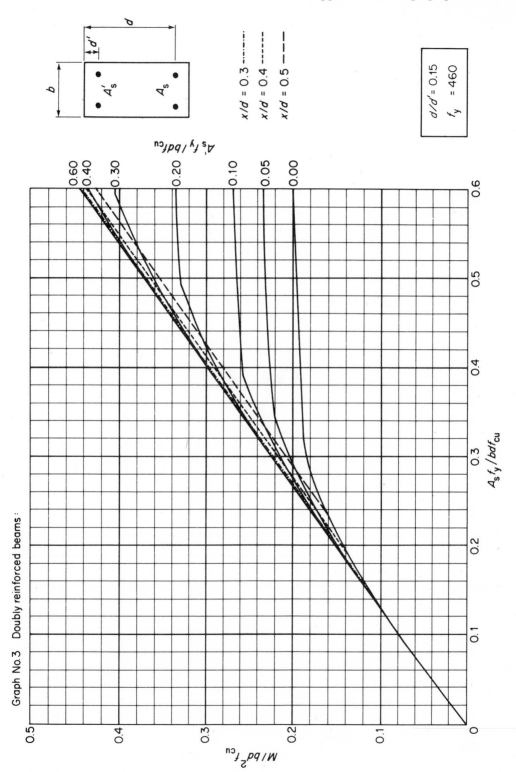

Graph No.3 Doubly reinforced beams:

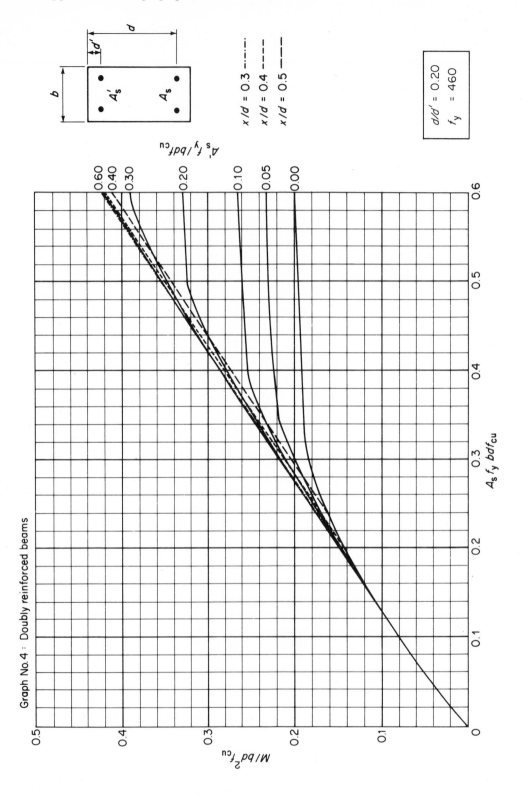

Graph No.4 : Doubly reinforced beams

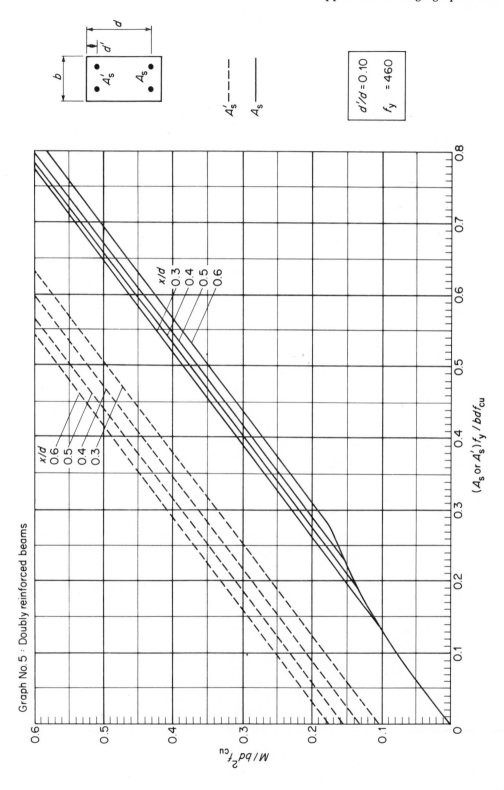

Graph No. 5 : Doubly reinforced beams

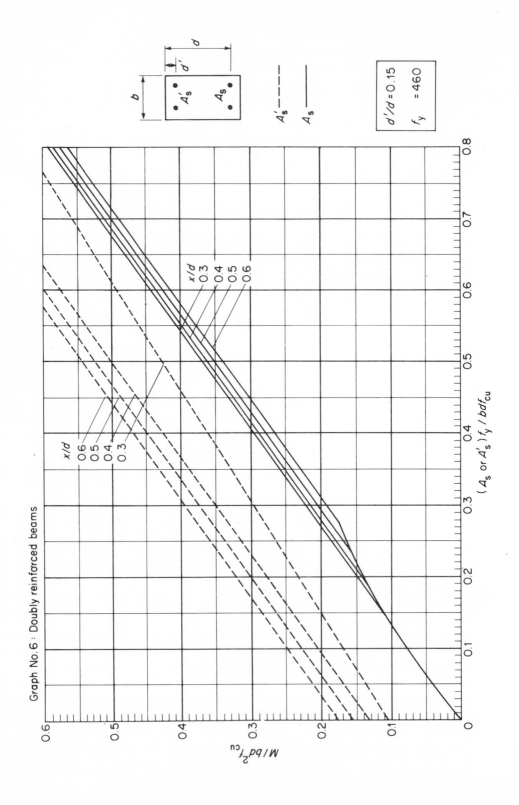

Graph No. 6 : Doubly reinforced beams

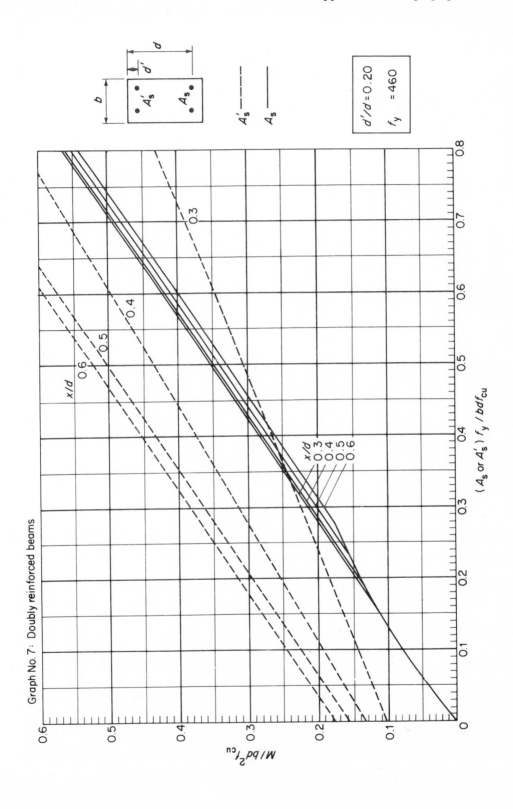

Graph No. 7: Doubly reinforced beams

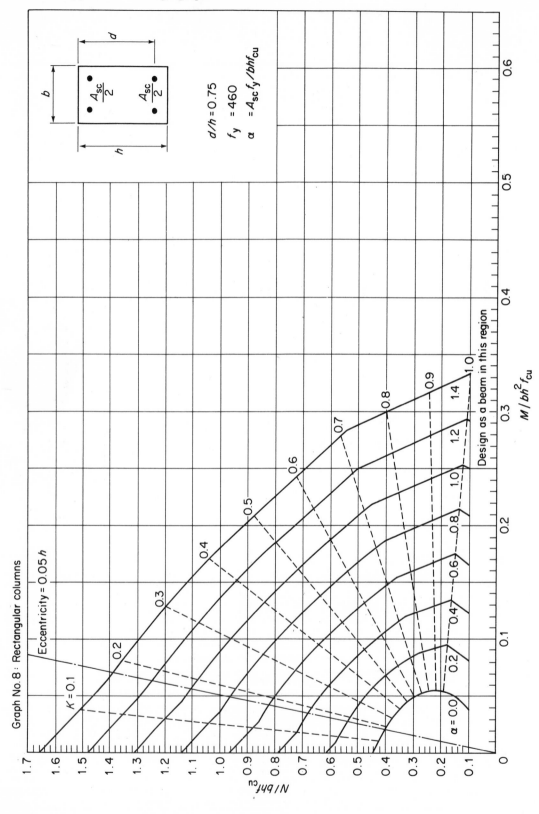

Graph No. 8 : Rectangular columns

Eccentricity = 0.05 h

$d/h = 0.75$

$f_y = 460$

$\alpha = A_{sc} f_y / bh f_{cu}$

Design as a beam in this region

$M / bh^2 f_{cu}$

$N / bh f_{cu}$

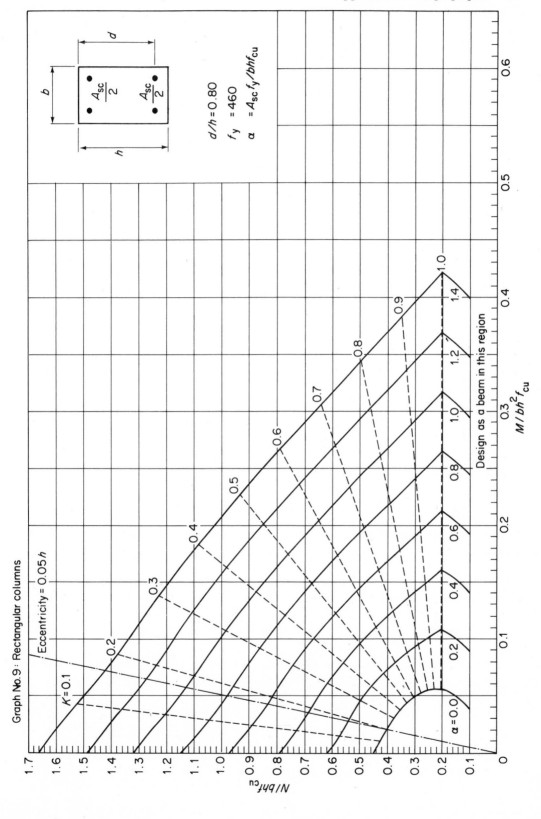

Graph No.9 : Rectangular columns

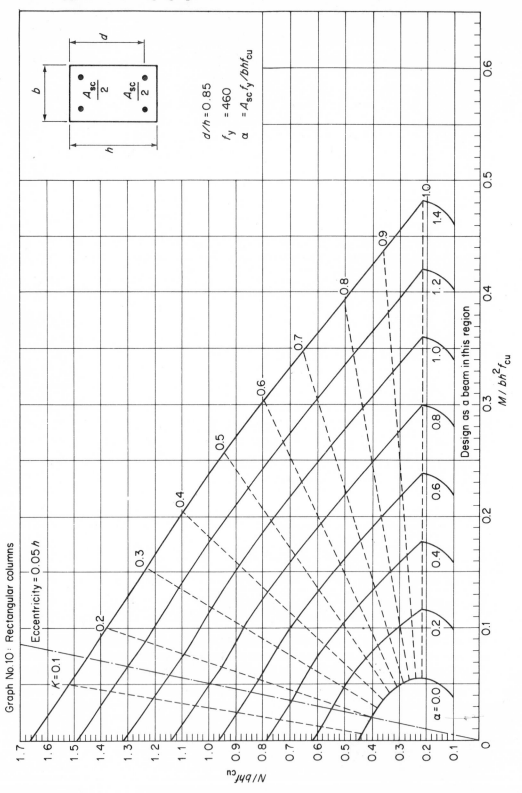

Graph No.10 : Rectangular columns

$d/h = 0.85$

$f_y = 460$

$\alpha = A_{sc} f_y / bh f_{cu}$

Eccentricity = 0.05 h

$M / bh^2 f_{cu}$

$N / bh f_{cu}$

Design as a beam in this region

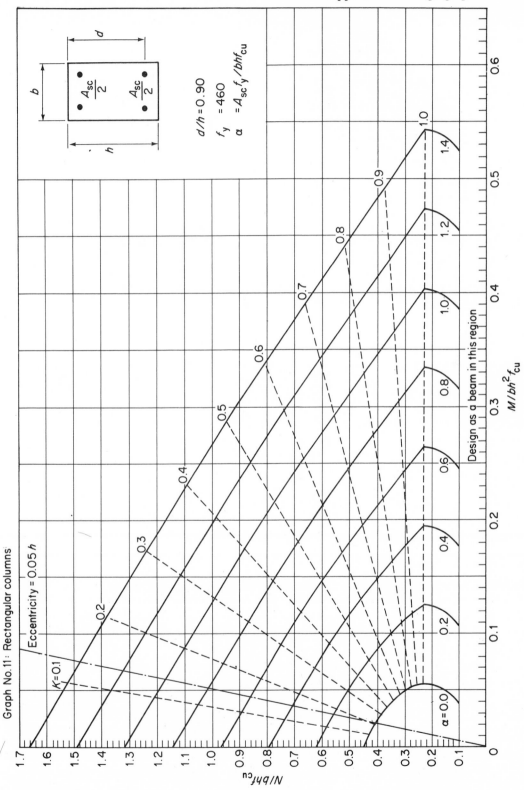

Graph No.11: Rectangular columns

Eccentricity = 0.05 h

$d/h = 0.90$
$f_y = 460$
$\alpha = A_{sc}f_y/bhf_{cu}$

M/bh^2f_{cu}

N/bhf_{cu}

Design as a beam in this region

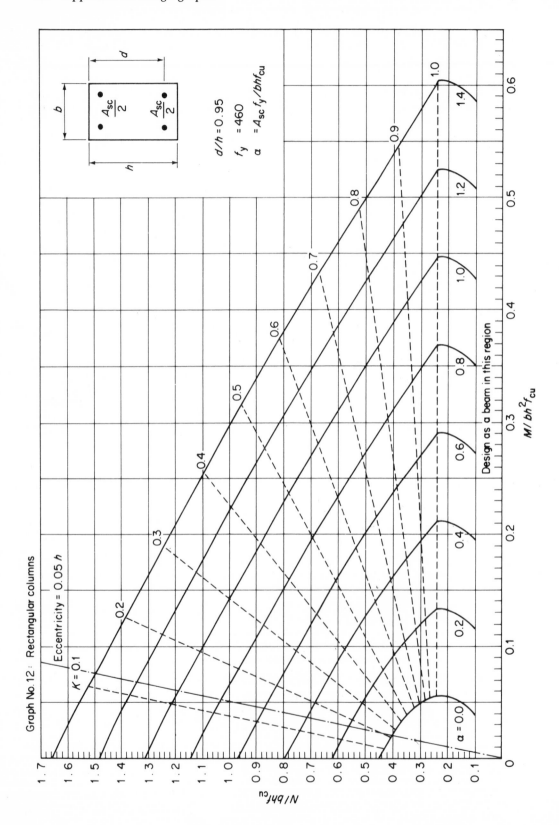

Graph No. 12 : Rectangular columns

Eccentricity = 0.05 h

$d/h = 0.95$
$f_y = 460$
$\alpha = A_{sc} f_y / bh f_{cu}$

$M / bh^2 f_{cu}$

$N / bh f_{cu}$

Design as a beam in this region

Graph No.13 : Pad foundations:

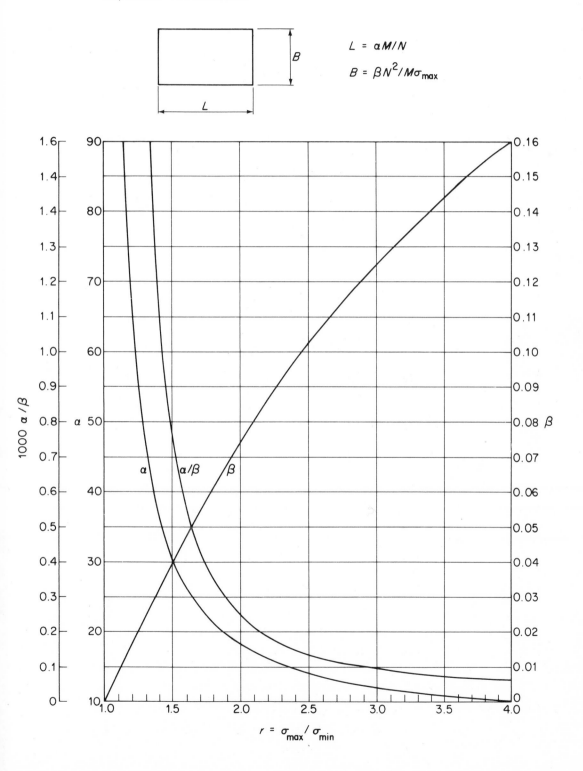

$$L = \alpha M / N$$

$$B = \beta N^2 / M \sigma_{max}$$

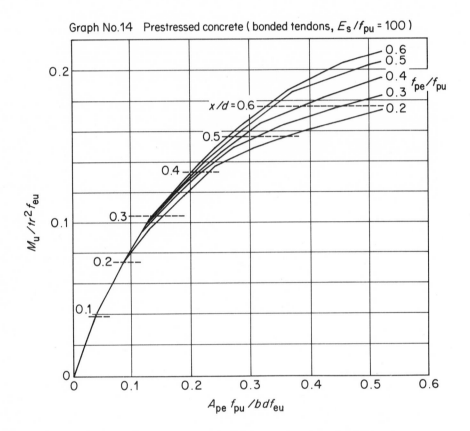

Graph No.14   Prestressed concrete (bonded tendons, $E_s/f_{pu} = 100$)

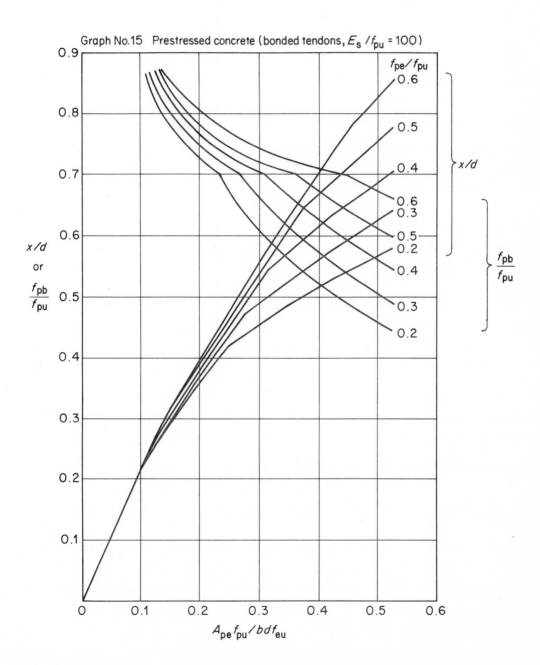

Graph No.15   Prestressed concrete (bonded tendons, E_s /f_{pu} = 100)

Appendix B2 Derivation of Design Graphs

B2.1 Doubly reinforced beams

B2.1.1 Graphs 2–4

The formulae from which these design graphs are constructed are derived from the general principles discussed in Chapter 6, based on the rectangular stress block. Recalling Equation (6.25),

$$M = F_c z + F_s'(d - d') \tag{B2.1}$$

where
$F_c z = K' b d^2 f_{cu}$, the ultimate moment of resistance of the singly reinforced section
$F_s' = f_s' A_s'$, the force in the compression reinforcement.

Substituting for K' from Equation (6.19) and writing the ultimate moment of resistance and the area of compression reinforcement in the dimensionless form required by the design graph,

$$\frac{M}{bd^2 f_{cu}} = 0.402\frac{x}{d} - 0.18\left(\frac{x}{d}\right)^2 + \frac{A_s' f_y}{bdf_{cu}}\left(1 - \frac{d'}{d}\right)\frac{f_s'}{f_y} \tag{B2.2}$$

For equilibrium of the section the tensile force from the tension reinforcement must be equal to the sum of the compressive forces from the concrete stress block and the compression reinforcement. Hence

$$f_s A_s = 0.402 b x f_{cu} + f_s' A_s'$$

Multiplying by $f_y / b d f_{cu}$ to express both reinforcement areas in dimensionless form, and transposing,

$$\frac{A_s f_y}{bdf_{cu}} = 0.402\frac{x f_y}{d f_s} \times \frac{A_s' f_y}{bdf_{cu}}\frac{f_s'}{f_s} \tag{B2.3}$$

The stresses in the reinforcement can also be expressed in terms of x/d by means of Equations (6.6) and (6.29), thus

$$f_s = 700(1 - x/d)/(x/d) \tag{B2.4}$$
$$f_s' = 700(x/d - d'/d)/(x/d) \tag{B2.5}$$

The graphs are plotted by evaluating Equations (B2.2) and (B2.3) for a series of values of x/d. Particular values of $A'_s f_y / b d f_{cu}$ are each represented by a separate line, and a complete graph is required for each value of d'/d.

Since the graphs are required to cover the elastic and plastic ranges of steel stress, f_s and f'_s are set to $0.87 f_y$ when the right-hand sides of Equation (B2.4) and (B2.5) exceed this value. It can be seen from these equations that in mild steel and high-yield steel the stress does not reach the design strength at the same value of x/d, so that although the axes of the graphs are dimensionless, the graphs are not independent of the yield stress except in the regions where the stress in both reinforcements is at the design strength. The graphs are therefore plotted for high-yield steel, which is the more likely to be used in practice.

At values of $x/d < d'/d$ the stress in the compression reinforcement becomes tensile. In this region the graphs for all values of $A'_s f_y / b d f_{cu}$ have been assumed to converge with the graph for $A'_s f_y / b d f_{cu} = 0$, which is conservative.

B2.2   Graphs 5–7

These graphs are intended for use only when the required ultimate moment of resistance is known and the areas of both tension and compression reinforcement are to be determined. They are based on the design formulae in cl 3.4.4.4, Pt 1 (see Section 6.3.3 in this book).

Assuming the stress in the compression reinforcement to be at the design strength Equations (6.26) and (6.27) may be expressed in dimensionless form as follows:

$$A'_s f_y / b d f_{cu} = (K - K')/(0.87(1 - d'/d)) \tag{B2.6}$$
$$A_s f_y / b d f_{cu} = K'/(0.87 z/d) + A'_s f_y /(b d f_{cu}) $$

that is

$$A_s f_y / b d f_{cu} = K'/(0.87 z/d) + (K - K')/(0.87(1 - d'/d)) \tag{B2.7}$$

If the compression reinforcement is elastic,

$$A'_s f_y / b d f_{cu} = (K - K') f_y /(f'_s (1 - d'/d)) \tag{B2.8}$$

where

> f'_s is given by Equation (B2.5)
> $z/d = 1 - 0.45 x/d$
> $K' = 0.402(\beta_b - 0.4) - 0.18(\beta_b - 0.4)^2$

Thus if x/d is given particular values of $\beta_b - 0.4$ and d'/d is fixed, Equations (B2.6)–(B2.8) are linear functions of K and can be plotted as shown in Graph Nos. 5–7. From Fig. 6.8 it can be seen that for the combinations $d'/d = 0.15$, $x/d = 0.3$, and $d'/d = 0.2$, $x/d = 0.3$ and 0.4, the stress in the compression reinforcement does not reach the design strength, necessitating the use of Equation (B2.8); in all other combinations Equation (B2.6) is used.

The lower part of the graph relates to singly reinforced beams.

B2.2   Singly reinforced beams (Graph 1)

Equations (B2.2) and (B2.3) can be modified to deal with singly reinforced beams simply by setting A_s' to zero. The imposition of a maximum value of $z = 0.95d$ (cl 3.4.4.1(e), Pt 1) results in the equation

$$A_s = M/(0.87f_y \times 0.95d) \tag{B2.9}$$

Transposing and writing in dimensionless form,

$$M/(bd^2f_{cu}) = 0.826A_sf_y/(bdf_{cu}) \tag{B2.10}$$

In the graph this result is achieved by drawing a straight line from the point represented by $x/d = 0.1111$ to the origin.

B2.3   Rectangular columns (Graphs 8–12)

B2.3.1   Short columns

Equations (9.6) and (9.7) may be written in dimensionless form as follows:

$$N/bhf_{cu} = 0.402x/h + n\alpha \tag{B2.11}$$
$$M/bh^2f_{cu} = 0.402x/h(0.5 - 0.45x/h) + m\alpha \tag{B2.12}$$

where

$$n = (f_1 - f_2)/2f_y$$
$$m = (2d/h - 1)(f_1 - f_2)/4f_y$$
$$\alpha = A_{sc}f_y/bhf_{cu}$$

f_1 and f_2 are the stresses in the more highly compressed and the less compressed reinforcement respectively (see Fig. 9.6)

Similarly, Equations (9.8) and (9.9) may be written in terms of the ratios x/h and d/h, thus

$$f_1 = 700(x/h - 1 + d/h)/(x/h) \tag{B2.13}$$
$$f_2 = 700(x/h - d/h)/(x/h) \tag{B2.14}$$

The steel stress reaches the design strength when f_1 or f_2 reach $\pm f_y/1.15$. Hence, from the last two equations:
f_1 is equal to the design strength in compression when

$$x/h \geqslant (1 - d/h)/(1 - f_y/805) \tag{B2.15}$$

and in tension when

$$x/h \leqslant (1 - d/h)/(1 + f_y/805) \tag{B2.16}$$

f_2 is equal to the design strength in compression when

$$x/h \geqslant (d/h)/(1 - f_y/805) \tag{B2.17}$$

and in tension when

$$x/h \leqslant (d/h)/(1 + f_y/805) \tag{B2.18}$$

When x/h lies outside the ranges indicated by these four expressions, the steel is elastic and its stress may be obtained from Equations (B2.13) and (B2.14).

The case when $0.9x \geqslant h$, i.e. when the concrete stress block covers the whole section, must also be considered. In this case f_1 is equal to the design strength in compression and there is no moment from the stress block. Hence, when x/h exceeds 1.111 Equations (B2.11) and (B2.12) become simply

$$N/bhf_{cu} = 0.4466 + n\alpha \qquad (B2.19)$$

$$M/bh^2f_{cu} = m\alpha \qquad (B2.20)$$

where

$$n = (1 + 1.15f_2/f_y)/2.3$$
$$m = (2d/h - 1)(1 - 1.15f_2/f_y)/4.6$$

The design graphs are plotted by evaluating Equations (B2.11) and (B2.12), or (B2.19) and (B2.20), for given values of x/h. Each value of α is represented by a separate line and a complete graph is required for each value of d/h. For particular values of x/h and d/h the equations are linear functions of α. Each value of x/h is therefore represented by a vector; and the points representing particular values of α are proportionally spaced along it. Thus for plotting by hand it is necessary only to compute coordinates for the two extreme values of α, the other points being determined by proportional division of the line joining these points.

Since Equations (B2.15) and (B2.16) are not independent of the yield stress, the graphs, like those for doubly reinforced beams, are based on $f_y = 460$ N/mm^2 and may only be used for high-yield steel, despite the fact that the axes of the graphs and the parameter α are in dimensionless form.

The minimum eccentricity of $0.05h$ is indicated by the chain-dotted line

$$N/bhf_{cu} = 20M/bh^2f_{cu} \qquad (B2.21)$$

To the left of this line the eccentricity is less than $0.5h$. *However, it should be remembered that the minimum eccentricity should not exceed 20 mm, which is less than $0.05h$ when $h > 400$ mm.*

At the bottom of the graph the axial force scale is cut off at $N = 0.1bhf_{cu}$, which is the maximum axial force that may be ignored in the design of a beam (cl 3.4.4.1, Pt 1).

B2.3.2 Slender columns

The dashed radial lines on the column design graphs represent the reduction factor K in Equation (9.13), which is defined as

$$K = (N_{uz} - N)/(N_{uz} - N_{bal}) \qquad (B2.22)$$

where

N is the design ultimate axial load
N_{uz} is the ultimate axial load capacity, given by

$$N_{uz} = 0.45f_{cu}A_c + 0.87f_yA_{sc} \qquad (B2.23)$$

in which A_c is the area of concrete in the section.

N_{bal} is the design axial load capacity of a balanced section (cl 3.8.1.1, Pt 1), or in other words, at axial loads below N_{bal} the stress in reinforcement A_2 is at the design strength in tension. In accordance with this definition N_{bal} is indicated by the discontinuities on the far right of the graphs. From Equation (B2.18), assuming high-yield steel, the balanced condition exists when $x/h = 0.6364d/h$. Substitution into Equation (B2.11) gives

$$N_{bal}/bhf_{cu} = 0.256d/h + n\alpha \tag{B2.24}$$

where, since $f_2 = f_y/1.15$,

$$n = (1.15f_1/f_y - 1)/2.3 \tag{B2.25}$$

Substituting $x/h = 0.6364d/h$ into Equation (B2.15) and putting $f_y = 460$ N/mm^2, it is seen that in a balanced section the stress in reinforcement A_1 reaches the design strength in compression when $d/h \geqslant 0.786$. This condition is fulfilled for all the design graphs except for $d/h = 0.75$. In this case substitution for x/h ard d/h into Equation (B2.13) gives $f_1 = 333.3$ N/mm^2. Hence, from Equation (B2.25), $n = 0.0725$. Substitution into Equation (B2.24) gives

$$N_{bal}/bhf_{cu} = 0.256d/h - 0.0725\alpha \tag{B2.26}$$

For all the other graphs $f_2 = -f_1$. Hence $n = 0$ and

$$N_{bal}/bhf_{cu} = 0.256d/h \tag{B2.27}$$

BS 8110 allows a general value of $N_{bal} = 0.25f_{cu}bd$ to be used. However, in order to be consistent with the above definition of N_{bal}, values have been calculated from the last two equations. The line representing $K = 1$ is then the line joining the values of N_{bal}, as indicated by the discontinuities on the design graphs. All the lines representing $K < 1$ lie above this line and may be obtained by transposing Equation (B2.22), thus

$$N = N_{uz} - K(N_{uz} - N_{bal}) \tag{B2.28}$$

Since A_c is usually taken as being equal to bh, both sides of this equation may be divided by bhf_{cu}. Substitution for N_{uz} and N_{bal} then gives

for $d/h = 0.75$
$$N/bhf_{cu} = 0.45 + 0.87\alpha - K(0.258 + 0.942\alpha) \tag{B2.29}$$

for $d/h \geqslant 0.8$

$$N/bhf_{cu} = (0.45 + 0.87\alpha)(1 - K) + 0.256Kd/h \tag{B2.30}$$

Values of N at the points of intersection of the K lines with the α lines may now be obtained.

B2.4 Pad foundations (Graph 13)

The maximum and minimum bearing pressure under a pad foundation subjected to uniaxial bending are given by Equations (11.2), which may be written as

$$\sigma_{max} = N/BL + 6M/BL^2$$
$$\sigma_{min} = N/BL - 6M/BL^2$$

Letting $r = \sigma_{max}/\sigma_{min}$

$$N/BL + 6M/BL^2 = r(N/BL - 6M/BL^2) \tag{B2.31}$$

The base area is obtained by dividing the axial load by the average bearing pressure, i.e.

$$BL = 2N/(\sigma_{max} + \sigma_{min}) = 2N/[\sigma_{max}(1 + 1/r)] \tag{B2.32}$$

Solving Equations (B2.31) and (B2.32) gives

$$L = \alpha M/N \tag{B2.33}$$
$$B = \beta N^2/M\sigma_{max} \tag{B2.34}$$

where

$$\alpha = 6(1 + r)/(r - 1) \tag{B2.35}$$
$$\beta = r(r - 1)/3(1 + r)^2 \tag{B2.36}$$

The graph is constructed by plotting α, β, and α/β against r for values of r from 1.0 to 4.0. The graphs for α and α/β tend to infinity when $r = 1$.

B2.5 Prestressed concrete (Graphs 14 and 15)

The basic equations for the analysis of a section in bending at the ultimate limit state for bonded tendons, according to the assumptions given in cl 4.3.7.1, Pt 1 (see Section 12.1.2) are as follows:

Assuming a rectangular concrete stress block and equating the compressive force to the tensile force (see Fig. 12.2(c))

$$b0.9 \times 0.45f_{cu} = A_{ps}f_{pb}$$

rearranging

$$x/d = 2.469[A_{ps}f_{pu}/(bdf_{cu})](f_{pb}/f_{pu}) \tag{B2.37}$$

This is Equation 53, cl 4.3.7.3, Pt 1, see Equation (12.3).

From the linear strain distribution over the depth of the section

$$0.0035/x = \varepsilon_{sb}/(d - x)$$

Rearranging, the bending strain in the steel

$$\varepsilon_{sb} = 0.0035(d/x - 1) \tag{B2.38}$$

Total strain in the steel, i.e. bending strain plus prestress strain

$$\varepsilon_s = \varepsilon_{sb} + \varepsilon_{sp} = \varepsilon_{sb} + (f_{pe}/f_{pu})(f_{pu}/E_s) \tag{B2.39}$$

Equations describing the trilinear stress–strain relationship for steel are

$$f_{pb}/f_{pu} = (E_s/f_{pu})\varepsilon_s \tag{B2.40}$$
$$f_{pb}/f_{pu} = (\varepsilon_s + 0.02)/(0.025\gamma_s + f_{pu}/E_s) \tag{B2.41}$$

It should be noted that values of x/d and f_{pb}/f_{pu} are related to $[A_{ps}f_{pu}/(bdf_{cu})]$, f_{pe}/f_{pu} and to E_s/f_{pu}. The values of f_{pu} and E_s vary with the type of prestressing steel as shown in Appendix A3. The values given in Table 12.1 appear to have been calculated using a conservative value of $E_s/f_{pu} = 100$.

Taking moments about the compressive force the moment of resistance

$$M_u = A_{ps}f_{pb}d(1 - 0.45x/d)$$

rearranging

$$M_u/(bd^2 f_{cu}) = [A_{ps} f_{pu}/(bd f_{cu})](f_{pb}/f_{pu})(1 - 0.45x/d) \qquad (B2.42)$$

Assuming $E_s/f_{pu} = 100$ and combining these equations it is possible to construct design graphs. The most important plots $M_u/(bd^2 f_{cu})$ against $A_{ps} f_{pu}/(bd f_{cu})$ as shown in Graph 14. However, this graph does not give very accurate values of the depth of the compression zone, nor does it give values of the steel stress. These can be determined from Graph 15.

Appendix C1 Densities (BS 648) and Specific Weights of Some Building Materials

Material	Density (kg/m^3)	Weight (kN/m^3)
Aluminium	2771	27.2
Asbestos cement	1922–2082	18.9–20.4
Asphalt	2082	20.4
Bitumen roofing felt	593	5.8
Brass	8426	82.7
Brickwork		
commons	2000	19.6
heavy pressed	2240	22
engineering	2400	23.5
Cement	1441	14.4
Concrete		
plain	2300	22.6
reinforced	2400	23.5
Copper	8730	85.6
Cork	128–240	1.3–2.4
Felt (roofing)	593	5.8
Fibre building board	160–400	1.6–3.9
Floors (hollow clay blocks with concrete ribs between blocks and 40 mm concrete topping)	1600	15.7
Glass plate	2787	27.3
Lead	11325	111.1
Plaster		
acoustic	800	7.8
fibrous	430	4.2
gypsum	1920	18.8
Steel (mild)	7849	77
Stone		
limestone	2082–2243	20.4–22
sandstone	2195–2403	21.5–23.6
granite	2595–2931	25.5–28.8
Timber		
oak	721–961	7.1–9.4
pitch-pine	673	6.6
Douglas fir	529	5.2

Appendix C2 Imposed Floor Loads for Some Buildings (BS 6399, Pt 1)

Type or part of building	Distributed load (kN/m^2)	Concentrated load applied over 300 mm square (kN)
Assembly areas, dance halls, gymnasia, and grandstands without fixed seating	5.0	3.6
Bedrooms		
domestic and institutions	1.5	1.8
hotels	2.0	1.8
Colleges		
classrooms, chapels	3.0	2.7
dining rooms	2.0	2.7
Corridors and footbridges		
crowd loading	4.0	4.5
loads greater than crowds	5.0	4.5
Factories and foundries	2.0–20.00	1.8–9.0
Garages		
vehicles < 2500 kg	2.5	9.0
vehicles > 2500 kg	5.0	9.0
Hospitals		
wards	2.0	1.8
operating theatres	2.0	4.5
Hotels		
bars and vestibules	5.0	—
kitchens	3.0	4.5
Offices		
filing and storage	5.0	4.5
general	2.5	2.7
with computing equipment	3.5	4.5
Self-contained dwelling units	1.5	1.4
Stairs		
domestic	3.0	4.5
other buildings	4.0	4.5
Storage	2.4 (per m in ht.)	7.0
Stationery stores	4.0 (per m in ht.)	9.0

Appendix C3 Imposed Vertical Roof Loads (BS 6399, Pt 3)

Roof type	Uniformly distributed load (kN/m^2)	Concentrated load (kN)
With access	1.5	1.8
No access and slope α		
$\alpha < 30°$	0.6	0.9
$\alpha = 30°$ to $60°$	$0.6[(60 - \alpha)/30]$	0.9
$\alpha > 60°$	zero	0.9

Appendix C4 Wind Pressures

On any point on the surface of a building the pressure from wind loading

$$p = 0.613 C_p (V S_1 S_2 S_3)^2 \text{ N/m}^2$$

where
C_p = pressure coefficient dependent on the shape of the building
V = basic wind speed which varies between 38 and 56 m/s in the United Kingdom
S_1 = topography factor which varies between 0.9 and 1.0
S_2 = ground roughness, building size and height above ground factor which varies between 0.47 and 1.27
S_3 = statistical probability factor related to period of exposure, normally taken as 1
The appropriate values of the factors for a particular structure are to be found in CP3, Ch. V, Pt 2.

Index

Additional moment, 233
aggregates, 83, 429
alkali-aggregate reaction, 83
anchorage,
    at ends of a member, 196, 380
    bars, 182
    bearing stress, 185
    hooks and bends, 184, 381
    links, 154
    pre-tensioned members, 359
    post-tensioned members, 356
analysis
    approximate analysis of continuous
        beams, 75
    serviceability limit state, 34
    structure, 1, 58, 372
    ultimate limit state, 34
area of bars, 438

Balanced section, 119
bar bending schedule, 5
bar mark, 7
beam,
    analysis of reinforced, 116
    analysis of prestressed, 325, 329
    bottom loaded floor beam, 156, 403
    continuous, 31, 51, 73, 371
    crack width, 94
    deflection, 84, 86, 339
    design formula, 121
    design graphs, 447
    flanged, 62, 131
    prestressed, 322
    shear strength, 148
    slenderness limit, 35, 328, 376
    torsion, 169
    ultimate moment of resistance, 118,
        323

bearing capacity, 290, 293
bearing stresses,
    inside bends, 185
    supports, 198
bearing pressure, 305
bending,
    moment envelope, 56
    moment distribution, 58
    resistance for prestressed concrete,
        322
bends in reinforcement, 185, 381
bent-up bars, 157, 238
biaxial bending, 231, 238, 308, 318, 385
bond length, 183, 380
bonded tendons, 324
bracing, 39, 219
braced frame, 39
buckling of,
    bars, 117, 219
    columns, 221, 224
bundled bars, 183
bursting forces, 356

Carbonation, 81
characteristic load, 23
characteristic strength, 12
chloride attack, 82
column,
    additional moment, 224, 233, 239
    analysis, 219, 230
    axially loaded, 227
    bending moment, 228
    biaxial bending, 231, 238
    bracing, 219
    effective height, 221
    graphs, 454
    minimum eccentricity, 224
    serviceability, 242

shear resistance, 168, 242
slender, 224, 232
starter bars, 315, 390
strip, 267, 394
supporting flat slabs, 260, 392
concrete,
    cover, 82, 103
    density, 23
    grade, 13
    lightweight, 429
connections,
    bars, 187
    beam-to-beam, 199
    beam-to-column, 204
    column-to-base, 207
    corbel, 208
    half joint, 212
    mechanical bar-to-bar, 188
    simple beam, 196
    welded bar-to-bar, 187, 189
continuous beams, 73, 51
contraflexure, points of, 69, 108
corrosion of reinforcement, 81
counterfort retaining wall, 289, 299, 411
cover to reinforcement, 82, 103
crack,
    control, 381
    width, 85, 94
    parallel to reinforcement, 82
cracking, early thermal, 98, 425
creep coefficient, 16
creep of concrete, 15, 344
critical section, 237, 311
critical perimeter, 313, 387
curing of concrete, 17, 82
curtailment,
    general, 29, 379, 382
    practical, 190
    rules, 193
    theoretical, 190

Deflection,
    long term, 89, 339
    reinforced beams, 2, 85
    short term, 89
density of materials, 469
design envelope, 27, 374
design formulae,
    beams, 121
    columns, 227
    pad foundations, 308, 312

design strength, 14
design graphs, 447
design graphs—derivation, 462
design graphs—use of,
    beams, 138
    columns, 229
    pad foundations, 309
design load, 26
design procedure—beams, 137
detailing, 6
doubly reinforced beams, 124
dowel force, 148
drawings, 8
ducts, 345
durability of concrete and steel, 80

Early thermal cracking, 98, 425
effective,
    depth, 117
    height of a column, 221
    width of flange, 131
    width of slab, 62, 392
elastic analysis,
    prestressed beams, 322
    slabs, 248, 262
end block,
    post-tensioned, 356
    pre-tensioned, 359
end plate, 356
envelope,
    bending moment, 56
    shear force, 56

Factor of safety, 2, 14, 26, 290
fans, yield line, 259
fire,
    beams, 103, 108
    columns, 103
    engineering design, 106, 400
    resistance, 100
    slabs, 103, 400
    standard test, 101
flange,
    beams, 131
    effective width, 131
flat slabs, 63, 284, 390, 429
foundations, 304
frame analysis and types, 39
friction,
    on a bearing, 211
    in a duct, 346

Grade of concrete, 13

Heat of hydration, 98
Hillerborg strip method, 262, 271, 276, 412, 420
hooks, 182, 197

Inclined bars, 157
infill panels, 39
isotropically reinforced slabs, 253

Jacking force, 342
Johansen yield line method, 35, 250
joints, *see* connections
joints in bars, 187

L beams, 131
lap bar connection, 187, 380
lateral buckling of beams, 35
lever arm, 122
lightweight concrete, 429
limit state design, 2
links,
    anchorage, 154
    buckling of compression bars, 117
    columns, 219
    minimum, 153
    spacing, 154
    vertical, 152
loads,
    characteristics, 23
    column, 64
    design, 26
    imposed floor, 470
    imposed roof, 471
    slab, 248
    wind, 472
long term deflection
    ordinary reinforced concrete beams, 89
    prestressed beams, 339
loss of prestress,
    anchorage, 345
    creep of concrete, 344
    elastic deformation, 343
    friction of ducts, 345
    relaxation of steel, 342
    shrinkage of concrete, 344
lower bound theorem for slabs, 250

Maximum,
    spacing of bars, 443

    percentage steel, 442
    spacing of links, 444
mean strength, 4
membrane action, 251
middle strip, 267, 394
minimum,
    lap length, 187
    percentage steel, 440
    spacing of steel, 442
modular ratio, 59
modulus of elasticity,
    concrete, 14, 343
    steel, 19
moment-curvature, 68, 119
moment redistribution, 67
moment of resistance,
    reinforced concrete beams, 116
    prestressed concrete beams, 322

N_{bal}, 465
neutral axis depth, 118, 120
nominal,
    compression reinforcement, 154
    links, 153
normal distribution, 3

Optimum cross section, 333
orthotropically reinforced slab, 253
over-reinforced beam, 119
overturning, 2, 38

Pad foundation, 164, 305
partial safety factor
    material, 14
    load, 26
pile foundation, 304, 315
prestressed concrete,
    class 1, 2 and 3 members, 334
    deflection, 339
    derivation of design graphs, 467
    design graphs, 460
    end blocks, 356
    flexural strength, 322
    loss of prestress, 342
    post-tensioning, 322
    pre-tensioning, 322
    shear strength, 349
    torsional strength, 169
punching shear, 149, 314, 316

Redistribution, 67, 120, 126, 135, 374

reinforcement,
  bar area tables, 438
  bends, 182, 197
  bond, 182
  characteristic strength, 13
  curtailment, 189
  design strength, 14
  hooks; 182, 197
  in beams, 116
  in columns, 219
  in pad foundations, 313
  in pile caps, 316
  lap length, 187
  maximum percentage, 442
  maximum spacing, 98, 443
  minimum percentage, 440
  minimum spacing, 442
  secondary, 316
  shear, 152
  torsion, 169
relaxation of steel, 342
retaining wall,
  base, 297, 291, 419
  counterfort, 289, 299, 411
  cantilever, 289, 292
  factor of safety, 290
  fill, 289
  gravity (mass), 289, 291
  overturning, 290
  settlement, 290, 298
  shear key, 293, 422
  stability, 290
  sliding, 290, 291
  stem, 294, 412
  surcharge, 293, 412
  tilt, 290, 298
ribbed slabs, 248
robustness, 2

Saint Venant torsion constant, 171
safety factor, 2, 14, 26
second moment of area, 59
section properties,
  reinforced concrete, 59
  prestressed concrete, 331
self weight, 23
service load, 1
serviceability limit state, 2
  columns, 242
  crack control, 381
  crack width, 2, 85

  deflection, 2, 3, 84, 86, 378
  fire, 85
  vibration, 2, 85
shear,
  bent-up bars, 157
  bond failure, 149
  concentrated loads, 160, 283
  cracked prestressed beams, 350
  failure, 148
  flanged beams, 150
  flat slabs, 160, 395, 434
  key, 293
  lag, 131
  links, 152
  pad foundation, 164, 313, 387
  pile caps, 166
  prestressed beams, 349
  reinforcement, 116, 142, 353, 378,
    441
  resistance of columns, 168
  stress, 150
  span/depth ratio, 148
  -torsion, 172
  uncracked prestressed concrete
    beams, 352
short columns, 225
shrinkage of concrete, 17, 89, 344
sign convention for,
  bending moment, 29, 41
  prestressed concrete, 331
  shear, 41
  structural analysis, 41
slabs,
  BS 8110 methods, 266
  concentrated loads, 248
  curtailment of reinforcement, 194,
    268, 379
  deflection, 399, 436
  detailing, 267
  edge beams, 256
  elastic analysis, 248, 262
  encastré, 275
  flat, 63, 284, 390, 429
  Hillerborg strip method, 262, 271,
    276, 412, 420
  lower bound theorem, 250
  methods of construction, 247
  modes of failure, 281
  nodal force approach, 251
  restrained, 266
  serviceability limit state, 247
  shear resistance, 160, 283

simply supported, one-way
   spanning, 265
square, 254
support beams, 256, 281
torsion, 268
two-way spanning, 265
types, 247
upper bound theorem, 250
virtual work approach, 251
waffle, 64, 247, 284
slender,
   beams, 35
   columns, 35
slenderness ratio, 224
slip at anchorage, 345
spacing of bars, 98, 442
span/depth ratio, 86, 378
specific weights of materials, 469
stability,
   columns, 226
   members, 35
   structure, 2, 36
staircases, 285
standard deviation, 4
stiffness of a member,
   bending, flexural, 58
   torsional, 171
stirrups, 152
strain,
   compatibility, 343
   distribution in bending, 324
   limitations, 117
stress block, 118, 356
stress-strain curves, 18
strip method, Hillerborg, 262, 271, 276,
   412
sub-frame
   continuous beam, 39, 40, 51
   one floor level, 39, 40, 48, 50, 53
sulphate attack, 84

Tee beams, 131
tendons, prestressed, 333
thermal,
   strain, 98
   cracking, 98

ties, 36
torsion,
   constant, 171
   failure modes, 170
   interaction with bending and shear,
     172
   plain concrete, 170
   prestressed beams, 169
   reinforcement, 173
   resistance, 169
   -shear, 442
   shear stress, 172
   stiffness (rigidity), 171
transfer of prestress, 342
transmission length, 359

Ultimate limit state, 2
   columns, 226
   reinforced beams, 116
   pad foundation, 306
   prestressed beams, 323
unbonded tendons, 324
unbraced frame, 39
under-reinforced beam, 119
upper bound theorem, slabs, 250

Vibration, 85

Wall, 119
waffle slab, 64, 247, 284
welded connection, 189
wind loading, 54, 472
working load, 1, 472

Yield line analysis,
   concentrated load, 259
   equilibrium method, 251
   fan mechanism, 259
   isotropically reinforced slab, 254
   Johansen method, 250
   lower bound theorem, 250
   nodal force method, 251
   orthotropically reinforced slab, 253
   upper bound theorem, 250
   virtual work method, 251